Scott Foresman SCIENCE

D1298666

Series Authors

Dr. Timothy Cooney
Professor of Earth Science and Science Education
Earth Science Department
University of Northern Iowa
Cedar Falls, Iowa

Michael Anthony DiSpezio
Science Education Specialist
Cape Cod Children's Museum
Falmouth, Massachusetts

Barbara K. Foots
Science Education Consultant
Houston, Texas

Dr. Angie L. Matamoros
Science Curriculum Specialist
Broward County Schools
Ft. Lauderdale, Florida

Kate Boehm Nyquist
Science Writer and Curriculum Specialist
Mount Pleasant, South Carolina

Dr. Karen L. Ostlund
Professor
Science Education Center
The University of Texas at Austin
Austin, Texas

Contributing Authors

Dr. Anna Uhl Chamot
Associate Professor and ESL Faculty Advisor
Department of Teacher Preparation and Special Education
Graduate School of Education and Human Development
The George Washington University
Washington, DC

Dr. Jim Cummins
Professor
Modern Language Centre and Curriculum Department
Ontario Institute for Studies in Education
Toronto, Canada

Gale Philips Kahn
Lecturer, Science and Math Education
Elementary Education Department
California State University, Fullerton
Fullerton, California

Vincent Sipkovich
Teacher
Irvine Unified School District
Irvine, California

Steve Weinberg
Science Consultant
Connecticut State Department of Education
Hartford, Connecticut

Scott Foresman

Editorial Offices: Glenview, Illinois; New York, New York
Sales Offices: Reading, Massachusetts; Duluth, Georgia; Glenview, Illinois; Carrollton, Texas; Menlo Park, California
www.sfscience.com

ISBN: 0-673-59312-6

Content Consultants

Dr. J. Scott Cairns
National Institutes of Health
Bethesda, Maryland

Jackie Cleveland
Elementary Resource Specialist
Mesa Public School District
Mesa, Arizona

Robert L. Kolenda
Science Lead Teacher, K-12
Neshaminy School District
Langhorne, Pennsylvania

David P. Lopath
Teacher
The Consolidated School District of New Britain
New Britain, Connecticut

Sammantha Lane Magsino
Science Coordinator
Institute of Geophysics
University of Texas at Austin
Austin, Texas

Kathleen Middleton
Director, Health Education
ToucanEd
Soquel, California

Irwin Slesnick
Professor of Biology
Western Washington University
Bellingham, Washington

Dr. James C. Walters
Professor of Geology
University of Northern Iowa
Cedar Falls, Iowa

Multicultural Consultants

Dr. Shirley Gholston Key
Assistant Professor
University of Houston-Downtown
Houston, Texas

Damon L. Mitchell
Quality Auditor
Louisiana-Pacific Corporation
Conroe, Texas

Classroom Reviewers

Kathleen Avery
Teacher
Kellogg Science/Technology Magnet
Wichita, Kansas

Margaret S. Brown
Teacher
Cedar Grove Primary
Williamston, South Carolina

Deborah Browne
Teacher
Whitesville Elementary School
Moncks Corner, South Carolina

Wendy Capron
Teacher
Corlears School
New York, New York

Jiwon Choi
Teacher
Corlears School
New York, New York

John Cirrincione
Teacher
West Seneca Central Schools
West Seneca, New York

Jacqueline Colander
Teacher
Norfolk Public Schools
Norfolk, Virginia

Dr. Terry Contant
Teacher
Conroe Independent School District
The Woodlands, Texas

Susan Crowley-Walsh
Teacher
Meadowbrook Elementary School
Gladstone, Missouri

Charlene K. Dindo
Teacher
Fairhope K-1 Center/Pelican's Nest Science Lab
Fairhope, Alabama

Laurie Duffee
Teacher
Barnard Elementary
Tulsa, Oklahoma

Beth Anne Ebler
Teacher
Newark Public Schools
Newark, New Jersey

Karen P. Farrell
Teacher
Rondout Elementary School District #72
Lake Forest, Illinois

Anna M. Gaiter
Teacher
Los Angeles Unified School District
Los Angeles Systemic Initiative
Los Angeles, California

Federica M. Gallegos
Teacher
Highland Park Elementary
Salt Lake School District
Salt Lake City, Utah

Janet E. Gray
Teacher
Anderson Elementary - Conroe ISD
Conroe, Texas

Karen Guinn
Teacher
Ehrhardt Elementary School - KISD
Spring, Texas

Denis John Hagerty
Teacher
Al Ittihad Private Schools
Dubai, United Arab Emirates

Judith Halpern
Teacher
Bannockburn School
Deerfield, Illinois

Debra D. Harper
Teacher
Community School District 9
Bronx, New York

Gretchen Harr
Teacher
Denver Public Schools - Doull School
Denver, Colorado

Bonnie L. Hawthorne
Teacher
Jim Darcy School
School Dist #1
Helena, Montana

Marselle Heywood-Julian
Teacher
Community School District 6
New York, New York

Scott Klene
Teacher
Bannockburn School 106
Bannockburn, Illinois

Thomas Kranz
Teacher
Livonia Primary School
Livonia, New York

Tom Leahy
Teacher
Coos Bay School District
Coos Bay, Oregon

Mary Littig
Teacher
Kellogg Science/Technology Magnet
Wichita, Kansas

Patricia Marin
Teacher
Corlears School
New York, New York

Susan Maki
Teacher
Cotton Creek CUSD 118
Island Lake, Illinois

Efraín Meléndez
Teacher
East LA Mathematics Science Center LAUSD
Los Angeles, California

Becky Mojalid
Teacher
Manarat Jeddah Girls' School
Jeddah, Saudi Arabia

Susan Nations
Teacher
Sulphur Springs Elementary
Tampa, Florida

Brooke Palmer
Teacher
Whitesville Elementary
Moncks Corner, South Carolina

Jayne Pedersen
Teacher
Laura B. Sprague School District 103
Lincolnshire, Illinois

Shirley Pfingston
Teacher
Orland School Dist 135
Orland Park, Illinois

Teresa Gayle Rountree
Teacher
Box Elder School District
Brigham City, Utah

Helen C. Smith
Teacher
Schultz Elementary
Klein Independent School District
Tomball, Texas

Denette Smith-Gibson
Teacher
Mitchell Intermediate, CISD
The Woodlands, Texas

Mary Jean Syrek
Teacher
Dr. Charles R. Drew Science Magnet
Buffalo, New York

Rosemary Troxel
Teacher
Libertyville School District 70
Libertyville, Illinois

Susan D. Vani
Teacher
Laura B. Sprague School
School District 103
Lincolnshire, Illinois

Debra Worman
Teacher
Bryant Elementary
Tulsa, Oklahoma

Dr. Gayla Wright
Teacher
Edmond Public School
Edmond, Oklahoma

ISBN: 0-673-59305-3

4567890 DOW 03 02 01 00

ii

Activity and Safety Consultants

Laura Adams
Teacher
Holley-Navarre Intermediate
Navarre, Florida

Dr. Charlie Ashman
Teacher
Carl Sandburg Middle School
Mundelein District #75
Mundelein, Illinois

Christopher Atlee
Teacher
Horace Mann Elementary
Wichita Public Schools
Wichita, Kansas

David Bachman
Consultant
Chicago, Illinois

Sherry Baldwin
Teacher
Shady Brook
Bedford ISD
Euless, Texas

Pam Bazis
Teacher
Richardson ISD
Classical Magnet School
Richardson, Texas

Angela Boese
Teacher
McCollom Elementary
Wichita Public Schools USD #259
Wichita, Kansas

Jan Buckelew
Teacher
Taylor Ranch Elementary
Venice, Florida

Shonie Castaneda
Teacher
Carman Elementary, PSJA
Pharr, Texas

Donna Coffey
Teacher
Melrose Elementary - Pinellas
St. Petersburg, Florida

Diamantina Contreras
Teacher
J.T. Brackenridge Elementary
San Antonio ISD
San Antonio, Texas

Susanna Curtis
Teacher
Lake Bluff Middle School
Lake Bluff, Illinois

Karen Farrell
Teacher
Rondout Elementary School, Dist. #72
Lake Forest, Illinois

Paul Gannon
Teacher
El Paso ISD
El Paso, Texas

Nancy Garman
Teacher
Jefferson Elementary School
Charleston, Illinois

Susan Graves
Teacher
Beech Elementary
Wichita Public Schools USD #259
Wichita, Kansas

Jo Anna Harrison
Teacher
Cornelius Elementary
Houston ISD
Houston, Texas

Monica Hartman
Teacher
Richard Elementary
Detroit Public Schools
Detroit, Michigan

Kelly Howard
Teacher
Sarasota, Florida

Kelly Kimborough
Teacher
Richardson ISD
Classical Magnet School
Richardson, Texas

Mary Leveron
Teacher
Velasco Elementary
Brazosport ISD
Freeport, Texas

Becky McClendon
Teacher
A.P. Beutel Elementary
Brazosport ISD
Freeport, Texas

Suzanne Milstead
Teacher
Liestman Elementary
Alief ISD
Houston, Texas

Debbie Oliver
Teacher
School Board of Broward County
Ft. Lauderdale, Florida

Sharon Pearthree
Teacher
School Board of Broward County
Ft. Lauderdale, Florida

Jayne Pedersen
Teacher
Laura B. Sprague School
District 103
Lincolnshire, Illinois

Sharon Pedroja
Teacher
Riverside Cultural Arts/History Magnet
Wichita Public Schools USD #259
Wichita, Kansas

Marcia Percell
Teacher
Pharr, San Juan, Alamo ISD
Pharr, Texas

Shirley Pfingston
Teacher
Orland School Dist #135
Orland Park, Illinois

Sharon S. Placko
Teacher
District 26, Mt. Prospect
Mt. Prospect, IL

Glenda Rall
Teacher
Seltzer Elementary
USD #259
Wichita, Kansas

Nelda Requenez
Teacher
Canterbury Elementary
Edinburg, Texas

Dr. Beth Rice
Teacher
Loxahatchee Groves Elementary School
Loxahatchee, Florida

Martha Salom Romero
Teacher
El Paso ISD
El Paso, Texas

Paula Sanders
Teacher
Welleby Elementary School
Sunrise, Florida

Lynn Setchell
Teacher
Sigsbee Elementary School
Key West, Florida

Rhonda Shook
Teacher
Mueller Elementary
Wichita Public Schools USD #259
Wichita, Kansas

Anna Marie Smith
Teacher
Orland School Dist. #135
Orland Park, Illinois

Nancy Ann Varneke
Teacher
Seltzer Elementary
Wichita Public Schools USD #259
Wichita, Kansas

Aimee Walsh
Teacher
Rolling Meadows, Illinois

Ilene Wagner
Teacher
O.A. Thorp Scholastic Acacemy
Chicago Public Schools
Chicago, Illinois

Brian Warren
Teacher
Riley Community Consolidated School District 18
Marengo, Illinois

Tammie White
Teacher
Holley-Navarre Intermediate School
Navarre, Florida

Dr. Mychael Willon
Principal
Horace Mann Elementary
Wichita Public Schools
Wichita, Kansas

Inclusion Consultants

Dr. Eric J. Pyle, Ph.D.
Assistant Professor, Science Education
Department of Educational Theory and Practice
West Virginia University
Morgantown, West Virginia

Dr. Gretchen Butera, Ph.D.
Associate Professor, Special Education
Department of Education Theory and Practice
West Virginia University
Morgantown, West Virginia

Bilingual Consultant

Irma Gomez-Torres
Dalindo Elementary
Austin ISD
Austin, Texas

iii

Unit A
Life Science

iv

v

Unit B

Physical Science

vi

vii

Unit C

Earth Science

viii

ix

Unit D

Human Body

x

Your Science Handbook

xi

Using Scientific Methods for Science Inquiry

The Scientific Methods pages are also on the **Flip Chart.**

- Read the introductory paragraph on page xii. Then ask children to recall some of the steps they have gone through when doing activities in science class in the past. (*Children may say they asked questions, did experiments, made charts, or completed other steps involved in science activities.*) Tell children that the steps they have described are part of the scientific methods they will read about on these pages.
- You may want to have children do the activity that is described on pages xii–xiii. The following materials will be needed for each group doing the activity: 3 glass bottles, water, pencil.
- Throughout the Scott Foresman Science program, Experiment activities follow the steps of scientific methods. Children will repeatedly use scientific methods as they complete Experiment activities.

Problem

Ask children if they can think of questions they might ask about how the sounds will be different. Examples include:

- Will the amount of water in the bottle affect the sound?
- Will more water in the bottle make a higher or lower sound?

Give your hypothesis.

Make sure that children pose their hypotheses as statements. Allow children to give their own hypotheses or to use the hypothesis that is proposed in the text.

Control the variables.

Ask children to identify what things will change and what things will stay the same as they do the experiment. (*changing variable: amount of water; controlled variables: size of bottles, kind of bottles, pencil used*) Allow children to vary the amounts of water in the bottles as proposed in their hypotheses.

Using Scientific Methods for Science Inquiry

Scientists use scientific methods to find answers to questions. Scientific methods have the steps shown on these pages. Scientists sometimes use the steps in different order. You can use these steps for your own science inquiries.

Problem
The problem is the question you want to answer. Inquiry has led to many discoveries in science. Ask your question.

How does the amount of water in a bottle affect the sound made when the bottle is tapped?

Give your hypothesis.
Tell what you think the answer is to the problem.

If the amount of water is more, then the sound will be lower when the bottle is tapped. ▶

Control the variables.
Change one thing when you test your hypothesis. Keep everything else the same.

Test your hypothesis.

Do experiments to test your hypothesis. You may need to do experiments more than one time to see if the results are the same each time.

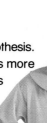

I'll tap each bottle with a pencil and observe the sound.

Collect your data.

Collect data about the problem. Record your data on a chart. You might make drawings or write words or sentences.

Tell your conclusion.

Compare your results and hypothesis. Decide if your hypothesis is right or wrong. Tell what you decide.

Inquire Further

Use what you learn to answer other problems or questions. You may want to do your experiment again or change your experiment.

▲ Does the size of a bottle affect the sound made when the bottle is tapped?

Test your hypothesis.

Ask children why is it important to repeat experiments. (*Results of experiments may differ from one test to another.*) Allow children to test their own hypotheses or the hypothesis described in the text. Remind children to repeat their test to ensure consistency.

Collect your data.

Ask children to describe different ways that data can be collected. (*making tables, drawings, lists, writing words or sentences, and so on*). Children should then use one of these methods or the method shown in the text to collect the data they gather during their test. Help children interpret their data.

Tell your conclusion.

Have children compare the data they gathered and interpreted with their hypotheses. Then ask: **Based on your data, is your hypothesis correct or incorrect?** Allow children to communicate their conclusions based on the data they gathered.

Inquire Further

Ask children what other problems they might like to solve or how they might change their experiment based on what they learned. Allow children to engage in further inquiry of their own design or based on the suggestion given in the text.

Using Process Skills for Science Inquiry

The Process Skills pages are also on the **Flip Chart.**

- Read the introductory paragraphs on page xiv. Then ask children how some of the process skills described are like the scientific methods they learned about on pages xii–xiii. (*"Giving Hypotheses" is like the Give your hypothesis step of scientific methods. "Collecting Data" is like the Collect your data step of scientific methods. "Experimenting" is like the Test your hypothesis step of scientific methods.*) Tell children that they will use many process skills as they do science activities.
- Process skills for all activities in Scott Foresman *Science* are called out both in the Student Edition and in the Teacher's Edition.
- A Skills Trace of Process Skills Development can be found in the Teacher's Edition at the beginning and at the end of each chapter.
- All of the process skills used in Scott Foresman *Science* are introduced here. Further activities involving each of the process skills can be found in the back of the book on pages 6–29.

Observing

Ask children if they can remember examples of science activities in which they observed by seeing, hearing, smelling, or touching. Discuss with children why, in science experiments, tasting and smelling should never be done without approval.

Communicating

Ask children to describe what they think is being shown in the picture that accompanies this process skill. (*parts of a plant*) Tell children that both the picture and its description are examples of communicating.

Classifying

Ask children to classify some of the objects in their desks into groups according to common properties. Have children communicate their methods of classification.

Estimating and Measuring

Provide children with nonstandard units and metric rulers. Then ask children to estimate and measure the length of several classroom objects.

Inferring

Place an object in a shoe box, then have a child hold and shake the box in an attempt to determine what is in it. Tell children that when they make reasonable guesses based on their observations, they are inferring. Ask children how they could infer what was in the bag shown in the picture that accompanies this process skill.

Using Process Skills for Science Inquiry

Scientists use process skills to do research. You will use process skills when you do the activities in this book.

When you test something, you use process skills. When you collect data, you use process skills. When you make conclusions and tell what you learn, you use process skills.

Observing

Your senses are seeing, hearing, smelling, touching, and tasting. Use your senses to find out about objects or things that happen.

Communicating

Use words, pictures, charts, and graphs to share what you learn.

Classifying

Sort or group objects by their properties.

Estimating and Measuring

Estimate means to tell what you think an object's measurement is. Make an estimate. Then measure the object.

Inferring

Make a conclusion or a guess from what you observe or from what you already know.

I think it is a...

Predicting

Tell what you think will happen.

Making Definitions

Use what you already know to describe something or tell what it means.

Making and Using Models

Make a model to show what you know about something.

Giving Hypotheses

Make a statement you can test to answer a problem or a question.

Collecting Data

Record what you observe and measure. Use graphs, charts, pictures, or words. Use what you learned to answer problems or questions.

Controlling Variables

Change one thing that may affect what happens. Keep everything else the same.

Experimenting

Plan and do an investigation to test a hypothesis or to answer a problem. Then make conclusions.

Predicting

Tell children that you will drop a book and a sheet of paper onto your desk. Ask children to predict which will make the louder sound.

Making Definitions

Give children a magnet and a variety of metal and nonmetal classroom objects. Ask children to find out what the magnet does to the objects. Then have children give an operational definition for a magnet.

Making and Using Models

Tell children that the model of a mountain in the picture accompanying this process skill is made from clay. Ask children how the model is like a real mountain and how it is different from a real mountain. (*like: same shape; different: made of different materials, different size, and so on*)

Giving Hypotheses

Remind children of the question and the hypothesis that were in the "Problem" step and the "Give your hypothesis" step of the scientific methods on page xii. (*Question: How does the amount of water in a bottle affect the sound made when the bottle is tapped? Hypothesis: If the amount of water is more, then the sound will be lower when the bottle is tapped.*) Ask children to share other questions or hypotheses they thought of when completing the experiment on pages xii–xiii.

Collecting Data

Remind children of the examples of collecting data from the "Collect your data" step of the scientific methods on page xiii. Tell children that this process skill is an important part of scientific methods. Ask children to tell about, or interpret, the data recorded on the chart that accompanies this process skill.

Controlling Variables

Remind children which variable changed and which variables were controlled in the experiment on pages xii–xiii. (*The amount of water changed; all other variables remained the same.*)

Experimenting

Ask children which step in scientific methods this process skill most closely matches. (*Test your hypothesis.*) Tell children that the child in the picture that accompanies this process skill is experimenting to find out whether light passes through different materials.

Activity Organizer

Process Skills observing

Materials paper towel, dropper, water, clock

Science Inquiry

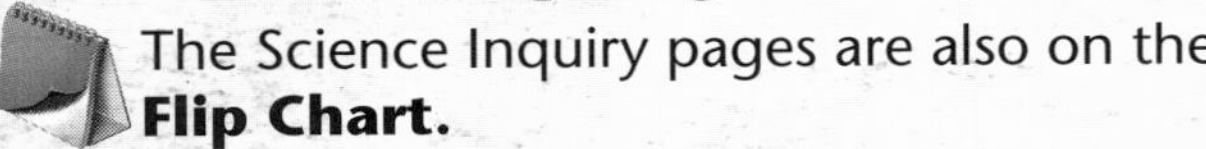

The Science Inquiry pages are also on the **Flip Chart.**

- The following science inquiry activity is an open-ended activity that allows children to discover what affects the rate of evaporation. Children can do activities such as this for science fair projects.
- The science inquiry activities and science fair project suggestions can be found on the Extended Inquiry pages at the beginning of each unit.

1. **Ask a question about living things, objects, or things that happen.** What can affect how long it takes a wet paper towel to dry? Tell children that they will investigate what affects how long it takes a wet paper towel to dry.
2. **Plan and do a simple investigation to answer your question.** Encourage children to point out different places that they can put wet paper towels. Places include dark areas of the classroom, sunny windowsills, or locations in front of a fan or open window. Ask children to plan an investigation to find out the answer to their question.
3. **Use some simple materials and tools to help you.** Have children use a dropper to put the same number of water drops on each towel. Have children use a clock to keep track of the time it takes for each towel to dry. Children should collect their data and record it in a chart.
4. **Use what you observed to answer your question.** Ask: **What affects how long it takes a wet paper towel to dry?** (*Children's answers should indicate that the paper towels dry faster in sunlight and in wind than in shady places.*)
5. **Share your information with your class.** Have children tell classmates about their investigations.

Inquire Further

Ask children to use thermometers to find out about the temperatures in each location they placed their paper towels.

Science Inquiry

As you use your science book, you will ask questions, do investigations, answer your questions, and then tell others what you learned. This is called science inquiry. You can use science inquiry to do this science project.

What can affe
how long it tak
a wet paper
towel to dry

1. **Ask a question about living things, objects, or things that happen.**
   What can affect how long it takes a wet paper towel to dry?
2. **Plan and do a simple investigation to answer your question.**
   Put a few drops of water on each of several paper towels. Test different ways to make the paper towels dry.
3. **Use some simple materials and tools to help you.**
   Use a dropper to put water on each paper towel. Use a clock to time how long it takes each paper towel to dry. Make a chart to show the steps in your experiment.

4. **Use what you observed to answer your question.**
   What affected how long it took for your paper towels to dry?
5. **Share your information with your class.**
   You can use words or pictures.

Unit A

Life Science

Chapter 1
Plants A 4

Chapter 2
Animals A 26

Chapter 3
Fossils A 46

Your Science Handbook

A1

In This Unit

In this unit, children learn about plants and animals. They learn about kinds of plants, seeds, parts of a plant, how plants grow and change, and how people use plants. Children learn about kinds of animals, how they grow and change, where they live, what they eat, and how they protect themselves. Finally, children learn how plants and animals of long ago were different from those of today.

Books for Teachers

Chapter 1

The Growing Classroom by Roberta Jaffe and Gary Appel. Ideas for using indoor and outdoor gardens to study science and nutrition. (Scott Foresman - Addison Wesley, ISBN 0-201-21539-X)

The Art and Science Connections: Hands-On Activities for Primary Students by Kimberly Tolley. Art and science concepts and processes integrated into creative art activities. (Scott Foresman - Addison Wesley, ISBN 0-201-45544-7)

Chapter 2

BugPlay by Marlene Nachbar Hapai and Leon H. Burton. Hands-on experiences with harmless insects. (Scott Foresman - Addison Wesley, ISBN 0-201-21540-3)

175 Amazing Nature Experiments by Thomas Keegan. Colorfully illustrated hands-on activities, games, and experiments. (Grisewood & Dempsey, ISBN 0-679-82043-4)

Chapter 3

Water, Stones, and Fossil Bones by Karen K. Lind. A collection of earth science activities, including a section on the earth's past. (National Science Teachers Association, ISBN 0-87355-101-X)

Dinosaur by David Norman and Angela Milner. Text and photographs explore the world of dinosaurs. (Knopf, ISBN 0-394-82253-6)

Science Background

What Is Life Science? Life science is the study of plants, animals, and other living things. For young children this means exploring the natural world around them. Life science can help answer questions such as: How does a living thing differ from a nonliving thing? What do living things need? How can we classify living things?

About the Photograph The photograph on this page shows a seedling and trees. Ask children to tell what they know about the life cycle of a plant. Point out that tall trees can grow from tiny seedlings like the one shown. Tell children they will learn more about trees and other plants as they study Chapter 3, "Plants."

Technology

You can use the **Teacher's Resource Planner** to plan and organize your curriculum.

	Chapter Concepts/ National Science Education Standards	Lessons/Vocabulary
Chapter 1	**Plants** p. A4 **Concepts** There are different kinds of plants. Plants need water, air, food, and light to grow. Parts of a plant are roots, stem, leaves, and flowers. Seeds are scattered by wind, water, and animals. Food and other useful products come from plants. **National Science Education Standards**  Content Standard C, p. 127 • **The characteristics of organisms** • **Life cycles of organisms** • **Organisms and their environment**	**Lesson 1** ***What are some kinds of plants? p. A6*** **Lesson 2** ***What does a plant need to grow? p. A8*** **Lesson 3** ***Experiment with plants. p. A10*** **Reading for Science** ***Using Vocabulary Words p. A12*** **Lesson 4** ***What are the parts of a plant? p. A14*** **Vocabulary** roots, stem, leaves, flowers **Lesson 5** ***How does a plant grow and change? p. A16*** **Lesson 6** ***What is inside a seed? p. A18*** **Lesson 7** ***How are seeds scattered? p. A20*** **Vocabulary** scatter **Lesson 8** ***How do people use plants? p. A22***
Chapter 2	**Animals** p. A26 **Concepts** There are different kinds of animals. Animals grow and change; live in various habitats; depend on plants and other animals for food; and protect themselves in different ways. **National Science Education Standards**  Content Standard C, p. 127 • **The characteristics of organisms** • **Life cycles of organisms** • **Organisms and their environment**	**Lesson 1** ***What are some kinds of animals? p. A28*** **Vocabulary** mammals, reptiles **Math in Science** ***Ordering p. A30*** **Lesson 2** ***How do frogs grow and change? p. A32*** **Vocabulary** life cycle, tadpole **Lesson 3** ***How do butterflies grow and change? p. A34*** **Vocabulary** chrysalis, pupa **Lesson 4** ***How can you make a model of a butterfly life cycle? p. A36*** **Lesson 5** ***Where do animals live? p. A38*** **Vocabulary** habitat, endangered **Lesson 6** ***What do animals eat? p. A40*** **Vocabulary** food chain **Lesson 7** ***How do animals protect themselves? p. A42*** **Vocabulary** camouflage
Chapter 3	**Fossils** p. A46 **Concepts** Fossils are evidence of life of long ago. Fossils provide evidence about dinosaurs. There were different kinds of dinosaurs. Dinosaurs were different lengths; dinosaurs became extinct. **National Science Education Standards**  Content Standard C, p. 127 • **The characteristics of organisms** • **Organisms and their environment**	**Reading for Science** ***Reading a Science Activity p. A48*** **Lesson 1** ***What are fossils? p. A50*** **Vocabulary** fossils **Lesson 2** ***How do we learn about dinosaurs? p. A52*** **Lesson 3** ***What are some kinds of dinosaurs? p. A54*** **Lesson 4** ***How long were some dinosaurs? p. A56*** **Lesson 5** ***What happened to the dinosaurs? p. A58*** **Vocabulary** extinct, paleontologists
Unit A Assessment	**Unit Performance Review** pp. A62–A63 **Writing for Science** p. A64	

Activity Opportunities

Student Edition
- Explore Activity *Classify plants.* p. A7
- Explore Activity *Make a light box.* p. A9
- Experiment Activity *Experiment with plants.* pp. A10–A11
- Explore Activity *Watch a plant grow.* p. A17
- Investigate Activity *What is inside a seed?* pp. A18–A19

Flip Chart
- Science Center Explore Activity *Describe plants.*
- Science Center Explore Activity *Make a plant.*
- Science Center Explore Activity *Design a seed.*

Teacher's Edition
- Activity Idea Bank, pp. A11a–A11b, A17a–A17b, A23a–A23b

Additional Resources
- Family Activity, Instructional Resources Package, pp. 1–2
- Vocabulary Preview, Instructional Resources Package, p. 3
- Graphic Organizer, Teacher's Assessment Package, p. 3
- Lab Manual, pp. 1, 3, 5–6, 7, 9, 11, 13, 15
- Interactive Transparency 1, Interactive Transparency Package
- Wall Chart, pp. 1, 2, 3, 4, 5

Technology
- *Life Science* National Lab **www.sfscience.com**

Student Edition
- Explore Activity *Guess the animal.* p. A29
- Investigate Activity *How can you make a model of a butterfly?* pp. A36–A37
- Explore Activity *Make a model of a food chain.* p. A41
- Explore Activity *Play a camouflage game.* p. A43

Flip Chart
- Science Center Explore Activity *Make a frog print.*
- Science Center Explore Activity *Make a model of a butterfly.*
- Science Center Explore Activity *Camouflage an animal.*

Teacher's Edition
- Activity Idea Bank, pp. A33a–A33b, A37a–A37b, A43a–A43b

Additional Resources
- Family Activity, Instructional Resources Package, pp. 9–10
- Vocabulary Preview, Instructional Resources Package, p. 11
- Graphic Organizer, Teacher's Assessment Package, p. 9
- Lab Manual, pp. 17, 18, 19, 21, 22, 23, 24
- Interactive Transparency 2, Interactive Transparency Package
- Wall Chart, pp. 6, 7, 8, 9, 10, 11, 12

Technology
- *Life Science* National Lab **www.sfscience.com**

Student Edition
- Explore Activity *Make a leaf print.* p. A51
- Investigate Activity *How long were some dinosaurs?* pp. A56–A57

Flip Chart
- Science Center Explore Activity *Make an imprint.*
- Science Center Explore Activity *Make a dinosaur rubbing.*

Teacher's Edition
- Activity Idea Bank, pp. A53a–A53b, A59a–A59b

Additional Resources
- Family Activity, Instructional Resources Package, pp. 17–18
- Vocabulary Preview, Instructional Resources Package, p. 19
- Graphic Organizer, Teacher's Assessment Package, p. 15
- Lab Manual, pp. 25, 26, 27, 28
- Interactive Transparency 3, Interactive Transparency Package
- Wall Chart, pp. 13, 14, 15, 16, 17, 18

Technology
- *Life Science* National Lab **www.sfscience.com**

Assessment Opportunities

Student Edition
- Lesson 1 Review, p. A7
- Lesson 2 Review, p. A9
- Lesson 4 Review, p. A15
- Lesson 5 Review, p. A17
- Lesson 7 Review, p. A21
- Lesson 8 Review, p. A23
- Chapter 1 Review, pp. A24–A25

Teacher's Edition
- Process Skills Development, pp. A5 & A25
- Assessment Rubric, p. A25

Teacher's Assessment Package
- Chapter 1 Review, p. 4
- Chapter 1 Assessment, pp. 5–6
- Portfolio Ideas, p. 1

Lab Manual
- Activity Rubric, pp. T1, T2, T3, T4

Technology
- **Practice & Assessment CD-ROM**
- **Production Studio**
- **The KnowZone™ at www.kz.com**
- **TestWorks™**

Student Edition
- Lesson 1 Review, p. A29
- Lesson 2 Review, p. A33
- Lesson 3 Review, p. A35
- Lesson 5 Review, p. A39
- Lesson 6 Review, p. A41
- Lesson 7 Review, p. A43
- Chapter 2 Review, pp. A44–A45

Teacher's Edition
- Process Skills Development, pp. A27 & A45
- Assessment Rubric, p. A45

Teacher's Assessment Package
- Chapter 2 Review, p. 10
- Chapter 2 Assessment, pp. 11–12
- Portfolio Ideas, p. 7

Lab Manual
- Activity Rubric, pp. T5, T6, T7, T8

Technology
- **Practice & Assessment CD-ROM**
- **Production Studio**
- **The KnowZone™ at www.kz.com**
- **TestWorks™**

Student Edition
- Lesson 1 Review, p. A51
- Lesson 2 Review, p. A53
- Lesson 3 Review, p. A55
- Lesson 5 Review, p. A59
- Chapter 3 Review, pp. A60–A61

Teacher's Edition
- Process Skills Development, pp. A47 & A61
- Assessment Rubric, p. A61

Teacher's Assessment Package
- Chapter 3 Review, p. 16
- Chapter 3 Assessment, pp. 17–18
- Portfolio Ideas, p. 13

Lab Manual
- Activity Rubric, pp. T8, T9, T10

Technology
- **Practice & Assessment CD-ROM**
- **Production Studio**
- **The KnowZone™ at www.kz.com**
- **TestWorks™**

Student Edition
- Unit A Performance Review, pp. A62–A63

Teacher's Edition
- Assessment Rubric, p. A63

Technology
- *Writing for Science* **www.sfscience.com**

Activity Organizer

Objective
Experiment to understand how liquids affect the growth of seeds.

Process Skills predicting, observing

Parallel Student Book Lesson
Chapter 1, Lesson 2

Materials 3 plastic cups; potting soil; grass seeds; water; different liquid substances, such as vinegar, liquid fertilizer, lemon juice, liquid soap, vegetable oil

EXTENDED INQUIRY

How can liquids change the rate at which seeds sprout and grow?

The following activity is a model of an inquiry-based science fair project for you to do with the class. A list suggesting individual science projects follows the activity. Use these steps of scientific inquiry.

Steps

1 Ask a question about objects, organisms, and events in the environment.

- Pose the following question to children: **How can you change the rate at which seeds sprout?**
- Ask children to predict the effect of different liquid substances on the growth of grass seed. Children will test the effect of these substances on the growth of grass seed.

2 Plan and conduct a simple investigation.

- Have children choose three liquids that they will pour on the grass seeds and label their cups accordingly. One of the liquids they choose should be water.
- Children should fill each cup with soil and place grass seed on top of the soil.
- Next, children should pour some of each liquid they chose over the seeds in the corresponding cup. Children should keep the seeds moist.

This activity follows methods of scientific inquiry suggested in the National Science Education Standards.

3 Employ simple equipment and tools to gather data and extend the senses.

To show how their seeds sprout and grow, children may want to:

- draw and label a diagram
- make a chart or graph
- draw a cartoon about the steps in seed growth

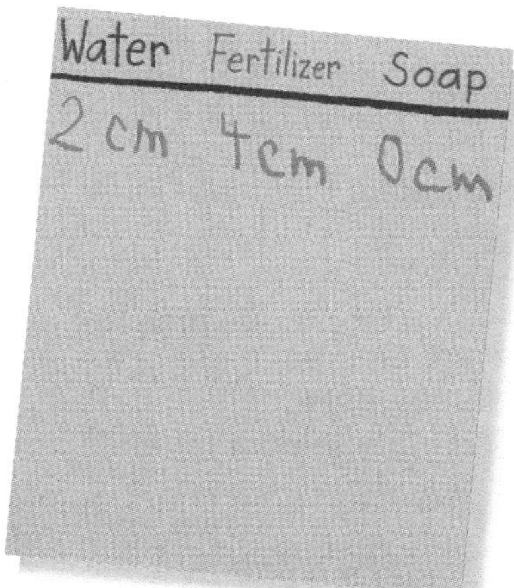

4 Use data to construct a reasonable explanation.

- Ask: **Were there any seeds that didn't sprout? Explain possible reasons why.** (*Possible answer: Some liquids may kill seeds.*)
- Ask: **What was similar about the seeds that sprouted quickly and grew well?** (*Possible answer: Using liquid fertilizer and water might make grass seedlings sprout and grow well.*)

5 Communicate investigations and explanations.

- Have children discuss their results. Children should describe the effects of all liquids they used on the sprouting of seeds and the growth of seedlings. Then ask children to group the liquids based on their effects on seeds and seedlings.

Inquire Further

Ask children if they think combining any of the liquids would make seeds sprout even faster or make the seedlings grow better. Ask how they think they could find out.

Science Fair Projects

Chapter 1 Plant Homes Invite children to make a miniterrarium using two 20-ounce clear plastic cups, gravel, soil, seedlings, and florist moss. Have children follow these steps: put one inch of soil on top of gravel in a cup, poke a hole in the soil and place the plant in the hole, put moss on top of the soil, and then add water until the soil is damp. Remove the rim from the other cup and help children firmly press it upside down into the planted cup. Have them place their cups in a warm, lighted area and observe daily.

Chapter 2 Snail Habitat Have children fill the bottom of a large, clear plastic jar with soil and place a lettuce leaf and a jar lid with about a teaspoon of water on the soil. Place a few snails in the jar and cover with mesh. Invite children to observe the animals in their habitat. Have children refresh the snails' water and food as needed.

Chapter 3 Dino Model Invite children to make clay models of their favorite dinosaurs. They can add features based on pictures from books about dinosaurs. Have them display their dinosaur with a chart telling about its size, what it ate, and what it looked like.

Technology

Children can participate in the Life Science extended inquiry *National Lab* at **www.sfscience.com.**

Unit Overview

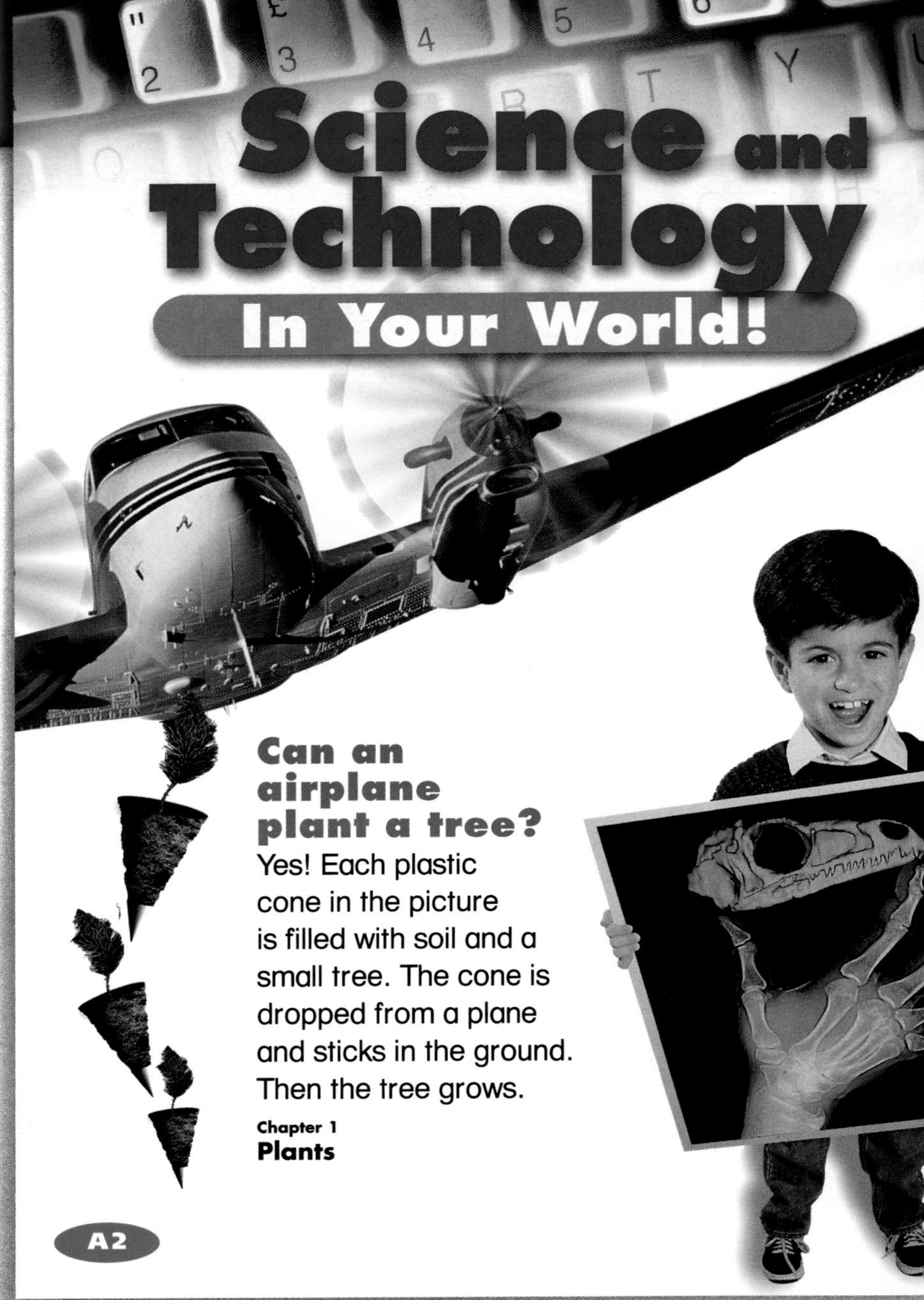

Science and Technology In Your World!

Can an airplane plant a tree?

Yes! Each plastic cone in the picture is filled with soil and a small tree. The cone is dropped from a plane and sticks in the ground. Then the tree grows.

Chapter 1
Plants

A2

Teaching Science and Technology

Unit A Life Science pages are also on the **Flip Chart.**

Have children look at the pictures. Talk about ways these pictures show examples of technology.

- A new invention is designed to plant forests in hard-to-get areas such as mountains. Trees are placed in plastic cones. The cones are dropped into the ground from airplanes. The plastic of the cone is biodegradable; wind and rain will wear it away so the tree can grow.
- The Robot Zoo is a traveling museum exhibit featuring eight animals whose body parts are made of different machines such as food processors and pistons. Each animal's "brain" or control center is a computer that allows the robots to move in ways that mimic their real-life counterparts.
- CT scans and X-rays make it possible for scientists to study dinosaur bones without destroying the bones.

Writing for Science

Persuasive
Write a Letter

Ask children to write a letter to the leader of their community persuading him or her to approve the use of cone devices to plant trees. Remind children to follow the steps of the writing process: prewrite, draft, revise, edit, and publish.

The Writing Process

The Writing Process

1. **Prewrite**
   - Talk with another person about things you can write about.
   - Choose one thing and draw a picture of it.
2. **Draft**
   Write sentences about your picture.
3. **Revise**
   Read what you wrote. Do you like it? Make changes if you want to.
4. **Edit**
   Check your writing to make sure it is correct. Make a neat copy.
5. **Publish**
   Share your picture and your writing with others.

Instructional Resources p. xi

What kind of animal has a long neck made of metal?

It's a giraffe in the Robot Zoo! The animals in the Robot Zoo look and move like real animals. Yet they are all made of metal machine parts.

Chapter 2
Animals

What can scientists learn from dinosaur bones?

Scientists use X-rays and other machines to learn about dinosaur bones. The bones can tell scientists how big the animal's eyes were, and how well it was able to hear and smell.

Chapter 3
Fossils

A3

INQUIRY

One aspect of inquiry involves asking questions. Give each child three index cards, one for each chapter in this unit. After they read the Science and Technology pages, children can write one question about each chapter. Throughout each chapter, children should use their text and other resources to look for the answer to their question. At the conclusion of each chapter, children should share the answer to their question with the class.

Math-Science Connection

Geometric Shapes

Direct children's attention to the picture of the airplane planting a tree. Have children name and describe the shape of the plastic container used to hold the soil and the tree. Then have children identify a cone-shaped item in the classroom and describe its characteristics. Ask: **Can it roll? Does it have sides and corners? How many faces does it have? Why do you think the cone shape was chosen for the tree?** Encourage children to explore other solid figures. Ask: **How are they like cones? How are they different?**

Chapter 1 Planning Guide

Lesson/Activity and Flip Chart	Objectives/Process Skills	Time Options/Activity Materials
Chapter Opener Student Edition pp. A4–A5 and **Flip Chart** ***How Did That Plant Get There?***		**Have less time?** Use the Graphic Organizer on Teacher's Assessment Package p. 3 for an overview of the lessons. Use the Flip Chart to teach lesson concepts and science activities. **Have more time?** Use the Flip Chart to reinforce and extend lesson concepts and activities. Use the Cross-Curricular Options in the Activity Idea Bank on Teacher's Edition pp. A11b, A17b, and A23b.
Lesson 1 Student Edition pp. A6–A7 ***What are some kinds of plants?*** **Explore Activity** ***Classify plants.*** **Flip Chart** ***Talk About Science***	**Objective** Classify plants based on their characteristics. **Process Skills** observing, classifying	**Kit Items** none **School-Supplied Items** magazines, catalogs, scissors, glue **Advance Prep** Bring in a variety of plants such as ivy, cacti, tulips, ferns.
Lesson 2 Student Edition pp. A8–A9 ***What does a plant need to grow?*** **Explore Activity** ***Make a light box.*** **Flip Chart** ***Talk About Science***	**Objective** Identify the basic needs of plants. **Process Skills** predicting, observing	**Kit Items** pinto bean seeds, cups, potting soil (*to prepare potted plants*) **School-Supplied Items** shoe boxes with lids **Advance Prep** Plant seeds about 10 days before doing the activity. Cut a hole in one end of each shoebox.
Lesson 3 Student Edition pp. A10–A11 and **Flip Chart** **Experiment Activity** ***Experiment with plants.***	**Objective** Experiment to determine what happens to a plant when it is deprived of light. **Process Skills** experimenting, predicting, observing (*formulating hypotheses, identifying and controlling variables, collecting data*)	**Kit Items** pinto bean seeds, cups, potting soil (*to prepare potted plants*) **School-Supplied Items** water, grocery bag **Advance Prep** Plant seeds about 10 days before doing the activity. Be sure the same kind of plants are used by all children.
Activity Idea Bank Teacher's Edition pp. A11a–A11b **Flip Chart** **Science Center Explore Activity** ***Describe plants.***	**Objective** Describe a plant. **Process Skills** observing	**Kit Items** none **School-Supplied Items** pictures of plants
Reading for Science Student Edition pp. A12–A13 ***Using Vocabulary Words***	**Objective** Use vocabulary words.	
Lesson 4 Student Edition pp. A14–A15 ***What are the parts of a plant?*** **Flip Chart** ***Talk About Science***	**Objectives** • Identify the parts of a plant. • Describe each part's function.	**Have more time?** Use the following teaching option: Interactive Transparency 1, Interactive Transparency Package
Lesson 5 Student Edition pp. A16–A17 ***How does a plant grow and change?*** **Explore Activity** ***Watch a plant grow.*** **Flip Chart** ***Talk About Science***	**Objective** Describe the growth and development of a plant. **Process Skills** observing, estimating and measuring	**Kit Items** pinto seeds (*pre-soaked*), plastic cup, potting soil **School-Supplied Items** water, ruler **Advance Prep** Punch holes in the bottom of each cup; soak seeds overnight; bring in fruit or vegetables with seeds.
Activity Idea Bank Teacher's Edition pp. A17a–A17b **Flip Chart** **Science Center Explore Activity** ***Make a plant.***	**Objective** Identify the parts of a plant. **Process Skills** observing, making and using models	**Kit Items** none **School-Supplied Items** art supplies
Lesson 6 Student Edition pp. A18–A19 and **Flip Chart** **Investigate Activity** ***What is inside a seed?***	**Objective** Identify the parts of a seed. **Process Skills** observing	**Kit Items** lima bean seeds (*pre-soaked*), hand lens **School-Supplied Items** none **Advance Prep** Presoak beans for at least two hours or overnight.
Lesson 7 Student Edition pp. A20–A21 ***How are seeds scattered?*** **Flip Chart** ***Talk About Science***	**Objective** Identify ways seeds can be scattered.	
Lesson 8 Student Edition pp. A22–A23 ***How do people use plants?*** **Flip Chart** ***Talk About Science***	**Objective** Identify products that come from plants.	
Activity Idea Bank Teacher's Edition pp. A23a–A23b **Flip Chart** **Science Center Explore Activity** ***Design a seed.***	**Objective** Discover characteristics of seeds that allow for better wind dispersal. **Process Skills** measuring, controlling variables	**Kit Items** clay, sponge, feathers, cork **School-Supplied Items** art supplies, meter stick
Chapter Review Student Edition pp. A24–A25 and **Flip Chart**		**Kit Items** none **School-Supplied Items** paper, pencil, crayons or markers **Advance Prep** Bring in picture books that show how plants grow; provide examples of flipbooks.

Lesson/Activity and Flip Chart	Additional Resources		Technology
Chapter Opener Student Edition pp. A4–A5 and **Flip Chart** ***How Did That Plant Get There?***	**Teacher's Assessment Package** • Graphic Organizer, p. 3 **Instructional Resources** • Family Activity, pp. 1–2 • Vocabulary Preview, p. 3	**Songs & Activities Package** • *How Did That Plant Get There?*, pp. 9–10 **Wall Chart,** p.1	**Practice & Assessment CD-ROM** **AudioText** **Production Studio** **www.sfscience.com** **Songs & Activities Package** **Teacher's Resource Planner CD-ROM**
Lesson 1 Student Edition pp. A6–A7 ***What are some kinds of plants?*** **Explore Activity** ***Classify plants.*** **Flip Chart** ***Talk About Science***	**Lab Manual** • Lab Manual, p.1 • Activity Rubric, p. T1	**Teacher Demonstration Kit** **Wall Chart,** p.2	
Lesson 2 Student Edition pp. A8–A9 ***What does a plant need to grow?*** **Explore Activity** ***Make a light box.*** **Flip Chart** ***Talk About Science***	**Lab Manual** • Lab Manual, p. 3 • Activity Rubric, p. T1	**Teacher Demonstration Kit**	
Lesson 3 Student Edition pp. A10–A11 and **Flip Chart** **Experiment Activity** ***Experiment with plants.***	**Lab Manual** • Lab Manual, pp. 5–6 • Activity Rubric, p. T2	**Teacher Demonstration Kit**	*Life Science* **Activity Video**
Activity Idea Bank Teacher's Edition pp. A11a–A11b **Flip Chart** **Science Center Explore Activity** ***Describe plants.***	**Lab Manual** • Lab Manual, p. 7 • Activity Rubric, p. T2		
Reading for Science Student Edition pp. A12–A13 ***Using Vocabulary Words***	**Instructional Resources** • Reading for Science, p. 4		
Lesson 4 Student Edition pp. A14–A15 ***What are the parts of a plant?*** **Flip Chart** ***Talk About Science***	**Interactive Transparency Package** • Interactive Transparency 1		
Lesson 5 Student Edition pp. A16–A17 ***How does a plant grow and change?*** **Explore Activity** ***Watch a plant grow.*** **Flip Chart** ***Talk About Science***	**Lab Manual** • Lab Manual, p. 9 • Activity Rubric, p. T3	**Teacher Demonstration Kit** **Wall Chart,** p. 3	
Activity Idea Bank Teacher's Edition pp. A17a–A17b **Flip Chart** **Science Center Explore Activity** ***Make a plant.***	**Lab Manual** • Lab Manual, p. 11 • Activity Rubric, p. T3		
Lesson 6 Student Edition pp. A18–A19 and ***Flip Chart*** **Investigate Activity** ***What is inside a seed?***	**Lab Manual** • Lab Manual, p. 13 • Activity Rubric, p. T4	**Teacher Demonstration Kit**	*Life Science* **Activity Video**
Lesson 7 Student Edition pp. A20–A21 ***How are seeds scattered?*** **Flip Chart** ***Talk About Science***		**Wall Chart,** p. 4	
Lesson 8 Student Edition pp. A22–A23 ***How do people use plants?*** **Flip Chart** ***Talk About Science***		**Wall Chart,** p. 5	
Activity Idea Bank Teacher's Edition pp. A23a–A23b **Flip Chart** **Science Center Explore Activity** ***Design a seed.***	**Lab Manual** • Lab Manual, p. 15 • Activity Rubric, p. T4		
Chapter Review Student Edition pp. A24–A25 and **Flip Chart**	**Teacher's Assessment Package** • Chapter 1 Assessment, p. 5–6		**Practice & Assessment CD-ROM** **Production Studio** **The Know Zone™ at www.kz.com** **TestWorks™**

Lab Manual

What are some kinds of plants?

Observe your pictures. How are the plants alike? How are they different?

Classify the pictures in as many ways as you can.

Glue your pictures to show one way you classified the plants. Label each side.

Student may identify similarities of parts (they all have roots, stem, leaves), of color (they may all be green), of size (if they are of comparable size).

Student may identify differences of size, shape, color.

Student may classify plants in terms of color, shape of leaves, size of leaves, size of stem, plants with/without fruit, plants with/without flowers.

Lab Manual p. 1

Lab Manual

What does a plant need to grow?

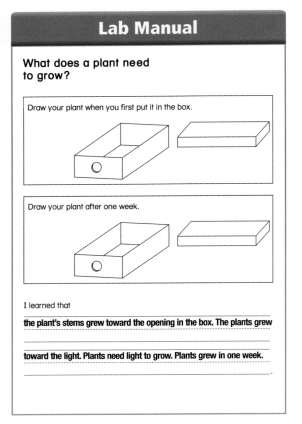

Draw your plant when you first put it in the box.

Draw your plant after one week.

I learned that

the plant's stems grew toward the opening in the box. The plants grew toward the light. Plants need light to grow. Plants grew in one week.

Lab Manual p. 3

Lab Manual

Experiment with plants.

Problem

What happens to plants that do not get light?

Give Your Hypothesis

If you put a plant in a dark place for a week, how will it look? Write what you think.

Hypotheses will vary. Student will probably anticipate some kind of change for the plant in a dark place over a period of one week. Students' predictions should reflect their hypotheses.

Control the Variables

Make sure that both plants get the same amount of water.

Test Your Hypothesis

Follow the steps to do the experiment.

Predict. How do you think the plants will look after one week?

Observe both plants after one week.

Lab Manual p. 5

Lab Manual

Collect Your Data

Draw your plants when you start. Draw your prediction for each plant. Draw what happened.

Covered plant

When I started	My prediction	What happened

Plant in light

When I started	My prediction	What happened

Tell Your Conclusion

What happens to plants that do not get light?

Students should conclude that plants will not stay healthy without light. Observations may include loss of color and less growth.

Inquire Further

What would happen to the covered plant if you put it in a light place now?

Responses will vary. Students may think that the plant's health could improve.

Lab Manual p. 6

Lab Manual

Describe plants.

Glue a picture of a plant to this paper.

Finish each sentence. Use the word bank on the flip chart.

Answers will vary. Students will use the phrases in the word bank to describe size, color, shape, and habitat.

This plant is

This plant is

Lab Manual p. 7

Reading for Science

Using Vocabulary Words

Make a science dictionary for Chapter 1. Write the science vocabulary words in your science dictionary. Write what the word means and draw a picture.

Word	Word Meaning	Picture
stem	The stem is the part of the plant that carries water to the leaves.	
roots	Roots hold a plant in the soil. They also take in water from the soil.	
leaves	The leaves use light, air, and water to make sugars that a plant needs to grow.	
flowers	Flowers make seeds.	
scatter	Scatter means to spread out.	

Instructional Resources
p. 4

Transparency

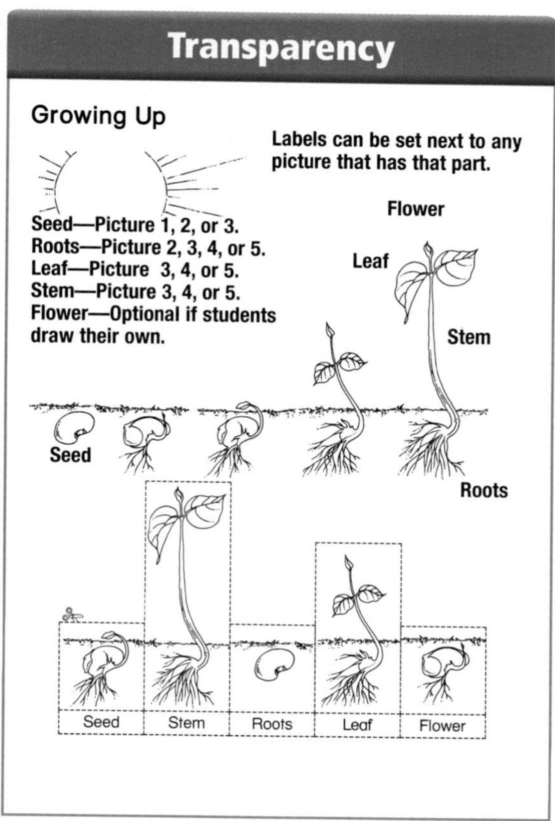

Growing Up
Labels can be set next to any picture that has that part.
Seed—Picture 1, 2, or 3.
Roots—Picture 2, 3, 4, or 5.
Leaf—Picture 3, 4, or 5.
Stem—Picture 3, 4, or 5.
Flower—Optional if students draw their own.
Flower
Leaf
Stem
Seed
Roots
Seed
Stem
Roots
Leaf
Flower

Interactive Transparency Package
Transparency 1

Lab Manual

How does a plant grow and change?

1. Make a book.
2. **Observe** and draw what you see every 2 or 3 days.
3. **Measure** your plants once a week. Record.

Measurements will vary.

Day ___

How does a plant grow and change?

Answers will vary. Student may observe the day when the stem first emerges from the soil. Recorded measurements will vary.

Day ___

The plant is ___ cm.

Day ___

Lab Manual
p. 9

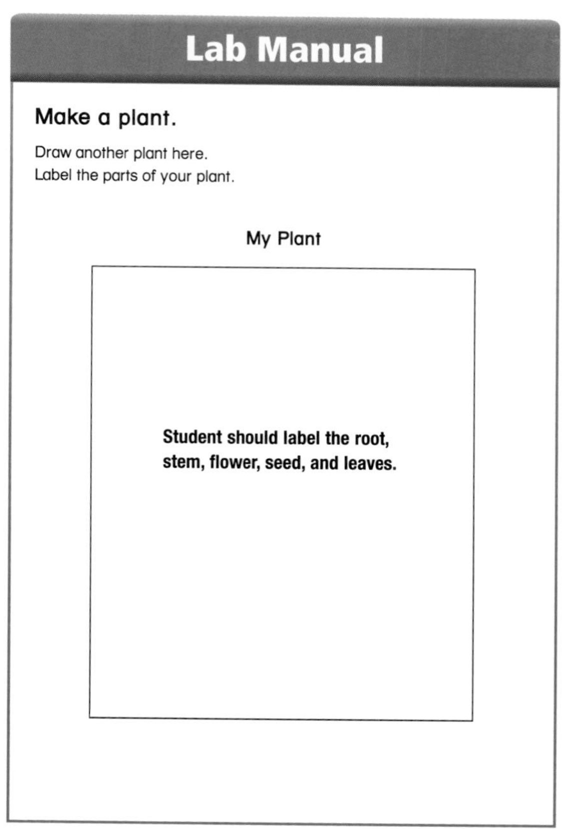

Lab Manual

Make a plant.

Draw another plant here.
Label the parts of your plant.

My Plant

Student should label the root, stem, flower, seed, and leaves.

Lab Manual
p. 11

Lab Manual

What is inside a seed?

1. Color and cut out the bean pieces and tiny plant. Punch the holes.
2. Use a paper fastener to put the model together.
3. Point to the stored food and the tiny plant.

Students will place the labels so that "tiny plant" is directed to the small leafy part of the diagram and "stored food" is directed to the larger seed area.

Lab Manual
p. 13

Lab Manual

Design a seed.

What materials did you use to make your seed?

Write or draw.

Answers will vary. Students may guess that their seeds can fly far away. Some may relate distance to the wind. Measurements of distance will vary.

How far will your seed fly?

Prediction

Results

Lab Manual
p. 15

Chapter 1 Assessment

Use the words in the box to finish each sentence.

stem	roots	leaves	flower

1. The **roots** hold the plant in the soil.
2. The **stem** carries water to the leaves.
3. The **flower** is the part of the plant that makes seeds.
4. The **leaves** make sugars that the plant needs to grow.

Write Yes or No.

yes 5. Fruits cover and protect seeds.

no 6. All plants have the same kinds of seeds.

yes 7. Seeds can travel in different ways.

yes 8. Plants can be used for many things including food and clothing.

yes 9. Plants need sunlight in order to grow.

no 10. All plants have bright flowers.

yes 11. New plants grow from seeds.

Teacher's Assessment Package
p. 5

Chapter 1 Assessment

Draw a line from each word to the correct part of the picture.

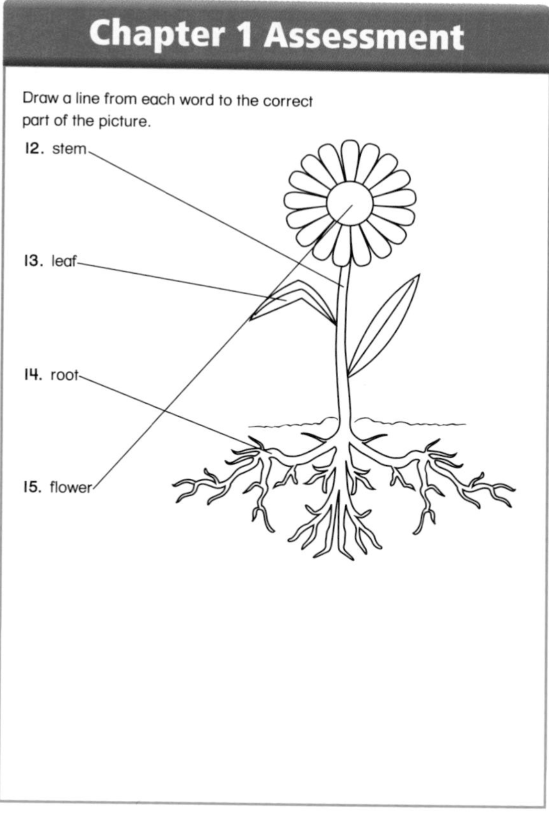

Teacher's Assessment Package
p. 6

Table of Contents

Introducing the Chapter

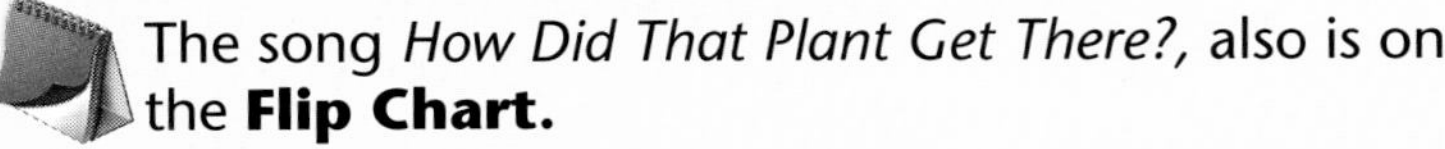

The song *How Did That Plant Get There?,* also is on the **Flip Chart.**

- Ask children what they know about plants. Tell them they will learn more about plants in this chapter.
- Distribute the Family Activity blackline master page.

Singing the Song

Have children sing the song *How Did That Plant Get There?,* on side 1 of the CTW cassette. Distribute pages 9–10 from the CTW Song Activity Book.

Reading Assist *Print Cues*

Write a question mark on the chalkboard. Read aloud the song title. Point out the question mark at the end of the title and explain that it signals a question. Ask children to find and read aloud other questions in the song.

Vocabulary Preview

Use Vocabulary Preview blackline master to introduce the vocabulary words for this chapter.

Lesson 4 roots, stem, leaves, flowers

Lesson 7 scatter

Chapter 1

Plants

How Did That Plant Get There?

Sing to the tune of *Where, Oh Where Has My Little Dog Gone?*

How, oh how did that plant get there?
It must have started from seed.
There's a stem, some leaves, and a bud on top,
And it's growing at a fast speed.

How, oh how did that plant get there?
And now what else does it need?
It needs air and water and light to grow,
On that we all can agree.

Technology

Practice & Assessment CD-ROM

AudioText

Production Studio

www.sfscience.com

Teacher's Resource Planner

Songs & Activities Package

CTW Song & Activity

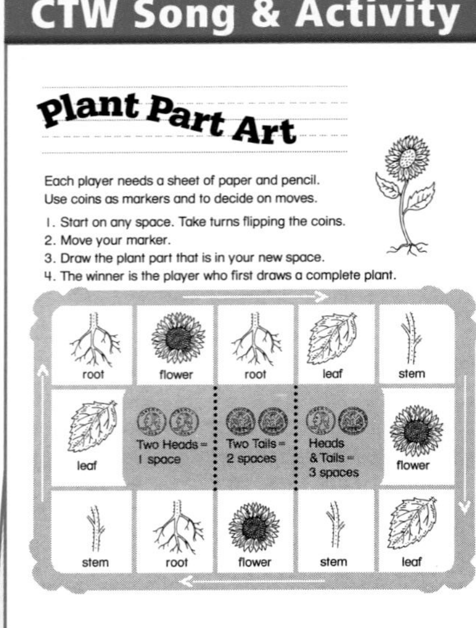

Plant Part Art
Each player needs a sheet of paper and pencil.
Use coins as markers and to decide on moves.
1. Start on any space. Take turns flipping the coins.
2. Move your marker.
3. Draw the plant part that is in your new space.
4. The winner is the player who first draws a complete plant.
root
flower
root
leaf
stem
leaf
Two Heads = 1 space
Two Tails = 2 spaces
Heads & Tails = 3 spaces
flower
stem
root
flower
stem
leaf

Songs & Activities Package pp. 9–10

But, how, oh how did that plant get there?
It makes me wonder indeed.
Was it wind or water or maybe a bird
That dropped off a traveling seed?

Original lyrics by Gerri Brioso and Richard Freitas.
Produced by Children's Television Workshop.

INQUIRY

Use a KWL chart at the beginning of each new chapter to encourage inquiry. In the *K* column, record what children already *know* about plants. In the *W* column, help children brainstorm a list of what they *want* to know. Throughout the chapter, ask children what they have *learned* and record their responses in the *L* column. A KWL chart is available on **Wall Chart** page 1.

Chapter 1 Skills Trace

Process Skills Development

	Observing	Classifying	Predicting	Experimenting	Estimating and Measuring
Skill Introduced	xiv	xiv	xv	xv	xiv
Skill Applied	A7 A9 A10–A11 A17 A18–A19	A7	A9 A10–A11	A10–A11	A17
Skill Assessed	End Matter 6–7	End Matter 10–11	End Matter 16–17	End Matter 28–29	End Matter 12–13

Family Activity

Science at Home

Dear Family:
Our class is starting Chapter 1. We will be learning about plants. These are the main ideas for Chapter 1.

- There are different kinds of plants.
- Plants need water, air, food, and light to grow.
- Parts of a plant are roots, stem, leaves, and flower.
- Flowers make seeds.
- Seeds are scattered by wind, water, and animals.
- Food and other useful products come from plants.

We will also be learning science vocabulary words for Chapter 1. By the end of Chapter 1, we will be able to read the vocabulary words and tell what they mean.

Word Bank
stem
roots
leaves
flowers
scatter

Home Projects

Here are some activities that will help your child understand the main ideas in Chapter 1. The activities are easy, fast, and fun.

Activities

- With your child, find out about plant parts we eat.

1. Look in the kitchen for plants we eat.
2. Look in magazines or a newspaper for plants we eat. Cut out the pictures.
3. Make a poster with the pictures.

Instructional Resources pp. 1–2

Vocabulary Preview

stem	roots
leaves	flower
scatter	oxygen
seeds	classify

Instructional Resources p. 3

Science Literature Library

Dandelion Adventures
by L. Patricia Kite.
Seven dandelion seed parachutes are carried away by the wind, each one landing in a different place, and eventually growing into new plants. A simple story to illustrate how common plants regenerate. (The Millbrook Press, ISBN 0-7613-0377-4)

Lesson Organizer

Objective
Classify plants based on their characteristics.

Process Skills observing, classifying

Materials
Kit Items none

School-Supplied Items magazines or catalogs, scissors, glue

Additional Resources
- Lab Manual
- Teacher Demonstration Kit
- Wall Chart

Introduce

Activate Prior Knowledge
Bring in different kinds of plants for children to observe. Help children identify each plant and ask them where they think it might grow.

Language Development *Scientific Language*
Explain that everyday speech and scientific language are sometimes the same and sometimes different. Read simple dictionary definitions of *tree* and *flower.* Ask children if these match their ideas of what the words mean. Discuss how they are different. Ask volunteers to find a tree, a large plant, and a flower in the picture.

Flip Chart
Have children identify the different kinds of plants in the picture: bean plants, flowers, trees, grass. Discuss the characteristics of each kind of plant.

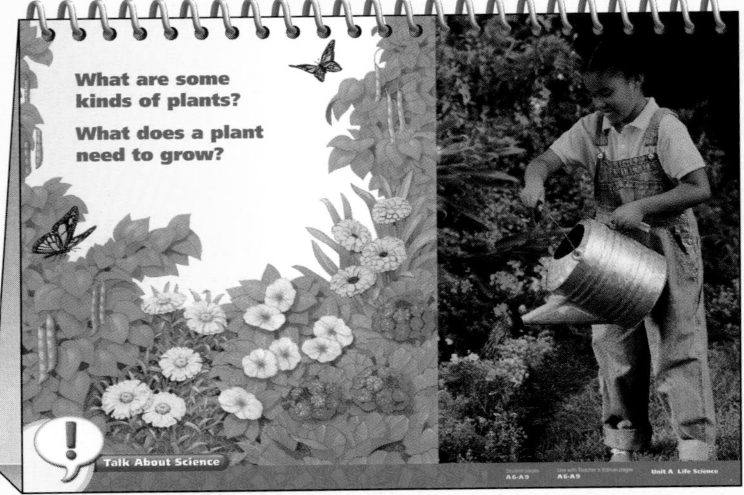

What are some kinds of plants?
What does a plant need to grow?
Talk About Science

What are some kinds of plants?

You see them every day. Some tower over you. Some are smaller than your little finger. What are they? If you guessed plants, you were right!

There are many kinds of plants. Most plants have leaves. Some leaves are wide and flat. Others are as thin as needles. What kinds of leaves do you see in the picture?[1]

Some plants have bright flowers. Some plants make fruits you can eat. Some grow best in hot, dry places. Others need lots of rain. What plants grow where you live?

[1] leaves of va[rious] sizes, shape[s], textures

Science Background
Plants can be classified into groups.
- Mosses are found in damp, shady places; most are shorter than an inch.
- Cone-bearing trees have cones that contain the seeds.
- Flowering plants have flowers and fruits.

Math-Science Connection
Take children for a nature walk and have them count the number of flowers, large plants, and trees they see. When they return to the classroom, make a bar graph to show their findings on **Wall Chart** page 2. Discuss what the graph shows.

Classify plants.

Materials

- scissors
- magazines or catalogs
- glue

Process Skills

- observing
- classifying

Steps

1. Cut out pictures of plants from your magazines.
2. **Observe** the pictures. How are the plants alike? How are they different?
3. **Classify** the pictures in as many ways as you can.

Share. Glue your pictures on a chart to show one way you can **classify** plants.

Lesson Review

1. How do some plants look different from others?
2. Where do plants live?
3. **Tell** two ways you can classify plants.

Teach and Apply

Student Page A6

Discuss how the plants are alike and different—color, type, size, kinds of leaves, flowers, fruit.

Student Page A7

Explore Activity

Time about 30 minutes

Grouping individual

Encourage children to find many ways to classify their pictures of plants, such as by color, size, shape, type. Children can complete Lab Manual page 1.

Reading Assist *Navigating the Page*

Direct children's attention to the page organization: lesson title, activity type, activity title, activity parts—Materials, Process Skills, Steps, Share—and Lesson Review. Discuss how to use these parts of the page.

Assess and Extend

Answers to Lesson Review

1. Children may say plants differ by color and shape of leaves, some have flowers and some do not, some plants make fruit.
2. Some plants grow in hot, dry places. Others need a lot of rain.
3. **Tell** (*Interview*) Children may say plants with leaves/plants without leaves; big plants/small plants; plants with flowers/plants without flowers.

Inquire Further

Ask the following question to guide further inquiry: **What can you learn about plants that grow in your community?** (*Answers may include kinds of local plants and what they need to live.*)

Lab Manual

What are some kinds of plants?

Observe your pictures. How are the plants alike? How are they different?

Classify the pictures in as many ways as you can.

Glue your pictures to show one way you classified the plants. Label each side.

Lab Manual
p. 1

Activity Rubric

Use the following activity scoring rubric to assess students' performance.

Scoring Criteria	1	2	3	4
Student followed instructions to perform the comparisons.				
Student observed similarities and differences based on pictures of plants.				
Student communicated his or her observations about the plants.				
Student completed the chart by classifying the plants using at least two characteristics.				
Student explained how the plants were classified in his or her chart.				

Scoring Key

4 points correct, complete, detailed
3 points partially correct, complete, detailed
2 points partially correct, partially complete, lacks some detail
1 point incorrect or incomplete, needs assistance

Lab Manual
p. T1

Enrichment

Display some field guides for plants. Challenge children to find listings of plants that are common to your community and then create a neighborhood field guide.

Higher Order Thinking *Apply*

Ask children to tell what kinds of plants usually grow outdoors and what kinds can be grown indoors.

Call 1-888-537-4908 with your Activity questions or comments.

Lesson Organizer

Objective
Identify the basic needs of plants.

Process Skills predicting, observing

Materials
Kit Items pinto bean seeds, cups, potting soil (*to prepare potted plants*)

School-Supplied Items shoe boxes with lids

Additional Resources
- Lab Manual
- Teacher Demonstration Kit

Introduce

Activate Prior Knowledge
Ask children what things help them live and grow. Write their answers on the chalkboard. (*Children's responses will probably include food, water, and air.*)

Language Development *Literature*
Read aloud stories that have references to plants, such as "Jack and the Beanstalk," "The Little Red Hen," and "The Tale of Peter Rabbit." Have children identify the different plants and discuss the importance of plants to the characters in the stories.

Flip Chart
Discuss what the girl in the picture is doing and why it is important. Ask: **What other things do the plants in the picture need to grow?** (*light, water, soil*)

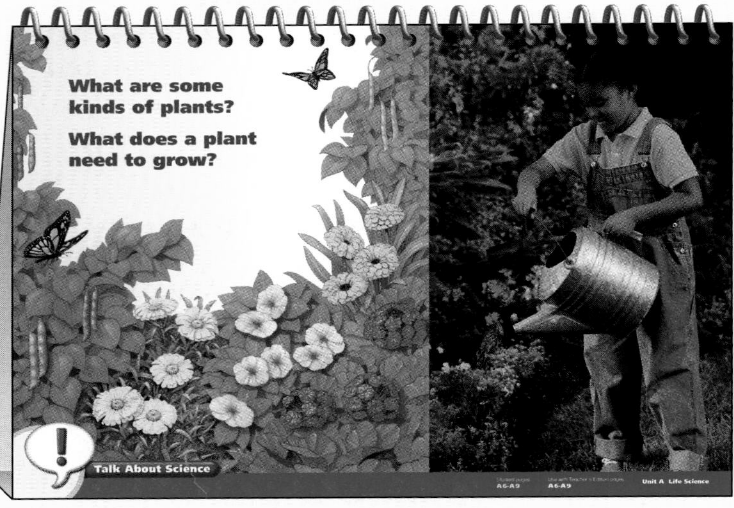

What does a plant need to grow?

Pretend this window box is yours. What would you plant in it? How would you help your plants grow?

Plants need light to grow well. Some plants need a lot of sunlight. Others need only a little sunlight.

These plants grow in soil. They need air and water, too. With the right amounts of light, air, and water, most plants can grow well.

People can help plants grow. How is the boy in the picture helping his plants grow?[1]

[1] watering

Science Background

Plants use the food they produce to make energy. To make food, plants need:

- light, as a source of energy
- air, as a source of carbon dioxide
- water, which they get from the soil, through the roots
- nutrients, such as nitrates and phosphates, which they get from the soil, dissolved in water

Possible Misconceptions Some children may think that all plants must have soil to make food. Plants need only the nutrients found in soil, and some plants can survive in water if the nutrients are provided.

Make a light box.

Materials

shoe box with lid

potted plant

Process Skills

- predicting
- observing

Steps

1. Make a light box like the one in the picture.
2. Cover the box with the lid. Place the box so the hole faces a sunny spot.
3. **Predict** how your plant will grow.
4. **Observe** your plant after one week.

Share. Draw how your plant grew in the box.

Lesson Review

1. What do plants need to help them grow?
2. How can people help plants grow?
3. **Tell** why your plant grew the way it did in the box.

A9

Lab Manual

What does a plant need to grow?

Draw your plant when you first put it in the box.

Draw your plant after one week.

I learned that

Lab Manual
p. 3

Activity Rubric

Use the following activity scoring rubric to assess students' performance.

Scoring Criteria	1	2	3	4
Student followed directions to make the plant comparisons.				
Student drew examples of plant growth at the beginning and end of one week.				
Student made a prediction about how the plant would grow.				
Student observed the plant after one week.				
Student wrote an explanation of what he or she learned.				

Scoring Key
4 points correct, complete, detailed
3 points partially correct, complete, detailed
2 points partially correct, partially complete, lacks some detail
1 point incorrect or incomplete, needs assistance

Lab Manual
p. T1

Teach and Apply

Student Page A8

Discuss how the boy in the picture is providing some of the things the plants need to grow.

Student Page A9

Explore Activity

Time about 30 minutes

Grouping cooperative groups of 4

Plant seeds about 10 days before doing the activity. In advance, cut a hole in one end of each shoe box. Bean plants work well for this activity. Be sure to use plants that are almost tall enough to touch the box lid.

Have children water their plants before putting them into the boxes and as needed during the week. Children can use Lab Manual page 3.

Reading Assist *Technical/Specialized Word*

Write the word *observe* on the chalkboard. Have children find it on page A9. Review the meaning of the word and point out that it will occur frequently in the science book.

What to Expect

Children should observe that the stems twist and turn as they grow toward the light.

Assess and Extend

Answers to Lesson Review

1. Plants need light, air, and water to grow.
2. People can help plants grow by providing light, air, soil, and water.
3. **Tell** (*Interview*) The plant needs light to grow. The plant followed the path through the box to the light.

Inquire Further

Ask the following question to guide further inquiry: **What would happen if you didn't water your plant for more than one week?** (*It would wilt.*)

Higher Order Thinking *Compare and Contrast*

Ask children to tell how the needs of people and plants are alike and different.

Call 1-888-537-4908 with your Activity questions or comments.

Activity Organizer

Objective

Experiment to determine what happens to a plant when it is deprived of light.

Process Skills experimenting, predicting, observing (*formulating hypotheses, identifying and controlling variables, collecting and interpreting data*)

Materials

Kit Items pinto bean seeds, cups, potting soil (*to prepare potted plants*)

School-Supplied Items water, grocery bag

Time about 30 minutes

Grouping cooperative groups of 4

Additional Resources

- Lab Manual
- Teacher Demonstration Kit

Introduce

Activity Summary

The Experiment Activity is also on the **Flip Chart.** In this activity, children use scientific methods to determine how a plant's growth is affected by a lack of light. To prepare potted plants, plant the seeds about 10 days before the activity. Children will find that plants exposed to sunlight will look green and healthy, while those kept in darkness will turn yellow.

Activate Prior Knowledge

Ask children to recall from Lesson 2 the three things plants need to grow. List air, water, and light on the chalkboard.

Using Scientific Language

Review the vocabulary of scientific methods on pages xii–xiii.

Reading Assist *Decoding*

In this experiment, it is helpful to review such words as *experiment, hypothesis, prediction,* and *conclusion* to make sure children can read and pronounce them. Use syllabication when necessary.

Experiment Activity

Experiment with plants.

Process Skills

- experimenting
- predicting
- observing

Materials

 2 potted plants

 water

grocery bag

Problem

What happens to plants that do not get light?

Give Your Hypothesis

If you put a plant in a dark place for a week, how will it look? Tell what you think.

Control the Variables

Make sure that both plants get the same amount of water.

Test Your Hypothesis

Follow these steps to do the experiment.

1. Water two plants.
2. Cover one plant. Put the other plant in the light.

A10

Science Background

The steps in this lesson follow general procedures scientists use to solve problems. Traditionally labeled scientific methods, these steps can be used in a variety of combinations.

Teaching Tips Bean plants work well for this experiment, but other options include pea, grass, or ivy plants. To control for variables, be sure to use the same kinds of plants. Depending on the type of plants used, they may need to be watered during the week.

Technology

Review the demonstration of this Experiment's procedure on the *Life Science* **Activity Video,** Segment 1.

3 **Predict.** How do you think the plants will look after one week?

4 **Observe** both plants after one week.

Collect Your Data

Use pictures like the ones shown. Draw your plants when you start. Draw your **prediction** for each plant. Draw what happened.

Tell Your Conclusion

Compare your results and hypothesis. What happens to plants that do not get light?

Inquire Further

What would happen to the covered plant if you put it in a light place now?

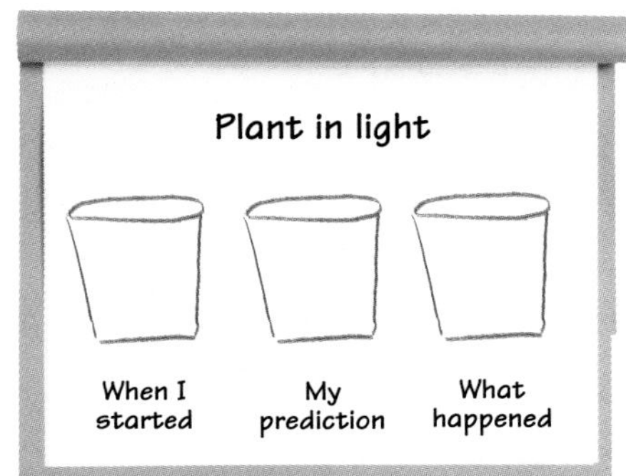

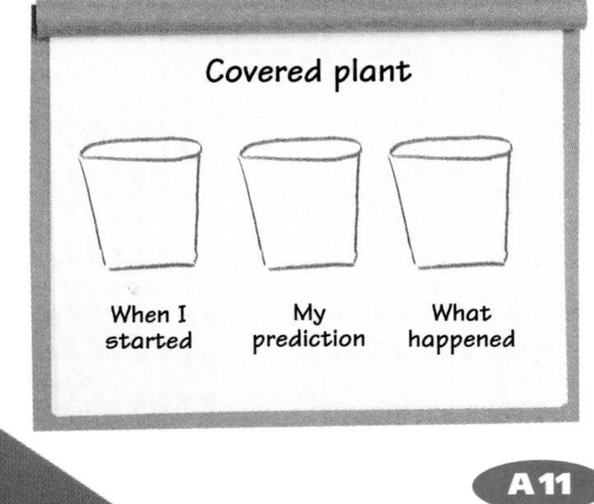

Teach and Apply

Problem

Ask children to share their ideas about how plants will look after being left in the sunlight and in the dark. Make a class chart of their predictions.

Give Your Hypothesis

Explain that a hypothesis is a possible answer to a problem. Have children record their hypotheses on Lab Manual page 5.

Control the Variables

Make sure both plants get the same amount of water.

Test Your Hypothesis

Have children observe their plants each day for changes.

Collect Your Data

Have children draw how their plants look and their predictions on the first day of the experiment. On the final day, have them draw what actually happened.

Assess and Extend

Tell Your Conclusion

Have children reread their hypothesis and compare it with their results. Children should conclude that plants will stay green and healthy when provided with air, water, and sunlight. Plants that do not get any light will turn yellow.

Inquire Further

Have children read the question on page A11 and work in small groups to find the answer. Have children record the question and answer on Lab Manual page 6.

Enrichment

Children place four plants in a sunny area and vary the amount of water each is given. They predict how each will grow, then check after one week and after two weeks.

Higher Order Thinking *Predict*

Ask: **Can a plant receive too much water? What do you think would happen to it?** (*Children might predict that plants receiving too much water may die.*)

Lab Manual

Experiment with plants.

Problem

What happens to plants that do not get light?

Give Your Hypothesis

If you put a plant in a dark place for a week, how will it look? Write what you think.

Control the Variables

Make sure that both plants get the same amount of water.

Test Your Hypothesis

Follow the steps to do the experiment.

Predict. How do you think the plants will look after one week?

Observe both plants after one week.

Lab Manual pp. 5–6

Activity Rubric

Use the following activity scoring rubric to assess students' performance.

Scoring Criteria	1	2	3	4
Student followed directions to perform the experiment.				
Student made a hypothesis about the plant kept in darkness for one week.				
Student controlled the water variable for each plant in the experiment.				
Student interpreted the data for the covered and uncovered plants by drawing pictures of the plants and making predictions.				
Student compared the result and hypothesis and explained the results of the experiment.				

Scoring Key

4 points correct, complete, detailed
3 points partially correct, complete, detailed
2 points partially correct, partially complete, lacks some detail
1 point incorrect or incomplete, needs assistance

Lab Manual p. T2

Call 1-888-537-4908 with your Activity questions or comments.

Science Center

Flip Chart

Describe plants.

Objective

Describe a plant.

Process Skills observing

Materials

Kit Items none

School-Supplied Items pictures of plants

Procedure

- Children look at pictures of plants and choose one to **observe**.
- Have children use the word bank to write descriptions of their plant.
- You can use **Lab Manual** page 7 with this activity.

What to Expect

Children's descriptions should include words and phrases from the word bank shown on the **Flip Chart.**

Lab Manual

Describe plants.

Glue a picture of a plant to this paper.

Finish each sentence. Use the word bank on the flip chart.

This plant is ____________

This plant is ____________

Lab Manual, p. 7

Connections

School and Community

Ideas for bringing the school and community together:

Field Trips

- local park or nature center
- plant nursery
- grocery store
- vegetable market

Guest Speakers

- florist
- botanist
- agricultural extension agent
- gardener

Themes

The activities on these pages can be used with classroom themes such as:

- plants
- growth
- gardening
- ecology

Books for Children

Children might enjoy these books about plants:

Why Do Leaves Change Color? by Betsy Maestro. The process leaves go through to change colors, with instructions on pressing leaves and making leaf rubbings. (HarperCollins, ISBN 0-06-445126-7)

Planting a Rainbow by Lois Ehlert. A mother and child plant a garden that becomes a rainbow of flowers to be picked and carried home. (Harcourt, ISBN 0-15-262610-7)

Cross-Curricular Options

LITERATURE

Plants That Never Ever Bloom

Use the book to learn about plants that do not bloom.

Materials *Plants That Never Ever Bloom* by Ruth Heller. (Grosset & Dunlap, ISBN 0-448-41092-3)

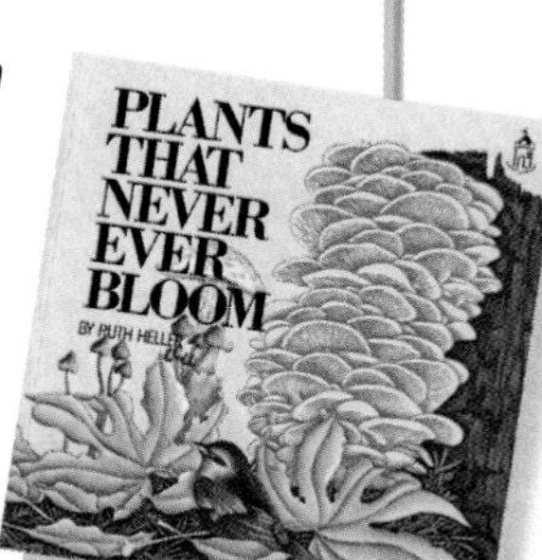

Procedure

- This rhyming book features mushrooms, algae, ferns, and other nonblooming plants.
- Let children study the illustrations, then design collages of nonblooming plants that live in the sea or on land.

Multiple Intelligences linguistic

Gifted and Talented Ask children to make a pictionary of plant words.

MATH

How Far Around?

Estimate circumference of tree trunks.

Materials string or yarn, scissors, ruler, meterstick, tape measure, poster board, pencil

Procedure

- Take children to a place that has trees.
- Partners cut a piece of string about the distance around a tree trunk. Then they measure the actual circumference with another piece of string.
- Back in the classroom, children measure each string and record the measurements. They compare estimates and measurements.

Multiple Intelligences logical-mathematical, spatial

ESL Display a ruler and a meterstick. Ask children to tell how many centimeters each measures.

WRITING

Scramble and Spell

Make and play a game.

Materials magazines, catalogs, glue, scissors, construction paper

Procedure

- Brainstorm a list of plant-related words and write them on the chalkboard.
- Have each child cut out letters from magazines and catalogs to spell a word and glue them onto paper in a scrambled way.
- Hold up a scrambled word and challenge children to identify it and spell it correctly.

Multiple Intelligences linguistic, spatial

ART

Leaf Rubbings

Compare leaves.

Materials variety of leaves, crayons with wrappers removed, white craft paper, tape

Procedure

- Demonstrate how to make a leaf rubbing: Tape a leaf, vein side down, onto white paper. Turn the paper over and rub the side of a crayon over the leaf.
- Invite children to choose several leaves and make their own rubbings.
- Have children compare the leaf shapes and patterns, including veins and edges.
- To expand the activity, have children make and compare rubbings of parts of different tree trunks.

Multiple Intelligences spatial, naturalist

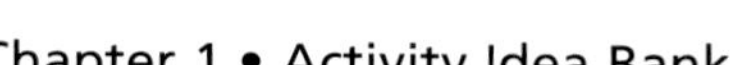

Reading Organizer

Objective

Use vocabulary words.

Additional Resources

- Reading for Science blackline master

Teaching Reading for Science

- The use of dark print is a familiar design element. In this book, dark print with yellow behind it cues the reader to important science terms. The dark print with yellow behind it helps call attention to words that may be unfamiliar.
- Creating a science dictionary actively involves children in constructing their understanding of vocabulary words. The science dictionary can be used to informally assess children's level of understanding of vocabulary words. In addition, children expand their science vocabulary as they write each word, write its meaning, and then draw a picture. These dictionary entries can be revisited and revised frequently as children explore the related science concepts.
- Have children read and complete the Reading for Science lesson and the Reading for Science blackline master.

Student Page A 12

- Invite children to point to the word in dark print with yellow behind it as you read the example sentence aloud. Discuss why the author used dark print for the word *stem.* Point out that the dark print calls attention to the word and lets the reader know it is an important science term.
- Have children tell in their own words what *stem* means. Discuss how the other words in the example sentence help them know the meaning of *stem.*

Using Vocabulary Words

In your science book, you will see some words in dark print with yellow behind them. Words in dark print look bigger than other words on the page.

These words are vocabulary words. When you read the sentence they are in, you will learn what the word means. Here is an example.

The **stem** is the part of the plant that carries water to the leaves.

Stem is the vocabulary word. The rest of the sentence tells what **stem** means.

A 12

ESL Strategy

Have children trace the stem in the picture with their fingers and identify the label. Explain that pictures and their labels can help us visualize, or see in our minds, what a word means. If you have a plant in your classroom, ask children to point to the stem.

When you see vocabulary words in this book, write them in your science dictionary. Then write what they mean and draw a picture.

stem
The stem is the part of the plant that carries water to the leaves.
stem

Turn the page.

Turn the page to learn some new vocabulary words.

Reading for Science

Using Vocabulary Words

Make a science dictionary for Chapter 1. Write the science vocabulary words in your science dictionary. Write what the word means and draw a picture.

Word	Word Meaning	Picture
stem	The stem is the part of the plant that carries water to the leaves.	

Instructional Resources p. 4

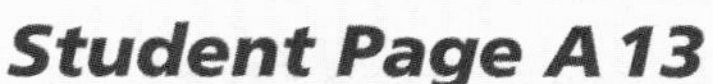

Student Page A 13

- Invite children to share their experiences using a dictionary. Focus the discussion on the purpose of a dictionary and the type of information found in it.
- Direct attention to the science dictionary entry on the page. Have children name ways this entry illustrates the meaning of *stem.*
- Point out that the vocabulary word *stem* names one part of a plant. Mention that grouping new words according to a theme, such as parts of a plant, can help children learn the new words.
- Help children make their own science dictionaries. Fold a sheet of colored construction paper and several sheets of writing paper. Place the construction paper on the outside of the stack. Staple the pages down the center, using a long-reach stapler.
- Children might want to copy their definitions from the science dictionary or put them into their own words.

Apply Reading for Science to Lesson 4

Children will use what they learned about vocabulary words to complete the next lesson.

Lesson Organizer

Objectives

- Identify the parts of a plant.
- Describe each part's function.

Vocabulary roots, stem, leaves, flowers

Additional Resources

- Interactive Transparency

Introduce

Activate Prior Knowledge

Show children a simple diagram of a plant, with roots, stem, leaves, and flowers. Have them write the names of the plant parts. Save children's work for use as a **baseline assessment.**

Language Development *Vocabulary*

Have children begin recording vocabulary words in their science dictionaries, as introduced in the Reading for Science lesson.

Flip Chart

Identify the plant parts in the picture and discuss what they do. Call out plant parts one at a time and have volunteers point to the part on the flowering plant.

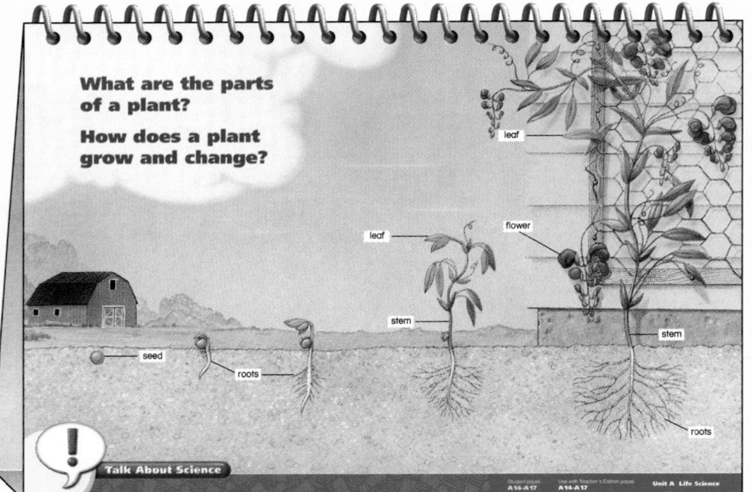

What are the parts of a plant?

A tree and a blade of grass do not look alike. Yet they both are plants. They both have the same parts.

What plant parts do you see in the picture?[1] Find the plant's roots. The **roots** hold the plant in the soil. They also take in water from the soil.

[1] roots, st leaves, a flower

Science Background

- Roots anchor the plant in the soil. Roots absorb water and minerals from the soil needed by the leaves to make food.
- Stems bring water and minerals from the roots to the leaves. Stems also bring food from the leaves to the rest of the plant.
- Leaves help plants receive light. Leaves use light to make sugars the plant uses for food. Most leaves are broad and flat to maximize the surface exposed to the sun.
- Flowers are the parts of the plant that make seeds that grow into the same type of plant. Most plants are pollinated by insects. The shapes, colors, and smells of their flowers attract the insects. Flowers that are tiny, green, and odorless are pollinated by the wind.

The **stem** is the part of the plant that carries water to the leaves. The **leaves** use light, air, and water to make sugars that the plant needs to grow.

Many plants have flowers. **Flowers** make seeds. New plants grow from the seeds.

Lesson Review

1. What are the parts of a plant?
2. How do leaves use light, air, and water?
3. **Tell** what each part of a plant does.

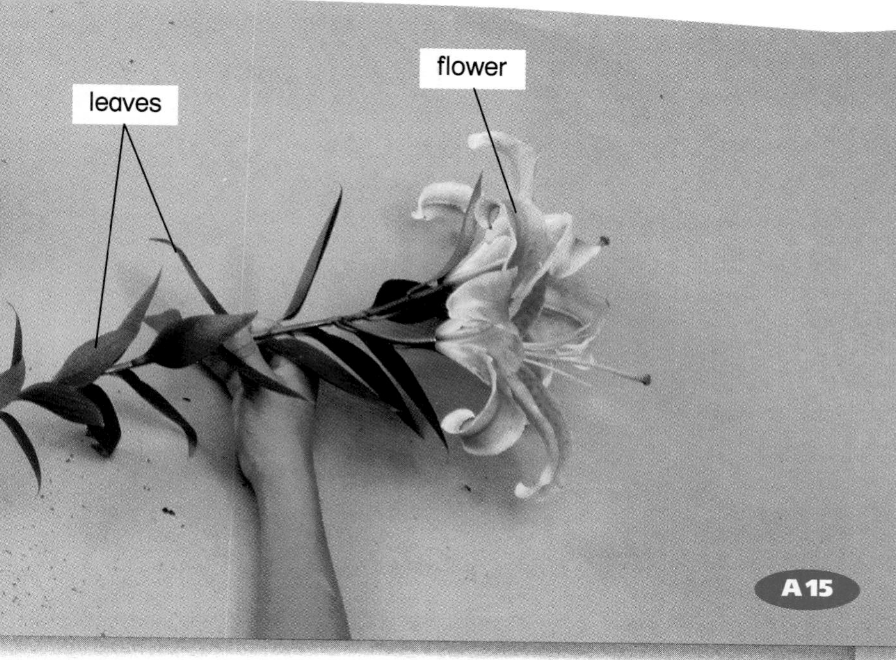

ESL Strategy

Point out that the vowel sound in *seeds* and *leaves* is the same, although the spelling is different. Note that there are a number of spellings for long vowel words. Mention other ways to write the long /e/: *e_e, ie, ei.*

Transparency

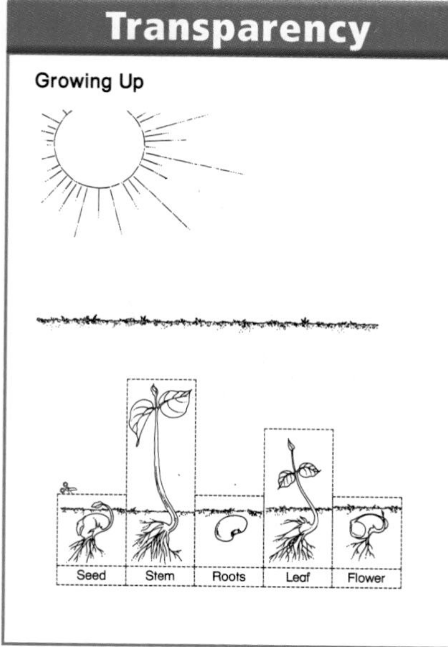

Interactive Transparency Package
Transparency 1

Teach and Apply

Student Pages A 14–A 15

After reading the pages, discuss how the various plant parts work together. Mention that there are nutrients—vitamins, minerals, proteins—in most soils that also help a plant grow. Like water, the nutrients are taken up through the roots.

Reading Assist *Vowel Combinations*
Help children identify the vowels or vowel combinations in the words *roots, stem, leaves,* and *flowers.* Review the sounds with children.

Assess and Extend

Answers to Lesson Review

1. The parts of a plant are the roots, stem, leaves, and flowers.
2. Leaves use light, air, and water to make sugars that the plant needs to grow.
3. **Tell** (***Interview***) Children's responses should include that roots hold the plant in the soil and take in water; the stem carries water to the leaves; the leaves make sugars that the plant needs to grow; and the flowers make seeds.

Check for Understanding

To follow up on the **baseline assessment,** show children once again the simple diagram of a plant. Ask them to tell the names of the plant parts and what each part does.

Reteach

- Use the Interactive Transparency to reteach Lesson 4 concepts.
- Have children make their own drawings of plants and label the parts. Encourage children to make their drawings colorful.

Lesson Organizer

Objective
Describe the growth and development of a plant.

Process Skills observing, estimating and measuring

Materials
Kit Items presoaked pinto seeds, plastic cup, potting soil

School-Supplied Items water, ruler

Additional Resources
- Lab Manual
- Teacher Demonstration Kit
- Wall Chart

Introduce

Activate Prior Knowledge
Discuss children's experiences with planting seeds.

Language Development *Make a List*
Help children brainstorm a list of kinds of seeds. Ask them to describe different things they have done with seeds, such as plant, cook, eat, and make pictures.

Flip Chart
Explain that the drawings in the picture are of the same plant. Discuss how the plant changes as it grows.

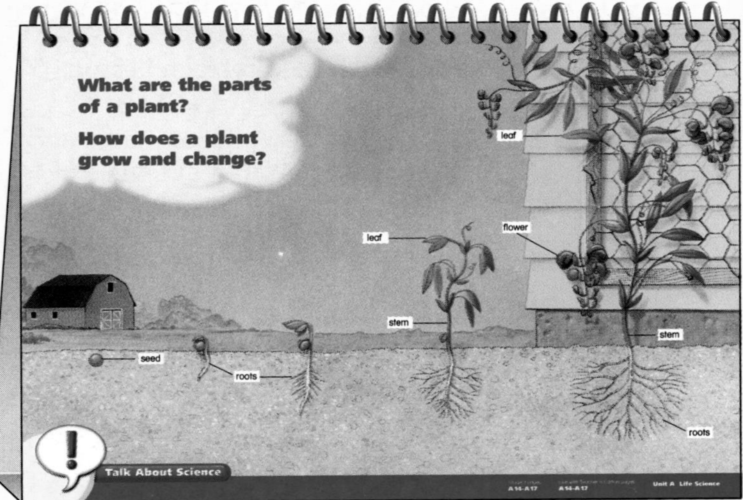

How does a plant grow and change?

Spring is here. The air is warm. Rain makes the soil soft and moist. Soon plants will start to grow.

Many plants grow from seeds. You can see a tiny plant inside this seed. The tiny plant uses the stored food as it grows.

Look at the picture of the growing plant. As the plant grows, the roots push down into the soil. Then the stem and leaves begin to grow.

Some plants make flowers too. The flowers will make seeds. Some of these seeds will grow into new plants. How will the new plants change as they grow?[1]

[1] **roots, stem, leaves, and flowers will grow**

Science Background

- Plants, like animals, grow by adding new cells. Almost all animal cells can reproduce, but only specialized tissue located at the ends of the plant can grow. The tip of the stem grows up toward the sky, and the tip of the root grows down into the earth.
- Some plants can also grow wider as well as taller.

Teaching Tips There are many other common seeds children can grow—green pepper, cantaloupe, pumpkin, tomato, or watermelon, for example.

Watch a plant grow.

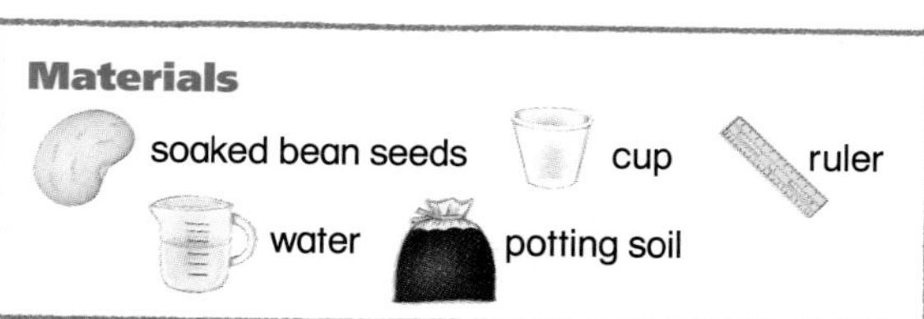

Materials

soaked bean seeds, cup, ruler, water, potting soil

Process Skills

- observing
- estimating and measuring

Steps

1. Put some potting soil in the cup.
2. Plant 2 or 3 seeds in the soil. Water the seeds.
3. Put your cup in a sunny spot.
4. **Observe** and draw what you see every 2 or 3 days.
5. **Measure** your plants once a week. Record.

Share. Compare your plants to a friend's plants.

Lesson Review

1. What is inside a seed?
2. How does a plant grow from a seed?
3. **Tell** how your plant has changed.

A17

Teach and Apply

Student Page A 16

Encourage children to talk about the changes taking place in the plant pictured.

Reading Assist *Summarizing*
Have children write the numbers 1 to 5 on a piece of paper. Encourage children to use words and/or pictures to summarize the major steps in the growth of a plant.

Student Page A 17

Explore Activity

Time about 1 hour over a number of weeks
Grouping individual

In advance, punch holes in the bottom of each cup and soak the seeds overnight. Encourage children to plant two or three seeds. Children need to keep soil moist. Demonstrate how to assemble the minibook on Lab Manual page 9.

What to Expect

Some seeds will grow into plants, and some will not.

Assess and Extend

Answers to Lesson Review

1. Inside a seed is a tiny plant and stored food.
2. First, roots grow into the soil. Then a stem grows up from the ground. Soon more leaves grow, and sometimes flowers appear.
3. **Tell** (*Interview*) Children may say that their plants got taller, grew leaves, or even died.

Inquire Further

Ask the following question to guide further inquiry: **How can the kind of soil affect the way seeds grow?**

Lab Manual

How does a plant grow and change?

1. Make a book.
2. **Observe** and draw what you see every 2 or 3 days.
3. **Measure** your plants once a week. Record.

Day ___ | How does a plant grow and change?
Day ___ | The plant is ___ cm.
Day ___

Lab Manual
p. 9

Activity Rubric

Use the following activity scoring rubric to assess students' performance.

Scoring Criteria	1	2	3	4
Student followed directions to complete this activity.				
Student planted bean seeds and observed changes every 2–3 days.				
Student made drawings to record his or her observations.				
Student measured and recorded the size of the plants once a week.				
Student compared his or her plants with those of a friend.				

Scoring Key
4 points correct, complete, detailed
3 points partially correct, complete, detailed
2 points partially correct, partially complete, lacks some detail
1 point incorrect or incomplete, needs assistance

Lab Manual
p. T3

Enrichment

Have children place two kinds of seeds in different plastic bags on moist paper toweling. Children use **Wall Chart** page 3 to compare the growth rates.

Higher Order Thinking *Sequence*
Ask children what they observed as their plant grew.

Call 1-888-537-4908 with your Activity questions or comments.

Science Center

Flip Chart

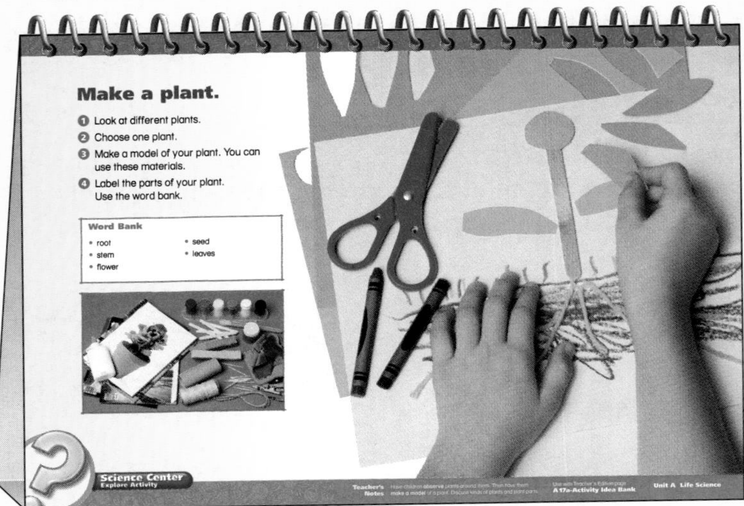

Make a plant.

Objective

Identify the parts of a plant.

Process Skills observing, making and using models

Materials

Kit Items none

School-Supplied Items art supplies

Procedure

- Children **observe** plants around them and **make a model** of a plant.
- Children label the parts of the plant.
- You can use **Lab Manual** page 11 with this activity.
- ***Teaching Tip*** Encourage children to think of all the plants around them. Children choose different types of plants to model.

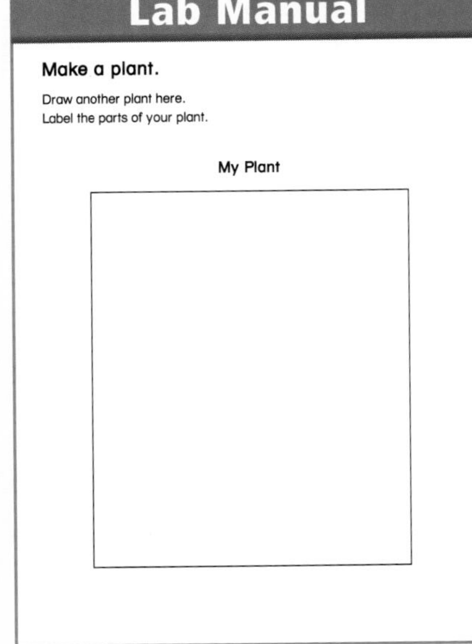
Lab Manual

Make a plant.

Draw another plant here.
Label the parts of your plant.

My Plant

Lab Manual, p. 11

Connections

School and Community

Ideas for bringing the school and community together:

Field Trips

- pumpkin farm
- apple orchard
- vegetable and/or flower garden

Guest Speakers

- forest ranger
- farmer
- gardener

Themes

The activities on these pages can be used with classroom themes such as:

- seasons
- growth and change
- flowers
- trees

Books for Children

Children might enjoy these books about plants:

Be a Friend to Trees by Patricia Lauber. The author describes the beauty and usefulness of trees and offers easy conservation suggestions. (HarperCollins, ISBN 0-06-445120-8)

How the Forest Grew by William Jaspersohn. This beautifully illustrated book traces the growth of a dense forest from a cleared field. (Morrow, ISBN 0-688-11508-X)

The Tremendous Tree Book by Barbara Brenner and May Garelick. Easy to understand information about trees, such as photosynthesis and animal dependency. (Boyds Mills Press, ISBN 1-56397-718-4)

Cross-Curricular Options

LITERATURE

Something Is Growing

Use the book to discuss how plants grow.

Materials *Something Is Growing* by Walter Lyon Krudop. (Atheneum, ISBN 0-064-45107-0)

Procedure

- Nobody notices when a boy plants a seed in a small patch of dirt in the city, until the plant grows and starts spreading out of control.
- Encourage children to talk about the parts of plants and how plants change as they grow.

Multiple Intelligences linguistic

Gifted and Talented Invite children to create a fantasy story about a plant that grows out of control in their community.

ART

Plant Prints

Make patterned plant prints.

Materials clean plant parts such as roots, stems, leaves, flower heads; poster paint; poster paper; cups

Procedure

- Pour different colors of paint into cups.
- Invite children to dip plant parts into the paint and use them to print a picture.
- Encourage children to identify the plant parts as stems, flowers, or roots. Children may want to take their completed artwork home to share with family members.

Multiple Intelligences spatial, logical-mathematical

WRITING

I Am a Plant

Write a story from the point of view of a plant.

Materials paper, pencil, crayons

Procedure

- Have children name a plant and pretend that they are that plant.
- Ask children where the plant lives—forest, garden, yard—what other plants live near it, and what problems the plant might face, such as people, weather, insects.
- Have children write and illustrate a story from the point of view of the plant.

I am a tulip.
I was sitting in the sun.
Then someone came and cut me.
Ouch! I was given a bath
in a long tube.

Multiple Intelligences linguistic

ESL Children can make picture/word cards of flowers and their names.

MUSIC

Let's Dance!

Enact the growth of a plant through dance.

Materials classical music cassette, cassette player

Procedure

- Discuss how a plant grows from seed to seedling to mature plant.
- Have groups of children decide what kind of plant they want to portray, such as tree, flower, cactus.
- Then have children show the stages of plant growth by moving to the music.
- Classmates can guess the kinds of plants being portrayed.

Multiple Intelligences bodily-kinesthetic, musical

Activity Organizer

Objective
Identify the parts of a seed.

Process Skills observing

Materials
Kit Items presoaked lima bean seeds, hand lens
School-Supplied Items none

Time about 20 minutes

Grouping cooperative groups of 2

Additional Resources
- Lab Manual
- Teacher Demonstration Kit

Introduce

The Lesson 6 Investigate Activity, *What is inside a seed?,* is on the **Flip Chart.**

Activate Prior Knowledge
Ask children if they have ever seen the inside of a seed. Have children draw a picture of the inside of a seed. Save their work for use as a **baseline assessment.**

Language Development *Vocabulary*
Discuss the meaning of the word *split,* "to break into parts."

What is inside a seed?

Process Skills
- observing

Materials
soaked bean seeds

hand lens

Steps
1. Observe your seed. Tell your partner what you see.
2. Split your seed into two parts with your fingernail.
3. Use a hand lens to observe the inside of the seed. Tell your partner what you see.
4. Draw a picture like this one. Label the tiny plant and the stored food.

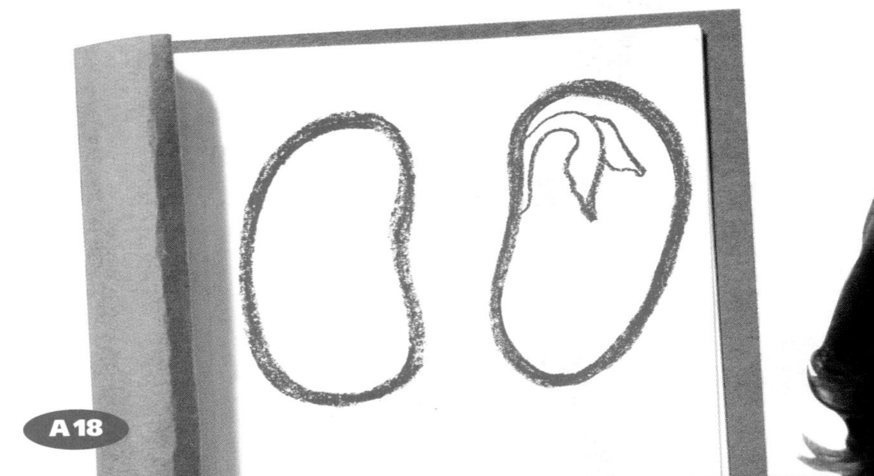

A18

Science Background
- The three main parts of a seed are the seed coat; the new plant, called the embryo; and sugars the plant uses until it can make its own food.
- The food is in the form of two seed leaves, which consist mainly of starch.

Teaching Tips Be sure to have plenty of soaked seeds ready for the activity. Soak them for at least two hours or overnight. Point out that in order to see smaller structures of living things it is often necessary to use magnifying tools such as a hand lens or a microscope. Note that many Native American cultures prohibit dissecting plants. These children should not be encouraged to participate in this part of the activity.

Technology

Review the demonstration of this Investigate's procedure on the *Life Science* **Activity Video,** Segment 2.

Think About Your Results

1. What are the parts of a seed?
2. How are the two halves of the seed different?

Inquire Further

How did the hand lens help you observe the seed? What in your classroom could you observe with a hand lens?

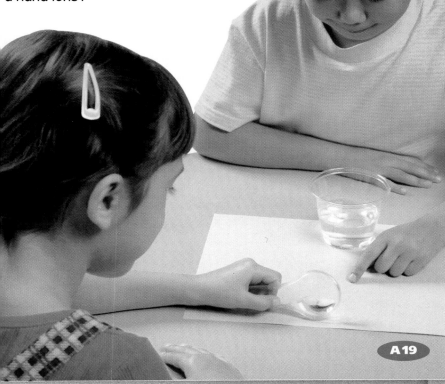

A19

Teach and Apply

- In this activity, children will split a bean seed. Provide paper towels for working with the wet seeds.
- Demonstrate how to split a seed into two parts with your fingernail.
- Children will observe the seed through a hand lens. Encourage them to help each other and share their observations.
- Children can complete Lab Manual page 13 as they do the activity.

Reading Assist *Irregular Plurals*

Point out that the word *half* forms its plural by changing the *f* to *v* and adding *-es*. Ask children if they know any other words that form plurals this way. (*calf, scarf, elf, hoof*)

What to Expect

Children will discover two inner parts, stored food and a new plant.

Assess and Extend

Answers to Think About Your Results

1. The parts of a seed are the stored food and the new plant.
2. Children may say that one half holds the new plant as well as food.

Inquire Further

Children may say that the hand lens helped them by enlarging their view of the seed. Answers will vary for other items they could observe with a hand lens.

Lab Manual

What is inside a seed?

1. Color and cut out the bean pieces and tiny plant. Punch the holes.
2. Use a paper fastener to put the model together.
3. Point to the stored food and the tiny plant.

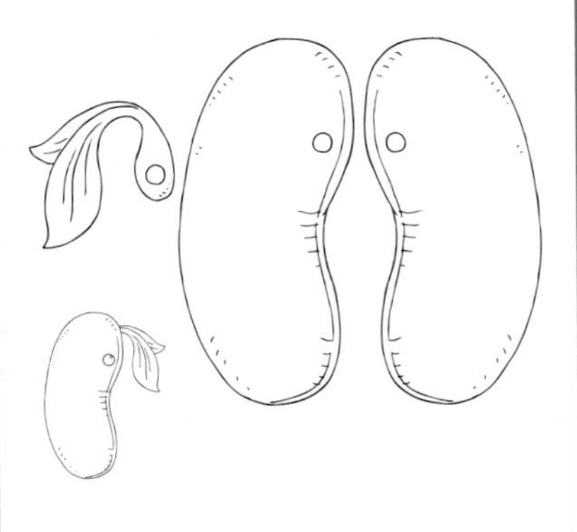

Lab Manual p. 13

Activity Rubric

Use the following activity scoring rubric to assess students' performance.

Scoring Criteria	1	2	3	4
Student followed directions to perform this activity.				
Student used a hand lens to observe the inside of a seed.				
Student observed the parts of a seed.				
Student used the parts of the drawing to make a model of a seed.				
Student explained how the two halves of the seed are different.				

Scoring Key

4 points correct, complete, detailed
3 points partially correct, complete, detailed
2 points partially correct, partially complete, lacks some detail
1 point incorrect or incomplete, needs assistance

Lab Manual p. T4

Check for Understanding

To follow up on the **baseline assessment,** have children draw a picture of the inside of a seed and compare it with their earlier drawing.

Enrichment

Have children try the activity again, using different kinds of seeds. Ask them to compare the insides of the seeds to determine how they are alike and different.

Higher Order Thinking *Infer*

Ask: **Why does a seed contain stored food?** (*Children might infer that the stored food nourishes the young plant until it can get nourishment from the earth.*)

Call 1-888-537-4908 with your Activity questions or comments.

Lesson Organizer

Objective
Identify ways seeds can be scattered.

Vocabulary scatter

Additional Resources
- Wall Chart

Introduce

Activate Prior Knowledge
Ask children to think about fruits they like and tell about the seeds in the fruits.

Language Development *Vocabulary*
Have children add *scatter* to their science dictionaries. Have children think of things besides seeds that can scatter or be scattered, for example, people in a crowd, chicken feed, dust.

Flip Chart
Have children find ways seeds are scattered in the picture. Ask: **Why do you think this is important?**

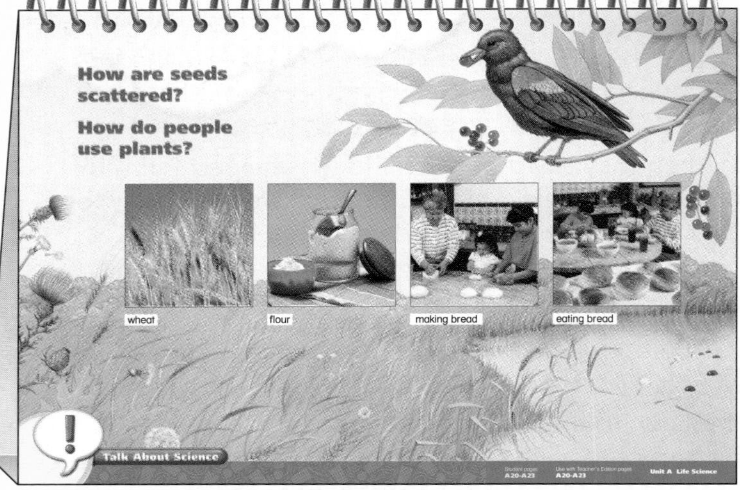

How are seeds scattered?

What is your favorite fruit? What kind of seeds does it have?

Fruits cover and protect seeds. The dandelion fruits in this picture have long feathery hairs that help them travel through the air. Find the fruits on this page that are shaped like wings. This shape helps them travel through the air.

When fruits travel, the seeds inside are scattered. **Scatter** means to spread out. Scattering helps carry seeds to new places where they can grow.

Science Background

- The fruit not only protects the seed but also helps it spread.
- When an animal eats a fruit, it also ingests the seeds. The seeds, surrounded by a protective coat, pass through the animal's digestive system and are released undamaged.
- Some fruits burst when ripe, shooting their seeds a considerable distance.

Teaching Tips Bring in different kinds of seeds for children to look at, such as seeds with wings—maple, elm, ash; seeds with parachutes—dandelion milkweed, cottonwood; and seeds that are dispersed by water—coconut, sedge, cranberry. Have children use **Wall Chart** page 4 to record the seed name and the way it is scattered.

Have you ever found burrs like these stuck to your shoes or clothes? Burrs are fruits that travel by hooking onto people's clothing or animals' fur.

Seeds can travel in other ways too. Animals can eat fruits and drop the seeds to the ground. Some fruits or seeds float on the water to new places.

Lesson Review

1. What does scatter mean?
2. How do animals scatter seeds?
3. **Draw** some ways seeds are scattered.

A21

ESL Strategy

Place a pile of paper clips or other small objects on a desktop or the floor. Discuss the meaning of *scatter* and ask children to demonstrate the meaning by scattering the paper clips.

Teach and Apply

Student Pages A20–A21

Discuss that seeds are scattered by wind, water, animals, and people. Relate the structure of a seed to how it is scattered. Discuss how animals help plants by carrying seeds and how plants help animals by providing food. You may want to introduce the term *interdependence.*

Reading Assist *Base Words*

Write these words on the chalkboard: *scatter, scattered, scattering.* Have children tell what is alike and different about each word. Discuss the meanings. Then have children find each word on page A20.

Assess and Extend

Answers to Lesson Review

1. *Scatter* means to spread out.
2. Animals scatter seeds by eating fruits and dropping the seeds. Also, burrs are scattered by getting hooked on animals' fur or people's clothing.
3. **Draw** (***Portfolio Assessment or Journal***) Children's pictures should show some ways seeds are scattered: wind, water, animals, or people.

Reteach

Supply children with a variety of seeds, hand lenses, a bowl of water, and a few cotton socks. Have children use the hand lenses to examine the seeds, blow the seeds to see which ones travel with wind, place some seeds into the water to see which ones can float, and place a sock on their hands to see which ones stick to clothing.

Lesson Organizer

Objective
Identify products that come from plants.

Additional Resources
- Wall Chart

Introduce

Activate Prior Knowledge
Have children brainstorm a list of things that come from plants. They could be foods, clothing, objects for everyday use, medicines, and so on. Save their lists for use as a **baseline assessment.**

Language Development *Scientific Language*
Ask children to tell what happens when they breathe. They may say air goes in and out of their bodies. Explain that the part of the air our bodies use is called oxygen. Oxygen is a gas in the air that living things need to stay alive.

Flip Chart
Discuss how the people in the pictures are using plants. Have children name other ways people use plants.

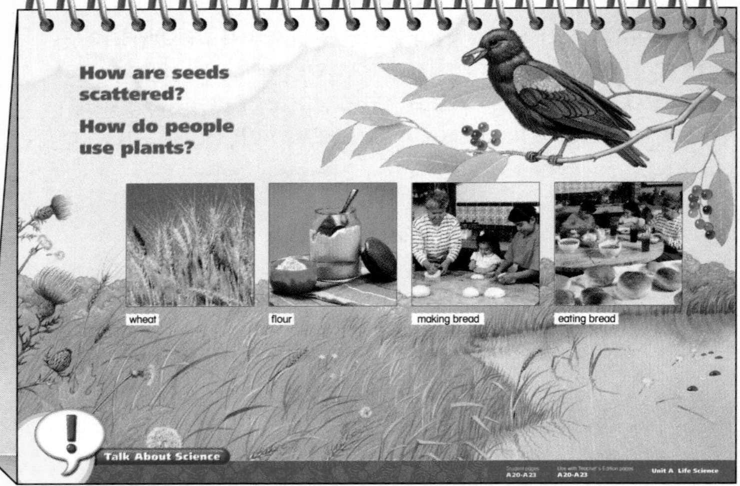

How do people use plants?

Look around you. Do you see anything made from a plant? Many things you use every day come from plants!

▲ Look at this cotton plant. Many socks are made from cotton.

◀ Many kinds of bread are made from wheat.

Science Background

- Plants are a source of food we eat and oxygen we breathe.
- We eat roots such as carrots, beets, turnips, yams; stems such as potatoes and asparagus; fruits such as apples, oranges, cucumbers, tomatoes, squash, eggplant; seeds such as beans, peas, corn, wheat, rice; leaves such as lettuce and cabbage; and flowers such as broccoli, cauliflower, artichokes.
- We use wood for lumber and paper.
- Many medicines are made from plant products.
- Rubber and cotton come from plants.

▲ Maybe you have used aloe vera. Aloe is used in lotions and gels for the skin. It comes from an aloe plant.

◀ Trees give off oxygen. People need oxygen to stay alive.

Lesson Review

1. What food comes from wheat?
2. What is cotton used for?
3. **Write** some ways you use plants every day.

A23

ESL Strategy

Point out that in English the word *plant* can be a noun or a verb. Use the word *plant* in these sentences and ask children to repeat the sentences and pantomime their meanings: **This plant grows in our classroom. I plant a seed by making a hole in the soil.**

Teach and Apply

Student Pages A22–A23

Discuss that plants are a source of food and other useful products. Mention that we use some plant products just as they come from the plant and others after they have been manufactured to change the plant material into something we can use. Use **Wall Chart** page 5 to categorize items mentioned in the lesson. Have children find other examples around the classroom and in books and magazines to add to the chart.

Reading Assist *Multiple Meanings*

The word *plant* can be used as a noun and as a verb. Have children read page A23 to find out how *plant* is used. Have volunteers give example sentences for both forms of the word.

Earth Science

Integrating the Sciences

In this lesson, children learn that plants provide many items for our use, such as fibers, cotton, oil, spices, lumber, rubber, medicines, paper, and so on. This lesson relates to Unit C, Chapter 1, which introduces other natural resources.

Assess and Extend

Answers to Lesson Review

1. Bread comes from wheat.
2. Children might say that cotton is used for clothing.
3. **Write** (*Portfolio Assessment or Journal*) Children might write that they use plants every day for food, shelter, clothing, medicines, and school supplies such as paper and pencils.

Check for Understanding

To follow up on the **baseline assessment,** have children revisit and add to their list of plant products.

Reteach

Ask children to bring two objects from home: one made from a plant and one not made from a plant.

Science Center

Flip Chart

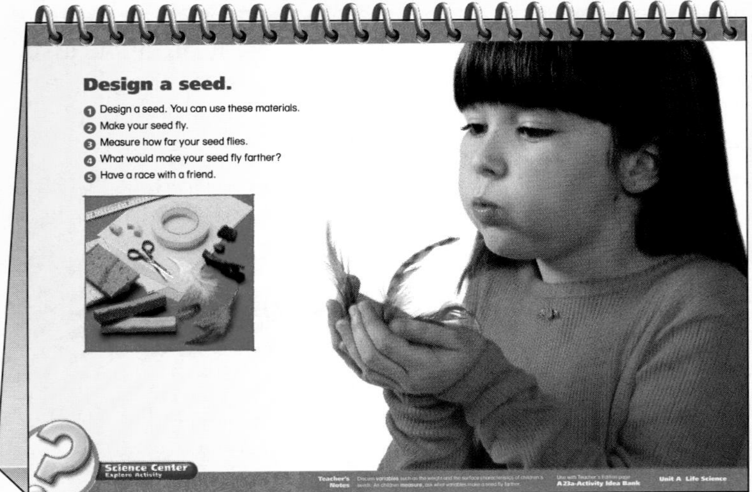

Design a seed.

Objective

Discover characteristics of seeds that allow for better wind dispersal.

Process Skills measuring, controlling variables

Materials

Kit Items clay, sponge, feathers, cork

School-Supplied Items paper, bark, scissors, masking tape, meterstick

Procedure

- Children make a model of a seed and predict how far their seed will travel.
- Children drop their seed. They can blow on it or drop it in a breezy place and **measure** the distance it flew. You can use **Lab Manual** page 15.
- Groups can have seed races and compare results. Encourage children to **control variables** by using the same starting point and/or same amount of air.

What to Expect

A seed will travel farther if it has longer flotation time. Lighter, featherlike seeds will fly farther.

Lab Manual

Design a seed.

What materials did you use to make your seed?

Write or draw.

How far will your seed fly?

Prediction

Results

Lab Manual, p. 15

Connections

School and Community

Ideas for bringing the school and community together:

Field Trips

- plant nursery
- arboretum

Guest Speakers

- gardener
- botanist

Themes

The activities on these pages can be used with classroom themes such as:

- growing and changing
- movement
- gardening
- systems

Books for Children

Children might enjoy these books about seeds and plants:

How a Seed Grows
by Helene J. Jordan.
A girl learns all about how seeds become flowers, plants, or trees. (HarperCollins, ISBN 0-06-445107-0)

Apple Picking Time
by Michele Benoit Slawson.
A community comes together to harvest the orchard crop each year. (Crown, ISBN 0-517-58971-0)

Seeds
by George Shannon.
Warren used to help his neighbor Bill in Bill's garden until Warren moved away. But they are able to share a garden again when Bill mails seeds to Warren. (Houghton Mifflin, ISBN 0-395-66990-1)

Cross-Curricular Options

LITERATURE

How to Make an Apple Pie and See the World

Use the book to identify plant products.

Materials *How to Make an Apple Pie and See the World* by Marjorie Priceman. (Knopf, ISBN 0-679-83705-1)

Procedure

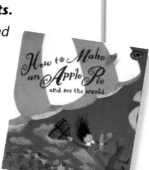

- A girl travels around the world to gather ingredients to make an apple pie.
- Help children identify and list plants and products mentioned in the book in a two-column chart. One column should list the plants, the other the products.

Multiple Intelligences linguistic

Gifted and Talented Children can add other plants and products to the chart.

MATH

Count the Kernels

Estimate, count, and record kernels.

Materials popcorn kernels, clear plastic jar with lid

Procedure

- Provide corn kernels. Explain that these are the seeds of a corn plant.
- Place the kernels in a jar and have children estimate how many there are. Record their estimates.
- Divide the kernels among children to count and record. Have children compare estimates with the actual count.

Multiple Intelligences logical-mathematical

WRITING

Plant Log

Write about how a plant grows.

Materials notebook, pencil, old potato with buds, cabbage, carrot, 3 plastic glasses, water, toothpicks

Procedure

- Discuss how a new plant can start from parts of a plant, such as the stems, roots, or leaves.
- Suspend each vegetable over water. Make sure the potato buds or eyes, the carrot bottom, and the cabbage leaf are always touching the water.
- Ask children to observe the plants each day and write their observations in their science journals.

Multiple Intelligences linguistic

ART

Seed Collage

Make a collage.

Materials different seeds such as sunflower, pumpkin, watermelon, peas, beans; drawing paper; glue

Procedure

- Have children make collages with seeds.
- Some children might make patterned designs; others might outline objects and then fill them in with seeds.

Multiple Intelligences spatial

Special Needs Children with visual limitations may want to use larger pasta pieces in different colors and shapes.

Review Organizer

Materials

Kit Items none

School-Supplied Items paper, pencil, crayons

Time about 30 minutes

Grouping cooperative groups of 4

Additional Resources

- Chapter 1 Assessment: Teacher's Assessment Package

Chapter Main Ideas

Lesson 1 Plants include trees, grass, flowers, bushes. Plants can be big and small. Some have flowers or fruits.

Lesson 2 Plants need water, air, food, and light.

Lesson 3 Plants need light to grow. If kept from light long enough, plants will die.

Lesson 4 The parts of a plant are the roots, stem, leaves, and flowers. The flowers produce seeds.

Lesson 5 Plants grow from seeds. The roots grow down into the soil and the stem grows up from the ground. Leaves and sometimes flowers grow.

Lesson 6 Stored food and a new plant are found inside a seed.

Lesson 7 Seeds are scattered by wind, water, animals, and people.

Lesson 8 People use plants for food and for materials such as cotton, wheat, and aloe vera. People also use the oxygen that plants release into the air.

Reviewing Science Words

1. Roots hold the plant in the soil and take in water. The stem carries water to the leaves. The leaves make sugars that the plant needs to grow.
2. Flowers make seeds.
3. Children's answers should include three of the following: wind, water, people, and animals.

Reviewing Science Ideas

1. A plant needs water, air, food, and light to grow.
2. People use plants for food, oxygen, and products such as cotton and lotions.

Chapter 1 Review

Reviewing Science Words

1. What do **roots**, **stems**, and **leaves** do?
2. What do **flowers** make?
3. Name three ways seeds are **scattered**.

Reviewing Science Ideas

1. Name things a plant needs to help it grow.
2. How do people use plants?

Technology

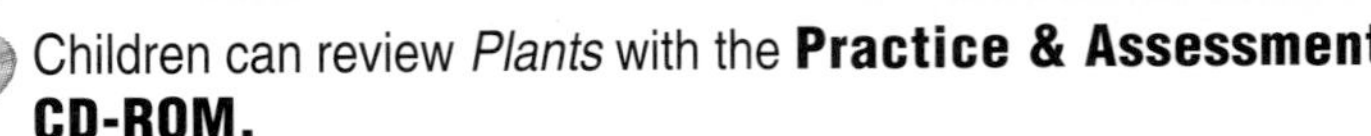

- Children can review *Plants* with the **Practice & Assessment CD-ROM.**

- Children can use the **Production Studio** to show what they've learned about *Plants*.
- Children can use The KnowZone™ at **www.kz.com** to review and test their science knowledge.

- You can use **TestWorks™** to customize assessment for your children.

Make a flip book.

Materials

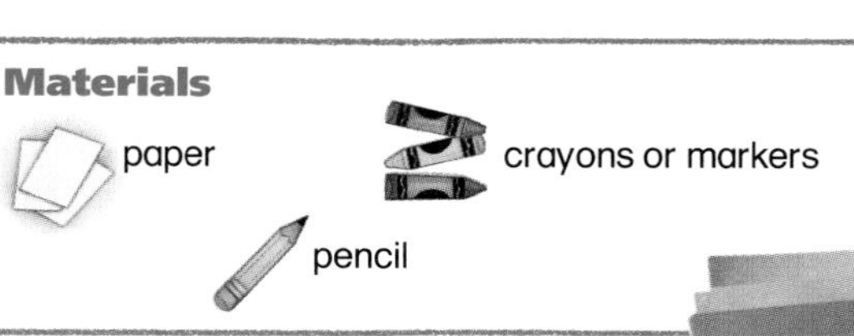

1. Have your teacher staple your papers along one edge.
2. Start on the first page. Draw a seed near the bottom edge of the paper.
3. On the next page, draw a seed just starting to grow.
4. Draw what the plant looks like as it grows. Make one drawing on each page.
5. Show your flip book to a friend. Flip the pages to see how a plant grows.

Chapter Assessment

Use the words in the box to finish each sentence.

stem	roots	leaves	flower

1. The ______________ hold the plant in the soil.
2. The ______________ carries water to the leaves.
3. The ______________ is the part of the plant that makes seeds.
4. The ______________ make sugars that the plant needs to grow.

Write Yes or No.

______ 5. Fruits cover and protect seeds.
______ 6. All plants have the same kinds of seeds.
______ 7. Seeds can travel in different ways.
______ 8. Plants can be used for many things including food and clothing.
______ 9. Plants need sunlight in order to grow.
______ 10. All plants have bright flowers.
______ 11. New plants grow from seeds.

Teacher's Assessment Package pp. 5–6

Assessment Rubric

	Growth of a Plant
4	Shows a good understanding of the growth and development of a plant.
3	Shows a partial understanding of the growth and development of a plant.
2	Has difficulty showing the growth and development of a plant.
1	Is unable to show the growth and development of a plant.

Performance Assessment Teaching Tips

- Before beginning the activity, have children brainstorm the parts of a plant and when each part might become visible in the growing process.
- Provide picture books that show how plants grow. Invite partners to look through books together and talk about how plants grow.
- Provide examples of flip books for children to examine. Point out how there are only small changes from page to page. Demonstrate how to flip the pages quickly.
- Many sizes of paper will work, but it is simplest to cut a stack of 8 1/2" x 11" paper into fourths, then staple along the short edge to provide maximum drawing space. The flip book works best with 5–10 pages in it.
- Suggest that children plan their flip books before actually beginning to draw. Ask questions such as: **How many pages will your flip book have? What new detail will you add to each page to make the plant seem like it is growing?**

Enrichment

Suggest that children continue the story of how a plant grows by creating a second flip book. Have children start this book with a flowering plant, show a seed from this plant being scattered, and finally a seed beginning to grow.

Chapter 1 Skills Trace

Process Skills Development

	Observing	Classifying	Predicting	Experimenting	Estimating and Measuring
Skill Introduced	xiv	xiv	xv	xv	xiv
Skill Applied	A7 A9 A10–A11 A17 A18–A19	A7	A9 A10–A11	A10–A11	A17
Skill Assessed	End Matter 6–7	End Matter 10–11	End Matter 16–17	End Matter 28–29	End Matter 12–13

Chapter Review pages are also on the **Flip Chart.**

Lesson/Activity and Flip Chart	Objectives/Process Skills	Time Options/Activity Materials
Chapter Opener Student Edition pp. A26–A27 and **Flip Chart** ***You've Changed a Lot***		**Have less time?** Use the Graphic Organizer on Teacher's Assessment Package p. 9 for an overview of the lessons. Use the Flip Chart to teach lesson concepts and science activities. **Have more time?** Use the Flip Chart to reinforce and extend lesson concepts and activities. Use the Cross-Curricular Options in the Activity Idea Bank on Teacher's Edition pp. A33b, A37b, and A43b.
Lesson 1 Student Edition pp. A28–A29 ***What are some kinds of animals?*** **Explore Activity** ***Guess the animal.*** **Flip Chart** ***Talk About Science***	**Objective** Classify animals. **Process Skills** communicating	**Kit Items** none **School-Supplied Items** drawing paper, pencil or crayons
Math in Science Student Edition pp. A30–A31 ***Ordering***	**Objective** Use sequencing to put events in order.	
Lesson 2 Student Edition pp. A32–A33 ***How do frogs grow and change?*** **Flip Chart** ***Talk About Science***	**Objective** Describe the growth and development of a frog.	
Activity Idea Bank Teacher's Edition pp. A33a–A33b **Flip Chart** **Science Center Explore Activity** ***Make a frog print.***	**Objective** Show the life cycle of a frog. **Process Skills** observing	**Kit Items** none **School-Supplied Items** stamp pad, paper, art supplies, frog picture book
Lesson 3 Student Edition pp. A34–A35 ***How do butterflies grow and change?*** **Flip Chart** ***Talk About Science***	**Objective** Describe the life cycle of a butterfly.	**Have more time?** Use the following teaching guide option: Interactive Transparency 2, Interactive Transparency Package
Lesson 4 Student Edition pp. A36–A37 and **Flip Chart** **Investigate Activity** ***How can you make a model of a butterfly life cycle?***	**Objective** Make a model of a butterfly life cycle. **Process Skills** making and using models	**Kit Items** modeling clay in assorted colors, pipe cleaners **School-Supplied Items** safety goggles, construction paper, scissors
Activity Idea Bank Teacher's Edition pp. A37a–A37b **Flip Chart** **Science Center Explore Activity** ***Make a model of a butterfly.***	**Objective** Understand the concept of symmetry and notice the symmetry on butterfly wings. **Process Skills** observing	**Kit Items** none **School-Supplied Items** construction paper, paint, scissors, pencil
Lesson 5 Student Edition pp. A38–A39 ***Where do animals live?*** **Flip Chart** ***Talk About Science***	**Objective** Identify features that enable animals to live in various habitats.	
Lesson 6 Student Edition pp. A40–A41 ***What do animals eat?*** **Explore Activity** ***Make a model of a food chain.*** **Flip Chart** ***Talk About Science***	**Objective** Explain how animals depend on plants and other animals for food. **Process Skills** making and using models	**Kit Items** paper plates, yarn **School-Supplied Items** index cards, crayons, masking tape
Lesson 7 Student Edition pp. A42–A43 ***How do animals protect themselves?*** **Explore Activity** ***Play a camouflage game.*** **Flip Chart** ***Talk About Science***	**Objective** Name some ways animals protect themselves. **Process Skills** collecting and interpreting data	**Kit Items** none **School-Supplied Items** 11" by 17" green construction paper; 20 1-inch green paper squares; 20 1-inch yellow paper squares; clock with a second hand **Advance Prep** Make sure that the large green paper is the same color as the small green squares. Make the green and yellow squares the same size.
Activity Idea Bank Teacher's Edition pp. A43a–A43b **Flip Chart** **Science Center Explore Activity** ***Camouflage an animal.***	**Objective** Devise animal camouflage that would protect an animal in a particular habitat. **Process Skills** observing	**Kit Items** none **School-Supplied Items** art supplies
Chapter Review Student Edition pp. A44–A45 and **Flip Chart**		**Kit Items** none **School-Supplied Items** big piece of paper, crayons or markers, books about animals

Lesson/Activity and Flip Chart	Additional Resources		Technology
Chapter Opener Student Edition pp. A26–A27 and **Flip Chart** ***You've Changed a Lot***	**Teacher's Assessment Package** • Graphic Organizer, p. 9 **Instructional Resources** • Family Activity, pp. 9–10 • Vocabulary Preview, p. 11	**Songs & Activities Package** • *You've Changed a Lot,* pp. 11–12 **Wall Chart,** p. 6	**Practice & Assessment CD-ROM** **AudioText** **Production Studio** **www.sfscience.com** **Songs & Activities Package** **Teacher's Resource Planner CD-ROM**
Lesson 1 Student Edition pp. A28–A29 ***What are some kinds of animals?*** **Explore Activity** ***Guess the animal.*** **Flip Chart** ***Talk About Science***	**Lab Manual** • Lab Manual, p. 17 • Activity Rubric, p. T5	**Teacher Demonstration Kit** **Wall Chart,** p. 7	
Math in Science Student Edition pp. A30–A3 ***Ordering***	**Instructional Resources** • Math in Science, p. 12		
Lesson 2 Student Edition pp. A32–A33 ***How do frogs grow and change?*** **Flip Chart** ***Talk About Science***		**Wall Chart,** p. 8	
Activity Idea Bank Teacher's Edition pp. A33a–A33b **Flip Chart** **Science Center Explore Activity** ***Make a frog print.***	**Lab Manual** • Lab Manual, p. 18 • Activity Rubric, p. T5		
Lesson 3 Student Edition pp. A34–A35 ***How do butterflies grow and change?*** **Flip Chart** ***Talk About Science***	**Interactive Transparency Package** • Interactive Transparency 2	**Wall Chart,** p. 9	
Lesson 4 Student Edition pp. A36–A37 and **Flip Chart** **Investigate Activity** ***How can you make a model of a butterfly life cycle?***	**Lab Manual** • Lab Manual, p. 19 • Activity Rubric, p. T6	**Teacher Demonstration Kit**	*Life Science* **Activity Video**
Activity Idea Bank Teacher's Edition pp. A37a–A37b **Flip Chart** **Science Center Explore Activity** ***Make a model of a butterfly.***	**Lab Manual** • Lab Manual, p. 21 • Activity Rubric, p. T6		
Lesson 5 Student Edition pp. A38–A39 ***Where do animals live?*** **Flip Chart** ***Talk About Science***		**Wall Chart,** p. 10	
Lesson 6 Student Edition pp. A40–A41 ***What do animals eat?*** **Explore Activity** ***Make a model of a food chain.*** **Flip Chart** ***Talk About Science***	**Lab Manual** • Lab Manual, p. 22 • Activity Rubric, p. T7	**Teacher Demonstration Kit** **Wall Chart,** p. 11	
Lesson 7 Student Edition pp. A42–A43 ***How do animals protect themselves?*** **Explore Activity** ***Play a camouflage game.*** **Flip Chart** ***Talk About Science***	**Lab Manual** • Lab Manual, p. 23 • Activity Rubric, p. T7	**Teacher Demonstration Kit** **Wall Chart,** p. 12	
Activity Idea Bank Teacher's Edition pp. A43a–A43b **Flip Chart** **Science Center Explore Activity** ***Camouflage an animal.***	**Lab Manual** • Lab Manual, p. 24 • Activity Rubric, p. T8		
Chapter Review Student Edition pp. A44–A45 and **Flip Chart**	**Teacher's Assessment Package** • Chapter 2 Assessment, pp. 11–12		**Practice & Assessment CD-ROM** **Production Studio** **The KnowZone™ at www.kz.com** **TestWorks™**

Lab Manual

What are some kinds of animals?

Draw your secret animal here.

Students' answers will vary. Descriptions of their secret animal may include mention of the size, shape, coloring, or other special features.

Write four things about your animal.

1.

2.

3.

4.

Lab Manual
p. 17

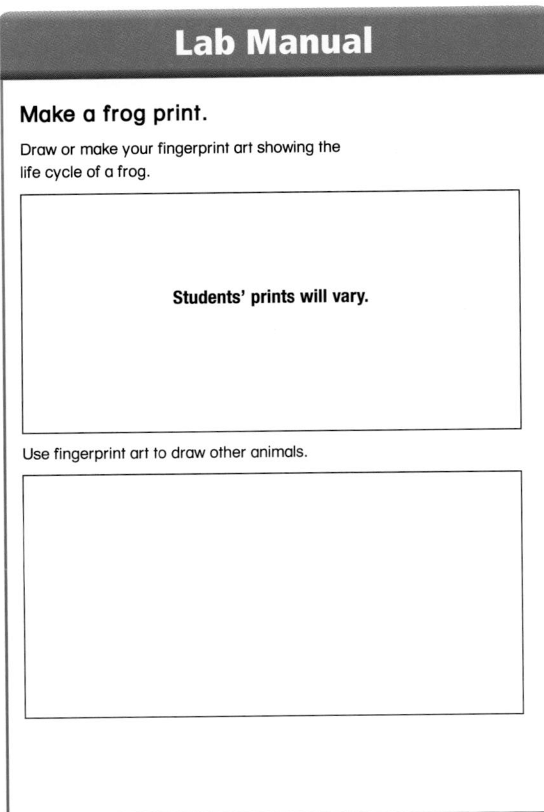

Lab Manual

Make a frog print.

Draw or make your fingerprint art showing the life cycle of a frog.

Students' prints will vary.

Use fingerprint art to draw other animals.

Lab Manual
p. 18

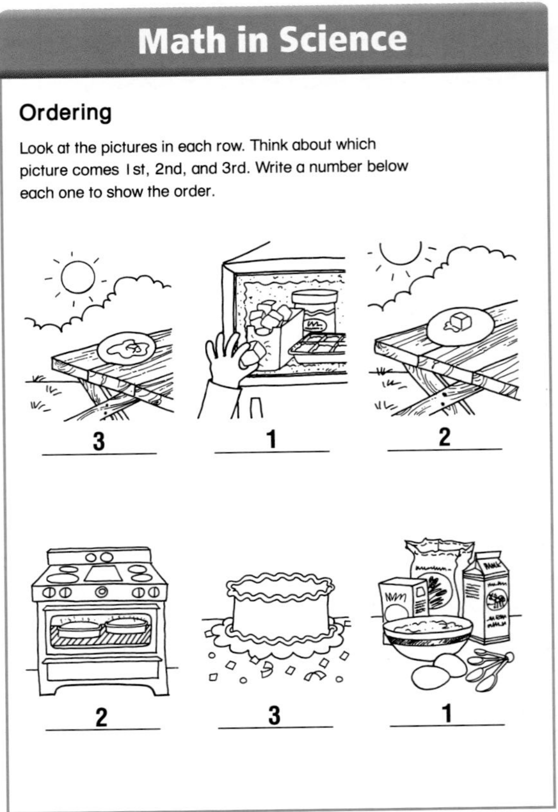

Math in Science

Ordering

Look at the pictures in each row. Think about which picture comes 1st, 2nd, and 3rd. Write a number below each one to show the order.

3	1	2
2	3	1

Instructional Resources
p. 12

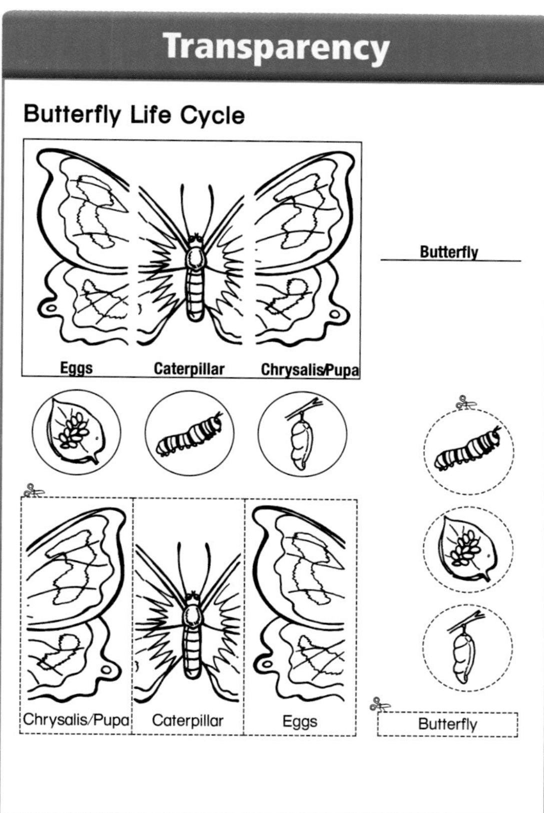

Transparency

Butterfly Life Cycle

Interactive Transparency Package
Transparency 2

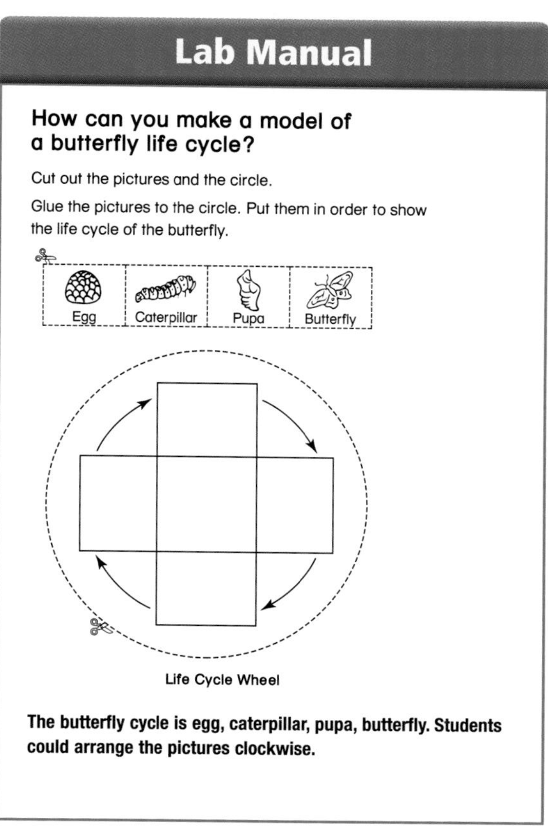

Lab Manual

How can you make a model of a butterfly life cycle?

Cut out the pictures and the circle.

Glue the pictures to the circle. Put them in order to show the life cycle of the butterfly.

The butterfly cycle is egg, caterpillar, pupa, butterfly. Students could arrange the pictures clockwise.

Lab Manual
p. 19

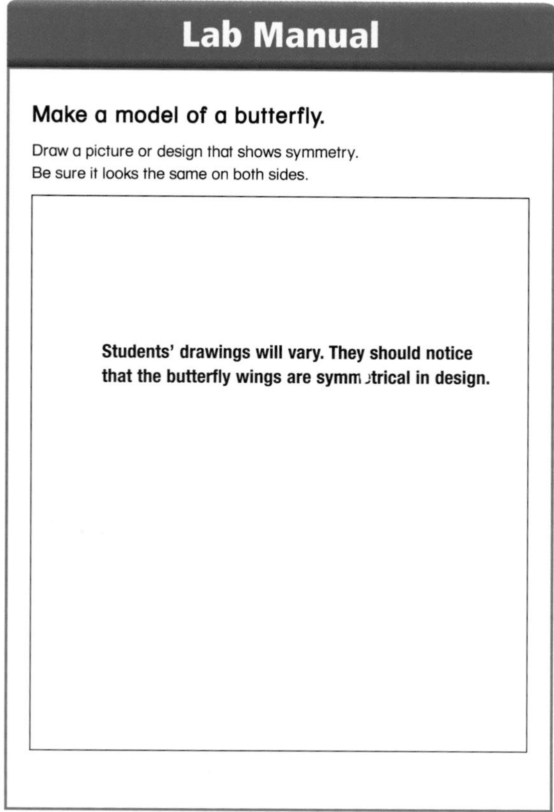

Lab Manual

Make a model of a butterfly.

Draw a picture or design that shows symmetry.
Be sure it looks the same on both sides.

Students' drawings will vary. They should notice that the butterfly wings are symmetrical in design.

Lab Manual
p. 21

Lab Manual

What do animals eat?

Draw pictures to make a model of a food chain.

Sun

Plant

Animal

Animal

Students' drawings will vary. Students will draw the sun, a plant (probably grass), and two animals (probably a bug and a lizard, or a lizard and a hawk).

Lab Manual
p. 22

Lab Manual

How do animals protect themselves?

Do the activity three times. Record your results.

1. I picked up ______ green squares.
   I picked up ______ yellow squares.
2. I picked up ______ green squares.
   I picked up ______ yellow squares.
3. I picked up ______ green squares.
   I picked up ______ yellow squares.

1. Which color did you pick up the most?

Students will probably pick up more yellow squares.

2. Tell why one color was picked up the most.

Answers will vary but may suggest that the yellow squares were easier to see because they were not camouflaged.

Lab Manual
p. 23

Lab Manual

Camouflage an animal.

Draw an animal that uses camouflage.

Students' drawings and explanations will vary.

How does camouflage help your animal hide?

Lab Manual
p. 24

Chapter 2 Assessment

Use the words in the box to finish each sentence.

habitat	mammals	life cycle	pupa

1. Animals with fur are called ________________.
2. Some animals change as they grow. This is called the ________________.
3. The place where an animal lives is its ________________.
4. A ________________ is the name of a caterpillar changing into a butterfly.

Write Yes or No.

________ 5. A tadpole is a full grown frog.

________ 6. A long neck helps a giraffe live in its habitat.

________ 7. Reptiles and mammals are the same kinds of animal.

________ 8. All animals eat plants to stay alive.

________ 9. A caterpillar forms a chrysalis before turning into a butterfly.

________ 10. Some animals protect themselves with sharp teeth and claws.

Teacher's Assessment Package p. 11

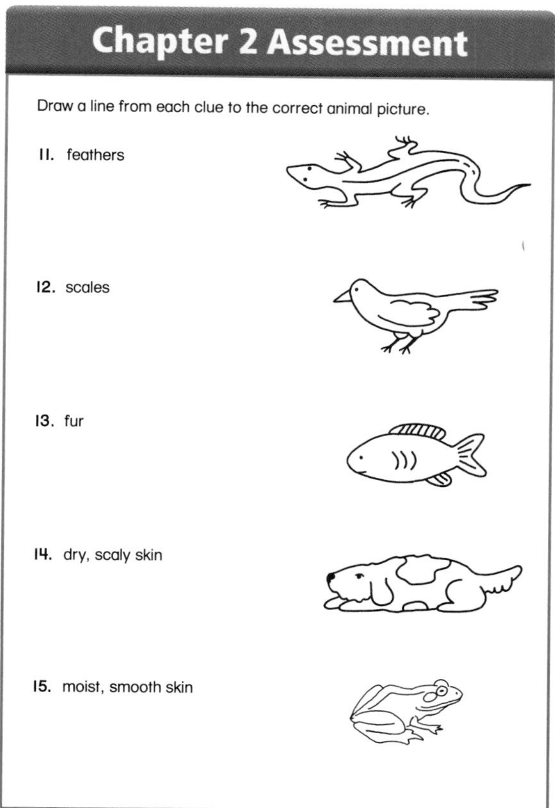

Chapter 2 Assessment
Draw a line from each clue to the correct animal picture.
11. feathers
12. scales
13. fur
14. dry, scaly skin
15. moist, smooth skin

Teacher's Assessment Package p. 12

Table of Contents

Introducing the Chapter

The song *You've Changed a Lot* is on the **Flip Chart.**

- Discuss when and where children notice animals in their daily lives.
- Distribute the Family Activity blackline master page.

Singing the Song

Have children sing the song *You've Changed a Lot* on side 1 of the CTW cassette. Distribute pages 11–12 from the CTW Song Activity Book.

Reading Assist *Word Meanings*

Have children preview the words to the song to find unfamiliar words. Discuss how children might determine the meaning of unfamiliar words. (*Use context clues, use picture clues, use a dictionary, ask someone.*) Help children determine the meaning of any unfamiliar words.

Vocabulary Preview

Use the Vocabulary Preview blackline master to introduce the vocabulary words for this chapter.

Lesson 1 mammals, reptiles, amphibians
Lesson 2 life cycle, tadpole
Lesson 3 chrysalis, pupa
Lesson 5 habitat, endangered
Lesson 6 food chain
Lesson 7 camouflage

Chapter 2

Animals

You've Changed a Lot

Sing to the tune of *Froggy Went a Courtin'*.

Hey, little frog, you've changed a lot, ah hum.
You had a tail that was very long, ah hum.
You grew four legs as the tail disappeared.
Now you hop, hop, hop all through the year.
Ah hum, ah hum, ah hum.

A26

Technology

Practice & Assessment CD-ROM

AudioText

Production Studio

www.sfscience.com

Teacher's Resource Planner

Songs & Activities Package

CTW Song & Activity

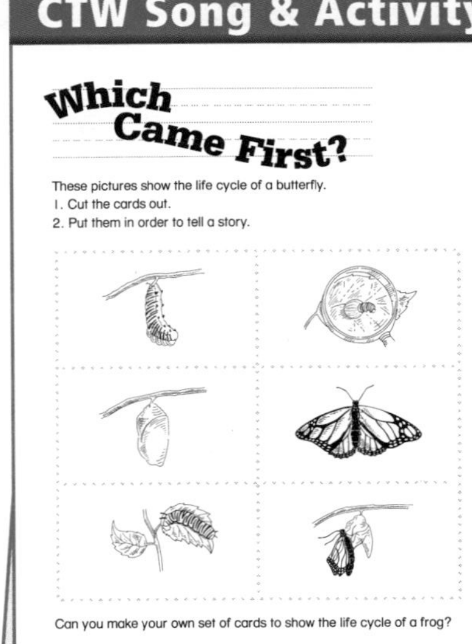
Which Came First?

These pictures show the life cycle of a butterfly.
1. Cut the cards out.
2. Put them in order to tell a story.

Can you make your own set of cards to show the life cycle of a frog?

Songs & Activities Package
pp. 11–12

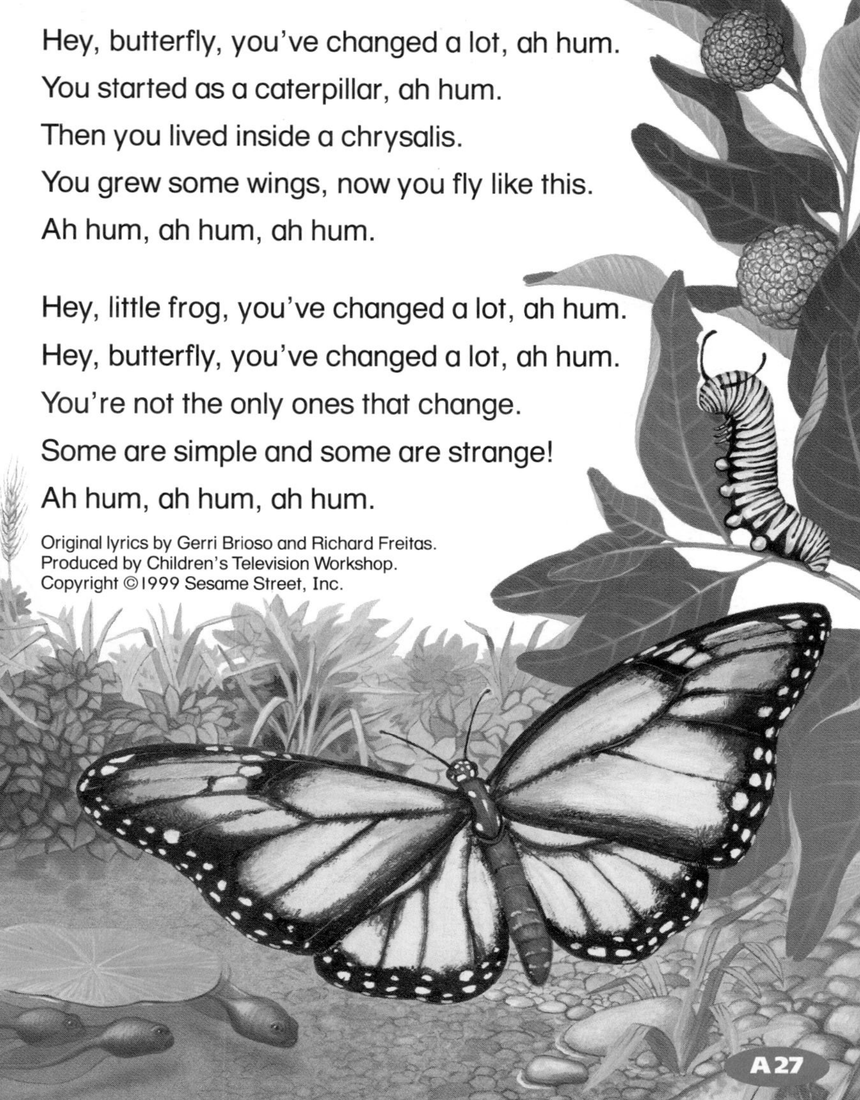

Hey, butterfly, you've changed a lot, ah hum.
You started as a caterpillar, ah hum.
Then you lived inside a chrysalis.
You grew some wings, now you fly like this.
Ah hum, ah hum, ah hum.

Hey, little frog, you've changed a lot, ah hum.
Hey, butterfly, you've changed a lot, ah hum.
You're not the only ones that change.
Some are simple and some are strange!
Ah hum, ah hum, ah hum.

Original lyrics by Gerri Brioso and Richard Freitas.
Produced by Children's Television Workshop.

A27

Family Activity

Science at Home

Dear Family:
Our class is starting Chapter 2. We will be learning about animals. These are the main ideas for Chapter 2.
- Many different kinds of animals share our world.
- Some animals, such as frogs and butterflies, change as they grow.
- A place where an animal lives is a habitat.
- Animals eat plants and other animals in the food chain.
- Animals protect themselves in many ways.

We will also be learning science vocabulary words for Chapter 2. By the end of Chapter 2, we will be able to read the vocabulary words and tell what they mean.

Word Bank
mammal
reptile
life cycle
tadpole
chrysalis
pupa
habitat
food chain
camouflage

Home Projects
Here are some activities that will help your child understand the main ideas in Chapter 2. The activities are easy, fast, and fun.

Activities
- Classify animals with your child by playing a game.
  1. Use eight pieces of paper.
  2. Write one of the words *mammal*, *reptile*, *bird*, and *fish* on four of the cards.
  3. Find and cut out a picture of each type of animal from a magazine. Paste them onto the remaining cards.

Instructional Resources pp. 9–10

Vocabulary Preview

mammal	reptile
life cycle	tadpole
chrysalis	pupa
habitat	food chain

Instructional Resources p. 11

INQUIRY

Use a KWL chart at the beginning of each chapter. In the *K* column, record what children *know* about animals. In the *W* column, list what they *want* to know. Throughout the chapter, ask children what they have *learned*. Record their responses in the *L* column. A KWL chart is available in the **Wall Chart** page 6.

Chapter 2 Skills Trace

Process Skills Development

	Communicating	Making and Using Models	Collecting Data
Skill Introduced	xiv	xv	xv
Skill Applied	A29	A36 A41	A43
Skill Assessed	End Matter 8–9	End Matter 20–21	End Matter 24–25

Science Literature Library

Animal Families
by Gene S. Stuart.
Spectacular photography depicting animals of various families engaged in their ordinary activities accompanies informative text about the featured species. (National Geographic Society, ISBN 0-7922-3610-6)

Lesson Organizer

Objective
Classify animals.

Vocabulary mammals, reptiles
Process Skills communicating

Materials
Kit Items none
School-Supplied Items drawing paper, pencil or crayons

Additional Resources
- Lab Manual
- Teacher Demonstration Kit
- Wall Chart

Introduce

Activate Prior Knowledge
Display several photographs of both living and nonliving things. Ask children how the things in the photographs are alike and how they are different.

Language Development *Make a List*
Ask children to brainstorm lists of living and nonliving things. Record their ideas on the chalkboard. Encourage children to tell the differences between the living and the nonliving things.

Flip Chart
Ask children to identify the animals in the picture. (*fox [mammal], turtle [reptile], heron [bird], fish, frog [amphibian]*) Discuss the animals' coverings and ways of moving.

What are some kinds of animals?

Look outside. Do you see buildings or cars or sidewalks? Those are nonliving things. What living things do you see? Do you see birds, squirrels, or other animals?

There are different kinds of animals. **Mammals** are animals that have fur or hair. Birds have feathers. Most **reptiles** have dry, scaly skin. Fish have scales. **Amphibians** have moist, smooth skin.

Animals can live on land, in water, or in the air. They can even live in trees or under the ground. Where do the animals in these pictures live?

A28

Science Background

- Animals can be divided into two groups—those without backbones (*invertebrates*) and those with backbones (*vertebrates*).
- Vertebrates are divided into groups (*classes*). Most animals belong to one of these groups: fish, amphibians, reptiles, birds, and mammals.
- Insects (*which are invertebrates*) are the most numerous type of animal on the earth.

Teaching Tips You may want to have available books with pictures of animals for children to use when they are choosing animals to draw. Suggest that children prepare a list of questions to use to help them guess the name of each animal. Encourage children to ask questions that will identify differences in the animals, such as number of legs, size, color, and body covering.

Guess the animal.

Materials

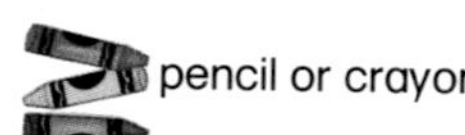

paper — pencil or crayons

Process Skills

- communicating (ask, answer)

Steps

1. This is a game you can play with your class.
2. Draw an animal. Keep it a secret.
3. When it is your turn, the class will **ask** you questions about your animal. You can only **answer** yes or no.
4. If no one guesses your animal in ten questions, you win. Show the class your picture.

Share. Tell why you chose that animal.

Lesson Review

1. What is a mammal?
2. Name some places animals live.
3. **Show** how your animal moves by acting it out.

A29

Lab Manual

What are some kinds of animals?

Draw your secret animal here.

Write four things about your animal.

1.

2.

3.

4.

Lab Manual p. 17

Activity Rubric

Use the following activity scoring rubric to assess students' performance.

Scoring Criteria	1	2	3	4
Student followed directions to complete this activity.				
Student drew an animal of his or her choice.				
Student wrote four characteristics of the animal he or she selected.				
Student interacted appropriately with the question-answer format in class.				
Students communicated his or her reasons for choosing the animal.				

Scoring Key

4 points correct, complete, detailed
3 points partially correct, complete, detailed
2 points partially correct, partially complete, lacks some detail
1 point incorrect or incomplete, needs assistance

Lab Manual p. T5

Call 1-888-537-4908 with your Activity questions or comments.

Teach and Apply

Student Page A28

Display **Wall Chart** page 7. Under each category, have children list characteristics of that type of animal and then names of specific animals that fit into that category.

Reading Assist *Plurals*

Remind children that although the plurals of most nouns are formed by adding *s* to the singular, some words are the same in singular and plural forms. Have children find all the plurals on the page and find the word that is the same in both forms. (*fish*)

Student Page A29

Explore Activity

Time about 25 minutes

Grouping individual, whole class

Suggest that children be creative in the questions they ask to guess the animals. Children can complete Lab Manual page 17 as they do the activity.

Assess and Extend

Answers to Lesson Review

1. A mammal is an animal that has fur or hair.
2. Some animals live on land, in the water, or in the air. Some live in trees or under the ground.
3. **Show** (*Performance Assessment*) Children's movements will vary based on the animals they choose.

Inquire Further

Ask the following question to guide further inquiry: **What are some ways animals' body coverings can help or protect the animals?** (*Possible answers: keep animals warm and dry*)

Enrichment

Display pictures of animals. Ask: **What kinds of animals have feathers?** (*fur, scales*) **Where do they live? How do they move? Name two animals that have feathers.** (*fur, scales*)

Higher Order Thinking *Generalize*

Have children tell what they look at first to help decide if an animal is a mammal or a reptile.

Math Organizer

Objective

Use sequencing to put events in order.

Additional Resources

- Math in Science blackline master

Teaching Math in Science

- In science, ordering skills help children understand time order relationships. Understanding time order relationships helps children see how events fit together. In addition to understanding time order relationships, ordering skills help children perform science experiments. Children need to use ordering skills to ensure that the steps in an experiment are performed in the same order or sequence each time. This helps ensure that independent variables are changed systematically.
- Communication is an important science process skill. The use of transition words such as *first, second, third, next, then,* and *last* can help children clearly communicate the order of events. The use of pictures, time lines, or flowcharts can help children visually represent a sequence of events.
- Have children read and complete the Math in Science lesson and the Math in Science blackline master.

Student Page A30

- Before beginning the page, explain that ordering means to put or do things in the right order. Children might be familiar with ordering from creating patterns in math.
- Have children observe as you model the use of transition words to discuss an order of events: **First, I find a pencil. Next, I sharpen the pencil. Finally, I write with the pencil.**
- After children discuss why the first set of pictures is in order, use transition words to point out that the sequence shows the time order of events.
- After you discuss why the second set of pictures is out of order, have children tell how they would rearrange the pictures to show the proper order.

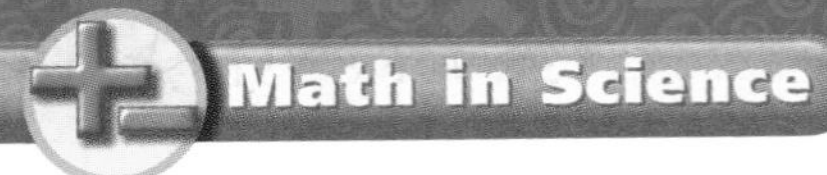

Ordering

These pictures are in order. Can you explain why?

1st 2nd 3rd

These pictures are not in order. Can you explain why?

ESL Strategy

Collect comic strips made up of three frames each. Cut apart the frames, shuffle them, and give each child one strip. Have children read the frames or look at the pictures to determine the story line, then put the frames in order. Have them use transition words such as *first, second, next,* and *last* to tell the story so it makes sense.

How would you put these pictures in order?[1]
Explain why.

[1] eggs cracking and bird coming out of egg; baby birds out of eggs; young bird

Turn the page to find out how ordering can help you learn more about animals.

A31

Student Page A31

- Before beginning the page, have children brainstorm a list of transition words they might use to help them communicate an order of events, such as *first, second, third, next, then, last,* and *finally.*
- Have children use transition words to tell in what order they would put the pictures.
- Read aloud the last statement. Then ask: **How do you think ordering can help you learn more about animals?** (*Possible answer: Ordering can help you know what an animal looks like as a baby and then as a grown-up.*)

Apply Math in Science to Lesson 2

Children will use what they learned about ordering to complete the next lesson.

Math in Science

Ordering

Look at the pictures in each row. Think about which picture comes 1st, 2nd, and 3rd. Write a number below each one to show the order.

Instructional Resources p. 12

Lesson Organizer

Objective
Describe the growth and development of a frog.

Vocabulary life cycle, tadpole

Additional Resources
- Wall Chart

Introduce

Activate Prior Knowledge
Ask children to draw a picture of what they think a young frog looks like. Save children's drawings for use as a **baseline assessment.**

Language Development *Story Starter*
Invite children to help you create a story about an animal that grew and changed. Ask children, in turn, to add at least one sentence to continue the following story: **Once upon a time, there was a young . . .**

Flip Chart

Point out the pictures that show the stages in the life cycle of a frog (*egg, tadpole, adult frog*). Ask: **How does a tadpole look different from an adult frog?**

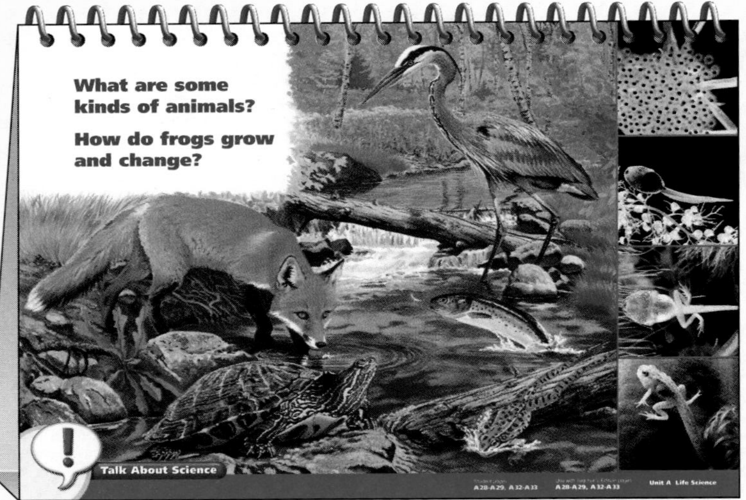

What are some kinds of animals?
How do frogs grow and change?
Talk About Science
Unit A Life Science

Amphibian

How do frogs grow and change?

What baby animals have you seen? You may have seen kittens or puppies. Some animals look a lot like their parents.

Not all baby animals look like their parents. Some animals go through many changes as they grow. This is called the **life cycle**.

These pictures are in order. They show the life cycle of a frog. When a baby frog hatches from an egg, it is called a **tadpole**. A tadpole has a tail and no legs, and it swims and breathes in the water.

As the tadpole grows, its legs form. It becomes a full-grown frog. How does the frog look different from the tadpole?[1]

[1] It has legs and no tail.

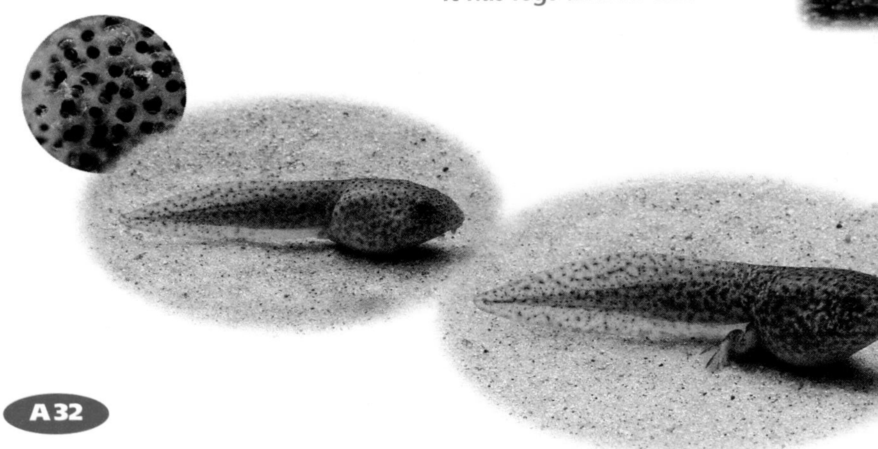

A32

Science Background

- Frogs belong to the group of vertebrates called amphibians.
- Frogs must lay their eggs in water, which is also where the eggs are fertilized. The eggs hatch into a larval form called a tadpole. Tadpoles breathe through gills and are plant eaters (*herbivores*). As the tadpole gets larger, it begins to grow legs and lungs and loses its tail and gills.
- Adult frogs are meat eaters (*carnivores*), eating mainly insects.

Possible Misconceptions Some children may think that the tadpole is an entirely different animal from the adult frog. Explain that the tadpole is a particular stage of development in the life cycle of a frog and is not a different animal.

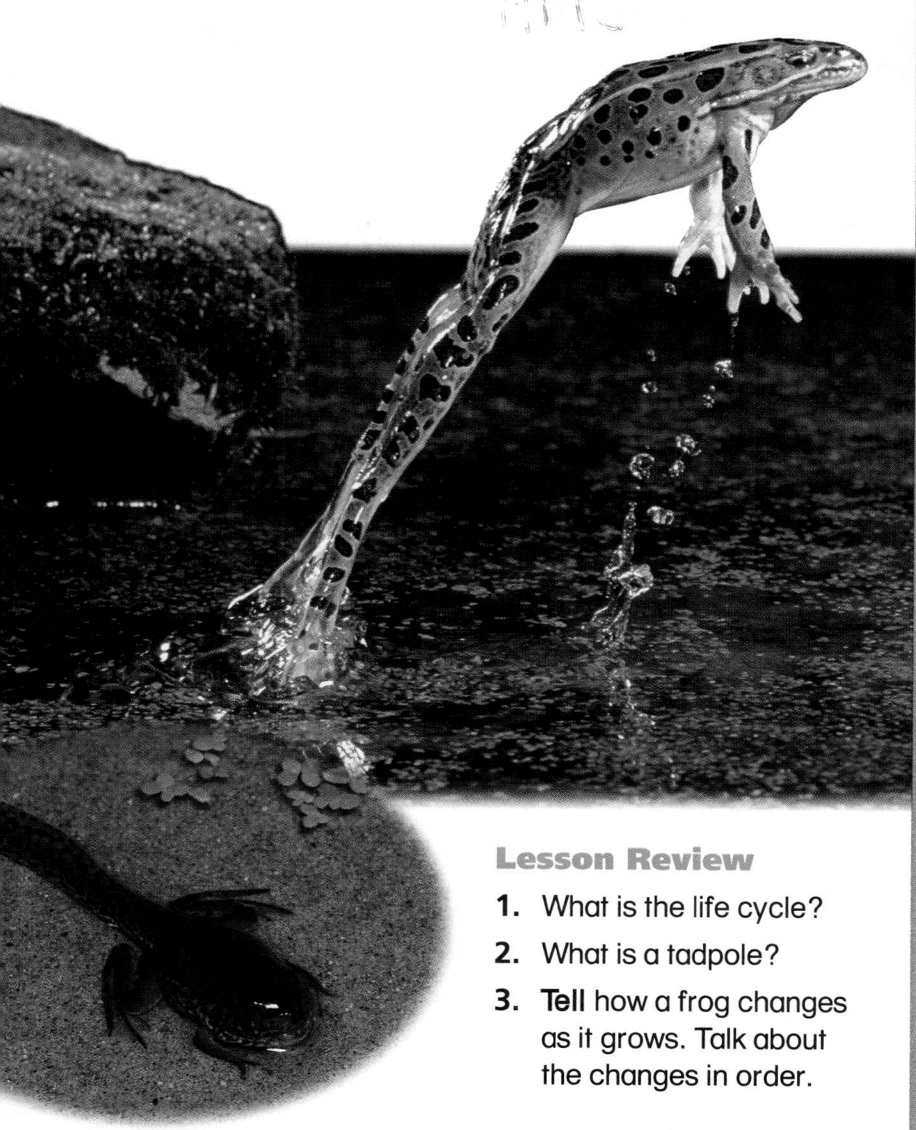

Lesson Review

1. What is the life cycle?
2. What is a tadpole?
3. **Tell** how a frog changes as it grows. Talk about the changes in order.

A33

ESL Strategy

Using **Wall Chart** page 8, point to each stage in the frog's life cycle as you describe it. Have children name each stage with you. Then cut out the pictures of the stages, scramble them, and have children attach them to the top of the chart in the correct order. Ask children to point to the pictures as they describe the life cycle.

Teach and Apply

Student Pages A32–A33

- Discuss the fact that all living things have a life cycle. Point out that frogs belong to a group of animals called amphibians. They are cold-blooded animals that live on land and in water. Explain that amphibians have wet, smooth skin instead of scales.
- Point out that many young animals look more similar to their parents than tadpoles do. However, they are not exactly like their parents. Lead a discussion about the differences children can see between other adult animals and their babies. Then challenge children to select an animal and draw a sequence of pictures like the ones of the frog in their books to show the life cycle of that animal.

Reading Assist *Use Picture Clues*

Encourage children to use the sequence of pictures as well as the text to help them understand how frogs grow and change.

Assess and Extend

Answers to Lesson Review

1. The changes animals go through as they grow are called the life cycle.
2. A tadpole is a baby frog.
3. **Tell** (*Interview*) Children's answers should include changes such as the growth of a tail, the legs forming, and so on.

Check for Understanding

To follow up on the **baseline assessment,** ask children to draw another picture of a tadpole and compare it with their original picture.

Reteach

Have children study the pictures and words in their textbooks and make a book titled *The Life Cycle of a Frog.* Tell them to draw and label a picture for each stage in the life of a frog.

Science Center

Flip Chart

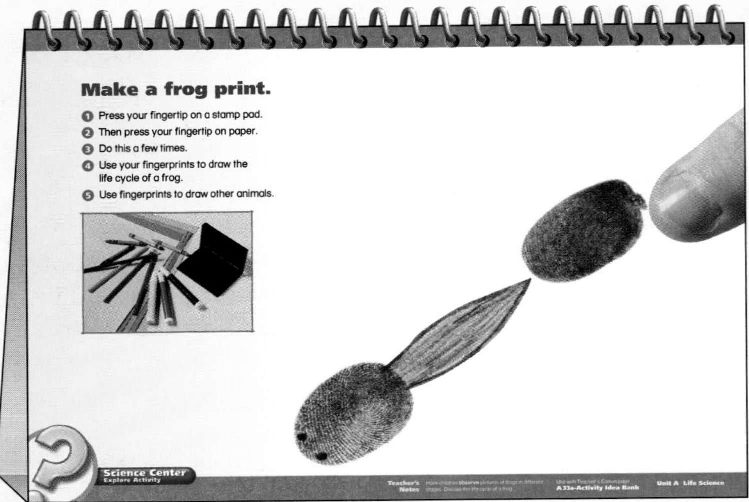

Make a frog print.
1 Press your fingertip on a stamp pad.
2 Then press your fingertip on paper.
3 Do this a few times.
4 Use your fingerprints to draw the life cycle of a frog.
5 Use fingerprints to draw other animals.
Science Center

Make a frog print.

Objective

Show the life cycle of a frog.

Process Skills observing

Materials

Kit Items none

School-Supplied Items stamp pad, paper, art supplies, frog picture book

Procedure

- Children **observe** the pictures of a frog's life cycle in the frog picture book. Help children name each stage.
- Children classify the stages of a frog's life cycle by ordering them in sequence. They may use their prints to communicate what happens in each stage.
- You can use **Lab Manual** page 18 with this activity.

What to Expect

Children's prints should include an egg, a tadpole, and a frog.

Lab Manual

Make a frog print.

Draw or make your fingerprint art showing the life cycle of a frog.

Use fingerprint art to draw other animals.

Lab Manual, p. 18

Connections

School and Community

Ideas for bringing the school and community together:

Field Trips

- nature center
- local pond
- city aquarium

Guest Speakers

- zoologist
- entomologist
- forest ranger
- game and fish commissioner

Themes

The activities on these pages can be used with classroom themes such as:

- animals
- metamorphosis
- pets
- woods
- ponds

Books for Children

Children might enjoy these books about animals:

Snakes by Patricia Demuth. Kinds, sizes, how they hunt, what dangers they face. (Price Stern Sloan, ISBN 0-448-40513-X)

The Very Quiet Cricket by Eric Carle. A cricket is unable to produce a chirp like other crickets. (Philomel, ISBN 0-399-21885-8)

What Keeps Them Warm? by Bill Gaynor. Nature's provisions for helping keep animals warm. (Learning Media, ISBN 0-478-20516-3)

Imagine by Alison Lester. Intricate pictures show a wide variety of animals that live in many different locations. (Houghton Mifflin, ISBN 0-395-66953-7)

Cross-Curricular Options

LITERATURE

Moonbear's Pet

Use the book to show sequence.

Materials *Moonbear's Pet* by Frank Asch. (Simon & Schuster, ISBN 0-689-80794-5), paper, crayons

Procedure

- Two friends, Bear and Little Bird, find a new pet. The pet begins to change shape, and both friends argue that it is becoming more like them. The new pet—a tadpole—puts a strain on the friends' relationship.
- Encourage children to guess what the new pet is as you read aloud and show the pictures.
- Invite children to make a book showing the sequence of development of the new pet. On each page, they can draw one stage in the development.

Multiple Intelligences linguistic

MATH

Sort and Graph

Make and analyze a bar graph.

Materials paper, crayons

Procedure

- Take a class poll of children's favorite animals.
- Then help children make a bar graph to illustrate the results of the poll.
- Discuss a title for the graph and how to label the side and bottom.

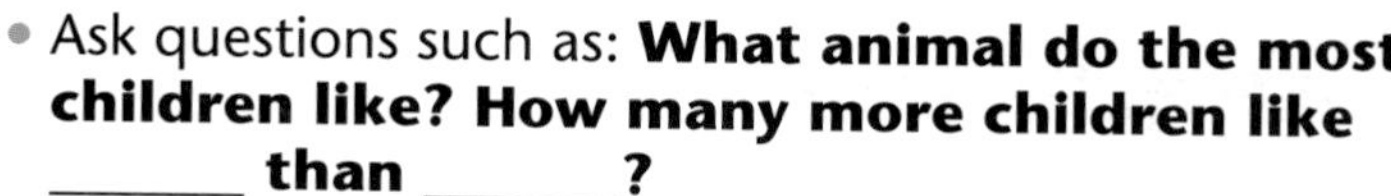

- Ask questions such as: **What animal do the most children like? How many more children like _______ than _______?**

Multiple Intelligences logical-mathematical

ESL Provide sentence frames using the words *most, fewest,* and *favorite* so children can create sentences.

WRITING

If Animals Could Talk...

Write animal dialogues.

Procedure

- Have children imagine that animals could talk and what a tadpole and frog or other parent and child animal might say to each other.
- Have children write a story about a young animal and its parent.

Multiple Intelligences linguistic

Gifted and Talented Challenge children to write their story in the form of a play and then work together to perform it.

ART

Clay Animals

Use clay to model stages in the life cycle of a frog.

Materials clay

Procedure

- Invite groups of children to work together to make clay models of different stages in the life cycle of a frog.
- Suggest that children combine their models and sequence them to create a display with labels.
- Children might create a pond backdrop for the display using colored paper and other materials.

Multiple Intelligences spatial, bodily-kinesthetic

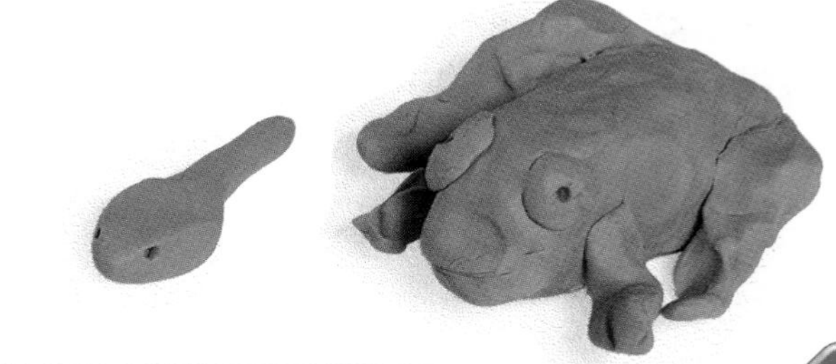

Lesson Organizer

Objective
Describe the life cycle of a butterfly.

Vocabulary chrysalis, pupa

Additional Resources
- Wall Chart
- Interactive Transparency

Introduce

Activate Prior Knowledge

Remind children of how a frog grows from an egg to a tadpole to a frog. Then ask children to draw a picture to show how they think the life of a butterfly begins. Save pictures for use as a **baseline assessment.**

Language Development *Make a List*

Help children brainstorm a list of baby animal names and the corresponding adult names, for example: tadpole/frog, kid/goat, calf/cow, colt/horse, fawn/deer. Tell children that they are going to learn about caterpillars and butterflies.

Flip Chart

Discuss with children the pictures showing the life cycle of a butterfly. Point out the eggs, the caterpillar, the pupa in its chrysalis, and the adult butterfly.

How do butterflies grow and change?

You may have seen many different kinds of butterflies. Not all butterflies look alike, but they have the same life cycle. How do butterflies change as they grow?

Find the eggs in the picture. A caterpillar hatches from an egg. The caterpillar eats a lot and grows very quickly.

Then the caterpillar makes a covering called a **chrysalis**. Now the caterpillar is called a **pupa**.

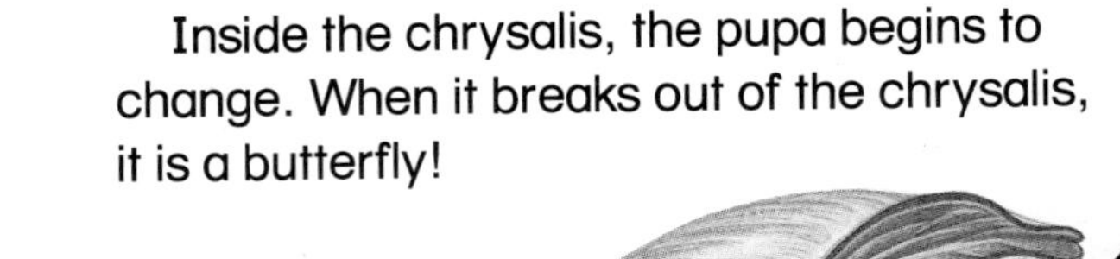

Inside the chrysalis, the pupa begins to change. When it breaks out of the chrysalis, it is a butterfly!

Science Background

Most insects grow and develop in one of two ways.

(1) In incomplete metamorphosis, the egg develops into a nymph, which develops into an adult, which lays eggs, completing the cycle. The nymph resembles the adult. Grasshoppers are an example.

(2) In complete metamorphosis, the egg develops into a larva, which develops into a pupa, which develops into an adult, which lays eggs, completing the cycle. The larva and pupa do not resemble the adult. Butterflies are an example.

Possible Misconceptions Some children may not realize that butterflies are insects. Point out that most insects have six legs, antennae, a mouth, body, and wings.

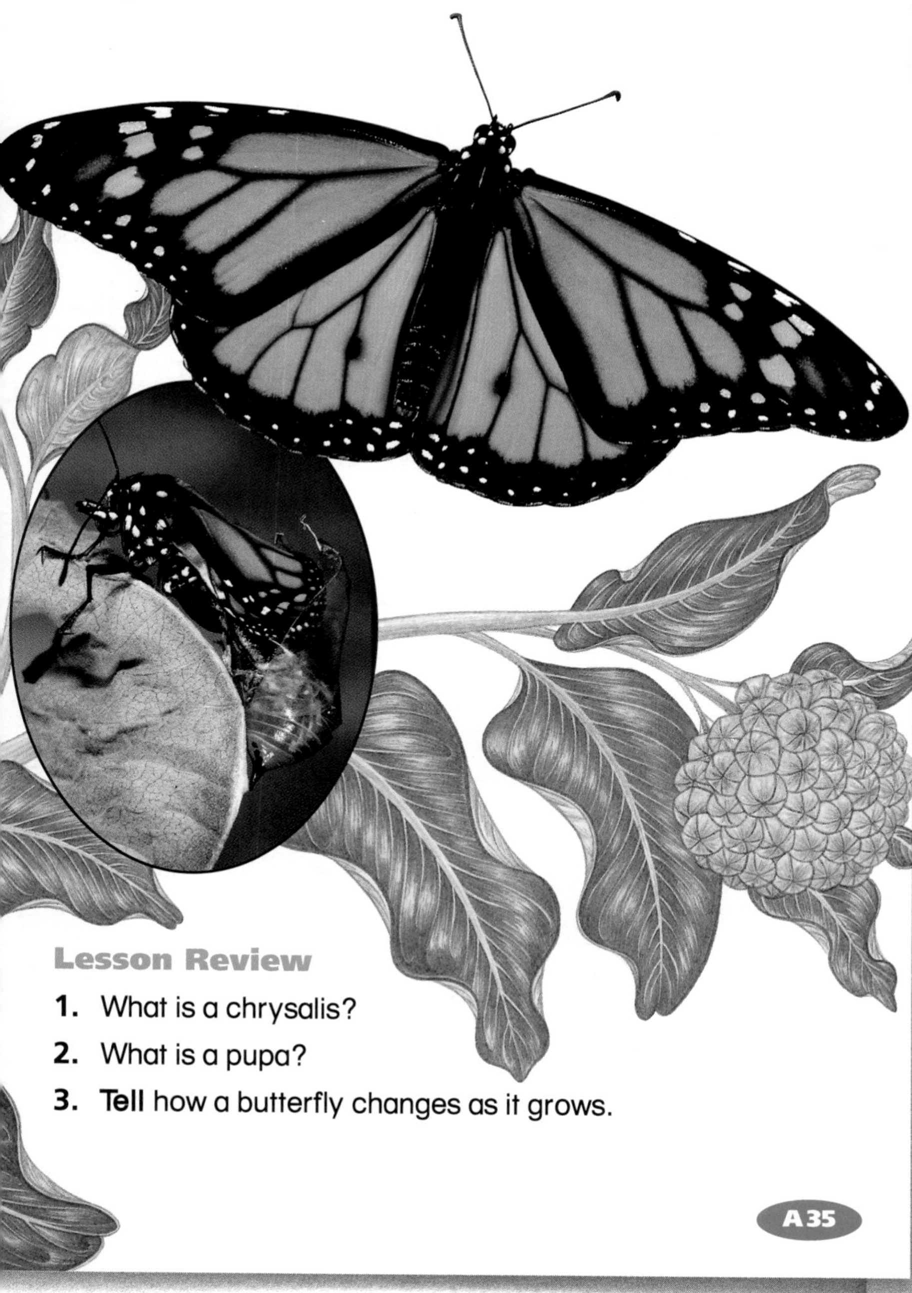

Lesson Review

1. What is a chrysalis?
2. What is a pupa?
3. **Tell** how a butterfly changes as it grows.

A35

ESL Strategy

Using **Wall Chart** page 9, point to each stage in the butterfly's life cycle as you describe it. Have children name each stage with you.

Transparency

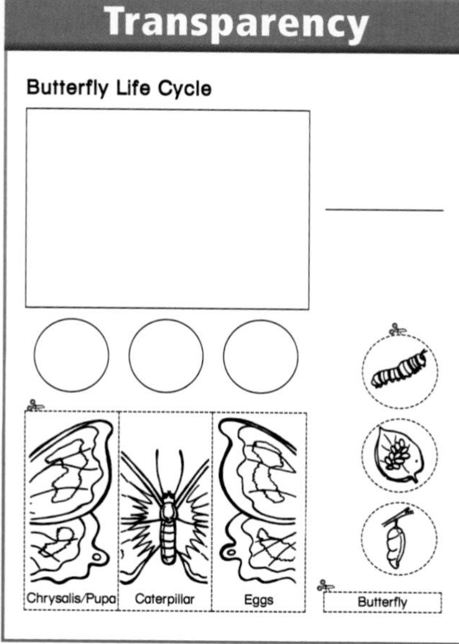

Interactive Transparency Package Transparency 2

Teach and Apply

Student Pages A34–A35

- After reading the text, help children identify each stage in the life cycle of a butterfly. Point out that a caterpillar, which looks like a worm, is the larva of the butterfly. The larva hatches from an egg and later changes into a pupa. Explain that although some animals resemble their parents from the beginning, butterflies and many other insects resemble their parents only after they go through several stages of development.
- Display **Wall Chart** page 9. Invite children to take turns labeling each stage in the life of a butterfly. Then, as a challenge, ask volunteers to label the body parts of the butterfly. Save the **Wall Chart** for use in the next lesson.

Reading Assist *Preview and Predict*

Using the lesson title and the pictures on the pages, have children predict what they will learn about in this lesson.

Assess and Extend

Answers to Lesson Review

1. A chrysalis is the covering made by a caterpillar.
2. A pupa is what a caterpillar is called when it is inside the chrysalis.
3. Tell (*Interview*) Children's answers should include changing from a caterpillar to a pupa to a butterfly. Children may mention that a butterfly has wings.

Check for Understanding

To follow up on the **baseline assessment,** have children add to or revise the pictures they drew in Activate Prior Knowledge.

Reteach

- Use the Interactive Transparency to reteach Lesson 3 concepts.
- Provide children with separate picture cards showing each stage in the development of a butterfly. Invite children to work with partners to place the pictures in order. Then have children take turns describing the development.

Activity Organizer

Objective
Make a model of a butterfly life cycle.

Process Skills making and using models

Materials

Kit Items modeling clay in assorted colors, pipe cleaners

School-Supplied Items safety goggles, construction paper, scissors

Time about 30 minutes

Grouping individual

Additional Resources
- Lab Manual
- Teacher Demonstration Kit

Introduce

The Lesson 4 Investigate Activity, *How can you make a model of a butterfly life cycle?*, is on the **Flip Chart.**

Activate Prior Knowledge

Invite children to list everything they know about butterflies. Suggest that they list what they know about the stages in the life of a butterfly, what it eats, what it looks like, and its body parts. Save the list for use as a **baseline assessment.**

Language Development *Drama*

Have children form groups of four. Assign each child in a group a stage in the butterfly's life cycle. Members act out what their stage would behave like. The class guesses the stages and puts them in the correct order.

Investigate Activity

How can you make a model of a butterfly life cycle?

Process Skills
- making and using models

Materials

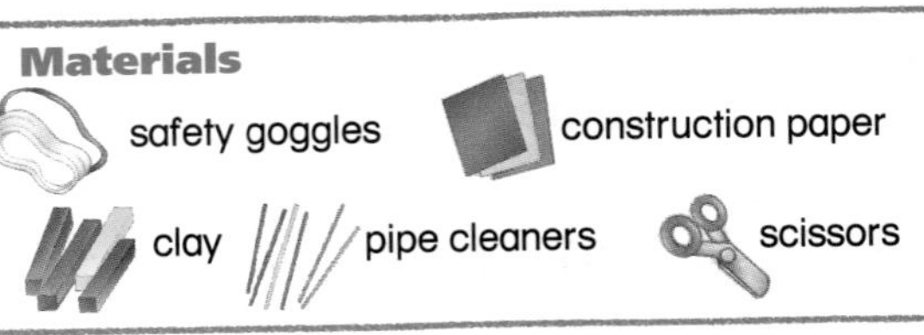

Steps
1. Put on your safety goggles.
2. Use clay to make models of an egg, a caterpillar, and a pupa in a chrysalis.
3. Now shape some clay into the body of a butterfly.
4. Add wings, legs, and antennae.
5. Use your models to show the life cycle of a butterfly.

A36

Science Background

- Butterflies usually fly during the day. Moths usually fly at night.
- The antennae of moths are usually feathery, while the antennae of butterflies are slender and end in small knobs.
- Moths have stout, furry bodies, while butterflies have thin, smooth bodies.

Math-Science Connection Point out that just as there are number patterns in math so there are patterns in nature. Invite children to examine the picture of the butterfly on page A35 and point out the color patterns on its wings. Then invite children to design their own butterflies.

Technology

Review the demonstration of this Investigate's procedure on the *Life Science* **Activity Video** Segment 3.

Think About Your Results

1. What are the stages of a butterfly's life?
2. How does the butterfly change in each stage?

 **Inquire Further**

How else could you show the stages of a butterfly's life?

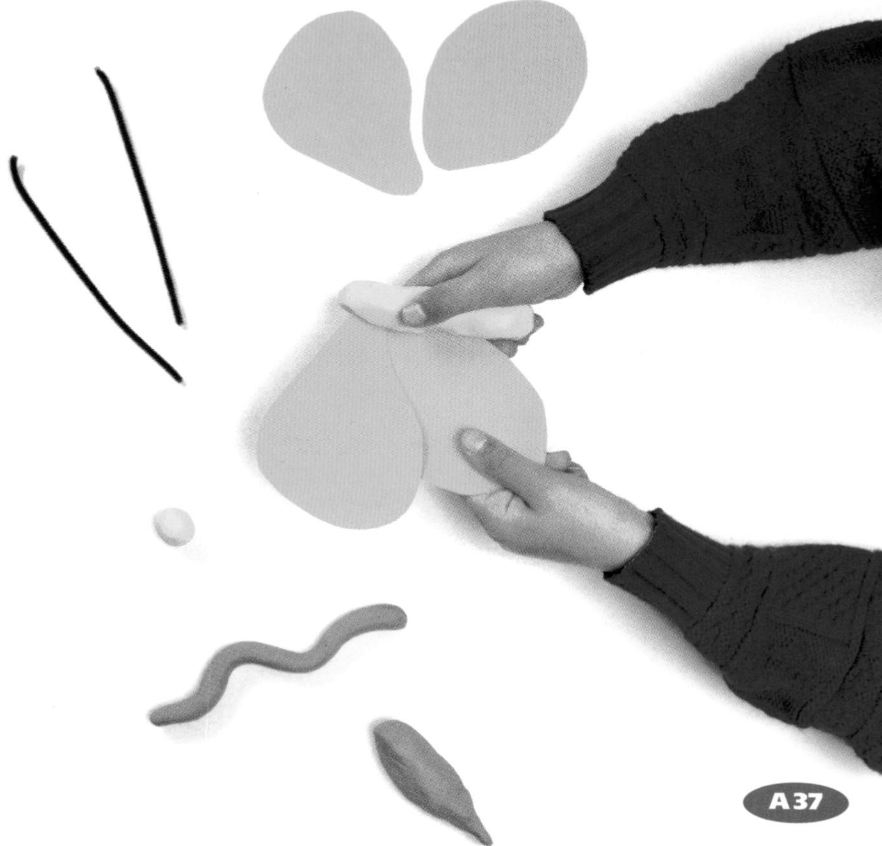

A37

Lab Manual

How can you make a model of a butterfly life cycle?

Cut out the pictures and the circle.

Glue the pictures to the circle. Put them in order to show the life cycle of the butterfly.

Egg | Caterpillar | Pupa | Butterfly

Life Cycle Wheel

Lab Manual
p. 19

Activity Rubric

Use the following activity scoring rubric to assess students' performance.

Scoring Criteria	1	2	3	4
Student followed directions to perform the activity.				
Student constructed a wheel model of various stages in the life of a butterfly.				
Student identified changes that occurred at each stage in the butterfly's life cycle.				
Student used safety practices in making his or her models.				
Student explained the life cycle of a butterfly using a model for visual reinforcement.				

Scoring Key
4 points correct, complete, detailed
3 points partially correct, complete, detailed
2 points partially correct, partially complete, lacks some detail
1 point incorrect or incomplete, needs assistance

Lab Manual
p. T6

 **Call 1-888-537-4908 with your Activity questions or comments.**

Teach and Apply

- In this activity, children will make clay models showing the stages in the life cycle of a butterfly.
- Be sure children make four separate models to represent the four stages—egg, caterpillar, pupa, and butterfly. Then have children display the models in the proper order.
- Suggest that children make a label for each stage on note cards and display them with the models.
- Children can complete Lab Manual page 19 as they do the activity.

Reading Assist *Vocabulary Development*

Explain that a model is a copy of a real object. Ask children why people use models. Elicit that objects are often too big or difficult to make in actual size.

What to Expect

When finished, children should have the complete life cycle of a butterfly shown in four models—egg, caterpillar, pupa, and butterfly.

Assess and Extend

Answers to Think About Your Results

1. The butterfly begins as an egg, becomes a caterpillar, forms a chrysalis and becomes a pupa, and then breaks out of the chrysalis as a butterfly.
2. In the beginning, it is a small egg. When it hatches, it is a furry caterpillar that eats and grows fat. Then it builds its covering and becomes a pupa. When it breaks out of its chrysalis, it has become a butterfly.

Inquire Further

Children might say that they could show the stages of a butterfly's life in pictures or by acting it out.

Check for Understanding

To follow up on the **baseline assessment,** have children revisit and add to their list about butterflies.

Enrichment

Invite children to use reference books to find pictures and more information about butterflies.

Higher Order Thinking *Generalize*

Ask children to tell why they think making models is a good way to learn about butterflies.

Science Center

Flip Chart

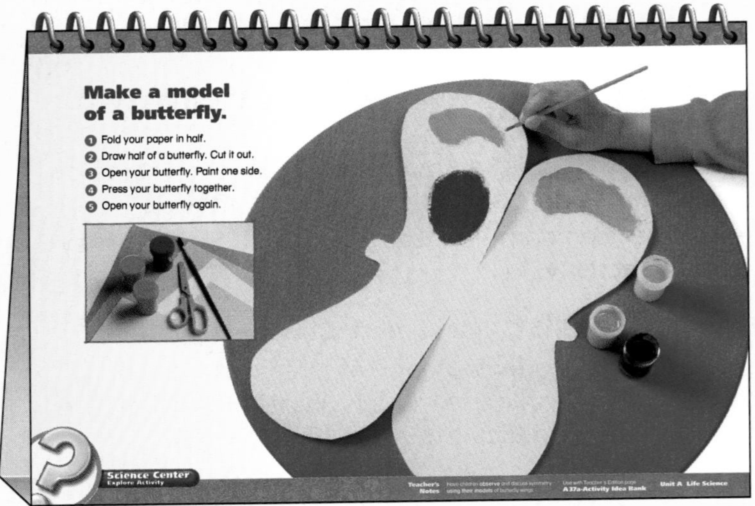

Make a model of a butterfly.

Objective

Understand the concept of symmetry and notice the symmetry on butterfly wings.

Process Skills observing, making and using models

Materials

Kit Items none

School-Supplied Items construction paper, paint, scissors, pencil

Safety Note *Talk to children about the proper use of scissors.*

Procedure

- Tell children that the midsection of the butterfly's body must be along the fold.
- Help children cut out paper to **make models** of butterflies.
- Ask children to **observe** what happens when they fold and press the sides together.
- Have children **use their models** to discuss how their butterflies are similar.
- You can use **Lab Manual** page 21 with this activity.

What to Expect

Children learn about symmetry. The wings on their butterfly models are symmetrical.

Lab Manual

Make a model of a butterfly.

Draw a picture or design that shows symmetry.
Be sure it looks the same on both sides.

Lab Manual, p. 21

Connections

School and Community

Ideas for bringing the school and community together:

Field Trips

- aviary
- nature center
- pond

Guest Speakers

- zoologist
- naturalist
- gardener

Themes

The activities on these pages can be used with classroom themes such as:

- insects
- habitats
- gardening or flowers

Books for Children

Children might enjoy these books about animals:

Dancers in the Garden by Joanne Ryder. Lyrical picture book about a day in the life of a hummingbird. (Sierra Club, ISBN 0-8715-6410-6)

All Kinds of Eyes by Bill Gaynor. Photo-rich book featuring the different kinds of eyes that animals have. (Learning Media, ISBN 0-478-20506-6)

Insects Are My Life by Megan McDonald. A girl shares her passion for insects with schoolmates, friends, and family. (Orchard Books, ISBN 0-531-07093)

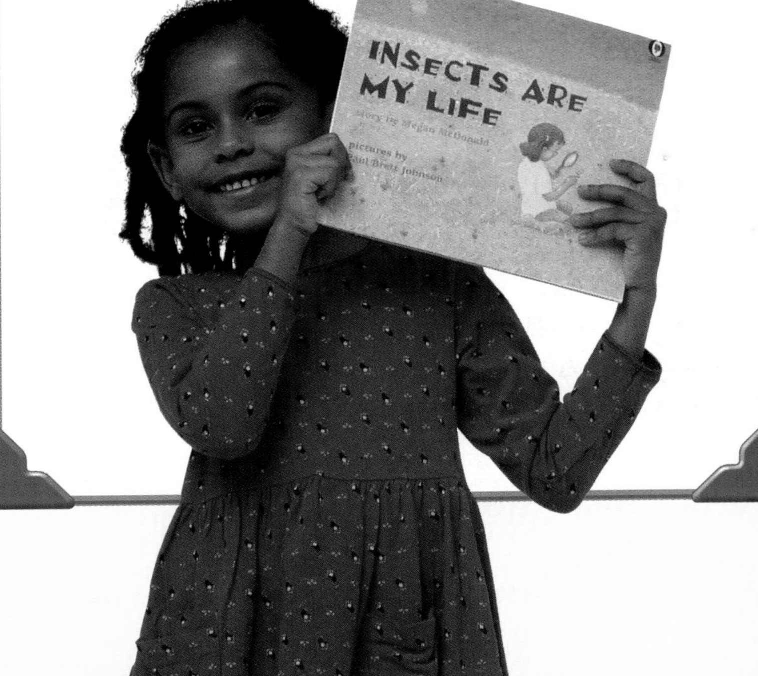

Cross-Curricular Options

LITERATURE

Chickens Aren't the Only Ones

Use the book to explore animals that lay eggs.

Materials *Chickens Aren't the Only Ones* by Ruth Heller. (Grossett & Dunlap, ISBN 0-448-40454-0)

Procedure

- As you read aloud, be sure to show children all the beautiful illustrations.
- Explain that this book shows animals as they really are. Point out that some books give plants and animals attributes they don't really have, such as being able to talk.
- Begin a bulletin board display titled "Animals That Lay Eggs." Have children contribute drawings and magazine cutouts of animals to the display.

Multiple Intelligences linguistic

MATH

All About Butterflies

Create and use data from a chart.

Materials books about butterflies, chart paper

Procedure

- Make a chart with these headings:

Kinds of butterflies	Characteristics

- Tell children that there are thousands of kinds of butterflies in the world.
- Have partners gather information about one kind of butterfly and record it on the chart.
- Then children can ask and answer questions about the information.

Multiple Intelligences logical-mathematical

Gifted and Talented Invite children to write about one kind of butterfly and present it to the class.

ART

Butterflies Fly

Make mobiles of butterflies.

Materials generic butterfly outlines, crayons or markers, scissors, yarn, hangers, books with color pictures of butterflies

Procedure

- Display pictures of different kinds of butterflies.
- Let children choose the one they like best and color in two or three outlines, cut them out, and color the other side.
- Help children cut different lengths of yarn and attach their butterflies to hangers. They can attach a label with the butterfly's name to another piece of yarn.
- Children can blow on their mobiles to make the butterflies fly.

Multiple Intelligences spatial

Special Needs You can enlarge the butterfly outlines for children with visual difficulties.

SOCIAL STUDIES

Map It!

Make a class map of butterfly migrations.

Procedure

- Provide books or have children select books from the library about the monarch butterfly.
- Invite them to read about the butterfly's migration.
- Then make a class map to illustrate some of the butterfly's paths.

Multiple Intelligences linguistic

Lesson Organizer

Objective

Identify features that enable animals to live in various habitats.

Vocabulary habitat, endangered

Additional Resources

- Wall Chart

Introduce

Activate Prior Knowledge

Have children select a duck, a giraffe, or a seal. Ask them to draw a picture of where the animal lives and write a sentence about why the animal lives there. Save pictures for use as a **baseline assessment.**

Language Development *Animal Riddles*

Children take turns describing an animal and asking others to guess what the animal is and where it lives. For example: I am furry. I look like I am wearing a mask. I climb trees. Who am I and where do I live? (*a raccoon; the forest*)

Flip Chart

Point out to children that each animal in the picture gets food, water, and shelter from its habitat. Explain how body parts (*legs, wings, and so on*) help an animal live in its habitat.

Where do animals live?
What do animals eat?
How do animals protect themselves?
Talk About Science
Unit A Life Science

Where do animals live?

Think about different animals you have seen. Where do these animals live?

A place where an animal lives is called its **habitat**. A habitat can be hot or cold or wet or dry. Animals get food, water, and shelter from their habitats. Many animals and plants become endangered when their habitats change. **Endangered** means that very few of these animals and plants are living.

What helps these animals live in their habitats? Webbed feet help a duck swim. A giraffe's long neck helps it reach leaves on tall trees. Seals have a thick layer of fat to help keep them warm. How does thick fur help seals live in their cold habitat?[1]

[1] It helps keep them warm.

Science Background

- Since animals depend on plants for food, the amount of plant life in an area determines how many animals can live there.
- The Antarctic landmass is too cold to support any plants, and no animals find food there. Penguins and seals sometimes rest on the land, but they get all their food from the sea.
- The tropical rain forests support more plant and animal life than any other habitat.

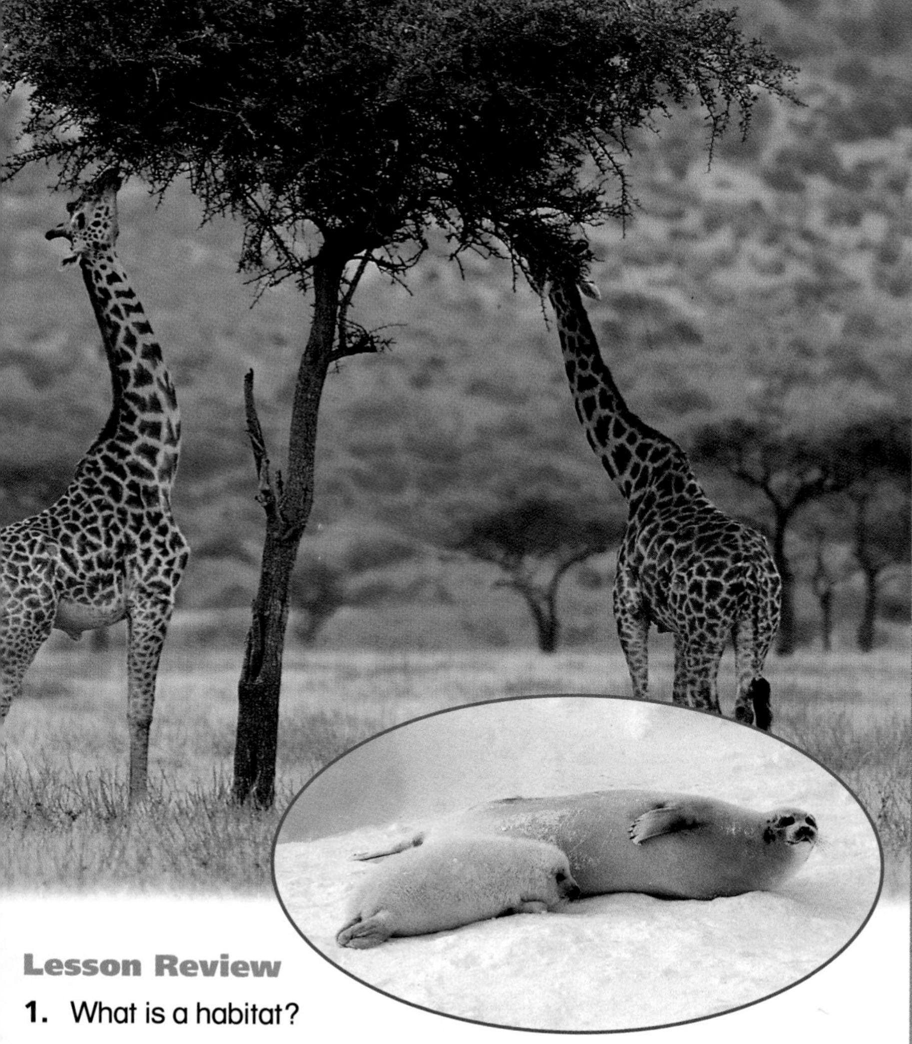

Lesson Review

1. What is a habitat?
2. What helps a giraffe live in its habitat?
3. **Draw** a habitat and an animal that lives there.

A39

ESL Strategy

Provide the following sentence frames for children to complete.
A ________ is a place where an animal lives. A (name an animal) lives in a ________ habitat. This habitat has ________ that the animal needs.

Teach and Apply

Student Pages A38–A39

- Point out that all living things need food, air, water, shelter, and space. Animals live in the habitat that can best provide them with each of these. Habitats vary based on temperature, amount of rain, and type of soil. These differences determine the types of animals and plants that live there. Explain that sometimes changes occur in habitats that make it difficult for plants and animals to live there. When this happens, the plants and animals can become endangered. Discuss the different environments shown on the page. Explain that some animals, like seals, also have blubber, a layer of fat under the skin, that keeps them warm.
- Display **Wall Chart** page 10. Have children list the giraffe, seal, and duck in the appropriate squares. Then discuss and list what each habitat is like, some animals that live there, and what body parts or features help the animals survive there. Challenge children to think about what would happen to different animals if you took them from one habitat and placed them in another.

Reading Assist *Vocabulary Department*

Point out the word *shelter* in the text and write it on the chalkboard. Then ask children to name different types of shelter that people and animals use.

Assess and Extend

Answers to Lesson Review

1. A habitat is a place where an animal lives.
2. A long neck helps a giraffe live in its habitat.
3. **Draw** (*Journal*) Children's drawings should show an animal that has some particular feature special to its habitat.

Check for Understanding

To follow up on the **baseline assessment,** ask children to revise or draw another picture of their animal and its habitat. Encourage them to add other animals to the picture that might also live there.

Reteach

Provide a variety of toy animals or pictures and have children group together animals that might live in the same habitat. Encourage children to describe the habitats and explain why they placed each animal in a certain one.

Lesson Organizer

Objective
Explain how animals depend on plants and other animals for food.

Vocabulary food chain
Process Skills making and using models

Materials
Kit Items paper plates, yarn
School-Supplied Items index cards, crayons, masking tape

Additional Resources
- Lab Manual
- Teacher Demonstration Kit
- Wall Chart

Introduce

Activate Prior Knowledge
Invite children to name foods they like to eat. Then ask them to tell why people need to eat food.

Language Development *Classify*
Have children tell which foods they like to eat come from plants and which come from animals.

Flip Chart
Explain that plants use the sun's energy to make food. Animals eat plants or other animals. Point out the food chain in the picture. (*plant, moth, bird, raccoon*)

Where do animals live?
What do animals eat?
How do animals protect themselves?
Talk About Science
Unit A Life Science

What do animals eat?

Splash! The river otter dives into the water to catch a fish.

Animals need plants and other animals to stay alive. Some animals eat plants. Some animals eat other animals.

Plants use energy from the sun to make food. Animals eat the plants for food. Then other animals eat those animals. This is called the **food chain**. Talk about the food chain in this picture.

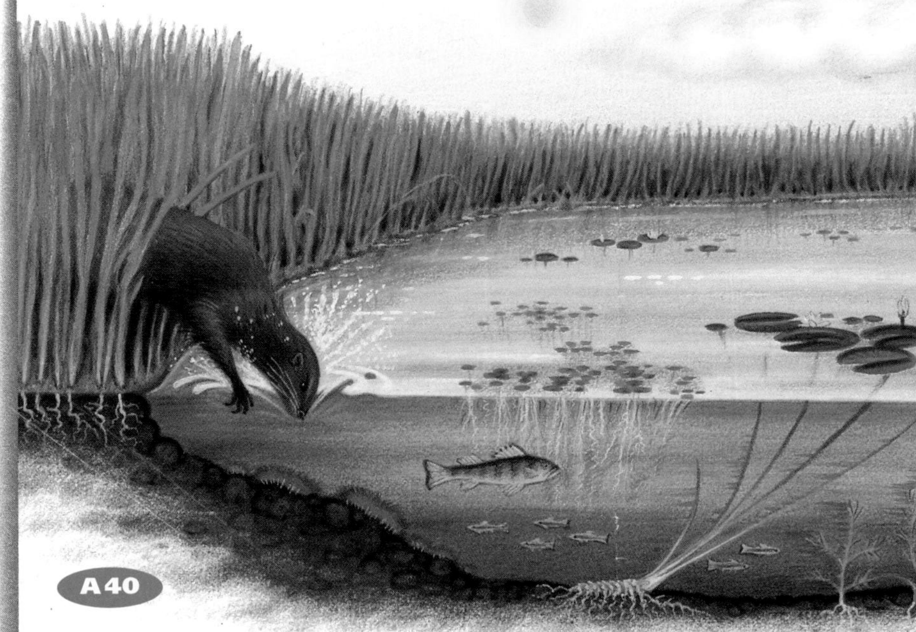

A40

Science Background
- All animals depend on plants for food. Animals that eat plants are called herbivores. Animals that eat other animals are called carnivores.
- Animals that eat both plants and animals are called omnivores.

Math-Science Connection
Work with children to list different animals and the foods they eat. Have children determine how this information could be graphed. Then have children work in small groups to graph specific information.

Make a model of a food chain.

Materials

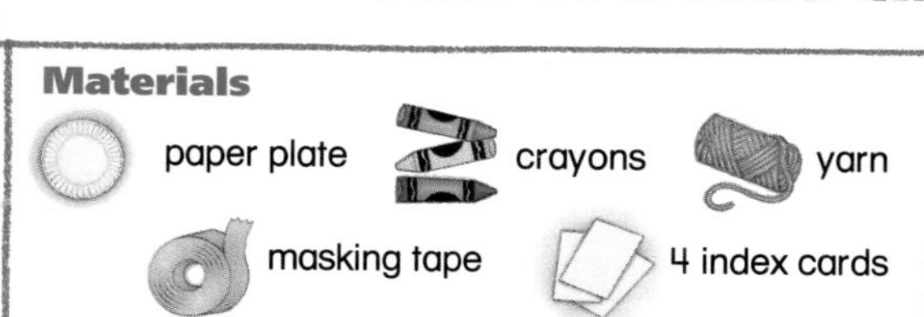

paper plate
crayons
yarn
masking tape
4 index cards

Process Skills

- making and using models

Steps

1. Color the plate yellow. This is your sun.
2. Draw these things, one on each card: a hawk, grass, a lizard, a bug.
3. Put the cards in order to make a model of a food chain.
4. Tape one end of the yarn to the back of the plate.
5. Tape the cards to the yarn in order.

Share. Tell about your food chain.

Lesson Review

1. What do animals eat?
2. What is the food chain?
3. **Tell** why the sun is important in a food chain.

A41

Lab Manual

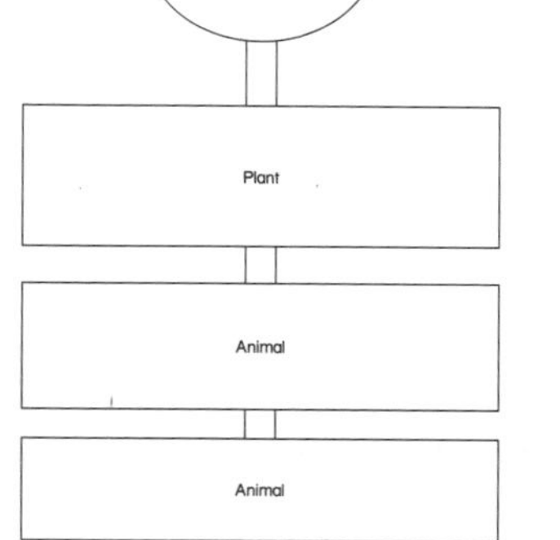

What do animals eat?

Draw pictures to make a model of a food chain.

Lab Manual
p. 22

Activity Rubric

Use the following activity scoring rubric to assess students' performance.

Scoring Criteria	1	2	3	4
Student followed directions to perform the activity.				
Student drew an example of a food chain with four components.				
Student ordered the proper sequence of a food chain example.				
Student made and used a model of a food chain.				
Student explained an example of the food chain.				

Scoring Key

4 points correct, complete, detailed
3 points partially correct, complete, detailed
2 points partially correct, partially complete, lacks some detail
1 point incorrect or incomplete, needs assistance

Lab Manual
p. T7

Teach and Apply

Student Page A40

Discuss the food chain and how it works. Then display **Wall Chart** page 11. Have children identify and list animals that eat other animals, animals that eat plants, and animals that eat both plants and animals.

Reading Assist *Use Illustrations*

Discuss the picture at the bottom of the page. Help children describe the animals and plants shown.

Student Page A41

Explore Activity

Time 20 minutes

Grouping individual

To help children understand the proper order of the food chain, ask questions such as, **What eats the grass?** or **What eats the bug?** Children can complete Lab Manual page 22 as they do the activity.

What to Expect

Children should tape the cards in the following order: grass, bug, lizard, hawk.

Assess and Extend

Answers to Lesson Review

1. Some animals eat plants; some eat other animals.
2. The food chain is the way animals depend on other animals and plants for food.
3. **Tell** (*Interview*) The sun is important because it is the energy source for all plant life.

Inquire Further

Ask the following question to guide further inquiry: **How do an animal's body parts help it obtain the food it eats?** (*Children may mention sharp teeth, claws, long neck, long tongue.*)

Enrichment

Challenge children to make another food chain using different animals.

Higher Order Thinking *Draw Conclusions*

Ask children to tell where people would belong on the food chain.

Call 1-888-537-4908 with your Activity questions or comments.

Lesson Organizer

Objective
Name some ways animals protect themselves.

Vocabulary camouflage

Process Skills collecting and interpreting data

Materials

Kit Items none

School-Supplied Items 11" by 17" green construction paper, 20 1-inch green paper squares, 20 1-inch yellow paper squares, clock with a second hand

Additional Resources

- Lab Manual
- Teacher Demonstration Kit
- Wall Chart

Introduce

Activate Prior Knowledge
Ask children to name an animal and tell what they know about how it protects itself.

Language Development *Game*
Have small groups of children secretly hide a few objects in the classroom for classmates to find. Talk about why some places were good hiding places.

Flip Chart
Discuss how camouflage would help protect the animals in the picture. Ask how else the animals could protect themselves. (*raccoon: run, scratch, bite; birds and moth: fly away*)

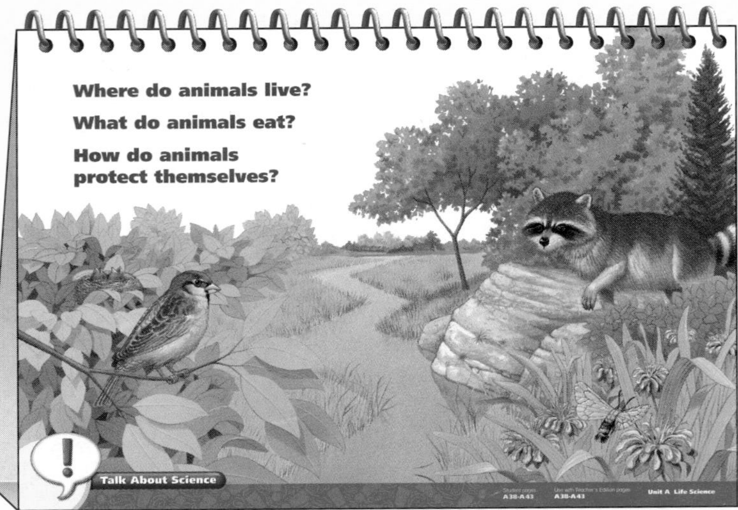

Where do animals live?
What do animals eat?
How do animals protect themselves?
Talk About Science

How do animals protect themselves?

There is an animal in this picture! Can you find it?

Some animals use color and shape to hide themselves. A color or shape that makes an animal hard to see is called **camouflage**.

Animals protect themselves in other ways too. Some animals can run quickly if they are being chased. Some animals have sharp teeth and claws for biting and scratching. Some animals have shells they can hide in. How does the animal in this picture protect itself?[1]

[1] Its color blen[ds into] the surroundi[ngs]

Science Background

- Some animals, such as fawns, protect themselves by hiding. They blend into the environment and are not detected by predators.
- Some animals, such as impalas, protect themselves by running away.
- Some animals, such as skunks or porcupines, protect themselves with defensive body parts. Skunks spray, and porcupines flap their quill-covered tail at potential predators.
- Some animals, such as monarch butterflies, are bad tasting.

Math-Science Connection

Display **Wall Chart** page 12. Have pairs take turns coloring a box to show whether they collected more green squares or more yellow ones. Have children count the boxes in each column. Discuss which color was collected more and why.

Play a camouflage game.

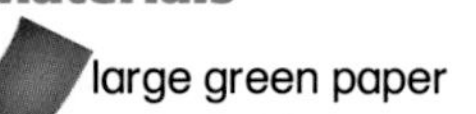

Materials

- large green paper
- 20 green paper squares
- 20 yellow paper squares
- clock with a second hand

Process Skills

- collecting and interpreting data

Steps

1. Take turns.
2. Have your partner put all of the squares on the large green paper.
3. Pick up as many squares as you can in ten seconds.
4. Collect data by counting how many squares of each color you picked up.

Share. Tell which color was easier to find and why.

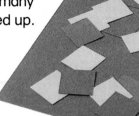

Lesson Review

1. What is camouflage?
2. What are some ways animals protect themselves?
3. **Tell** how camouflage can help an animal hide on a leaf.

A43

Lab Manual

How do animals protect themselves?

Do the activity three times. Record your results.

1. I picked up _____ green squares.
   I picked up _____ yellow squares.
2. I picked up _____ green squares.
   I picked up _____ yellow squares.
3. I picked up _____ green squares.
   I picked up _____ yellow squares.

1. Which color did you pick up the most?
2. Tell why one color was picked up the most.

Lab Manual p. 23

Activity Rubric

Use the following activity scoring rubric to assess students' performance.

Scoring Criteria	1	2	3	4
Student followed directions to perform the activity.				
Student learned that color is a type of camouflage.				
Student learned that camouflage helps protect animals.				
Student collected and recorded data about color selections for three trials.				
Student reported on the quantitative data and suggested a hypothesis to support the data.				

Scoring Key

4 points correct, complete, detailed
3 points partially correct, complete, detailed
2 points partially correct, partially complete, lacks some detail
1 point incorrect or incomplete, needs assistance

Lab Manual p. T7

Teach and Apply

Student Page A42

Point out that some animal behaviors are learned, such as hiding in their shell or burrowing into the ground. Others are ways animals have adapted over time, such as with camouflage or with sharp teeth and claws.

Reading Assist *Decode Words*

Point out that the word *camouflage* begins with the hard *c* sound. Ask children to find other words on the page that begin with this sound. (*can, color*)

Student Page A43

Explore Activity

Time 15 minutes

Grouping cooperative groups of 2

Suggest that children cover their eyes while partners put the squares in place. Instruct children to use only one hand and pick up only one square at a time. Children might use Lab Manual page 23.

What to Expect

Most children will pick up more yellow squares than green squares because they are easier to see.

Assess and Extend

Answers to Lesson Review

1. Camouflage is a color or shape that makes an animal hard to see.
2. Answers may include running fast, using sharp teeth or claws, hiding in a shell, and using camouflage.
3. **Tell** (*Interview*) An animal that is close to the same color as the leaf is harder for another animal to spot.

Inquire Further

Ask the following question to guide further inquiry: **What are some ways size can help protect an animal?** (*Big animals are strong; small animals can hide.*)

Enrichment

Invite children to pantomime some ways animals protect themselves, then name the animals.

Higher Order Thinking *Evaluate*

Ask children to tell why animals need to protect themselves.

Call 1-888-537-4908 with your Activity questions or comments.

Science Center

Flip Chart

Camouflage an animal.
1 Think about where animals live.
2 Choose a place.
3 Use art materials to make a picture of that place.
4 Hide animals in your picture.
Science Center

Camouflage an animal.

Objective

Devise animal camouflage that would protect an animal in a particular habitat.

Process Skills observing

Materials

Kit Items none

School-Supplied Items art supplies

Procedure

- Children **observe** animals or pictures of animals in their natural habitats to find out how animals use camouflage.
- Children use their observations to make model of a habitat and an animal that is camouflaged in that environment.
- You can use **Lab Manual** page 24 with this activity.

What to Expect

Children discover that an animal that uses camouflage has a body covering that helps it blend into its surroundings.

Lab Manual

Camouflage an animal.

Draw an animal that uses camouflage.

How does camouflage help your animal hide?

Lab Manual, p. 24

Connections

School and Community

Ideas for bringing the school and community together:

Field Trips

- local pond
- aquarium
- nature center

Guest Speakers

- naturalist/ecologist
- veterinarian
- forest ranger

Themes

The activities on these pages can be used with classroom themes such as:

- animal habitats
- animal foods

Books for Children

Children might enjoy these books about animals:

See How They Grow: Duck by Dorling Kindersley. The development of a duck, from egg to nearly grown duck. (Lodestar Books, ISBN 0-525-67346-6)

Crafty Chameleon by Mwenye Hadithi and Adrienne Kennaway. A little chameleon gets the better of two bullies by using his camouflage ability. (Little, Brown, ISBN 0-316-33771-4)

What Newt Could Do for Turtle by Jonathan London. The little newt looks for a way to match Turtle's generous contributions to their relationship. (Candlewick Press, ISBN 0-7636-0580-8)

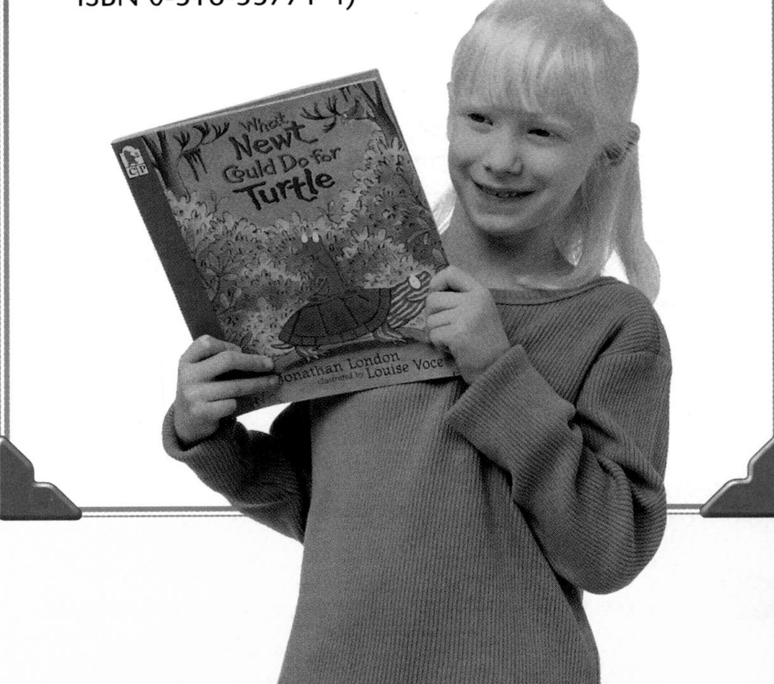

Cross-Curricular Options

LITERATURE

A House Is a House for Me

Use the book to learn about animal homes.

Materials *A House Is a House for Me* by Mary Ann Hoberman. (Puffin Books, ISBN 0-14-050394-3)

Procedure

- Told in rhyme, this lively book explores all kinds of houses.
- Children may enjoy memorizing and reciting some of the lines about animals.
- Have children choose one verse from the book and illustrate it.

Multiple Intelligences linguistic

Gifted and Talented Challenge children to design a habitat they would like to live in.

LANGUAGE ARTS

I Went Walking

Play a cumulative speaking game.

Procedure

- Choose a specific animal habitat, such as the woods or desert.
- The first person begins, "I was walking in the woods and I saw a beaver." The second person says, "I was walking in the woods and I saw a beaver and a chipmunk." Children continue, repeating all the animals said before and adding one name each time. Challenge children to continue the game as long as they can.

Multiple Intelligences linguistic

Special Needs A hearing-impaired child and a partner might adapt the game to play with animal cards.

WRITING

Puzzlers

Create word search puzzles.

Materials 1-inch or larger grid paper, pencil

Procedure

- Have partners create hidden-word searches.
- Assign each pair a habitat. Have them list names of animals and plants that live in that habitat.
- Then have them create word search puzzles with the words.
- Duplicate the puzzles so classmates can find the hidden words.

Multiple Intelligences linguistic

ART

Animal Masks

Make animal masks.

Materials paper bags, paper plates, ribbon, yarn, crayons, paints, animal reference books

Procedure

- Provide reference books. Then organize children into groups of 4. Have each child in the group choose either a mammal, an insect, a fish, a bird, a reptile, or an amphibian to learn more about.
- Invite each child to create a mask of the chosen animal.
- When children wear or display their masks, have them share information about their animals.

Multiple Intelligences spatial, linguistic

Review Organizer

Materials

Kit Items none

School-Supplied Items big piece of paper, crayons or markers, books about animals

Time about 30 minutes

Grouping cooperative groups of 4

Additional Resources

- Chapter 2 Assessment: Teacher's Assessment Package

Chapter Main Ideas

Lesson 1 There are different kinds of animals.

Lesson 2 A frog's life cycle is: egg; tadpole; frog.

Lesson 3 A butterfly's life cycle is: egg; caterpillar; pupa in a chrysalis; butterfly.

Lesson 4 A model of a butterfly's life cycle includes an egg, a caterpillar, a pupa, and a butterfly.

Lesson 5 Animals live in habitats. Some animals are endangered.

Lesson 6 Animals eat plants or other animals.

Lesson 7 Animals protect themselves with color and shape, sharp teeth or claws, or behaviors such as hiding in a shell or running fast.

Reviewing Science Words

1. Mammals have fur or hair.
2. Reptiles have dry, rough skin.
3. A tadpole has a tail and no legs. A frog has legs and no tail. A tadpole lives in water. A frog lives on land.
4. Answers should include discussion of the egg, the caterpillar, the pupa, the chrysalis, and the butterfly.
5. A habitat is a place where an animal lives.
6. They became endangered because their habitats changed.
7. Plants make food. Animals eat the plants for food.
8. Camouflage helps some animals hide to protect themselves.

Reviewing Science Ideas

1. Answers may include birds, fish, mammals, reptiles.
2. Answers may include camouflage, sharp teeth or claws, poison, hiding in a shell, and running fast.

Chapter 2 Review

Reviewing Science Words

1. How are **mammals** different from other animals?
2. What kind of skin do **reptiles** have?
3. What is the skin of an **amphibian** like?
4. How is a **tadpole** different from a frog?
5. Tell about a butterfly's **life cycle**. Talk about the **pupa** and the **chrysalis**.
6. What is a **habitat**?
7. Why do some plants and animals become **endangered**?
8. Why are plants an important part of the **food chain**?
9. How can **camouflage** help some animals?

Reviewing Science Ideas

1. What are some kinds of animals?
2. How do some animals protect themselves?

A44

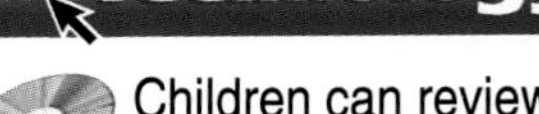
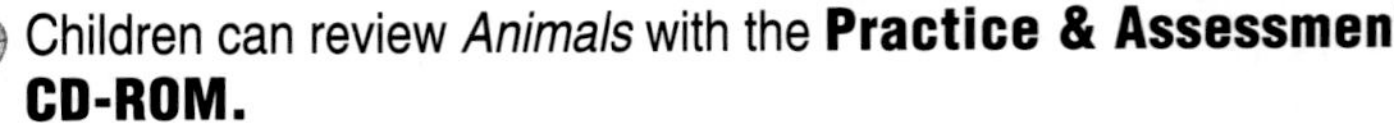

Technology

Children can review *Animals* with the **Practice & Assessment CD-ROM.**

Children can use the **Production Studio** to show what they've learned about *Animals.*

WWW Children can use The KnowZone™ at **www.kz.com** to review and test their science knowledge.

You can use **TestWorks™** to customize assessment for your children.

Make a poster.

Materials

- big piece of paper
- books about animals
- crayons or markers

1. Work with a group.
2. Read about animal habitats.
3. Choose a habitat.
4. Talk about which animals live in the habitat.
5. Draw the habitat and the animals on the big piece of paper.

Chapter Assessment

Use the words in the box to finish each sentence.

habitat	mammals	life cycle	pupa

1. Animals with fur are called ________.
2. Some animals change as they grow. This is called the ________.
3. The place where an animal lives is its ________.
4. A ________ is the name of a caterpillar changing into a butterfly.

Write Yes or No.

________ 5. A tadpole is a full grown frog.

________ 6. A long neck helps a giraffe live in its habitat.

________ 7. Reptiles and mammals are the same kinds of animal.

________ 8. All animals eat plants to stay alive.

________ 9. A caterpillar forms a chrysalis before turning into a butterfly.

________ 10. Some animals protect themselves with sharp teeth and claws.

Teacher's Assessment Package pp. 11–12

Assessment Rubric

	Habitats
4	Shows a good understanding of animals that live in a particular habitat and characteristics of the habitat.
3	Shows a partial understanding of animals that live in a particular habitat and characteristics of the habitat.
2	Has difficulty identifying animals that live in a particular habitat and characteristics of the habitat.
1	Is unable to identify animals that live in a particular habitat and characteristics of the habitat.

Performance Assessment Teaching Tips

- Before beginning the activity, review the word *habitat* and have children brainstorm a list of animal habitats such as ocean, desert, forest, and backyard.
- Have each group select a different habitat to research and draw. Provide nature magazines and picture books for children to use as reference.
- After children complete their posters, have them tell about the pictures they drew. Ask questions such as: **What habitat did you draw? How does your picture model the real habitat? What animals live in that habitat? How does the habitat provide food, air, water, shelter, and space for the animals that live there? How do the animals protect themselves in that habitat?**
- Display the complete posters as one continuous mural titled "Animals in Our World."

Enrichment

Have children do a research project on animals living in their group's habitat. Each child can focus on a different animal in that habitat. Children can write about how the habitat provides food, water, air, shelter, and space for their animals.

Chapter 2 Skills Trace

Process Skills Development

	Communicating	Making and Using Models	Collecting Data
Skill Introduced	xiv	xv	xv
Skill Applied	A29	A36 A41	A43
Skill Assessed	End Matter 8–9	End Matter 20–21	End Matter 24–25

Chapter Review pages are also on the **Flip Chart.**

Chapter 3 Planning Guide

Lesson/Activity and Flip Chart	Objectives/Process Skills	Time Options/Activity Materials
Chapter Opener Student Edition pp. A46–A47 and **Flip Chart** ***Fossils Here, Fossils There***		**Have less time?** Use the Graphic Organizer on Teacher's Assessment Package p. 15 for an overview of the lessons. Use the Flip Chart to teach lesson concepts and science activities. **Have more time?** Use the Flip Chart to reinforce and extend lesson concepts and activities. Use the Cross-Curricular Options in the Activity Idea Bank on Teacher's Edition pp. A53b and A59b.
Reading for Science Student Edition pp. A48–A49 ***Reading a Science Activity***	**Objective** Read a science activity.	
Lesson 1 Student Edition pp. A50–A51 ***What are fossils?*** **Explore Activity** ***Make a leaf print.*** **Flip Chart** ***Talk About Science***	**Objective** Explain what fossils are and how they are formed. **Process Skills** observing	**Kit Items** modeling clay in assorted colors **School-Supplied Items** leaves
Lesson 2 Student Edition pp. A52–A53 ***How do we learn about dinosaurs?*** **Flip Chart** ***Talk About Science***	**Objective** Explain that fossils provide evidence about dinosaurs.	**Have more time?** Use the following teaching guide option: Interactive Transparency 3, Interactive Transparency Package
Activity Idea Bank Teacher's Edition pp. A53a–A53b **Flip Chart** **Science Center Explore Activity** ***Make an imprint.***	**Objective** Observe different imprints that various objects make in wet sand. **Process Skills** observing, inferring	**Kit Items** fine sand, foil pan **School-Supplied Items** water; objects to imprint such as pasta, eraser, spoon, comb
Lesson 3 Student Edition pp. A54–A55 ***What are some kinds of dinosaurs?*** **Flip Chart** ***Talk About Science***	**Objective** Identify some dinosaurs and their characteristics.	
Lesson 4 Student Edition pp. A56–A57 and **Flip Chart** **Investigate Activity** ***How long were some dinosaurs?***	**Objective** Measure the length of a dinosaur. **Process Skills** estimating and measuring	**Kit Items** red yarn **School-Supplied Items** meterstick or tape measure, scissors
Lesson 5 Student Edition pp. A58–A59 ***What happened to the dinosaurs?*** **Flip Chart** ***Talk About Science***	**Objective** Identify events that may have caused the extinction of dinosaurs.	
Activity Idea Bank Teacher's Edition pp. A59a–A59b **Flip Chart** **Science Center Explore Activity** ***Make a dinosaur rubbing.***	**Objective** Make and tell about a dinosaur rubbing. **Process Skills** observing, communicating	**Kit Items** none **School-Supplied Items** foam tray, paper, crayons, pencil
Chapter Review Student Edition pp. A60–A61 and **Flip Chart**		**Kit Items** none **School-Supplied Items** modeling clay

Lesson/Activity and Flip Chart	Additional Resources		Technology
Chapter Opener Student Edition pp. A46–A47 and **Flip Chart** ***Fossils Here, Fossils There***	**Teacher's Assessment Package** • Graphic Organizer, p. 15 **Instructional Resources** • Family Activity, pp. 17–18 • Vocabulary Preview, p. 19	**Songs & Activities Package** • *Fossils Here, Fossils There,* pp. 13–14 **Wall Chart,** p. 13	**Practice & Assessment CD-ROM** **AudioText** **Production Studio** **www.sfscience.com** **Songs & Activities Package** **Teacher's Resource Planner CD-ROM**
Reading for Science Student Edition pp. A48–A49 ***Reading a Science Activity***	**Instructional Resources** • Reading for Science, p. 20		
Lesson 1 Student Edition pp. A50–A51 ***What are fossils?*** **Explore Activity** ***Make a leaf print.*** **Flip Chart** ***Talk About Science***	**Lab Manual** • Lab Manual, p. 25 • Activity Rubric, p. T8	**Teacher Demonstration Kit** **Wall Chart,** p. 14	
Lesson 2 Student Edition pp. A52–A53 ***How do we learn about dinosaurs?*** **Flip Chart** ***Talk About Science***	**Interactive Transparency Package** • Interactive Transparency 3	**Wall Chart,** p. 15	
Activity Idea Bank Teacher's Edition pp. A53a–A53b **Flip Chart** **Science Center Explore Activity** ***Make an imprint.***	**Lab Manual** • Lab Manual, p. 26 • Activity Rubric, p. T9		
Lesson 3 Student Edition pp. A54–A55 ***What are some kinds of dinosaurs?*** **Flip Chart** ***Talk About Science***		**Wall Chart,** p. 16	
Lesson 4 Student Edition pp. A56–A57 and **Flip Chart** **Investigate Activity** ***How long were some dinosaurs?***	**Lab Manual** • Lab Manual, p. 27 • Activity Rubric, p. T9	**Teacher Demonstration Kit** **Wall Chart,** pp. 17, 18	*Life Science* **Activity Video**
Lesson 5 Student Edition pp. A58–A59 ***What happened to the dinosaurs?*** **Flip Chart** ***Talk About Science***			
Activity Idea Bank Teacher's Edition pp. A59a–A59b **Flip Chart** **Science Center Explore Activity** ***Make a dinosaur rubbing.***	**Lab Manual** • Lab Manual, p. 28 • Activity Rubric, p. T10		
Chapter Review Student Edition pp. A60–A61 and **Flip Chart**	**Teacher's Assessment Package** • Chapter 3 Assessment, pp. 17–18		**Practice & Assessment CD-ROM** **Production Studio** **The KnowZone™ at www.kz.com** **TestWorks™**

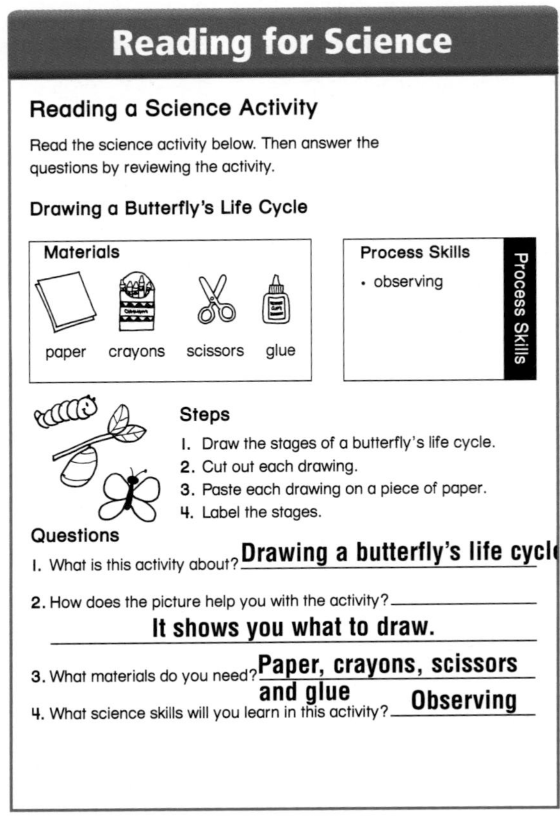

Reading for Science

Reading a Science Activity

Read the science activity below. Then answer the questions by reviewing the activity.

Drawing a Butterfly's Life Cycle

Materials

paper crayons scissors glue

Process Skills

- observing

Process Skills

Steps

1. Draw the stages of a butterfly's life cycle.
2. Cut out each drawing.
3. Paste each drawing on a piece of paper.
4. Label the stages.

Questions

1. What is this activity about? **Drawing a butterfly's life cycle**
2. How does the picture help you with the activity? **It shows you what to draw.**
3. What materials do you need? **Paper, crayons, scissors and glue**
4. What science skills will you learn in this activity? **Observing**

Instructional Resources
p. 20

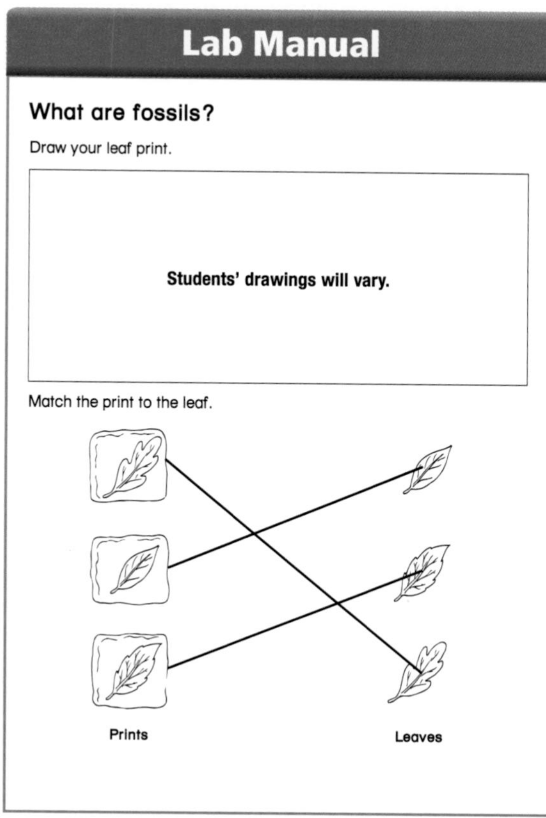
Lab Manual
What are fossils?
Draw your leaf print.
Students' drawings will vary.
Match the print to the leaf.
Prints
Leaves

Lab Manual
p. 25

Transparency
Plant Eaters and Meat Eaters
Plant eaters
Meat eaters

Interactive Transparency Package
Transparency 3

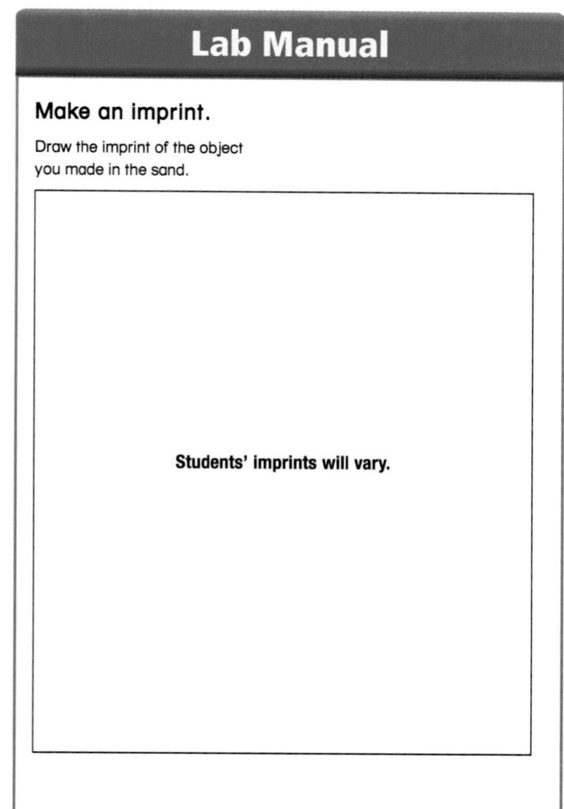
Lab Manual
Make an imprint.
Draw the imprint of the object
you made in the sand.
Students' imprints will vary.

Lab Manual
p. 26

Lab Manual

How long were some dinosaurs?

Students' choice of dinosaurs and their measurements will vary. Their choice of objects of similar length will depend on their choice of dinosaurs.

1. Which dinosaur did you measure?

2. How long was that dinosaur?

3. List 3 things that are about the same length as the dinosaur.

Lab Manual
p. 27

Lab Manual

Make a dinosaur rubbing.

Draw a picture of another kind of dinosaur.
Write a sentence about it.

Answers will vary depending on students' choice of dinosaurs.

Lab Manual
p. 28

Chapter 3 Assessment

Draw a circle around the words that finish each sentence.

1. Fossils can form when plants and animals are buried in ___________.

   water leaves mud

2. Over many years, buried remains turn into ___________.

   mud rock sand

3. Fossils can tell us the ___________ of dinosaurs.

   names size sounds

Use the words in the box to finish each sentence.

fossils	extinct	paleontologist

4. A ___________ is a scientist who studies fossils.
5. Some scientists think that a meteor caused the dinosaurs to die and become ___________.
6. We can see how dinosaurs looked by looking at ___________.

Teacher's Assessment Package
p. 17

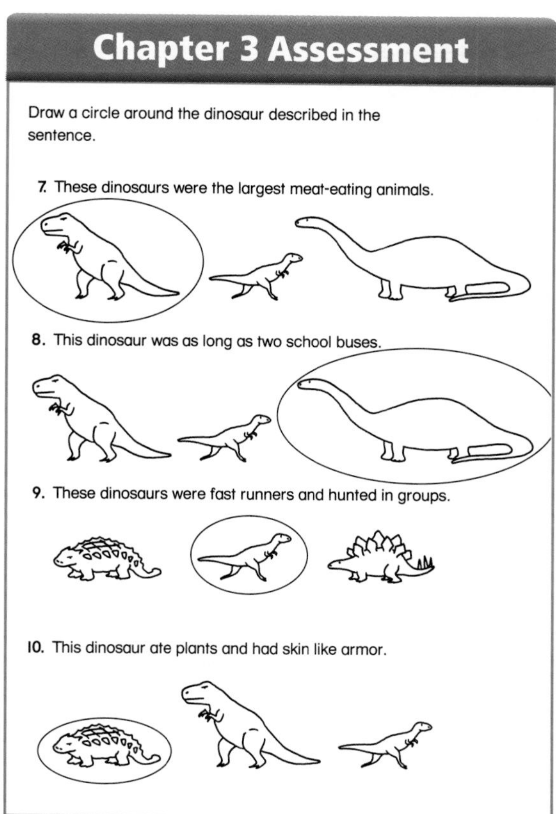
Chapter 3 Assessment

Draw a circle around the dinosaur described in the sentence.

7. These dinosaurs were the largest meat-eating animals.
8. This dinosaur was as long as two school buses.
9. These dinosaurs were fast runners and hunted in groups.
10. This dinosaur ate plants and had skin like armor.

Teacher's Assessment Package
p. 18

Table of Contents

Introducing the Chapter

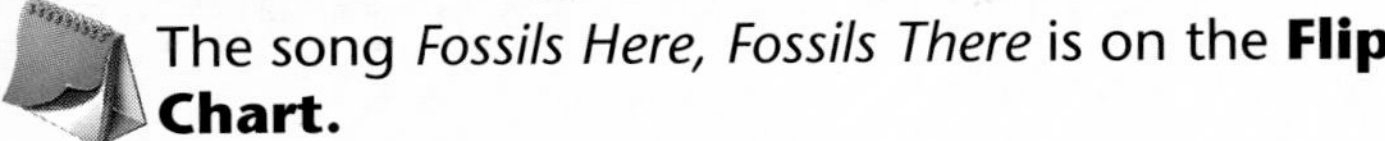

The song *Fossils Here, Fossils There* is on the **Flip Chart.**

- Begin a word web about dinosaurs by placing the word *dinosaur* in a center circle. As children describe dinosaurs, write their descriptive words around the center circle. Tell children that in this chapter they will learn more about dinosaurs.
- Distribute the Family Activity blackline master page.

Singing the Song

Have children sing the song *Fossils Here, Fossils There* on side 1 of the CTW cassette. Distribute pages 13–14 of the CTW Song Activity Book.

Reading Assist *Decode Words*

Write the word *ground* on the chalkboard. Underline the letters *ou* as you say the word *ground* aloud. Explain that together the letters *o* and *u* stand for /ou/ in the word *ground.* Ask children to find other words in the song with the same /ou/ they hear in *ground.* (*around, underground, found*)

Vocabulary Preview

Use Vocabulary Preview blackline master to introduce the vocabulary words for this chapter.

Lesson 1 fossils
Lesson 5 extinct, paleontologists

Chapter 3

Fossils

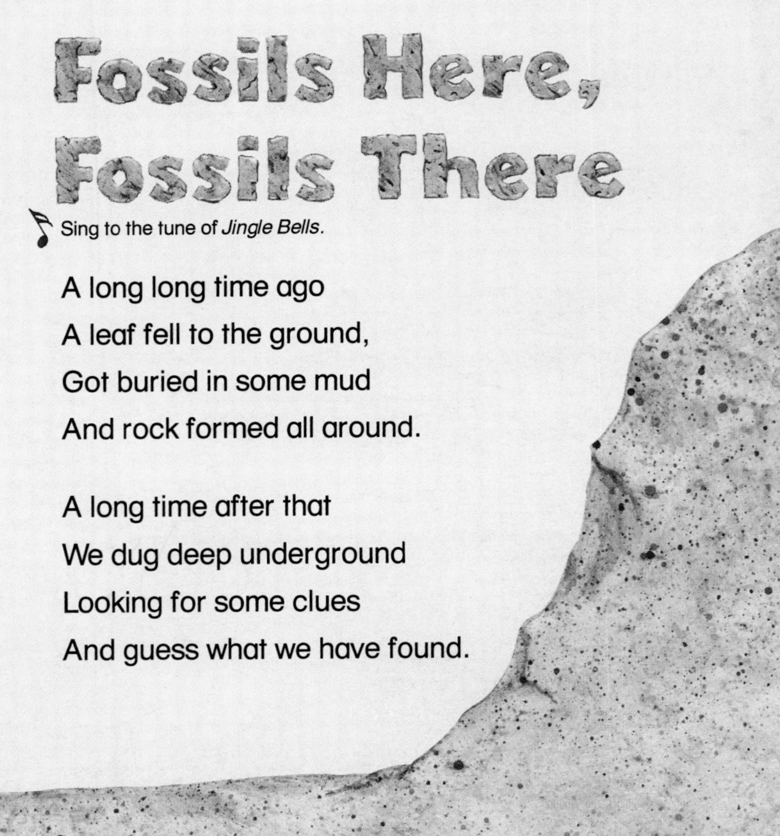

Fossils Here, Fossils There

Sing to the tune of *Jingle Bells.*

A long long time ago
A leaf fell to the ground,
Got buried in some mud
And rock formed all around.

A long time after that
We dug deep underground
Looking for some clues
And guess what we have found.

A46

Technology

Practice & Assessment CD-ROM

AudioText

Production Studio

www.sfscience.com

Teacher's Resource Planner

Songs & Activities Package

CTW Song & Activity

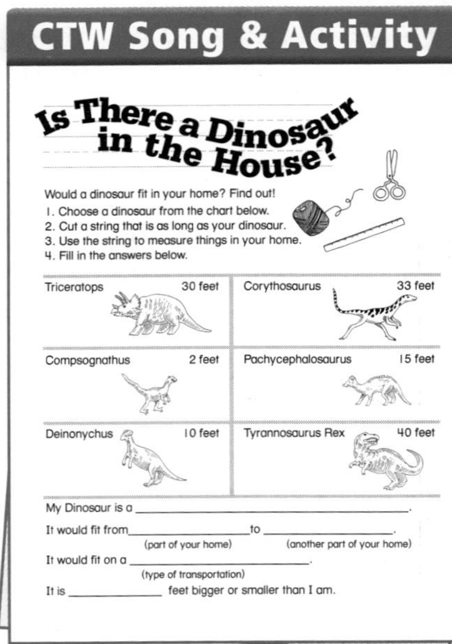

Is There a Dinosaur in the House?

Would a dinosaur fit in your home? Find out!
1. Choose a dinosaur from the chart below.
2. Cut a string that is as long as your dinosaur.
3. Use the string to measure things in your home.
4. Fill in the answers below.

Triceratops 30 feet	Corythosaurus 33 feet
Compsognathus 2 feet	Pachycephalosaurus 15 feet
Deinonychus 10 feet	Tyrannosaurus Rex 40 feet

My Dinosaur is a ________.
It would fit from ________ (part of your home) to ________ (another part of your home).
It would fit on a ________ (type of transportation).
It is ________ feet bigger or smaller than I am.

Songs & Activities Package
pp. 13–14

Fossils here, fossils there,
Fossils far and near.
Fossils give us clues to things
That are no longer here.

Family Activity — Science at Home

Dear Family:
Our class is starting Chapter 3. We will be learning about fossils. These are the main ideas for Chapter 3.

- Fossils are prints or remains of plants and animals.
- Fossils help us learn about dinosaurs.
- There were hundreds of kinds of dinosaurs.
- Dinosaurs became extinct and scientists are not sure why.

We will also be learning science vocabulary words for Chapter 3. By the end of Chapter 3, we will be able to read the vocabulary words and tell what they mean.

Word Bank
fossils
extinct
paleontologists

Home Projects

Here are some activities that will help your child understand the main ideas in Chapter 3. The activities are easy, fast, and fun.

Activities

- With your child, compare dinosaurs to animals living today.
  1. Divide a piece of paper into three columns.
  2. In the first column list all the dinosaurs you know.
  3. In the second column write one characteristic for each dinosaur you listed.
  4. Think of one living animal that shares each characteristic. Write the name of this animal in the third column.

Instructional Resources
pp. 17–18

Vocabulary Preview

fossils	extinct
paleontologist	observe
skeleton	measure
meteor	remains

Instructional Resources
p. 19

INQUIRY

Use a KWL chart at the beginning of each new chapter to encourage inquiry. In the *K* column, record what children already *know* about fossils. In the *W* column, help children brainstorm a list of what they *want* to know. Throughout the chapter, ask children what they have *learned* and record their responses in the *L* column. A KWL chart is available on **Wall Chart** page 13.

Chapter 3 Skills Trace

Process Skills Development	Observing	Estimating and Measuring
Skill Introduced	xiv	xiv
Skill Applied	A49 A51	A56–A57
Skill Assessed	End Matter 6–7	End Matter 12–13

Science Literature Library

Digging Up Dinosaurs
by Aliki.
Children are introduced to various kinds of dinosaurs while learning how scientists discover, preserve, and reconstruct fossils. (HarperTrophy, ISBN 0-06-445078-3)

Reading Organizer

Objective
Read a science activity.

Additional Resources
- Reading for Science blackline master

Teaching Reading for Science

- Reading a science activity for understanding includes the following: reading the title and looking at any pictures for clues about the activity; reading the materials list to know what is needed for the activity; reading the process skills to understand the focus and to set the purpose for the activity; and reading the steps to visualize what must be done from beginning to end.
- Science activities actively involve children in science concepts. The strategies children apply to reading this science activity can be applied to science activities in general.
- Have children read and complete the Reading for Science lesson and the Reading for Science blackline master.

Student Page A48

- Ask children if they have ever used written directions to make a favorite food or to play a game. Discuss how the information is organized and what kind of information is included in these types of written directions.
- Have children point to each component of the science activity on page A49 as you read aloud the explanatory information on page A48.

Reading a Science Activity

Look at page A49. What is the title of the activity? The title can give you clues about what you will be doing.

Now look at the picture. How does the picture help you understand the activity?

What materials will you need? Get all the materials ready before you start.

Find the Process Skills box. This box tells you what science skills you will be using. Process Skill words are in red.

Read the steps. When you're ready to start, be sure to do the steps in order.

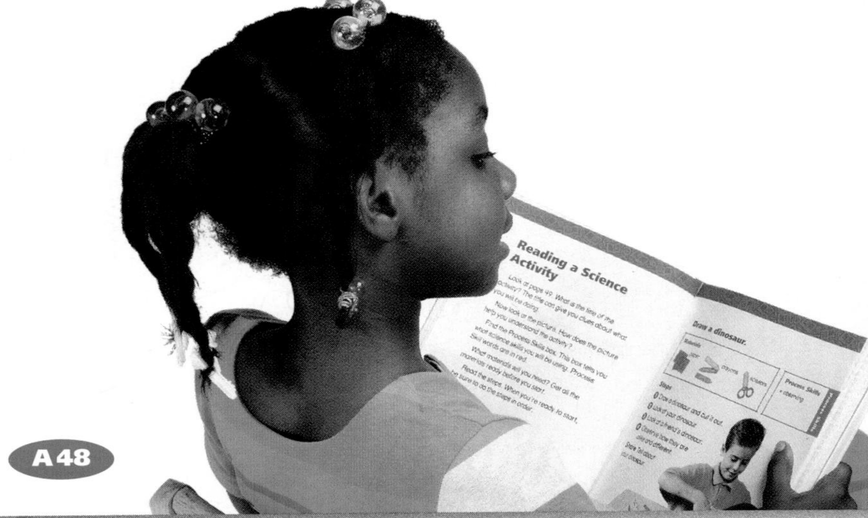

A48

ESL Strategy

Discuss the purpose of each component by asking questions such as: **Why do you read the title and look at the picture first? Why is it important to know what the process skill is? How do you know what materials you will need? How do you know what steps to follow? Why are the steps numbered?** Encourage children to answer in complete sentences.

Draw a dinosaur.

Materials
paper crayons scissors

Process Skills
- observing

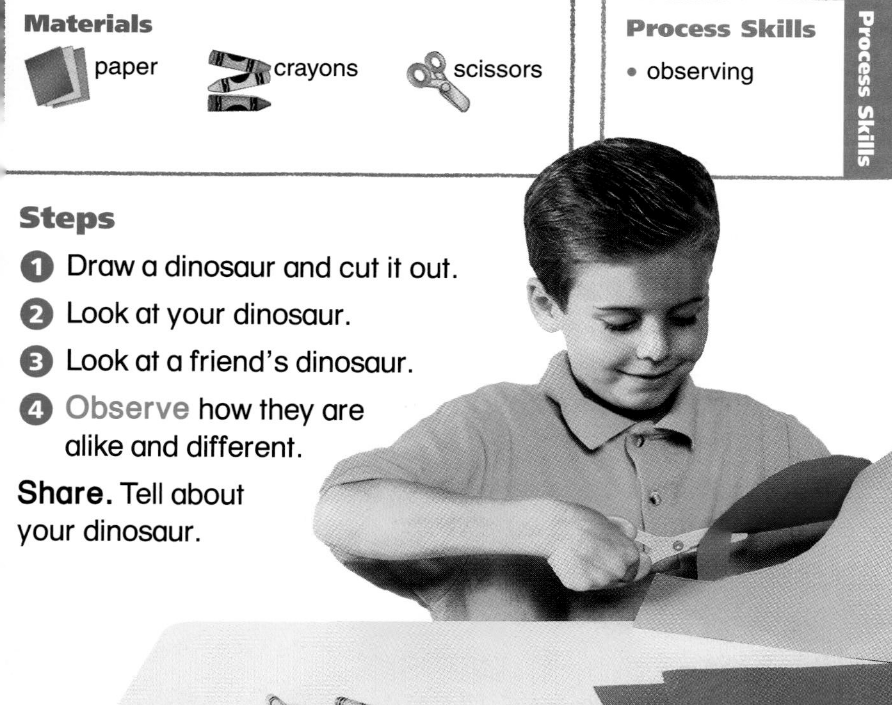

Steps

1. Draw a dinosaur and cut it out.
2. Look at your dinosaur.
3. Look at a friend's dinosaur.
4. Observe how they are alike and different.

Share. Tell about your dinosaur.

Turn the page to read a lesson and a science activity.

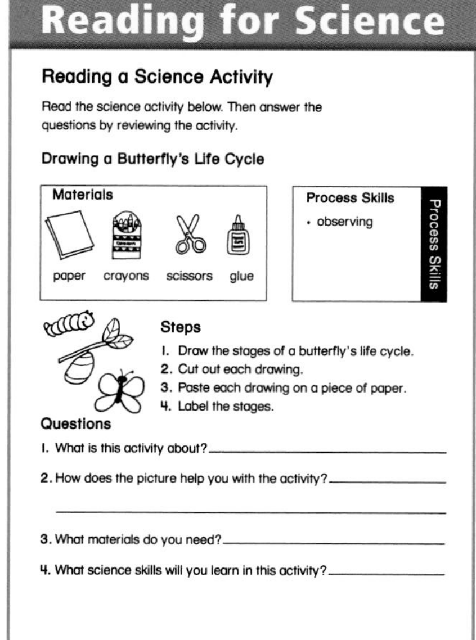

Reading for Science

Reading a Science Activity

Read the science activity below. Then answer the questions by reviewing the activity.

Drawing a Butterfly's Life Cycle

Materials: paper, crayons, scissors, glue

Process Skills
- observing

Steps
1. Draw the stages of a butterfly's life cycle.
2. Cut out each drawing.
3. Paste each drawing on a piece of paper.
4. Label the stages.

Questions
1. What is this activity about? ____________
2. How does the picture help you with the activity? ____________
3. What materials do you need? ____________
4. What science skills will you learn in this activity? ____________

Instructional Resources p. 20

Student Page A49

- Discuss how the information is organized on the page and why that organizational format is important.
- Ask children to look at the page and summarize how to read a science activity.
- Have children explain why the science process skill **observing** is important for this science activity. Point out that children use the skill as they make their drawings and as they compare finished drawings.

Apply Reading for Science to Lesson 1

Children will use what they learned about reading a science activity to complete the next lesson.

Lesson Organizer

Objective
Explain what fossils are and how they are formed.

Vocabulary fossils
Process Skills observing

Materials
Kit Items modeling clay (*assorted colors*)
School-Supplied Items leaves

Additional Resources
- Lab Manual
- Teacher Demonstration Kit
- Wall Chart

Introduce

Activate Prior Knowledge
Display several pictures of fossils. Ask children what they think the fossils are and how they think they were formed.

Language Development *Make a List*
Point out that a fossil is a nonliving object made from a once-living plant or animal. Use **Wall Chart** page 14 and have children take turns recording one living thing and one nonliving thing they see on the chart. Discuss how they know the difference.

Flip Chart
Discuss the pictures of plant and animal fossils. Explain that long ago the plant and animal parts were buried in mud. The mud hardened into rock.

What are fossils?
How do we learn about dinosaurs?
Talk About Science
Unit A Life Science

What are fossils?

Think about animals that live in your neighborhood. You have probably seen dogs, cats, birds, and squirrels.

Other kinds of animals lived in the past. You can learn about them by studying fossils. **Fossils** are prints or remains of plants and animals that lived long ago.

Sometimes parts of plants or animals that have died get buried in mud. Over many years, the mud can turn to rock. The remains become fossils in the rock.

These fossils show how some plants and animals looked long ago. Which look like plants and animals that you have seen?[1] Which look different?[2]

[1] fern, grasshopper, snake
[2] trilobite

▲ trilobit

▼ grass

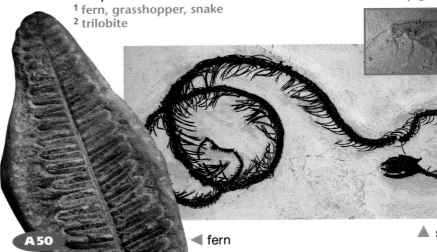

◀ fern

▲ sn

A50

Science Background
- A fossil is a print or the preserved remains of an organism that lived a long time ago. Many fossils are formed from the hard parts of organisms, such as shell, teeth, and bones.
- Trilobites and crabs are both arthropods. Trilobites are extinct. They have no direct descendants, only arthropod relatives, such as the crab.

Math-Science Connection
Provide small groups of children with drawings or pictures showing different stages of fossil formation. Challenge them to place the drawings in the right order and number them.

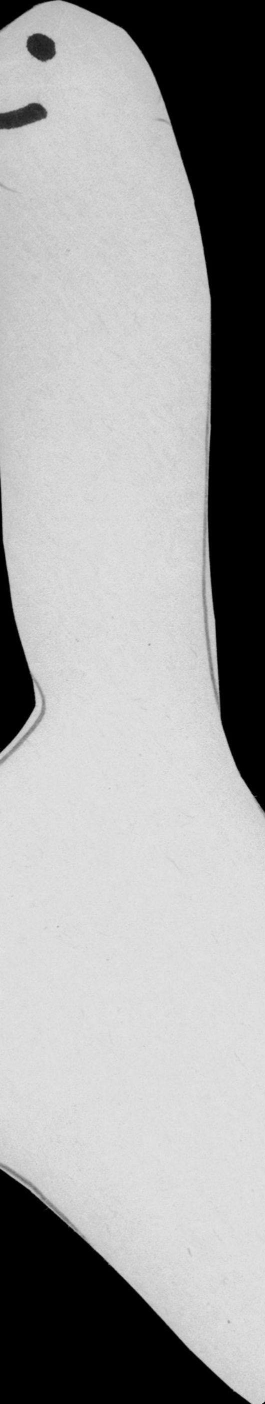

Make a leaf print.

Materials

clay
leaves

Process Skills
- observing

Steps

1. Make your clay thin and flat.
2. Press a leaf into the clay.
3. Take the leaf out. Observe the print.
4. Put your leaf and print with other children's leaves and prints.
5. Observe each print. Try to match each print with its leaf.

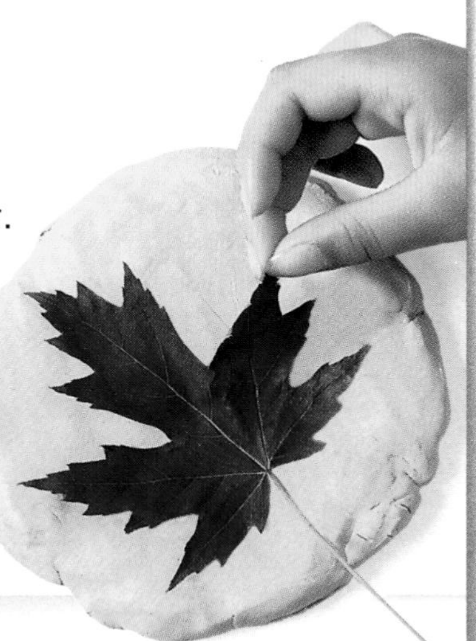

Share. Compare your leaf print to other children's prints.

Lesson Review

1. What are fossils?
2. How do fossils form?
3. **Tell** how your print is like your leaf and how it is different.

A51

Lab Manual

What are fossils?

Draw your leaf print.

Match the print to the leaf.

Prints Leaves

Lab Manual p. 25

Activity Rubric

Use the following activity scoring rubric to assess students' performance.

Scoring Criteria	1	2	3	4
Student followed directions to complete the activity.				
Student drew an imprint of a leaf.				
Student compared his or her leaf print with others made in class.				
Student observed each leaf print and matched the print with the leaf source.				
Student compared the likeness of the leaf print to the leaf source.				

Scoring Key
4 points correct, complete, detailed
3 points partially correct, complete, detailed
2 points partially correct, partially complete, lacks some detail
1 point incorrect or incomplete, needs assistance

Lab Manual p. T8

Call 1-888-537-4908 with your Activity questions or comments.

Teach and Apply

Student Page A50

Explain that fossils help us learn about the plants and animals that lived a very long time ago. Fossils allow scientists to figure out what these animals looked like and even how they behaved.

Reading Assist *Context Clues*

Remind children that when they come to an unfamiliar word in their reading they can use the other words in the sentence to help them understand the meaning.

Student Page A51

Explore Activity

Time 30 minutes

Grouping individual

Children can use Lab Manual page 25.

Integrating the Sciences

Earth Science In this lesson, children learn how animal remains can become fossils in rock. In Unit C, Chapter 1, children learn about different kinds of rocks.

Assess and Extend

Answers to Lesson Review

1. Fossils are prints or remains of plants and animals that lived long ago.
2. Fossils form when remains get buried in mud that over a long period of time turns to rock.
3. **Tell** (*Interview*) The leaf and the print are shaped the same, but the leaf is colorful, lightweight, and living; the print is gray, heavier, and nonliving.

Inquire Further

Ask the following question to guide further inquiry: **What can you learn about plants and animals by studying their fossils?** (*You can learn what they looked like and how they lived.*)

Higher Order Thinking *Infer*

Ask children to tell what parts of plants and animals do not make fossils.

Lesson Organizer

Objective

Explain that fossils provide evidence about dinosaurs.

Additional Resources

- Interactive Transparency
- Wall Chart

Introduce

Activate Prior Knowledge

Ask children how they think scientists learn about plants and animals that lived long ago. List children's answers on the chalkboard or on chart paper and save for use as a **baseline assessment.**

Language Development *Make a List*

Encourage children to brainstorm a list of "dinosaur" words. The list might include words such as *bones, skeleton,* and *fossils.*

Flip Chart

Have children describe the dinosaur in the picture. Ask them how fossils such as bones and teeth helped scientists learn about the dinosaurs.

What are fossils?
How do we learn about dinosaurs?
Talk About Science
Unit A Life Science

How do we learn about dinosaurs?

Have you ever seen a living dinosaur? Of course not! Yet you probably have an idea of what some dinosaurs looked like. People have learned a lot about dinosaurs from fossils.

Fossils give clues about the past. You can find out what dinosaurs looked like by looking at fossils of their bones. Look at the skeleton of the Stegosaurus. The Stegosaurus had bony plates on its back and sharp spikes on its tail.

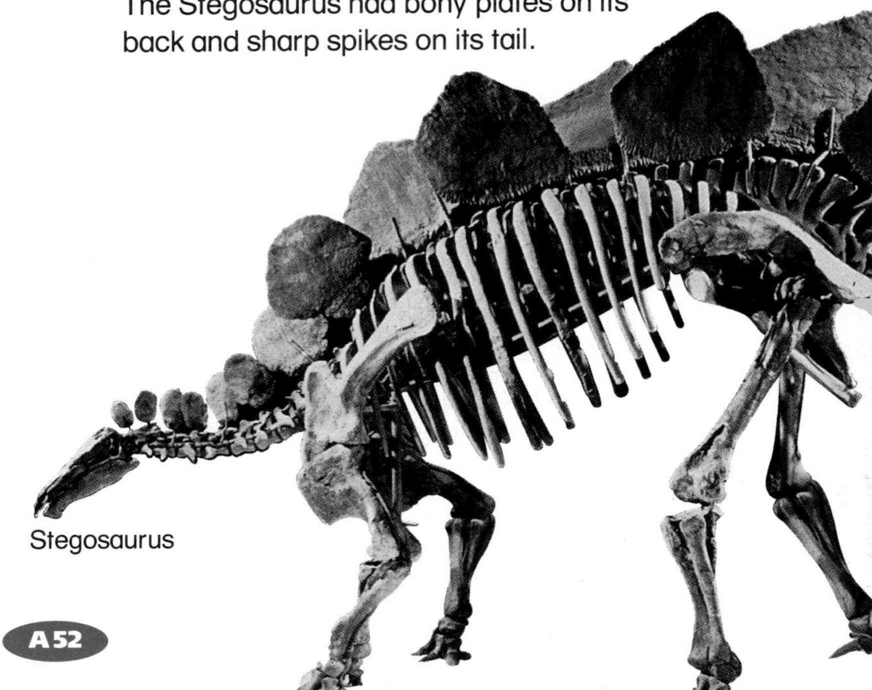

Stegosaurus

A52

Science Background

- Dinosaur fossils have been found on all continents except Antarctica.
- The oldest dinosaur fossil is 235 million years old. By 200 million years ago, dinosaurs had become common.
- Fossils show that dinosaurs were the dominant animals on the earth for more than 100 million years, but the last dinosaur died about 65 million years ago.

Possible Misconceptions Some children may think that people lived on the earth at the same time as the dinosaurs. Point out that dinosaurs existed long before humans; cartoon depictions of cave dwellers and dinosaurs are inaccurate.

You can learn about what dinosaurs ate by looking at fossils of their teeth. The Centrosaurus apertus ate plants. It had a sharp beak for grabbing plants and leaves. It had short teeth for chewing plants. The Tyrannosaurus rex had long, sharp teeth for eating meat.

Centrosaurus apertus

Tyrannosaurus rex

Lesson Review

1. What can you learn about dinosaurs by looking at their fossils?
2. How did a beak help the Centrosaurus apertus eat plants?
3. **Tell** what you can learn about the Stegosaurus by looking at its bones.

ESL Strategy

Be sure that children understand what a fossil is. Point to one or two of the fossils in this and the previous lesson and ask children to tell in complete sentences what it is and what made it.

Transparency

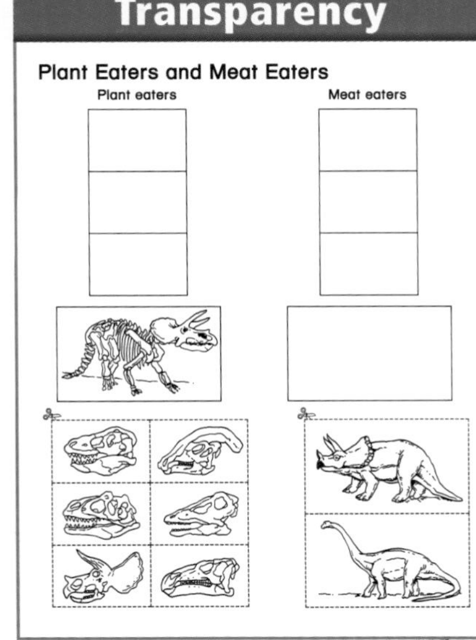

Interactive Transparency Package Transparency 3

Teach and Apply

Student Pages A 52–A 53

- Invite children to examine the photo of the dinosaur skeleton. Help children realize that finding out about dinosaurs is similar to putting together a puzzle. Point out that the scientists first had to determine how to put the bone fossils together, and then they used clues from the skeleton to discover what the dinosaur actually looked like.
- Lead a discussion about the similarities and differences in the two fossils. Help children compare the size and the special features of each one.

Reading Assist *Syllables*

Children may need help reading and pronouncing the dinosaur names. Write the words on the chalkboard, drawing a line between each syllable. Encourage children to read each one and then say all the parts together.

Assess and Extend

Answers to Lesson Review

1. You can learn how they looked and what they ate.
2. The *Centrosaurus apertus* had a beak for grabbing plants and short teeth for chewing.
3. **Tell** (*Interview*) Children may mention the bony plates on the *Stegosaurus*'s back or the spikes on its tail.

Check for Understanding

As a follow up to the **baseline assessment,** review children's list of ways scientists learn about plants and animals that lived long ago. Invite children to correct or add to their list.

Reteach

- Use the Interactive Transparency to reteach Lesson 2 concepts.
- Use pictures in books or plastic models to display a variety of dinosaurs. Discuss similarities and differences. Compare characteristics such as teeth, overall size, special body features, and so on. Ask children to pick a characteristic and tell how scientists use that characteristic to tell what the dinosaurs were like, for example, a dinosaur with sharp teeth probably ate meat. Record children's responses on **Wall Chart** page 15.

Science Center

Flip Chart

Make an imprint.
1 Add water to the sand.
2 Choose an object.
3 Press your object into the wet sand.
4 Observe the imprint.
5 Have friends guess what object made your imprint.
Science Center

Make an imprint.

Objective

Observe different imprints that various objects make in wet sand.

Process Skills observing, inferring

Materials

Kit Items fine sand, foil pan

School-Supplied Items water; objects to imprint such as pasta, eraser, spoon, comb

Safety Note Be sure that children wash their hands after touching the sand.

Procedure

- In advance, fill the pans partially with sand or other material such as clay, flour, salt, or sugar.
- Have each child pick an object and **observe** the imprint it makes in the sand.
- Invite volunteers to display imprints. Ask children to **infer** which objects made the imprints.
- You can use **Lab Manual** page 26 with this activity.

What to Expect

Children observe how different objects make different imprints in the sand.

Lab Manual

Make an imprint.

Draw the imprint of the object you made in the sand.

Lab Manual, p. 26

Connections

School and Community

Ideas for bringing the school and community together:

Field Trips

- natural history museum
- science museum

Guest Speakers

- paleontologist
- geologist
- museum curator
- zoologist

Themes

The activities on these pages can be used with classroom themes such as:

- dinosaurs
- paleontology
- rocks
- animals
- the earth

Books for Children

Children might enjoy these books about fossils and dinosaurs:

Dinosaurs Walked Here and Other Stories Fossils Tell by Patricia Lauber. Photographs of dozens of fossils with explanations of what kind of animal or plant each fossil once was. (Aladdin, ISBN 0-689-71603-6)

Fossils Tell of Long Ago by Aliki. How fossils are formed and what clues they give us about the past. (HarperCollins, ISBN 0-06-445093-7)

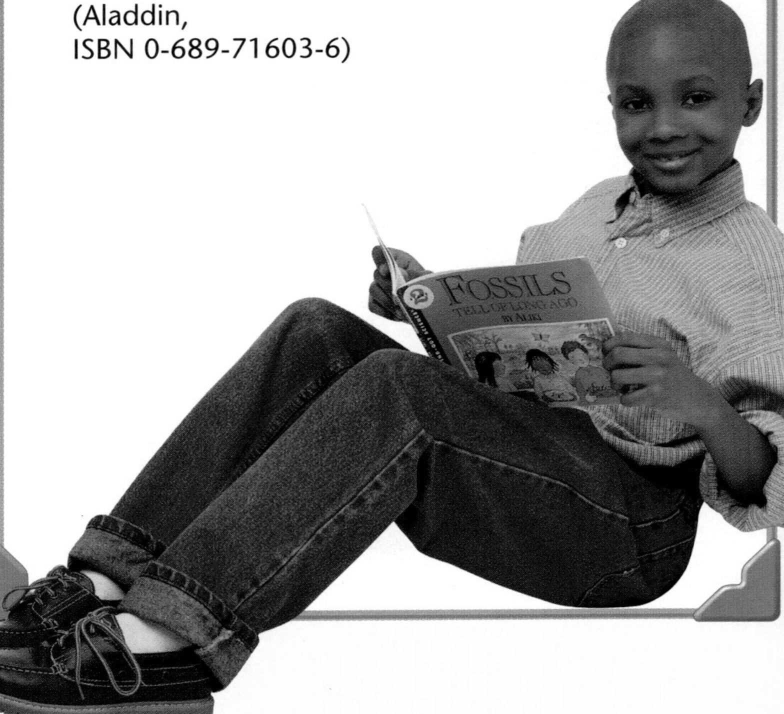

Cross-Curricular Options

LITERATURE

Dinosaur Bones

Use the book discuss fossils.

Materials *Dinosaur Bones* by Aliki. (HarperCollins, ISBN 0-06-445077-5)

Procedure

- This book describes how scientists study fossil remains to provide information about how dinosaurs lived millions of years ago.
- As you read the book, create a list of the dinosaurs named and invite children to add information they learn about these dinosaurs.

Multiple Intelligences linguistic

Gifted and Talented The back of the book provides extra information about dinosaurs. Children might use this as a springboard to do research about one of the dinosaurs named.

SOCIAL STUDIES

Who Goes There?

Guess what made the imprint.

Materials clay; variety of classroom objects such as pencil, toys, shells, buttons

Procedure

- Partners take turns. One child secretly chooses an object and makes an imprint in a piece of clay.
- The partner looks at the imprint and guesses what made the imprint.
- Have partners exchange roles.

Multiple Intelligences spatial

WRITING

What If...?

Write a paragraph about a fossil.

Procedure

- Ask children to imagine that they discovered a dinosaur fossil in their backyard. Encourage them to think about what they would do with it.
- Have children write a paragraph explaining what actions they would take.

Multiple Intelligences linguistic

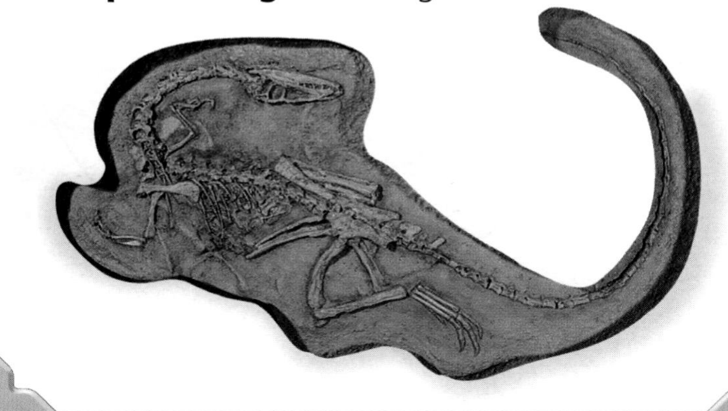

LANGUAGE ARTS

Be a Footprint Detective

Keep a journal of footprints.

Materials notebook, pencil

Procedure

- Invite children to look for different footprints in mud, on sidewalks or floors, and so on.
- Have them draw pictures of the footprints in a journal and write what the creatures probably look like based on the footprint.

Multiple Intelligences linguistic, spatial, naturalist

ESL Show children pictures of animals and have them say the animal names with you.

Lesson Organizer

Objective

Identify some dinosaurs and their characteristics.

Additional Resources

- Wall Chart

Introduce

Activate Prior Knowledge

Invite children to name as many different kinds of dinosaurs as they can. Record their responses as a word web on the chalkboard or on chart paper. Save children's work for use as a **baseline assessment.**

Language Development *Create a Story*

Ask children to sit in a circle and create an oral story to describe how different their lives would be if they were as big as a giant dinosaur such as *Tyrannosaurus rex.*

Flip Chart

Discuss the characteristics of the dinosaurs in the picture, such as sizes, shapes, and so on. Point out that some dinosaurs ate plants and others ate meat.

What are some kinds of dinosaurs?
What happened to the dinosaurs?
Talk About Science

What are some kinds of dinosaurs?

Did you know that there were hundreds of different kinds of dinosaurs? Some were small and fast. Others were very big and very heavy. How many dinosaurs can you name?

Compare the dinosaurs in the picture. Tyrannosaurus rex was the largest meat-eating animal that we know of. It was as long as a school bus and as tall as a small house.

Alamosaurus was as long as two school buses. It had a long neck for reaching tall plants.

Tyrannosaurus rex
Dromaeosaurus
A 54

Science Background

- Although some dinosaur species were smaller than a person, some were larger than an elephant. One of the largest, *Brachiosaurus,* was 23 meters long, stood 12 meters tall, and weighed 80,000 kilograms.
- Types of dinosaurs include: the giant herbivores, such as *Brachiosaurus* and *Apatosaurus*, previously known as *Brontosaurus; Tyrannosaurus rex,* one of the largest and certainly most famous of the carnivores; the horned dinosaur *Triceratops;* and the armored dinosaur *Ankylosaurus.*

Possible Misconceptions Children may think that all animals living during the Age of Dinosaurs were dinosaurs. This is not true. Reptiles such as the flying pterosaurs and the aquatic ichthyosaurs and plesiosaurs were not dinosaurs. Many mammals and birds lived at the same time as the dinosaurs and pterosaurs for more than 100 million years but were not common until dinosaurs became extinct.

Dromaeosaurus was about as long as your bed. It was a fast runner and hunted in groups.

Ankylosaurus was a plant eater. How do you think Ankylosaurus protected itself?

Lesson Review

1. How long was a Tyrannosaurus rex?
2. How did a long neck help the Alamosaurus?
3. **Tell** how two of the dinosaurs in the picture are different from each other.

ESL Strategy

As you discuss the terms length and height, have children pantomime the difference by holding their hands far apart lengthwise for length and high over their heads for height.

Teach and Apply

Student Pages A 54–A 55

- Point out that some people think all dinosaurs lived during the same time period, but this is not true. Many different dinosaurs existed and lived at various times. The dinosaurs shown on these pages all lived in the late Cretaceous period and in the same region of the world.
- Explain the difference between length and height. Point out that when we say that *Tyrannosaurus rex* was as long as a school bus, we are talking about its length. When we say it was as tall as a house, we are talking about its height.

Reading Assist *Syllables*

Continue helping children learn to read and pronounce dinosaur names. Write each word on the chalkboard and draw a line between each syllable. Point out that each name ends in *saurus,* which means "lizard." Encourage children to read each word part and then say all the parts together.

Assess and Extend

Answers to Lesson Review

1. *Tyrannosaurus rex* was as long as a school bus.
2. A long neck helped the *Alamosaurus* reach tall plants.
3. **Tell** (*Interview*) Answers will vary. Children may compare dinosaurs by length, by what they ate, or by their height.

Check for Understanding

To follow up on the **baseline assessment,** invite children to add dinosaur names to the word web begun earlier. Encourage children to add new facts or characteristics about each dinosaur.

Reteach

To help children become more familiar with different kinds of dinosaurs, use **Wall Chart** page 16. Invite children to compare the dinosaurs pictured and take turns adding information about one of the dinosaurs in the appropriate section on the chart. They should include information about the dinosaur's size, behavior, eating habits, protection features, and other interesting facts.

Activity Organizer

Objective
Measure the length of a dinosaur.

Process Skills estimating and measuring

Materials
Kit Items red yarn
School-Supplied Items meterstick or tape measure, scissors

Time about 20 minutes

Grouping cooperative groups of 4

Additional Resources
- Lab Manual
- Teacher Demonstration Kit
- Wall Charts

Introduce

The Lesson 4 Investigate Activity, *How Long were some dinosaurs?*, is on the **Flip Chart.**

Activate Prior Knowledge

Display several instruments of measurement, such as a meterstick, a tape measure, and a ruler. Invite children to tell how these items might be used. Ask volunteers to demonstrate how to use each one.

Language Development *Vocabulary*

Point out that the word *measure* means to find out the size of something by comparing it to something else, such as a meterstick.

How long were some dinosaurs?

Process Skills
- estimating and measuring

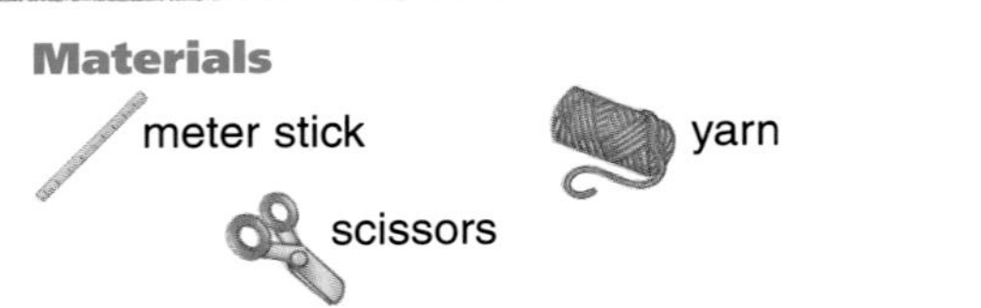

Materials
meter stick
yarn
scissors

Steps
1. Choose a dinosaur from the chart.
2. Use a meter stick to measure.
3. Roll out your yarn until it is the length of your dinosaur.
4. Use your yarn to find something else that is about the same length as your dinosaur.

Dinosaur	Length
Ceratosaurus	6 meters
Megalosaurus	9 meters
Allosaurus	12 meters
Alamosaurus	21 meters
Brachiosaurus	23 meters
Diplodocus	26 meters

Dinosaur	
Length	
Object that is the same length	

Science Background

- *Brachiosaurus* was 23 meters long, about the length of a tennis court. Its weight was the equivalent of 14 elephants. This dinosaur was as high as a four-story building.

Math-Science Connection Use **Wall Chart** page 17.
Invite children to measure one or more of the fossils shown on the chart. You may wish to have children use a variety of nonstandard measurement tools, such as string, connecting cubes, or paper clips, or standard measures. As children measure the fossils have them compare the lengths with other items in the room.

Technology

Review the demonstration of this Investigate's procedure on the *Life Science* **Activity Video,** Segment 4.

Think About Your Results

1. What is about the same length as your dinosaur?
2. What would be about the same length as two dinosaurs?

Inquire Further

How else could you measure the length of a dinosaur?

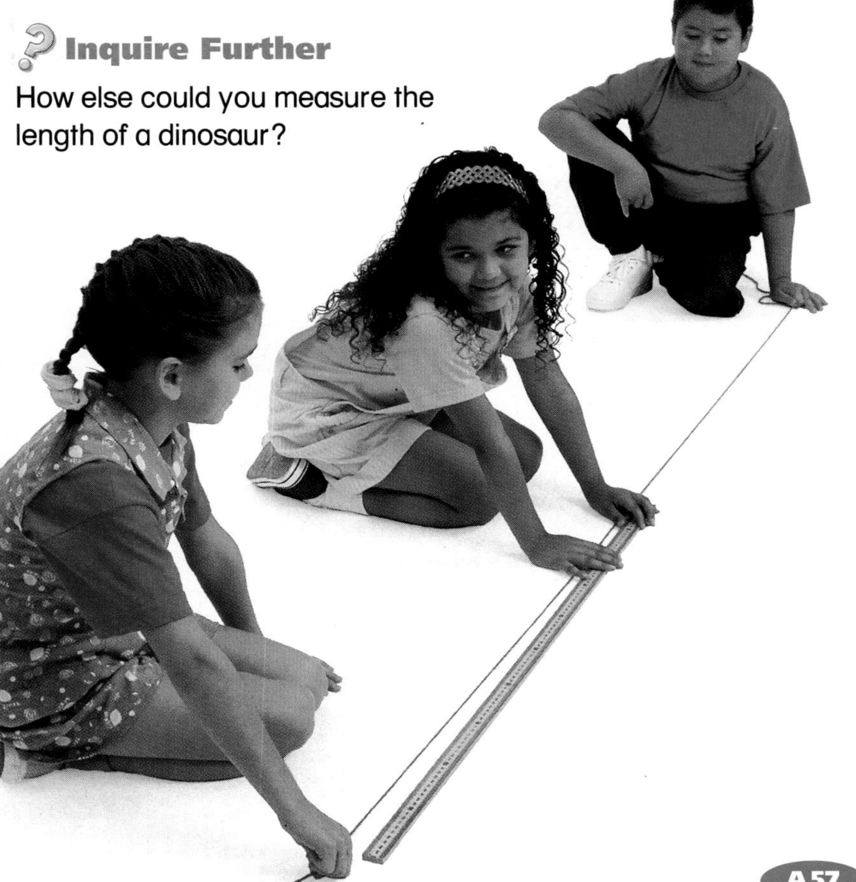

Lab Manual

How long were some dinosaurs?

1. Which dinosaur did you measure?
2. How long was that dinosaur?
3. List 3 things that are about the same length as the dinosaur.

Lab Manual p. 27

Activity Rubric

Use the following activity scoring rubric to assess students' performance.

Scoring Criteria	1	2	3	4
Student followed directions to complete this activity.				
Student used a meter stick to measure objects.				
Student compared measurements to length of various dinosaurs.				
Student estimated and measured objects in relation to dinosaur measurements.				
Student investigated the length of objects approximately the same length of a dinosaur.				

Scoring Key
4 points correct, complete, detailed
3 points partially correct, complete, detailed
2 points partially correct, partially complete, lacks some detail
1 point incorrect or incomplete, needs assistance

Lab Manual p. T9

Teach and Apply

- In this activity, children measure the length of various dinosaurs. First demonstrate how to measure with a meterstick: one child places the meterstick on the floor; the other child puts his or her finger at the end of the meterstick to mark the spot; and the first child moves the meterstick to the next position. The length of each dinosaur in feet: *Ceratosaurus,* 20 feet; *Megalosaurus,* 30 feet; *Allosaurus,* 40 feet; *Alamosaurus,* 69 feet; *Brachiosaurus,* 75 feet; and *Diplodocus,* 85 feet.
- Suggest that each child in a group have a different job. One holds the end of the yarn, while another unwinds the yarn from the other end and cuts it when done. A third child places the meterstick down while the fourth child marks the end of the meter stick placement each time.
- Children can use Lab Manual page 27.

Reading Assist *Picture Clues*

Suggest that children look at the pictures showing children measuring to help them follow the steps needed to complete the activity.

What to Expect

Children will discover that dinosaurs were many different sizes. They may also realize how large the dinosaurs were in comparison to themselves.

Assess and Extend

Answers to Think About Your Results

1. Children should name items that are close to the same length as their dinosaur.
2. Answers will depend on which two dinosaurs children are measuring.

Inquire Further

Children might name both standard and nonstandard tools of measurement.

Enrichment

Invite children to make a bar graph comparing the lengths of each dinosaur. Use **Wall Chart** page 18.

Higher Order Thinking *Hypothesize*

Ask children to tell what they think the world would be like if some people were as big as the largest dinosaurs.

Call 1-888-537-4908 with your Activity questions or comments.

Lesson Organizer

Objective
Identify events that may have caused the extinction of dinosaurs.

Vocabulary extinct, paleontologists

Introduce

Activate Prior Knowledge

On a sheet of paper, have children answer the question, **What do you think happened to the dinosaurs?** Save children's ideas for use as a **baseline assessment.**

Language Development *Scientific Language*

Discuss the idea that different species of plants and animals that are no longer living or found on the earth are said to be *extinct.* Help children realize that once something becomes extinct, it can never come back.

Flip Chart

Tell children that scientists are not sure what happened to the dinosaurs. Many scientists believe that dinosaurs died when a meteor crashed into the Earth.

What happened to the dinosaurs?

Dinosaurs lived on the earth for millions of years. Now only their fossils are left. What do you think happened to the dinosaurs?

Dinosaurs are extinct. An **extinct** animal is a kind of animal that no longer lives on the earth.

We can learn about extinct animals by studying the fossils they left behind. Scientists who study fossils are called **paleontologists**.

Science Background

- The fossil record indicates that there have been five major mass extinctions. In each, more than half the existing species became extinct. A mass extinction about 215 million years ago wiped out the ancestors to the dinosaurs that were dominant before them and enabled the dinosaurs and pterosaurs to dominate. Another, about 65 million years ago, wiped out the dinosaurs and pterosaurs. This allowed the mammals and birds to dominate.
- A widely accepted theory of this last mass extinction was the impact of a giant meteorite hitting the earth. Large amounts of dust and smoke were thrown into the atmosphere, blocking out sunlight for many years. A period of cold temperatures was created worldwide. Mammals and birds, insulated with fur and feathers, were better adapted to withstand the cold.

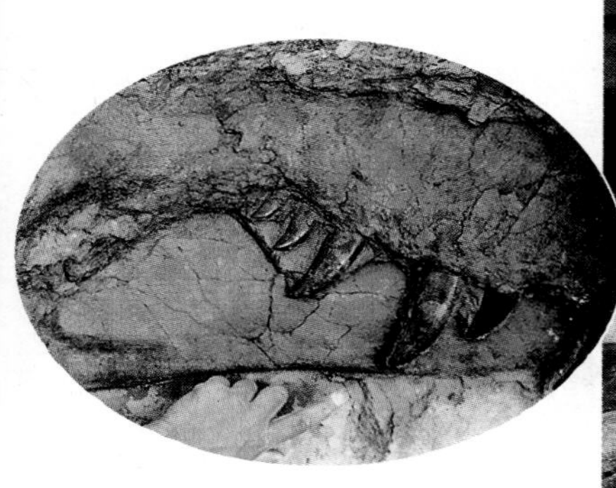

Scientists do not know for sure what happened to the dinosaurs. Some scientists believe that a meteor crashed into the earth. Dust from the meteor may have blocked the sunlight, causing plants to die. Without plants to eat, dinosaurs could not live.

Paleontologists are still learning about dinosaurs from the fossils they find.

Lesson Review

1. What does extinct mean?
2. What do paleontologists do?
3. **Tell** what some scientists believe happened to the dinosaurs.

A59

ESL Strategy

Ask children to point to specific things in the photographs and then use a complete sentence to describe what they're pointing to. For example, **Show me the paleontologist. This is the paleontologist.**

Teach and Apply

Student Pages A58–A59

- Discuss how changes in water and land affect plants and animals.
- Point out that many animals today are endangered, or on the verge of becoming extinct. Not all endangered animals will become extinct.

Reading Assist *Verb Tenses*

Have children find *lives* and *lived* on page A58. Help them identify the tense of each verb.

Assess and Extend

Answers to Lesson Review

1. Extinct means a type of animal that no longer lives on the earth.
2. Paleontologists study fossils.
3. **Tell** (*Interview*) Some scientists believe that dust from a meteor that crashed into the earth may have blocked sunlight, causing plants to die. Dinosaurs could not live without plants to eat.

Check for Understanding

As a follow-up to the **baseline assessment,** have children look at the reasons they gave earlier for the dinosaurs' extinction. Then have them add to their reasons based on what they learned in the lesson.

Reteach

Invite small groups of children to work cooperatively to draw pictures showing an idea of how dinosaurs became extinct. Encourage them to share their drawings.

Science Center

Flip Chart

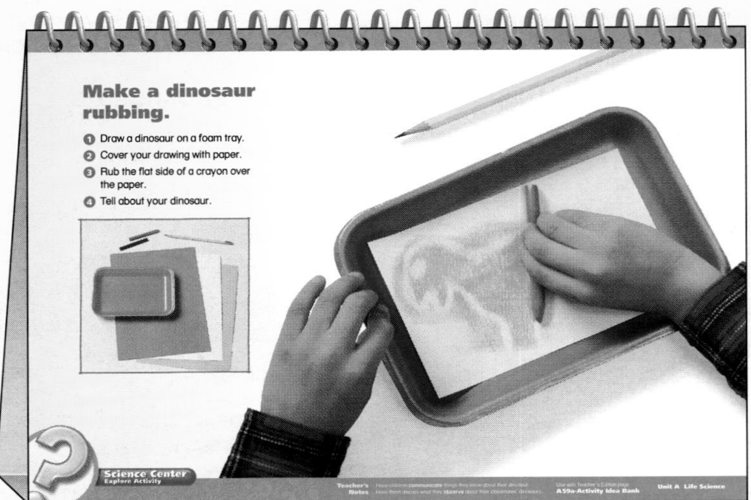

Make a dinosaur rubbing.

Objective

Make and tell about a dinosaur rubbing.

Process Skills observing, communicating

Materials

Kit Items none

School-Supplied Items foam tray, paper, crayons, pencil

Procedure

- In advance, cut the drawing paper to fit the foam trays and tear paper off crayons.
- Encourage children to pick different dinosaurs to draw.
- Have children press their pencils firmly when they draw the dinosaur outlines.
- Children **observe** the rubbings they made in order to **communicate** what they know about dinosaurs.
- You can use **Lab Manual** page 28 with this activity.

What to Expect

Children use dinosaur outlines to make rubbings and tell what they know about dinosaurs.

Lab Manual

Make a dinosaur rubbing.

Draw a picture of another kind of dinosaur.
Write a sentence about it.

Lab Manual, p. 28

Connections

School and Community

Ideas for bringing the school and community together:

Field Trips

- natural history museum
- bird sanctuary

Guest Speakers

- paleontologist
- archeologist

Themes

The activities on these pages can be used with classroom themes such as:

- dinosaurs
- environments
- sizes
- sounds

Books for Children

Children might enjoy these books about dinosaurs:

A Boy Wants a Dinosaur by Hiawyn Oram. Alex decides he wants a dinosaur for a pet, but after a few misadventures he settles for a rabbit. (Farrar, Straus, ISBN 0-374-40889-0)

If Dinosaurs Came to Town by Dom Mansell. A fantasy about dinosaurs in a modern-day setting. (Little, Brown, ISBN 0-316-67028-6)

What Happened to Patrick's Dinosaurs? by Carol Carrick. A boy's imaginative explanation of why dinosaurs became extinct. (Clarion, ISBN 0-89919-797-3)

What Happened to the Dinosaurs? by Franklyn M. Branley. Some of the scientific theories of what happened to the dinosaurs. (HarperCollins, ISBN 0-06-445105-4)

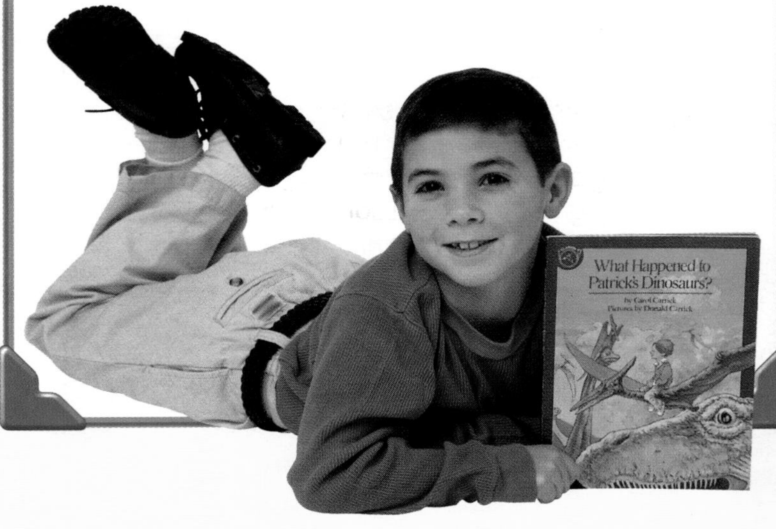

Cross-Curricular Options

LITERATURE

Prehistoric Pinkerton

Use this book to discuss dinosaurs.

Materials *Prehistoric Pinkerton* by Steven Kellogg. (Dial, ISBN 0-8037-0322-8)

Procedure

- A young girl dresses up her dog in a Stegosaurus costume and takes him on a field trip to a museum.
- Remind children that paleontologists learn about dinosaurs by studying their bones.
- Have children share facts about the real Stegosaurus. Then invite children to draw pictures of a Stegosaurus and write one or two facts about it.

Multiple Intelligences linguistic, spatial

Gifted and Talented Some children might write a newspaper account of what happened on a real or imaginary trip to a dinosaur museum.

MATH

A Dinosaur Puzzler

Make a dinosaur puzzle with geometric shapes.

Materials lightweight cardboard, crayons, scissors, ruler, envelope

Procedure

- Have children draw a picture of a dinosaur.
- On the reverse side, have children use a ruler to divide the puzzle into geometric shapes.
- Have children cut out the shapes and put them in an envelope with the dinosaur's name on the front.
- Children take turns working the puzzles.

Multiple Intelligences spatial

Special Needs Children with fine-motor limitations can tell a partner how to position the pieces to complete the puzzle.

SOCIAL STUDIES

Studying Clues

Study evidence to learn more about a person.

Materials paper bag; assorted small objects such as, toys, pictures related to sports, hobbies, pets

Procedure

- Prepare bags for small groups to use. Place a variety of objects in each bag and write a fictitious name on each.
- Explain that each bag provides clues about a person. Invite children in the group to take turns choosing an object from the bag and telling something about the person. Have the group compile a list of the person's characteristics.

Multiple Intelligences spatial

ART

Fossil Art

Make a fossil of a dinosaur.

Materials variety of pasta pieces, soft clay

Procedure

- Invite children to make models of a dinosaur fossil. Have children look at pictures to get an idea of the shape of a dinosaur skeleton.
- First they pat the clay into a flat shape. Then they press the pasta pieces into the clay in the shape of a dinosaur skeleton. They gently pull the pasta pieces out to create the fossil art.

Multiple Intelligences spatial

ESL To make sure children recognize the different dinosaur names, say each name as children point to the picture of the dinosaur on Student Edition pages A54–A55.

Review Organizer

Materials

Kit Items modeling clay

School-Supplied Items none

Time about 20 minutes

Grouping individual

Additional Resources

- Chapter 3 Assessment: Teacher's Assessment Package

Chapter Main Ideas

Lesson 1 Fossils are prints or remains of plants and animals that lived long ago. Fossils form when remains get buried in mud that over time turns to rock.

Lesson 2 Fossils give us clues about what dinosaurs looked like and what they ate.

Lesson 3 There were hundreds of types of dinosaurs. Some were small and some were big. Some were fast and some were slow. Some ate plants and some ate meat.

Lesson 4 Dinosaurs varied in length and height, from very short to very tall and long.

Lesson 5 Events that may have caused the extinction of dinosaurs include a lack of sunlight due to an explosion of a meteor.

Reviewing Science Words

1. Fossils are prints or remains of plants and animals that lived long ago.
2. Answers may include lack of sunlight, which was caused by a meteor.
3. Paleontologists learn about dinosaurs by studying fossils.

Reviewing Science Ideas

1. Fossils form when the remains of plants or animals that have died get buried in mud that over time turns to stone. The remains form fossils.
2. We learn about dinosaurs from their fossils.
3. Children may mention that *Tyrannosaurus rex* was as long as a school bus, *Alamosaurus* was as long as two school buses, *Dromaeosaurus* was a fast runner, and *Ankylosaurus* had bony plates and spikes at the end of its tail.

Chapter 3 Review

Reviewing Science Words

1. What are **fossils**?
2. What might have caused the dinosaurs to become **extinct**?
3. How do **paleontologists** learn about dinosaurs?

Reviewing Science Ideas

1. How do fossils form?
2. How do we learn about dinosaurs?
3. Describe some different kinds of dinosaurs.

A60

Technology

 Children can review *Fossils* with the **Practice & Assessment CD-ROM.**

 Children can use the **Production Studio** to show what they've learned about *Fossils.*

 Children can use The KnowZone™ at **www.kz.com** to review and test their science knowledge.

 You can use **TestWorks™** to customize assessment for your children.

Make a clay dinosaur.

Materials

clay

1. Choose a dinosaur.
2. Make a model of your dinosaur out of clay.
3. Tell about your dinosaur. Talk about its size and what it ate.

A 61

Chapter Assessment

Draw a circle around the words that finish each sentence.

1. Fossils form when plants and animals are buried in ____________.
   water   leaves   mud
2. Over many years, buried remains turn into ____________.
   mud   rock   sand
3. Fossils can tell us the ____________ of dinosaurs.
   names   size   sounds

Use the words in the box to finish each sentence.

fossils	extinct	paleontologist

4. A ____________ is a scientist who studies fossils.
5. Some scientists think that a meteor caused the dinosaurs to die and become ____________.
6. We can see how dinosaurs looked by looking at ____________.

Teacher's Assessment Package pp. 17–18

Assessment Rubric

	Dinosaurs
4	Shows a good understanding of some characteristics of a dinosaur.
3	Shows a partial understanding of some characteristics of a dinosaur.
2	Has difficulty describing some characteristics of a dinosaur.
1	Is unable to describe characteristics of a dinosaur.

Performance Assessment Teaching Tips

- Before beginning the activity, tape waxed paper on children's desks to keep the clay from sticking.
- Explain to children that they will use the clay to make a model of a dinosaur. Ask children to share previous experiences with dinosaur models, such as plastic models. Discuss how models are the same as or different from real dinosaurs.
- Provide additional picture resources of dinosaurs for children to refer to as they make their dinosaur models.
- Review characteristics of various dinosaurs. For example, point out that *Alamosaurus* had a long neck for reaching tall plants. Mention that a child who makes a model of an *Alamosaurus* will want to be sure it has a long neck.
- Suggest that children plan their models before actually beginning to make them from clay. Ask questions such as: **What size is your dinosaur? How will you design your model to show size? Was your dinosaur a meat eater or a plant eater? How will you design your model to show what your dinosaur ate?**

Enrichment

When the dinosaur models are finished, invite children to create background pictures that provide more information about their dinosaurs. For example, if their dinosaurs were really big, their backgrounds might show smaller dinosaurs to help get across the concept of how big their dinosaurs were.

Chapter 3 Skills Trace

Process Skills Development

	Observing	Estimating and Measuring
Skill Introduced	xiv	xiv
Skill Applied	A 49 A 51	A 56–A 57
Skill Assessed	End Matter 6–7	End Matter 12–13

Chapter Review pages are also on the **Flip Chart.**

Review Organizer

Using Multiple Intelligences

The following activities can be used to assess children's understanding of Unit A concepts. Assign the activities based on each child's strongest learning modality. The following chart shows which intelligences are developed in each assessment option.

Activity	Intelligence
Make a puzzle.	spatial
Put on a skit.	bodily-kinesthetic
Play a game.	linguistic

Plan your game day.

Unit Performance Review pages are also on the **Flip Chart.**

Have individuals or groups of children choose one or more of the following activities in which to participate. You may want to set aside a portion of one or more days when children can work on their projects and then present them to classmates.

Make a puzzle.

Before they begin drawing, encourage children to think about the parts of the plant or animal they will draw. You may want to provide an envelope for each child in which to place his or her puzzle pieces. Remind children to write their names on the envelopes. Ask questions such as these to suggest things partners might share when they tell about their pictures: Where does the plant or animal live? What does it need to live? Does it move? If so, how?

Put on a skit.

Children might work individually or in pairs to create skits that reflect something they've learned about life science, such as how a plant grows, how an animal eats or moves, how a person cares for a plant or animal, how an animal cares for its baby, how a scientist learns about a dinosaur. Classroom plants or stuffed animals can serve as props.

Play a game.

Before children begin the game, you may want to brainstorm with the class lists of words that tell about plants and animals. Point out to children that they are classifying their words into two groups, plants and animals.

Unit A Performance Review

You have learned a lot about plants and animals. You have learned about dinosaurs too. Think of something you would like to show your classmates. Have a game day to celebrate life!

Plan your game day.

1. Pick a project you would like to do.
2. Find the things you will need to do your project.
3. Think about how to best present your project so others will understand.

Make a puzzle.

Draw a picture of a plant or animal on heavy paper. Cut your picture into pieces to make a puzzle. Give your puzzle to a partner to put together. Tell your partner about your picture.

A 62

Put on a skit.

Act out one thing you learned. You can use props to help. Have your skit tell a story. You can work with a partner.

Play a game.

With a partner, write words about plants and animals on cards. Turn the cards over. Make a spinner. Take turns spinning the spinner and turning over a card. If the word on the card and the word on the spinner go together, keep the card. If they do not, turn the card over. Play until all the cards are taken.

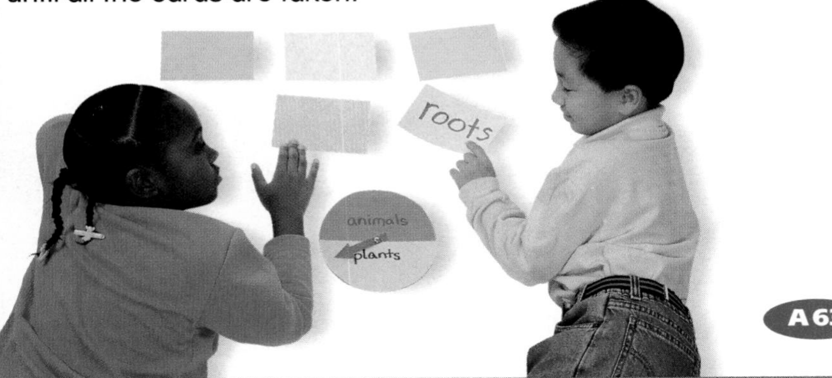

A63

Assessment Rubric

	Make a puzzle.	Put on a skit.	Play a game.
4	Creates and describes a puzzle that shows a good understanding of plant or animal characteristics.	Presents a skit that shows a good understanding of something learned about life science.	Chooses words that show a good understanding of vocabulary related to plants and animals.
3	Creates and describes a puzzle that shows a fair understanding of plant or animal characteristics.	Presents a skit that shows a fair understanding of something learned about life science.	Chooses words that show a fair understanding of vocabulary related to plants and animals.
2	Has difficulty creating and describing a puzzle that shows an understanding of plant or animal characteristics.	Has difficulty presenting a skit that shows an understanding of something learned about life science.	Has difficulty choosing words that show an understanding of vocabulary related to plants and animals.
1	Is unable to create and describe a puzzle that shows an understanding of plant or animal characteristics.	Is unable to present a skit that shows an understanding of something learned about life science.	Is unable to choose words that show an understanding of vocabulary related to plants and animals.

Portfolio Assessment

Suggested items from this unit to include in children's portfolios are listed on the following pages in the Teacher's Assessment Package:

- Chapter 1: page 1
- Chapter 2: page 7
- Chapter 3: page 13

Unit A Performance Assessment

- The formal Performance Assessment for this unit is on pages 28A–28B of the Lab Manual Teacher's Edition.
- The student recording sheet for the formal Performance Assessment for this unit is on pages 29–30 of the Lab Manual, both in the Teacher's Edition and the Student Edition.

Writing Organizer

Objective
Write a description.

Teaching Writing for Science

The Writing for Science page is also on the **Flip Chart.**

Explain to children that their purpose is to write a description. Point out that they will share their writing with their classmates.

Writing About a Plant, Animal, or Dinosaur

Guide children through the steps of the writing process.

1. **Prewrite** Talk with your partner about things you can write about. Choose a plant, animal, or dinosaur. Draw a picture of it.
   Encourage partners to discuss ideas. You may want to model this step by having children help you work through the thinking process. Let them hear how you might select a topic. After children draw a picture, they should use describing words to tell about it.
2. **Draft** Write sentences about your picture.
   Tell children that the most important thing is to get their main ideas on paper. Remind them that they can add details afterward.
3. **Revise** Read what you wrote. Do you like it? Make changes if you want to.
   Help children focus on making the ideas in their writing better. Point out that they can correct errors in capitalization, spelling, and so on during the next step.
4. **Edit** Check your writing to make sure it is correct. Make a neat copy.
   Have children ask themselves: Did I use correct spelling? Did I use capital letters correctly? Did I use the correct mark at the end of each sentence?
5. **Publish** Share your picture and your writing with others. You can make a booklet or find another way to share.
   Some children may prefer to share their writing orally in front of the class or in small groups.

Writing about a Plant, Animal, or Dinosaur

Before you write a description, you need to choose a topic. Then think about words that describe your topic. When you describe something, you can tell how it looks, sounds, feels, smells, or tastes.

1. **Prewrite** Talk with your partner about things you can write about. Choose a plant, animal, or dinosaur. Draw a picture of it.
2. **Draft** Write sentences about your picture.
3. **Revise** Read what you wrote. Do you like it? Make changes if you want to.
4. **Edit** Check your writing to make sure it is correct. Make a neat copy.
5. **Publish** Share your picture and your writing with others. You can make a booklet or find another way to share.

A 64

Writing Rubric

	4	3	2	1
Follows steps of writing process in order				
Communicates specific details and information				
Includes ideas related to topic				
Writes clear sentences				
Uses correct capitalization				

Scoring Key **Total Score** ______
4 points correct, complete, detailed
3 points partially correct, complete, detailed
2 points partially correct, partially complete, lacks some detail
1 point incorrect or incomplete, needs assistance

Technology

Children can share their descriptions at **www.sfscience.com.**

Unit B
Physical Science

B1

Science Background

What Is Physical Science? Physical science is the study of everything we see around us and things we do not see, such as air and gas. For young children this means exploring such things as light, sound, heat, and magnets. Physical science can help answer questions such as these: How fast does an object fall? How does electricity work? Why can you mix some things together and take them apart again but not others?

About the Photograph The photograph on this page shows the launch of a space shuttle. Ask children to tell what they know about space vehicles and what makes them move. Tell children they will learn more about what makes things move in Chapter 3, "Force, Magnets and Electricity."

Technology

You can use the **Teacher's Resource Planner** to plan and organize your curriculum.

In This Unit

In this unit, children learn about matter, sound, heat, light, force, magnets, and electricity. They explore the properties and the states of matter and how matter can be mixed and changed. They learn about different sounds, investigate heat, and experiment with light and shadows. Finally, they discover how objects and electricity move, and they explore gravity and magnets.

Books for Teachers

Chapter 1

Science on a Shoestring by Herb Strongin. Inexpensive, hands-on activities designed to introduce children to the themes of matter, change, and energy. (Scott Foresman - Addison Wesley, ISBN 0-201-25760-2)

Matter by Christopher Cooper. Text and photographs provide an excellent resource for learning about the elements that make up the physical world. (Dorling Kindersley, ISBN 1-879431-88-2)

Chapter 2

Rubber-Band Banjos and a Java-Jive Bass: Projects and Activities on the Science of Music and Sound by Alex Sabbeth. Projects and activities, including how to make simple musical instruments. (John Wiley, ISBN 0-471-15675-2)

The Science Explorer Out and About by Pat Murphy, Ellen Klages, Linda Shore, and the staff of the Exploratorium. Exciting hands-on projects including several tricks with mirrors that demonstrate the reflection of light. (Henry Holt, ISBN 0-8050-4537-6)

Chapter 3

Understanding Electricity by Gary Gibson. Hands-on experiments and activities that provide an introduction to basic principles of electricity. (Copper Beech Books, ISBN 0-7613-0462-2)

Janice VanCleave's Electricity by Janice VanCleave. Children can have fun and learn about simple principles of electricity as they follow experiments suggested in this book. (John Wiley, ISBN 0-471-31010-7)

Chapter	Chapter Concepts/ National Science Education Standards	Lessons/Vocabulary
Chapter 1	**Matter** p. B4 **Concepts** Objects can be sorted according to their properties. Matter is anything that takes up space and has weight. The states of matter are solid, liquid, and gas. A solid has a definite volume, a liquid takes its shape from its container, and a gas can change shape and volume. Matter can be mixed, as well as changed from one state to another. **National Science Education Standards**  Content Standard B, p. 123 • **Properties of objects and materials**	**Math in Science** *Sorting p. B6* **Lesson 1** *What are the properties of objects? p. B8* **Vocabulary** properties **Lesson 2** *What is matter? p. B10* **Vocabulary** matter **Lesson 3** *What are the states of matter? p. B12* **Vocabulary** states of matter, solid, liquid, gas **Lesson 4** *How can matter be mixed? p. B14* **Lesson 5** *How can matter be changed? p. B16* **Lesson 6** *How fast can you melt an ice cube? p. B18*
Chapter 2	**Sound, Heat, and Light** p. B22 **Concepts** Sounds are made when objects vibrate. The volume and pitch of a sound can change. Heat comes from many sources and moves from warmer objects and places to cooler ones. Heat moves through metal more easily than plastic or foam. Some sources of light also give off heat. Light is made up of many colors, and travels in a straight line. When light hits objects it can pass through, bounce off, bend, or be blocked. An object's shadow becomes smaller as it moves away from a light source. **National Science Education Standards**  Content Standard B, p. 123 • **Light, heat, electricity and magnetism**	**Lesson 1** *How can you make sounds? p. B24* **Vocabulary** vibrate, volume **Lesson 2** *What is pitch? p. B26* **Vocabulary** pitch **Lesson 3** *What are some sources of heat? p. B28* **Vocabulary** source **Lesson 4** *Which container will warm up fastest? p. B30* **Lesson 5** *What are some sources of light? p. B32* **Reading for Science** *Using a Word Web p. B34* **Lesson 6** *How does light move? p. B36* **Lesson 7** *Experiment with shadows. p. B38*
Chapter 3	**Force, Magnets, and Electricity** p. B42 **Concepts** Force is the push or pull that makes something move. Gravity is the force between the earth and objects. Magnets push or pull certain metal objects. Opposite poles attract, like poles repel. Electricity travels in a path called a circuit. If the circuit is broken or part of it is removed, the circuit will not work. It is important to follow safety rules when using electricity. **National Science Education Standards**  Content Standard B, p. 123 • **Position and motion of objects** • **Light, heat, electricity and magnetism**	**Reading for Science** *Cause and Effect p. B44* **Lesson 1** *What makes objects move? p. B46* **Vocabulary** force **Lesson 2** *What is gravity? p. B48* **Vocabulary** gravity **Lesson 3** *What is a magnet? p. B50* **Vocabulary** pole, attract, repel **Lesson 4** *What can a magnet attract? p. B52* **Lesson 5** *How many paper clips will a magnet pick up? p. B54* **Lesson 6** *How does electricity move? p. B56* **Vocabulary** circuit **Lesson 7** *How do you use electricity safely? p. B58*
Unit B Assessment	**Unit Performance Review** pp. B62–B63 **Writing for Science** p. B64	

Activity Opportunities

Student Edition
- Explore Activity *Sort objects.* p. B9
- Explore Activity *Compare objects.* p. B11
- Explore Activity *Find out what mixes with water.* p. B15
- Investigate Activity *How fast can you melt an ice cube?* pp. B18–B19

Flip Chart
- Science Center Explore Activity *Guess what is in the bag.*
- Science Center Explore Activity *Make a mixture.*

Teacher's Edition
- Activity Idea Bank, pp. B13a–B13b, B19a–B19b

Additional Resources
- Family Activity, Instructional Resources Package, pp. 25–26
- Vocabulary Preview, Instructional Resources Package, p. 27
- Graphic Organizer, Teacher's Assessment Package, p. 21
- Lab Manual, pp. 31, 33, 35, 36, 37, 38
- Interactive Transparency 4, Interactive Transparency Package
- Wall Chart, pp. 19, 20, 21, 22

Technology
- *Physical Science* National Lab **www.sfscience.com**

Student Edition
- Explore Activity *Make sounds.* p. B25
- Explore Activity *Make a pitch finder.* p. B27
- Investigate Activity *Which container will warm up fastest?* pp. B30–B31
- Explore Activity *Go on a scavenger hunt.* p. B37
- Experiment Activity *Experiment with shadows.* pp. B38–B39

Flip Chart
- Science Center Explore Activity *Explore sounds.*
- Science Center Explore Activity *Measure temperature.*
- Science Center Explore Activity *Play a mirror game.*

Teacher's Edition
- Activity Idea Bank, pp. B27a–B27b, B31a–B31b, B39a–B39b

Additional Resources
- Family Activity, Instructional Resources Package, pp. 33–34
- Vocabulary Preview, Instructional Resources Package, p. 35
- Graphic Organizer, Teacher's Assessment Package, p. 27
- Lab Manual, pp. 39, 40, 41, 43–44, 45, 46, 47–48, 49
- Interactive Transparency 5, Interactive Transparency Package
- Wall Chart, pp. 23, 24, 25, 26

Technology
- *Physical Science* National Lab **www.sfscience.com**

Student Edition
- Explore Activity *Make an object move.* p. B47
- Explore Activity *Explore gravity.* p. B49
- Explore Activity *Push and pull magnets.* p. B51
- Explore Activity *Go fishing with a magnet.* p. B53
- Investigate Activity *How many paper clips will a magnet pick up?* pp. B54–B55
- Explore Activity *Light a bulb.* p. B57

Flip Chart
- Science Center Explore Activity *Move an object.*
- Science Center Explore Activity *Use a magnet.*
- Science Center Explore Activity *Explore electricity.*

Teacher's Edition
- Activity Idea Bank, pp. B49a–B49b, B55a–B55b, B59a–B59b

Additional Resources
- Family Activity, Instructional Resources Package, pp. 41–42
- Vocabulary Preview, Instructional Resources Package, p. 43
- Graphic Organizer, Teacher's Assessment Package, p. 33
- Lab Manual, pp. 51, 52, 53, 54, 55, 56, 57, 58, 59
- Interactive Transparency 6, Interactive Transparency Package
- Wall Chart, pp. 27, 28, 29, 30, 31

Technology
- *Physical Science* National Lab **www.sfscience.com**

Assessment Opportunities

Student Edition
- Lesson 1 Review, p. B9
- Lesson 2 Review, p. B11
- Lesson 3 Review, p. B13
- Lesson 4 Review, p. B15
- Lesson 5 Review, p. B17
- Chapter 1 Review, pp. B20–B21

Teacher's Edition
- Process Skills Development, pp. B5 & B21
- Assessment Rubric, p. B21

Teacher's Assessment Package
- Chapter 1 Review, p. 22
- Chapter 1 Assessment, pp. 23–24
- Portfolio Ideas, p. 19

Lab Manual
- Activity Rubric, pp. T11, T12, T13

Technology
- **Practice & Assessment CD-ROM**
- **Production Studio**
- **The KnowZone™ at www.kz.com**
- **TestWorks™**

Student Edition
- Lesson 1 Review, p. B25
- Lesson 2 Review, p. B27
- Lesson 3 Review, p. B29
- Lesson 5 Review, p. B33
- Lesson 6 Review, p. B37
- Chapter 2 Review, pp. B40–B41

Teacher's Edition
- Process Skills Development, pp. B23 & B41
- Assessment Rubric, p. B41

Teacher's Assessment Package
- Chapter 2 Review, p. 28
- Chapter 2 Assessment, pp. 29–30
- Portfolio Ideas, p. 25

Lab Manual
- Activity Rubric, pp. T14, T15, T16, T17

Technology
- **Practice & Assessment CD-ROM**
- **Production Studio**
- **The KnowZone™ at www.kz.com**
- **TestWorks™**

Student Edition
- Lesson 1 Review, p. B47
- Lesson 2 Review, p. B49
- Lesson 3 Review, p. B51
- Lesson 4 Review, p. B53
- Lesson 6 Review, p. B57
- Lesson 7 Review, p. B59
- Chapter 3 Review, pp. B60–B61

Teacher's Edition
- Process Skills Development, pp. B43 & B61
- Assessment Rubric, p. B61

Teacher's Assessment Package
- Chapter 3 Review, p. 34
- Chapter 3 Assessment, pp. 35–36
- Portfolio Ideas, p. 31

Lab Manual
- Activity Rubric, pp. T18, T19, T20, T21, T22

Technology
- **Practice & Assessment CD-ROM**
- **Production Studio**
- **The KnowZone™ at www.kz.com**
- **TestWorks™**

Student Edition
- Unit B Performance Review, pp. B62–B63

Teacher's Edition
- Assessment Rubric, p. B63

Technology
- *Writing for Science* **www.sfscience.com**

Activity Organizer

Objective
Experiment to find out how the surface of a ramp changes the way things slide.

Process Skills predicting, observing

Parallel Student Book Lesson
Chapter 3, Lesson 1

Materials board; chair or cardboard box; block, toy car or other object; materials for covering ramp such as sandpaper, wax paper, cloth

EXTENDED INQUIRY

How does the surface of a ramp affect how things move?

The following activity is a model of an inquiry-based science fair project for you to do with the class. A list suggesting individual science projects follows the activity. Use these steps of scientific inquiry.

Steps

1 Ask a question about objects, organisms, and events in the environment.

- Pose the following question to children: **How does the surface of a ramp change the way things slide?**
- Have children choose three materials such as wax paper, sandpaper, and cloth. Then create a ramp by resting a board against a child-size chair, cardboard box or pail. Ask children to predict how the surface of the ramp will change the way things move down the ramp. Children will cover the board with the different materials and slide the same object down on each surface.

This activity follows methods of scientific inquiry suggested in the National Science Education Standards.

2 Plan and conduct a simple investigation.

- Have children take turns covering the board with different materials, resting the board against a chair, box, or pail to create a ramp, and sliding a block, toy car or other object down the ramp.
- Children should try to set up the ramp at exactly the same angle each time.
- Have children describe the movement of the object with each surface.

3 Employ simple equipment and tools to gather data and extend the senses.

To show how the surface of the ramp changes the way the object moves, children may want to:

- record their findings in a chart
- draw and label pictures to illustrate their findings
- label and display the fabrics to show how they affected the way the objects moved down the ramp

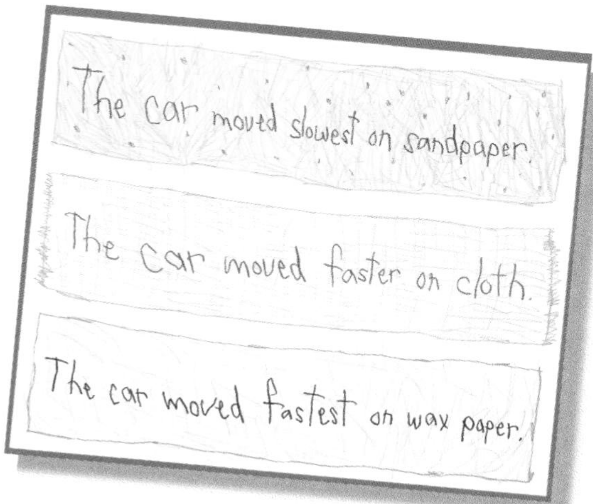

The car moved slowest on sandpaper.
The car moved faster on cloth.
The car moved fastest on wax paper.

4 Use data to construct a reasonable explanation.

- Ask: **How does the surface of the ramp affect the way things move down the ramp?** (*Possible answers: Things move faster down smooth surfaces than rough surfaces.*)
- Ask: **Do you think the results would be different if you used a shorter ramp?** (*Possible answer: The distance the object moved would be different, but the object would still move more quickly on the smoother surface.*)

5 Communicate investigations and explanations.

- Have children discuss their observations. Children should compare the results to their predictions. They should recognize that objects moved more easily and faster on the smooth surface than on the rough surface.

Inquire Further

Ask children to predict what might happen if they used other materials to cover the ramp. Ask what they could do to find out.

Science Fair Projects

Chapter 1 Cookbook
Have children create a class cookbook of recipes that involve mixtures, such as fruit salads, tossed salads, trail mix, and fruit punch.

Chapter 2 String Phones
Children can explore transmissions of sound vibrations. Have them connect paper cups with string. They thread the ends of the string through tiny holes in the bottoms of the cups and tie the ends onto a bread tie. Have children find out what happens if someone pinches the string while they are using their "telephones."

Chapter 3 Magnetism Invite children to investigate how the strength of a magnet is affected by various materials. Children place a handful of paper clips on the table and hold a magnet 2 centimeters and then 4 centimeters away. They record how many paper clips the magnet attracts each time. Next, children place all of the clips in a container of water and suspend the magnet the same distance from the clips as before. They compare the results.

Technology

Children can participate in the Physical Science extended inquiry *National Lab* at **www.sfscience.com.**

Unit Overview

Teaching Science and Technology

Unit B Physical Science pages are also on the **Flip Chart.**

Have children look at the pictures. Talk about ways these pictures show examples of technology.

- The balloon is filled with cold air generated by a large, gas-powered portable fan. Burners are mounted on the balloon's basket to heat the air, and an aperture is attached to the bottom of the balloon. Hot air is then blasted into the opening, and the balloon rises. Hydrogen or helium gases are superior to heated air in lifting a balloon and are more often used.
- Holograms like this dinosaur image are actually flat. A laser beam was used to create tiny grooves on the surface of the lollipop. When light hits the grooves, it bends and bounces, making it appear as if the dinosaur could leap off the lollipop.
- This new invention is designed to be worn by anyone who works or plays in the ocean. It produces an electric field that annoys sharks and drives them away.

Science and Technology In Your World!

What makes this balloon go up?

First the balloon is filled with cold air. Then the air is heated. Hot air is lighter than the air around it. So the balloon is able to float.

Chapter 1
Matter

These lollipops have special lines on them.

When light hits the lines, the light bends and bounces. The way the light moves makes the pictures of dinosaurs appear.

Chapter 2
Sound, Heat, and Light

B2

Writing for Science

Narrative

Write a Story

Ask children to think about things that might happen if they rode in a hot-air balloon and then write a story to tell about their ride. Remind children to follow the steps of the writing process: prewrite, draft, revise, edit, and publish.

The Writing Process

The Writing Process

1. Prewrite
   - Talk with another person about things you can write about.
   - Choose one thing and draw a picture of it.
2. Draft
   Write sentences about your picture.
3. Revise
   Read what you wrote. Do you like it? Make changes if you want to.
4. Edit
   Check your writing to make sure it is correct. Make a neat copy.
5. Publish
   Share your picture and your writing with others.

Instructional Resources p. xi

A special machine uses electricity to make sharks swim away.

Some divers use these machines when they go in deep water. These machines may soon be put on surfboards and life jackets too.

Chapter 3
Force, Magnets, and Electricity

B3

INQUIRY

One aspect of inquiry involves asking questions. Give each child three index cards, one for each chapter in this unit. After they read the Science and Technology pages, have children write one question about each chapter. Throughout each chapter, children should use their text and other resources to look for the answer to their question. At the conclusion of each chapter, children should share the answer to their question with the class.

Math-Science Connection

Compare Weights

Point out that the reason that a hot-air balloon floats is that the hot air and helium inside are lighter than the air around it. Show children various items in the room, such as a stapler, a pencil, or a book. Have them guess whether the items are lighter or heavier than 1 pound or 1 kilogram. Use a scale and help children weigh the objects to find out.

Chapter 1 Planning Guide

Lesson/Activity and Flip Chart	Objectives/Process Skills	Time Options/Activity Materials
Chapter Opener Student Edition pp. B4–B5 and **Flip Chart** ***Ice-Cold Lemonade***		**Have less time?** Use the Graphic Organizer on Teacher's Assessment Package p. 21 for an overview of the lessons. Use the Flip Chart to teach lesson concepts and science activities. **Have more time?** Use the Flip Chart to reinforce and extend lesson concepts and activities. Use the Cross-Curricular Options in the Activity Idea Bank on Teacher's Edition pp. B13b, and B19b.
Math in Science Student Edition pp. B6–B7 ***Sorting***	**Objective** Sort objects.	
Lesson 1 Student Edition pp. B8–B9 ***What are the properties of objects?*** **Explore Activity** ***Sort objects.*** **Flip Chart** ***Talk About Science***	**Objective** State the properties of objects. **Process Skills** observing	**Kit Items** none **School-Supplied Items** common classroom objects
Lesson 2 Student Edition pp. B10–B11 ***What is matter?*** **Explore Activity** ***Compare objects.*** **Flip Chart** ***Talk About Science***	**Objective** Define matter. **Process Skills** predicting, observing	**Kit Items** pan balance **School-Supplied Items** classroom objects
Lesson 3 Student Edition pp. B12–B13 ***What are the states of matter?*** **Flip Chart** ***Talk About Science***	**Objective** Describe the properties of solids, liquids, and gases.	
Activity Idea Bank Teacher's Edition pp. B13a–B13b **Flip Chart** **Science Center Explore Activity** ***Guess what is in the bag.***	**Objective** Identify the properties of objects. **Process Skills** communicating, inferring	**Kit Items** none **School-Supplied Items** brown paper bags, variety of classroom objects
Lesson 4 Student Edition pp. B14–B15 ***How can matter be mixed?*** **Explore Activity** ***Find out what mixes with water.*** **Flip Chart** ***Talk About Science***	**Objective** Identify mixtures and solutions. **Process Skills** observing	**Kit Items** plastic cup with lid **School-Supplied Items** water, oil, juice, other liquids; confetti, sand, other solids
Lesson 5 Student Edition pp. B16–B17 ***How can matter be changed?*** **Flip Chart** ***Talk About Science***	**Objective** Tell how matter can be changed.	**Have more time?** Use the following teaching guide option: Interactive Transparency 4, Interactive Transparency Package
Lesson 6 Student Edition pp. B18–B19 and **Flip Chart** **Investigate Activity** ***How fast can you melt an ice cube?***	**Objective** Identify ways that heat can change the state of matter. **Process Skills** predicting, observing	**Kit Items** plastic-coated plate **School-Supplied Items** ice cube, clock
Activity Idea Bank Teacher's Edition pp. B19a–B19b **Flip Chart** **Science Center Explore Activity** ***Make a mixture.***	**Objective** Observe how matter can change when mixing things together. **Process Skills** measuring, observing	**Kit Items** liquid starch, 10-ounce plastic cup **School-Supplied Items** white glue, craft stick, measuring spoons
Chapter Review Student Edition pp. B20–B21 and **Flip Chart**		**Kit Items** none **School-Supplied Items** paper, pencil

Lesson/Activity and Flip Chart	Additional Resources		Technology
Chapter Opener Student Edition pp. B4–B5 and **Flip Chart** ***Ice-Cold Lemonade***	**Teacher's Assessment Package** • Graphic Organizer, p. 21 **Instructional Resources** • Family Activity, pp. 25–26 • Vocabulary Preview, p. 27	**Songs & Activities Package** • *Ice-Cold Lemonade*, pp. 15–16 **Wall Chart,** p. 19	**Practice & Assessment CD-ROM** **AudioText** **Production Studio** **www.sfscience.com** **Songs & Activities Package** **Teacher's Resource Planner CD-ROM**
Math in Science Student Edition pp. B6–B7 ***Sorting***	**Instructional Resources** • Math in Science, p. 28		
Lesson 1 Student Edition pp. B8–B9 ***What are the properties of objects?*** **Explore Activity** ***Sort objects.*** **Flip Chart** ***Talk About Science***	**Lab Manual** • Lab Manual, p. 31 • Activity Rubric, p. T11	**Teacher Demonstration Kit** **Wall Chart,** p. 20	
Lesson 2 Student Edition pp. B10–B11 ***What is matter?*** **Explore Activity** ***Compare objects.*** **Flip Chart** ***Talk About Science***	**Lab Manual** • Lab Manual, p. 33 • Activity Rubric, p. T11	**Teacher Demonstration Kit**	
Lesson 3 Student Edition pp. B12–B13 ***What are the states of matter?*** **Flip Chart** ***Talk About Science***		**Wall Chart,** p. 21	
Activity Idea Bank Teacher's Edition pp. B13a–B13b **Flip Chart** **Science Center Explore Activity** ***Guess what is in the bag.***	**Lab Manual** • Lab Manual, p. 35 • Activity Rubric, p. T12		
Lesson 4 Student Edition pp. B14–B15 ***How can matter be mixed?*** **Explore Activity** ***Find out what mixes with water.*** **Flip Chart** ***Talk About Science***	**Lab Manual** • Lab Manual, p. 36 • Activity Rubric, p. T12	**Teacher Demonstration Kit** **Wall Chart,** p. 22	
Lesson 5 Student Edition pp. B16–B17 ***How can matter be changed?*** **Flip Chart** ***Talk About Science***	**Interactive Transparency Package** • Interactive Transparency 4		
Lesson 6 Student Edition pp. B18–B19 and **Flip Chart** **Investigate Activity** ***How fast can you melt an ice cube?***	**Lab Manual** • Lab Manual, pp. 37 • Activity Rubric, p. T13	**Teacher Demonstration Kit**	*Physical Science* **Activity Video**
Activity Idea Bank Teacher's Edition pp. B19a–B19b **Flip Chart** **Science Center Explore Activity** ***Make a mixture.***	**Lab Manual** • Lab Manual, p. 38 • Activity Rubric, p. T13		
Chapter Review Student Edition pp. B20–B21 and **Flip Chart**	**Teacher's Assessment Package** • Chapter 1 Assessment, pp. 23–24		**Practice & Assessment CD-ROM** **Production Studio** **The KnowZone™ at www.kz.com** **TestWorks™**

Math for Science

Sorting

Think about how you can sort the fish into groups.
Look at the sizes and colors.

Sort the fish into two groups. Draw them in the tanks below.

Children can sort the fish in two different ways: large and small or solid-color and striped.

Instructional Resources
p. 28

Lab Manual

What are the properties of objects?

Classify your objects by size. Draw them here.

Students' answers will vary. Objects of similar smaller size might include paper clips, erasers, rings. Objects of similar larger size might include books, folders, papers. Objects of similar shape might include pencils, crayons, rulers, chalk, markers.

Classify your objects by shape. Draw them here.

Find another way to classify your objects.
Draw them here.

Lab Manual
p. 31

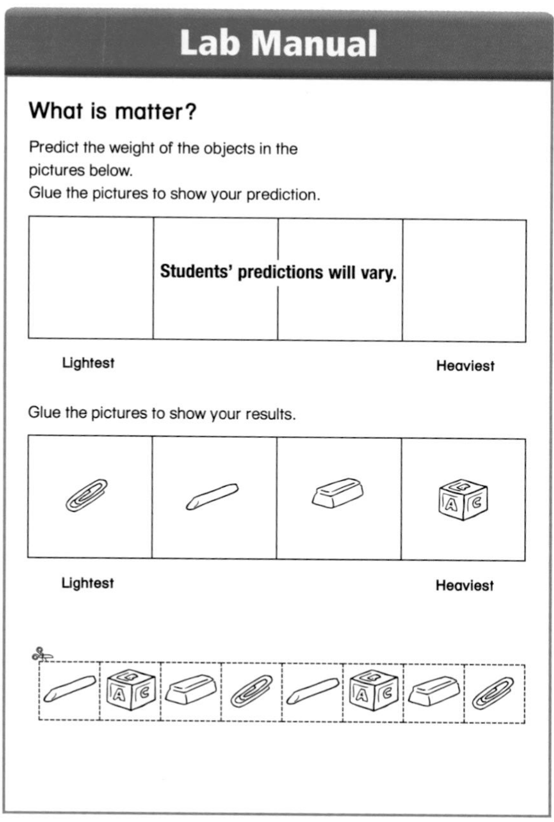

Lab Manual

What is matter?

Predict the weight of the objects in the pictures below.
Glue the pictures to show your prediction.

Students' predictions will vary.

Lightest Heaviest

Glue the pictures to show your results.

Lightest Heaviest

Lab Manual
p. 33

Lab Manual

Guess what is in the bag.

Choose an object and write a riddle.
Ask a friend to guess your object.

Students' responses will vary because the choice of objects will vary.

I am ________.
color

I am ________.
shape

I am ________.
size

I am ________.
a solid, liquid, or gas

What am I? ________

Lab Manual
p. 35

Lab Manual

How can matter be mixed?

Write the name of each material you test.
Draw how each material looked after shaking and then after two minutes.

The materials that students select will vary. Their reports on the materials used after shaking and after two minutes will vary.

The material I used: ______

After shaking. After 2 minutes.

The material I used: ______

After shaking. After 2 minutes.

Lab Manual
p. 36

Transparency

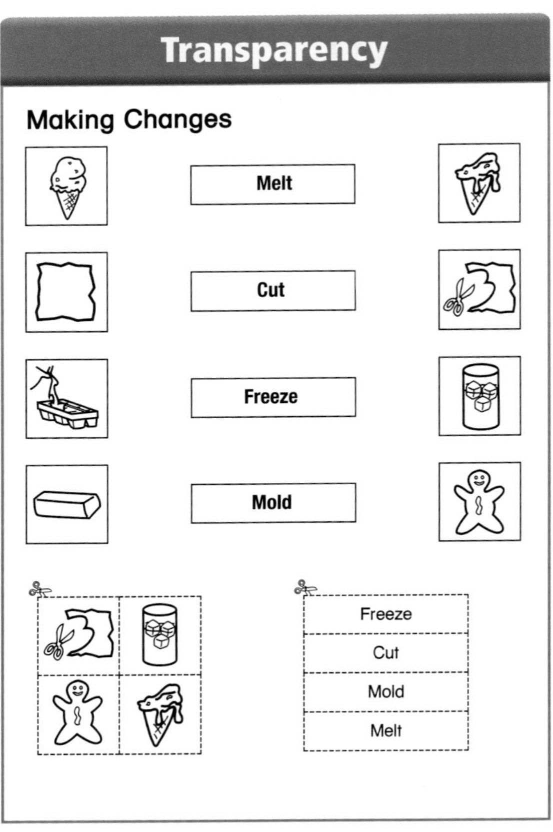

Interactive Transparency Package
Transparency 4

Lab Manual

How fast can you melt an ice cube?

Plan

To make my ice cube melt, I will ______

Prediction

I predict the ice cube will melt in ______ minutes.

Record your starting and ending times.

Start

End

Results

The ice cube melted in ______ minutes.

Students' predictions will vary. Their plans to melt their ice cubes will also vary. The time for melting will vary.

Lab Manual
p. 37

Lab Manual

Make a mixture.

Write what each material feels like and looks like.
Draw a picture of each material.

Material	Description	Picture
Glue		
Starch		
Mixture		**Students' descriptions and pictures of the mixture they made from glue and starch will vary.**

Lab Manual
p. 38

Chapter 1 Assessment

Draw a circle around the object described in the sentence.

1. This object is round and has stripes.

2. This object is large and floats.

Complete each sentence with one of these words: gas, solid, or liquid.

3. A **solid** has a size and shape of its own.
4. A **liquid** can be poured.
5. When a **solid** melts, it becomes a liquid.
6. A **gas** can change size and shape.

Draw a circle around the picture in each group that is a different state of matter.

7.

8.

Teacher's Assessment Package
p. 23

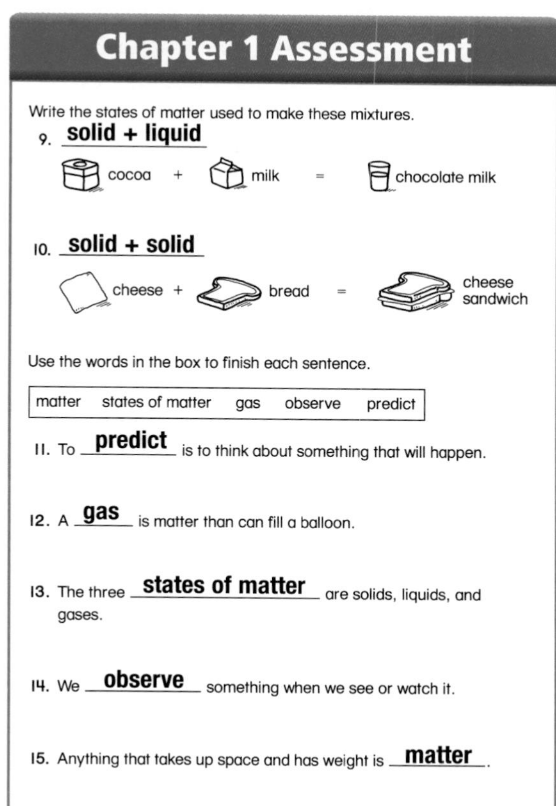

Chapter 1 Assessment

Write the states of matter used to make these mixtures.

9. **solid + liquid**

cocoa + milk = chocolate milk

10. **solid + solid**

cheese + bread = cheese sandwich

Use the words in the box to finish each sentence.

matter	states of matter	gas	observe	predict

11. To **predict** is to think about something that will happen.
12. A **gas** is matter than can fill a balloon.
13. The three **states of matter** are solids, liquids, and gases.
14. We **observe** something when we see or watch it.
15. Anything that takes up space and has weight is **matter**.

Teacher's Assessment Package
p. 24

Table of Contents

Introducing the Chapter

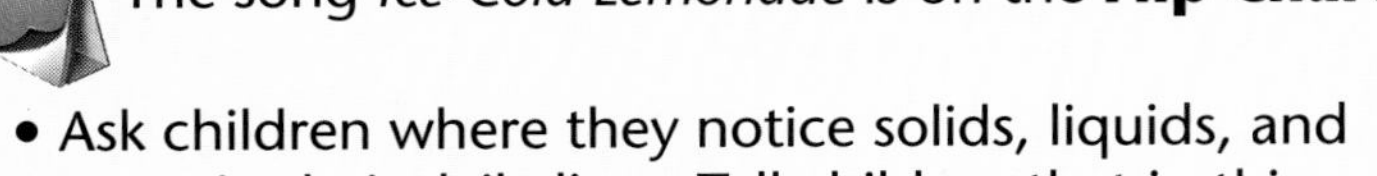

The song *Ice-Cold Lemonade* is on the **Flip Chart.**

- Ask children where they notice solids, liquids, and gases in their daily lives. Tell children that in this chapter they will learn more about these states of matter.
- Distribute the Family Activity blackline master page.

Singing the Song

Have children sing the song *Ice-Cold Lemonade* on side 1 of the CTW cassette. Distribute pages 15–16 from the CTW Song Activity Book.

Reading Assist *Contractions*

Write the words *there is* and *there's* on the chalkboard. Mention that *there's* is a contraction. Explain that a contraction is made by putting two words together. Point to the apostrophe in *there's.* Explain that the apostrophe takes the place of the letter *i* when the words *there* and *is* are put together. Ask children to find other contractions in the song. (*what's, they're*)

Vocabulary Preview

Use the Vocabulary Preview blackline master to introduce the vocabulary words for this chapter.

Lesson 1 properties
Lesson 2 matter
Lesson 3 states of matter, solid, liquid, gas

Chapter 1

Matter

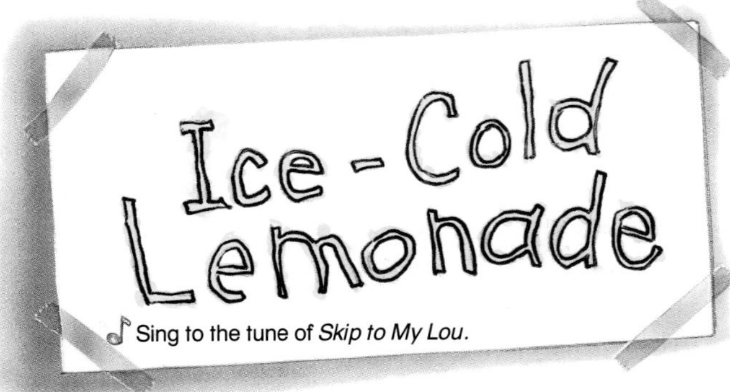

Sing to the tune of Skip to My Lou.

There's water in the pitcher, ready to pour.
There's water in the pitcher, ready to pour.
Pour it in the ice trays we bought at the store.
Then put them in the freezer.

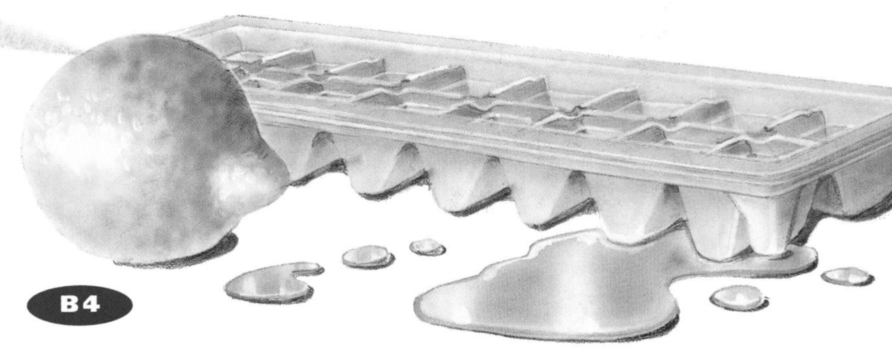

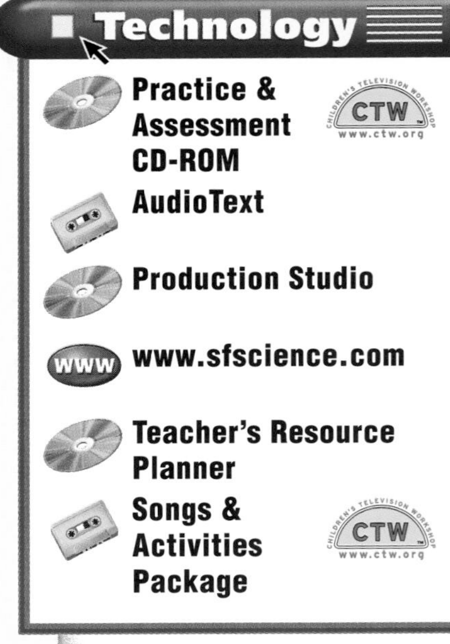

Technology
Practice & Assessment CD-ROM
CTW
www.ctw.org
AudioText
Production Studio
www.sfscience.com
Teacher's Resource Planner
Songs & Activities Package
CTW
www.ctw.org

CTW Song & Activity

What Might Have Happened?

1. Look at the pictures below.
2. How do things change from the picture on the left to the picture on the right?
3. Draw or write what might have caused each change.

Ice cubes on a plate — Water on the same plate
A piece of paper — Paper cut into small pieces
Sugar, lemon, water — Glass of lemonade
Unlit candle — Smaller version of candle

Songs & Activities Package
pp. 15–16

Wait a little while, then take them out.
The water has changed, what's this about?
It turned into ice, without a doubt.
What can we make with ice cubes?

Put the ice in the glass and go to the store.
Buy some lemons, you know what they're for.
But when you come back, there's no ice anymore.
All you have is water.

Original lyrics by Gerri Brioso and Richard Freitas.
Produced by Children's Television Workshop.

B5

Family Activity

Science at Home

Dear Family:

Our class is starting Chapter 1. We will be learning about matter. These are the main ideas for Chapter 1.

- Anything that takes up space and weight is matter.
- Matter has properties such as color, shape, and size.
- There are three states of matter.
- Matter can be mixed together.
- You can change the shape or the state of matter.

We will also be learning science vocabulary words for Chapter 1. By the end of Chapter 1, we will be able to read the vocabulary words and tell what they mean.

Word Bank

properties
matter
states of matter
solid
liquid
gas

Home Projects

Here are some activities that will help your child understand the main ideas in Chapter 1. The activities are easy, fast, and fun.

Activities

- You can identify properties of matter by playing a guessing game with your child.

1. Choose objects around your neighborhood and list their properties only. Include color, shape, weight, or anything that makes an object special.
2. List the properties for each object until your child identifies it, then switch roles with your child.

Instructional Resources
pp. 25–26

Vocabulary Preview

properties	liquid
matter	gas
states of matter	predict
solid	balance

Instructional Resources
p. 27

INQUIRY

Use a KWL chart at the beginning of each new chapter to encourage inquiry. In the *K* column, record what children think they already *know* about matter. In the *W* column, help children brainstorm a list of what they *want* to know about matter. Throughout the chapter, ask children what they have *learned* about matter and record their responses in the *L* column. A KWL chart is available in the **Wall Chart** page 19.

Chapter 1 Skills Trace

Process Skills Development	Observing	Predicting
Skill Introduced	xiv	xv
Skill Applied	B9 B11 B15 B18–B19	B11 B18–B19
Skill Assessed	End Matter 6–7	End Matter 16–17

Science Literature Library

Lemonade for Sale
by Stuart J. Murphy.
Members of the Elm Street Kid's Club make and sell lemonade to earn money to fix up their clubhouse. Elementary graphing concepts are introduced as the children create a bar graph to keep track of their sales. Making lemonade can spark discussion involving concepts of mixing and changing matter. (HarperCollins, ISBN 0-06-446715-5)

Math Organizer

Objective
Sort objects.

Additional Resources
- Math in Science blackline master

Teaching Math in Science

- Sorting objects builds on children's prior math experiences with the concepts of color, shape, and size. As children sort objects, they develop a sense of the relationships among objects. They also recognize that one object can belong to more than one group depending on the sorting scheme. For example, a blue ball can belong to a group of blue objects, a group of round objects, and a group of objects that bounce.
- In order to sort objects, children perform several steps. First, they compare and contrast the objects to find how the objects are alike and different. Then they use this information to identify a common characteristic. Next, they organize or group the objects based on the common characteristic. Finally, they use the common characteristic to name the group so that others will know how the objects have been sorted.

Student Page B6

- Have volunteers share experiences they have had with sorting objects.
- If possible, use a set of attribute blocks to model ways to sort. Some children may notice that in addition to sorting attribute blocks by color and shape, the blocks can be sorted by thickness and size.
- Hold up a blue block. Have children point to the group of blocks on the page to which the blue block could be added and discuss why. (*It can be added to the blue group because the block is blue.*) Repeat with other color blocks.

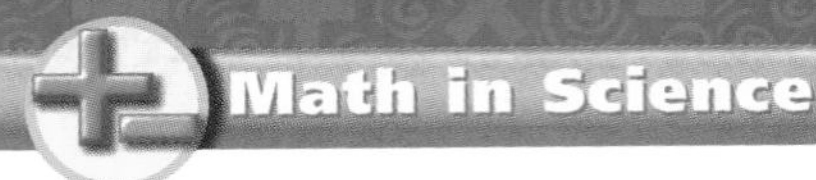

Sorting

When you put objects into groups, you are sorting. These blocks are sorted by color.

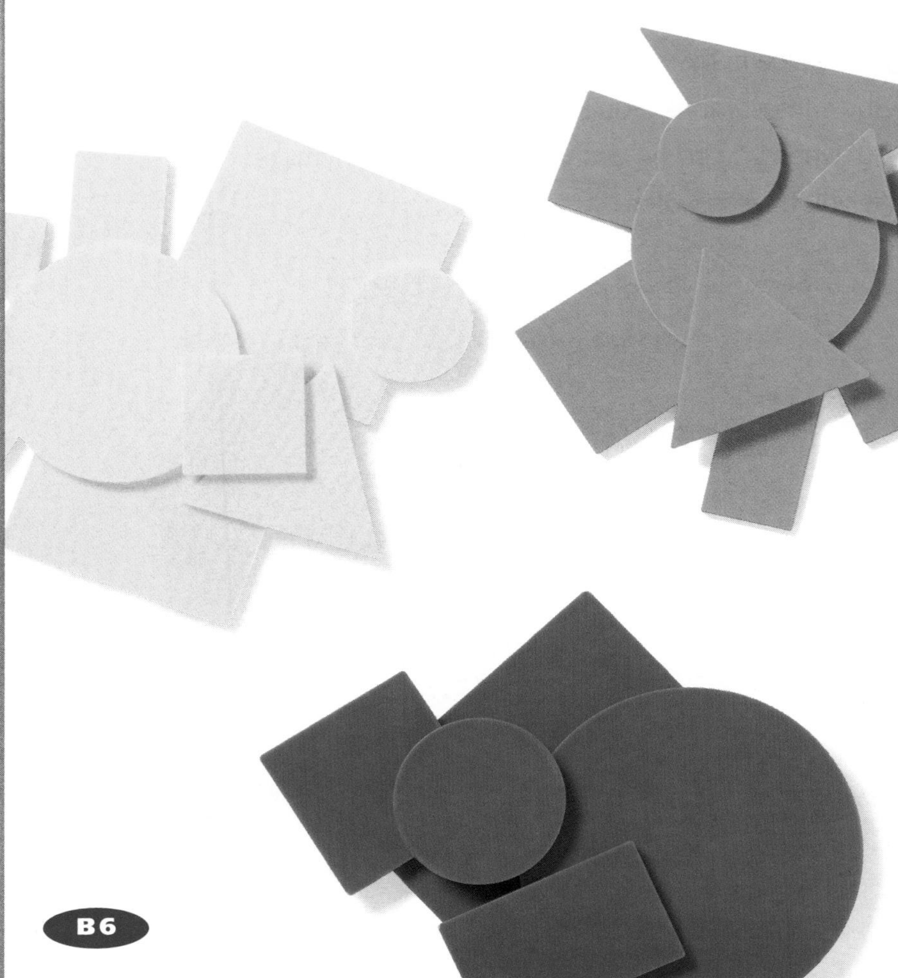

B6

ESL Strategy

Provide a collection of items such as buttons, socks, and paper shapes. Have children select an item and name it. Ask children to describe the item by telling about its shape, color, size, use, or texture. Encourage children to speak in complete sentences, modeling for them if necessary. Then ask children to find another item that is like the first in some way. Have children name the item and tell how it is like the first object. Continue with other objects.

[1] by size, by number of corners, by round/not round or square/not square, and so on

These blocks are sorted by shape. Find another way to sort the blocks.[1]

Turn the page to find out how sorting can help you learn about objects.

Student Page B7

- Point out that these are the same blocks as the ones pictured on page B6. Discuss how the groupings have changed by asking questions such as: **How many groups of objects were shown on page B6?** (3) **How many are shown on page B7?** (4) **Why did the number of groups change?** (*The blocks are grouped differently on page B7.*)
- Have children point to each group of objects as volunteers name the shape that describes the group.
- Ask volunteers to sort the blocks in a different way. As they name different ways to sort the blocks, have children point to blocks on the page that would belong to the new group.
- If possible, provide a mixture of blocks to small groups of children. Have one child in each group sort the blocks. Then have other children in the group guess how the blocks are sorted. Children can take turns sorting the blocks.

Apply Math in Science to Lesson 1

Children will use what they learned about sorting objects to complete the next lesson.

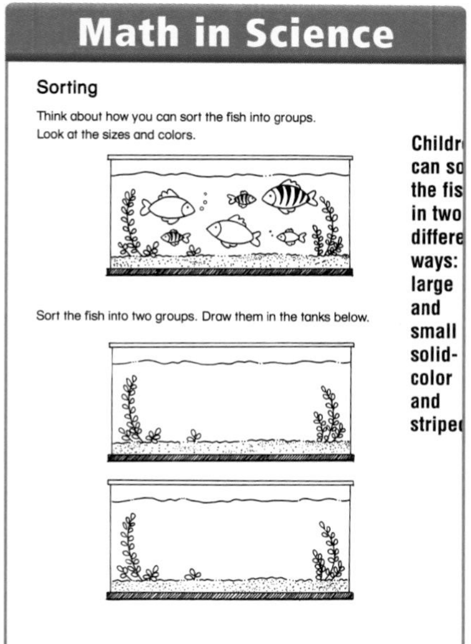

Math in Science

Sorting

Think about how you can sort the fish into groups.
Look at the sizes and colors.

Sort the fish into two groups. Draw them in the tanks below.

Childr can so the fis in two differe ways: large and small solid-color and striped

Instructional Resources p. 28

Lesson Organizer

Objective
State the properties of objects.

Vocabulary properties
Process Skills observing

Materials
Kit Items none
School-Supplied Items common classroom objects

Additional Resources
- Lab Manual
- Teacher Demonstration Kit
- Wall Chart

Introduce

Activate Prior Knowledge

Provide children with bite-size pieces of several fruits, such as banana, orange, and apple. Have children use their five senses to describe the fruit.

Language Development *Word Webs*

Display **Wall Chart** page 20. Explain that the *properties* of an object tell what the object is like. Have children name words describing what each fruit is like as you record them on the web.

Flip Chart

Have volunteers name properties of an object in the picture. Have classmates guess the object being described.

What are the properties of objects?
What is matter?
What are the states of matter?
Talk About Science

What are the properties of objects?

Find a toy in the picture that is green, round, and bounces. Which toy is it?

You're right! The ball is green, round, and bounces. You used the ball's properties to tell it apart from the other toys.

Some **properties** of objects are color, shape, and size. How much an object weighs and how it feels are other properties.

Find the sailboat. Do you think it floats? Whether an object floats or sinks is a property. What are some other properties of the sailboat?[1]

[1] plastic, red yellow sail

B8

Science Background

We can observe and describe the physical properties of any substance. Each substance has certain physical properties that make it different from other substances. Our senses (*sight, hearing, touch, smell, taste*) help us recognize properties. Some properties of matter that we can observe and describe are size, shape, color, and texture.

Science Across Cultures Invite children to bring from home toys that are common in different cultures, for example, nesting dolls or wind-up toys. Invite children to share their toys and describe their properties.

Sort objects.

Materials

common classroom objects

Process Skills

- observing

Steps

1. Gather some objects from your classroom.
2. Observe the objects. Describe them to a friend.
3. Sort your objects by color.
4. Now sort your objects by shape.
5. Find another way to sort your objects.

Share. Find as many ways to sort your objects as you can. Tell a friend about some of the ways you found.

Lesson Review

1. What are some properties of the ball in the picture?
2. What are some properties of objects?
3. **Tell** four ways you can sort objects.

B9

Lab Manual

What are the properties of objects?

Classify your objects by size. Draw them here.

Classify your objects by shape. Draw them here.

Find another way to classify your objects. Draw them here.

Lab Manual
p. 31

Activity Rubric

Use the following activity scoring rubric to assess students' performance.

Scoring Criteria	1	2	3	4
Student followed directions to perform the activity.				
Student classified common classroom objects by size.				
Students classified common classroom objects by shape.				
Students observed similarities among size and shape classifications.				
Student represented some of the properties of matter.				

Scoring Key
4 points correct, complete, detailed
3 points partially correct, complete, detailed
2 points partially correct, partially complete, lacks some detail
1 point incorrect or incomplete, needs assistance

Lab Manual
p. T11

 **Call 1-888-537-4908 with your Activity questions or comments.**

Teach and Apply

Student Page B8

Ask children to find objects in the picture that are the same in some way. Explain that objects with the same property can be classified in a group together.

Reading Assist *Decoding Words*
Write the word *weighs* on the chalkboard and have children find it on page B8. Point out that the *eigh* spelling pattern is pronounced as long /*a*/. Encourage children to name other words with *eigh,* such as *weight, sleigh,* and *eight.*

Student Page B9

Explore Activity

Time about 15 minutes

Grouping cooperative groups of 2

Point out some ways objects can be sorted, such as by size, materials they are made of, use, weight, or texture. Children can use Lab Manual page 31.

 ***Safety Note*** *Tell children not to taste any classroom objects.*

Assess and Extend

Answers to Lesson Review

1. The ball is green and round, and it bounces.
2. Some properties of objects are color, shape, size, weight, texture, and whether they sink or float.
3. **Tell** (*Interview*) Children might mention size, shape, color, material, use, weight, and buoyancy.

Inquire Further

Ask the following question to guide further inquiry: **What are some properties of objects in your classroom?**

Enrichment
Have children choose one of their groupings and then order the objects by another property.

Higher Order Thinking *Apply*
Ask: **What senses would you use to describe the properties of a dog?**

Lesson Organizer

Objective
Define matter.

Vocabulary matter
Process Skills predicting, observing

Materials
Kit Items pan balance
School-Supplied Items classroom objects

Additional Resources
- Lab Manual
- Teacher Demonstration Kit

Introduce

Activate Prior Knowledge
Place a block in one closed paper bag and a scarf in another. Ask children how they can determine some of the properties of each object without opening the bags.

Language Development
Multiple-Meaning Words
Point out that the word *matter* has more than one meaning. Discuss some of the meanings.

Flip Chart
Discuss the meaning of the word *matter* in science. Ask: **How do you know all the objects in the picture are made of matter?** (*because they all take up space and have weight*)

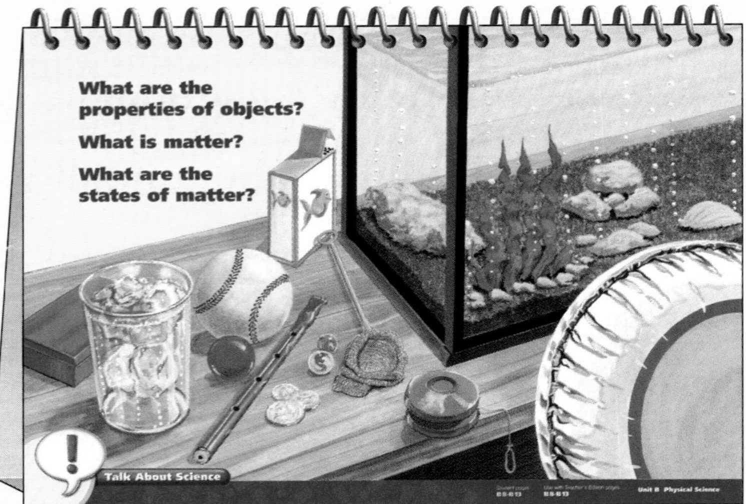
What are the properties of objects?
What is matter?
What are the states of matter?
Talk About Science
Unit B Physical Science

What is matter?

Can you find the football on the bed and the shoes on the floor? What else do you see in this bedroom?

Everything in this room is made of matter. In fact, everything around you is made of matter.

Matter is anything that takes up space and has weight. What do you see in your classroom that is made of matter?[1]

[1] desks, tables, bulletin b… chairs, books, and so on

Some things that you cannot see are made of matter. Even the air around you is matter.

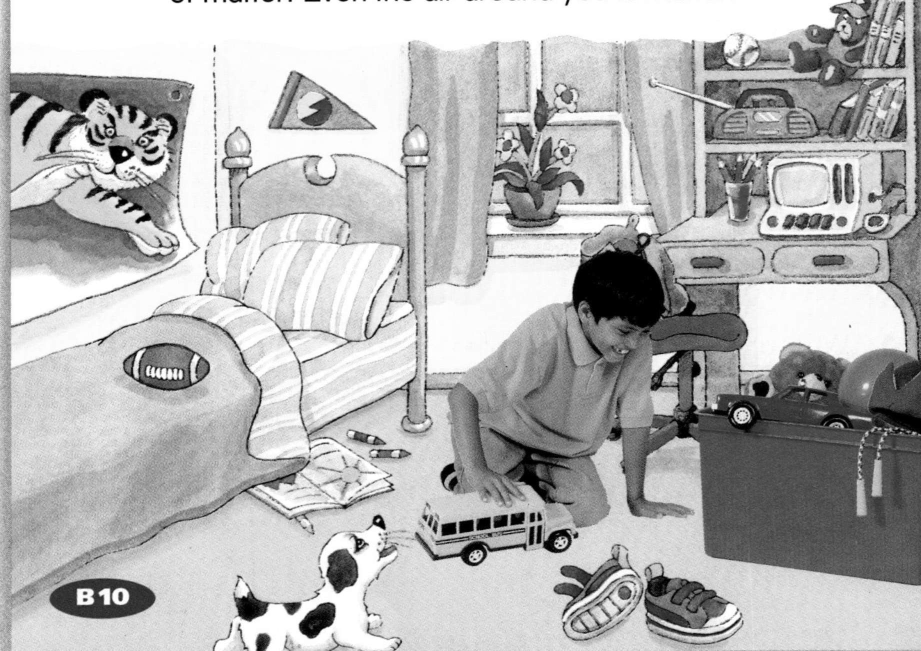
B10

Science Background
Matter is anything that takes up space and has mass. The term *weight* is substituted for *mass* at this grade level, even though the concepts are not identical. Weight is the pull of gravity on mass and can vary. Mass is how much material an object has in it.

Possible Misconceptions Help children realize that the air around them is made of matter. Point out that although we cannot see it, air takes up space and has weight.

Compare objects.

Materials

pan balance common classroom objects

Process Skills

- predicting
- observing

Process Skills

Steps

1. How would you put your objects in order from lightest to heaviest? Predict.
2. Put one object in each pan. Observe.
3. Compare the weight of each object.
4. Put the objects in order from lightest to heaviest. Record.

Share. Compare your results with your prediction.

Lesson Review

1. What is matter?
2. What are some things that are made of matter?
3. **Tell** how a balance can help you learn about matter.

B11

Teach and Apply

Student Page B 10

Have children quickly name things they see in the classroom. Help children realize that everything around them is matter. Ask children to name ways they might describe matter. (*by its properties, such as color, weight, shape, texture, and size*)

Student Page B 11

Explore Activity

Time about 10 minutes

Grouping cooperative groups of 4

Demonstrate how to use the pan balance. Encourage children to hold the objects to help them make their predictions. Help children realize that bigger objects are not necessarily heavier than smaller ones.

Reading Assist *Specialized Words*

Point out that when we *predict* we are making a thoughtful or reasonable guess about something, and that usually we test our guesses to see if we are correct.

What to Expect

Results may be different based on specific objects used.

Assess and Extend

Answers to Lesson Review

1. Matter is anything that takes up space and has weight.
2. Answers may include people, desks, tables, chairs, chalkboards, bulletin boards, pencils, paper.
3. **Tell** (*Interview*) Children may say that a balance can help them learn how objects compare to each other.

Inquire Further

Ask the following question to guide further inquiry:
How could a ruler help you compare matter?

Lab Manual

What is matter?

Predict the weight of the objects in the pictures below.
Glue the pictures to show your prediction.

Lightest Heaviest

Glue the pictures to show your results.

Lightest Heaviest

Lab Manual
p. 33

Activity Rubric

Use the following activity scoring rubric to assess students' performance.

Scoring Criteria	1	2	3	4
Student followed directions to complete the activity.				
Student made predictions about the weight of specific objects.				
Student observed the comparative weights of specific objects.				
Student ordered the predicted and actual weights of specific objects.				
Student compared objects according to weights.				

Scoring Key
4 points correct, complete, detailed
3 points partially correct, complete, detailed
2 points partially correct, partially complete, lacks some detail
1 point incorrect or incomplete, needs assistance

Lab Manual
p. T11

Enrichment

Have children select other objects made of matter and repeat the activity.

Higher Order Thinking *Analyze*

Ask: **How can you find out if something is matter?** (*see if it takes up space and has weight*)

Call 1-888-537-4908 with your Activity questions or comments.

Lesson Organizer

Objective
Describe the properties of solids, liquids, and gases.

Vocabulary states of matter, solid, liquid, gas

Additional Resources
- Wall Chart

Introduce

Activate Prior Knowledge

Invite children to cut out or draw pictures of a solid, a liquid, or a gas. Have them glue the pictures onto a sheet of paper folded into thirds and then label each one. Save their papers for use as a **baseline assessment.**

Language Development *Make a Chart*

Encourage children to share their pictures of solids, liquids, and gases. Use their ideas to complete **Wall Chart** page 21.

Flip Chart

Discuss the properties of a solid, liquid, and gas. Name objects on the **Flip Chart.** Have children tell which state of matter each object is.

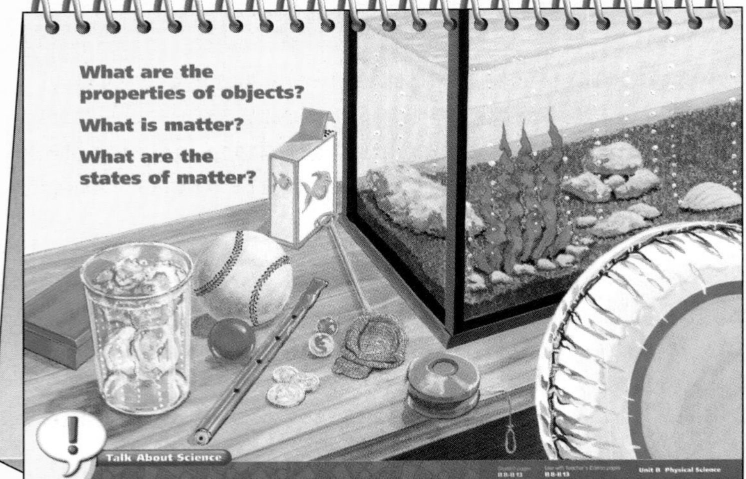

What are the properties of objects?
What is matter?
What are the states of matter?
Talk About Science

What are the states of matter?

Look up! Look down! Look all around! What do you see?

You know that everything around you is made of matter. There are three states of matter. The **states of matter** are solids, liquids, and gases.

A **solid** has a size and shape of its own. Which things in the picture are solids?[1]

[1] backpack, pencil, orange, notebook, and so on

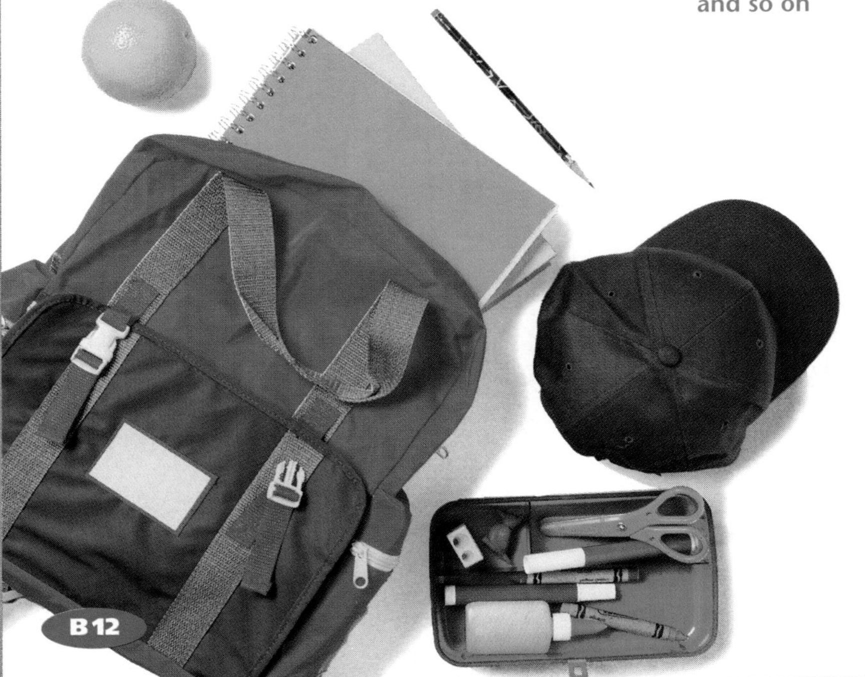

Science Background

- The word *volume* means "the amount of space that matter takes up."
- A solid has a definite shape and volume because its molecules are held in place and cannot move freely.
- A liquid has a definite volume. It takes the shape of its container.
- A gas has neither a definite volume nor a definite shape. It takes the shape and volume of its container.

Technology

Children explore properties of solids, liquids, and gases at **www.sfscience.com**

A **liquid** takes the shape of its container. Paint is a liquid. What other liquids do you know about?[2] [2]water, juice, and so on

A **gas** can change shape and size. When you fill a balloon with gas, the gas takes the shape and size of the balloon. You know that air is all around you. Air is made of gases you cannot see.

Lesson Review

1. What is a solid?
2. What is a liquid?
3. **Write** a list of some solids, liquids, and gases.

B13

ESL Strategy

Display pictures of a solid, a liquid, and a gas. Have children identify the state of matter of each. Encourage them to speak in complete sentences.

Teach and Apply

Student Pages B 12–B 13

After children read the pages, have them list the properties of each state of matter on paper. Discuss some examples of each state, especially gases. Point out that some gases, such as oxygen, are necessary for us to live; some, such as carbon dioxide, are necessary for plants to live; and some, such as carbon monoxide, which is produced by cars, are harmful.

Reading Assist *Word Meaning*

Ask children what they think the word *states* means. Then discuss how here the word refers to ways matter can be grouped.

Assess and Extend

Answers to Lesson Review

1. A solid is matter with a size and shape of its own.
2. A liquid is matter that takes the shape of its container.
3. **Write** (*Portfolio Assessment or Journal*) Solids may include books and pencils. Liquids may include water and juice. Gases may include air as well as the carbon dioxide in carbonated drinks.

Check for Understanding

To follow up on the **baseline assessment,** ask children to make adjustments to the papers they began in Activate Prior Knowledge. Encourage children to tell how they know each picture shows a liquid, a solid, or a gas.

Enrichment

Have children classify the foods they ate for breakfast or lunch as solid, liquid, or gas. If appropriate, point out that carbonated beverages contain a gas.

Reteach

Provide children with solids (*such as a spoon, a block, and a feather*) and liquids (*such as water, milk, syrup*) to explore. Discuss the properties of each one. Use various types of containers to aid your discussion. Then use the air around you or a balloon filled with air to discuss the properties of a gas.

Science Center

Flip Chart

Guess what is in the bag.

Objective

Identify the properties of objects.

Process Skills communicating, inferring

Materials

Kit Items none

School-Supplied Items brown paper bags, variety of classroom objects

Procedure

- Invite children to discuss the properties of objects.
- Have children work in pairs. They take turns **communicating** the properties of the object and **inferring** what is in the bag.
- You can use **Lab Manual** page 35 with this activity.

What to Expect

Children use different properties, such as shape, size, and texture, to describe objects.

Lab Manual

Guess what is in the bag.

Choose an object and write a riddle.
Ask a friend to guess your object.

I am ____________ .
color

I am ____________ .
shape

I am ____________ .
size

I am ____________ .
a solid, liquid, or gas

What am I? ____________

Lab Manual, p. 35

Connections

School and Community

Ideas for bringing the school and community together:

Field Trips

- science museum
- restaurant kitchen

Guest Speakers

- chemist
- chef

Themes

The activities on these pages can be used with classroom themes such as:

- classifying and sorting
- atmosphere
- the earth

Books for Children

Children might enjoy these books about matter:

Air Is All Around You by Franklyn M. Branley. Directions for two simple experiments about air. (HarperCollins, ISBN 0-06-445048-1)

Solids and Liquids by David Glover. Experiments and chemical reactions that examine solids and liquids. (Kingfisher Books, ISBN 1-85697-934-2)

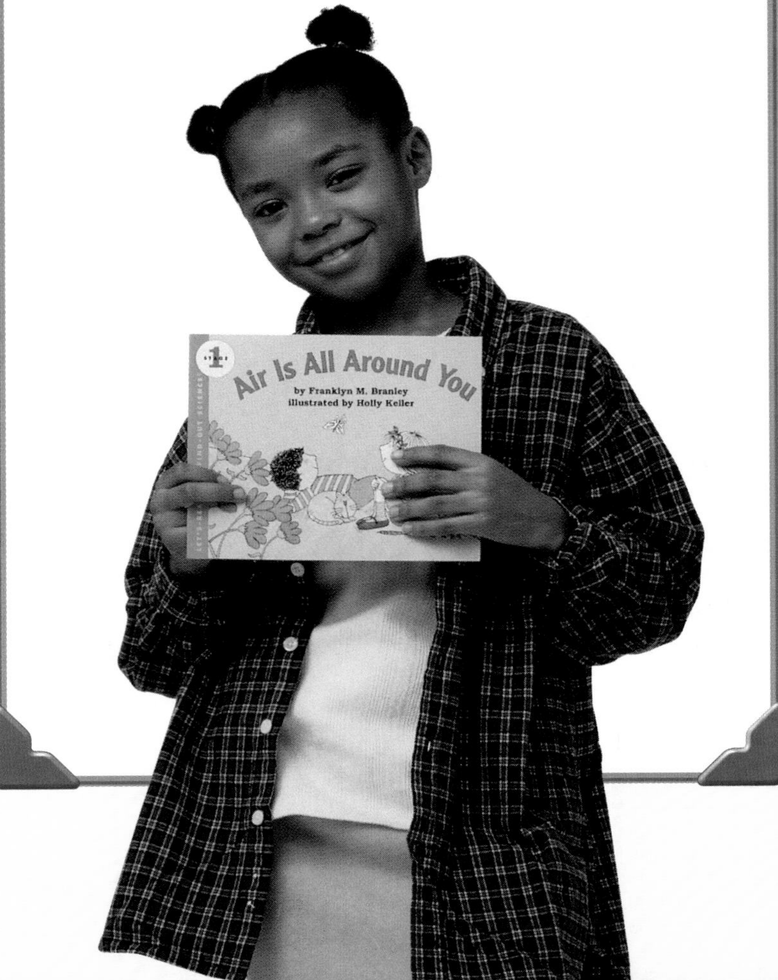

Cross-Curricular Options

LITERATURE

Puddle Jumper

Use the book to discuss a wooden toy.

Materials *Puddle Jumper: How a Toy Is Made* by Ann Morris. (Lothrop, Lee & Shepard, ISBN 0-688-10205-0)

Procedure

- After reading the story aloud to children, review how the lumber was changed to make a toy.
- Discuss the solids—paper, saw, pencil, shaper, sander, and so on—and how they were used to make and form the toy.
- Point out how the paint—a liquid—was used to change the product.

Multiple Intelligences linguistic

Gifted and Talented Some children might design a sculpture or other object from small pieces of wood or plastic foam.

MATH

Sort It!

Sort blocks or beads.

Materials different-shaped blocks, beads, and buttons

Procedure

- Have children sort the blocks, beads, or buttons by size, color, shape, texture, or number of holes.
- Challenge children to explain their sorting criteria.

Multiple Intelligences spatial

WRITING

A Penny for Your Thoughts

List the properties of different objects.

Materials pennies, blocks, apple, cotton, sealed plastic bag with air inside, cup of apple juice, cup of water

Procedure

- Display the materials.
- On the board list questions that children can use to describe properties of the objects: Is it hard or soft? Does it float? Is it smooth or rough? Can you see it? Does it move?
- Have children list as many properties as possible for one or more of the objects.

Multiple Intelligences spatial, linguistic

Special Needs Children with limited writing ability can dictate the properties for a partner to record.

ART

Fun Bubblers!

Design bubble wands and blow bubbles.

Materials wire, straws, paper cups, juice cans, tape, scissors, bucket, dishwashing liquid, water, tablespoon, safety goggles

Procedure

- Children can design creative bubble wands.
- In a bucket, make a bubble solution with 10 parts water and 1 part dishwashing liquid.
- Have children test their bubble wands outdoors.
- Discuss that air in the bubbles is gas and that the detergent and water are liquids.

Multiple Intelligences spatial

Lesson Organizer

Objective

Identify mixtures and solutions.

Process Skills observing

Materials

Kit Items plastic cup with lid

School-Supplied Items water; oil, juice, other liquids; confetti, sand, other solids

Additional Resources

- Lab Manual
- Teacher Demonstration Kit
- Wall Chart

Introduce

Activate Prior Knowledge

Have children predict what might happen if they mix together different solids, or a solid and a liquid. Record children's ideas on **Wall Chart** page 22. Save for use as a **baseline assessment.**

Language Development *Specialized Words*

Talk about the meaning of the word *mixture.* What mixtures can children name?

Flip Chart

Have children identify pictures in which matter has been mixed. Ask: **In which picture have two solids been mixed together? In which picture have two liquids been mixed together?**

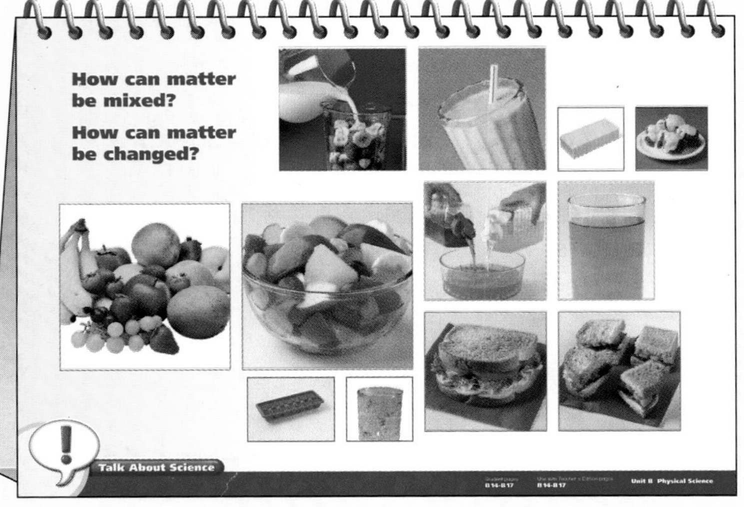

How can matter be mixed?

Help your family make dinner. Toss the salad. Stir the lemonade. As you cook, you are mixing different kinds of matter.

What would you put in a salad? You might put in some lettuce, carrots, and tomatoes. When you toss the salad, you are mixing solids together.

How could you make a dressing for the salad? You might mix oil and vinegar together. Then, you are mixing two liquids.

Look at the lemonade in the picture. It is made of a solid mixed with a liquid.

Look around you. What things do you see in your classroom that are mixed together?

B14

Science Background

- A substance is a particular kind of matter that has a uniform and definite composition. Granulated sugar is a substance. It is 100 percent sucrose.
- Mixtures consist of a physical blend of two or more substances. Lemonade is a mixture of sugar, lemon juice, and water. Soil is a mixture of rocks, soluble nutrients, organic matter, gases, and water.

Name Science

Matter is anything that takes up space and has weight.

Two things cannot be in the same place at the same time.

#1 EXPERIMENT:

We need: marbles → oooooooo

glass of water →

Marbles will be dropped into the glass of water.

1. Draw what you think will happen.

2. Draw what actually happened.

Explain:

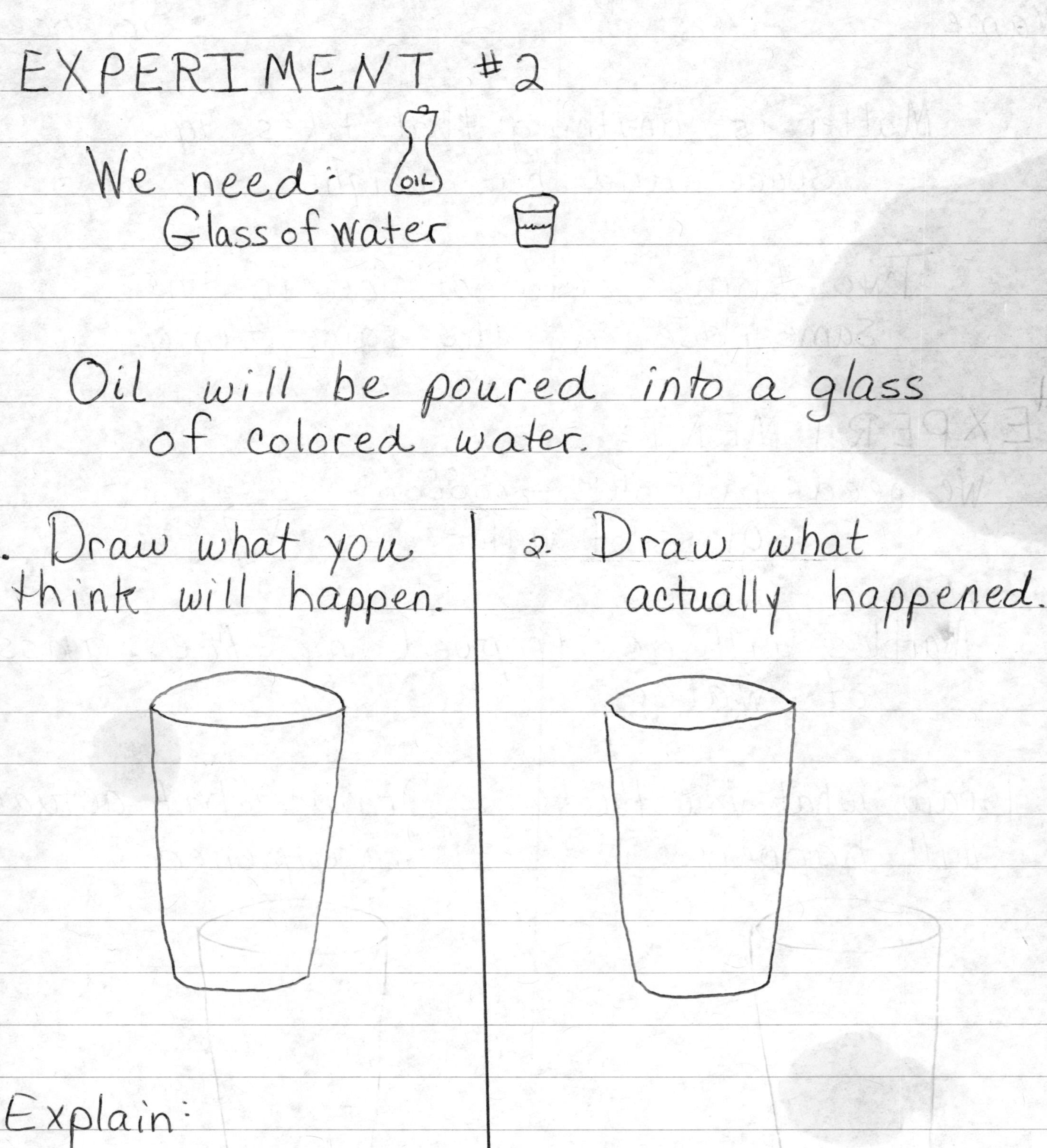

EXPERIMENT #2

We need: OIL
Glass of water

Oil will be poured into a glass of colored water.

1. Draw what you think will happen.

2. Draw what actually happened.

Explain:

Find out what mixes with water.

Materials

- water
- oil, juice, other liquids
- sand, confetti, other solids
- cup with lid

Process Skills

- observing

Steps

1. Put some water in a cup.
2. Add one of the solids or liquids.
3. Put the lid on the cup and shake the cup gently.
4. Put the cup down. Observe.
5. Wait 2 minutes. Observe again.
6. Do the activity again with a different material.

Share. Tell how your materials mixed with water.

Lesson Review

1. Name two solids that can be mixed.
2. Name a solid that can be mixed with a liquid.
3. **Write** two ways that different materials can mix with water.

B15

Lab Manual

How can matter be mixed?

Write the name of each material you test. Draw how each material looked after shaking and then after two minutes.

The material I used: ______ After shaking. After 2 minutes.

The material I used: ______ After shaking. After 2 minutes.

Lab Manual p. 36

Activity Rubric

Use the following activity scoring rubric to assess students' performance.

Scoring Criteria	1	2	3	4
Student followed directions to complete the activity.				
Student observed how different materials appeared after being shaken in water.				
Student described how different materials looked after soaking in water for two minutes.				
Student collected data for materials submerged and shaken in water.				
Student recorded the appearance of the matter under observation in controlled situations.				

Scoring Key
4 points correct, complete, detailed
3 points partially correct, complete, detailed
2 points partially correct, partially complete, lacks some detail
1 point incorrect or incomplete, needs assistance

Lab Manual p. T12

Teach and Apply

Student Page B14

Help children realize that mixing some things together is reversible, but some mixtures cannot be separated easily.

Reading Assist *Word Meaning*
Discuss the word *dressing.* Help children realize that in this context the word refers to something people put on salads. Children may also relate other meanings.

Student Page B15

Explore Activity

Time about 20 minutes

Grouping cooperative groups of 4

Before children mix each combination, encourage them to predict the result. Children can complete Lab Manual page 36 as they do the activity.

What to Expect
Some substances mix with water, some do not mix, and some initially mix but then settle to the bottom in time.

Assess and Extend

Answers to Lesson Review

1. Lettuce and carrots can be mixed.
2. Lemonade powder can be mixed with water.
3. **Write** (*Journal*) Children might write that juice mixes completely while sand settles over time.

Check for Understanding

To follow up on the **baseline assessment,** have children check to see if their predictions were correct. Invite children to fill in the last row with a mixture discovery of their choice.

Inquire Further

Ask the following question to guide further inquiry:
How can salt be separated from water?

Higher Order Thinking *Evaluate*

Ask: **Why do you think people started mixing things together?** (*Children may answer because they were curious or because they thought things would taste, look, or feel better together.*)

Call 1-888-537-4908 with your Activity questions or comments.

Lesson Organizer

Objective
Tell how matter can be changed.

Additional Resources
- Interactive Transparency

Introduce

Activate Prior Knowledge
Ask children how many ways they can change a piece of paper. Record their ideas on the chalkboard. Children may mention cutting, coloring, painting, folding, crumpling, or getting the paper wet. Save children's ideas for use as a **baseline assessment.**

Language Development *Game*
Invite children to play "Melt or Freeze." Have children move freely around the room until you say either "melt" or "freeze." If you say "melt," children should pretend they are melting into a puddle on the ground. If you say "freeze" children should freeze in their position.

Flip Chart
Have children identify pictures in which matter has changed. Ask: **Which pictures show a solid changed to a liquid? Which pictures show a liquid changed to a solid?**

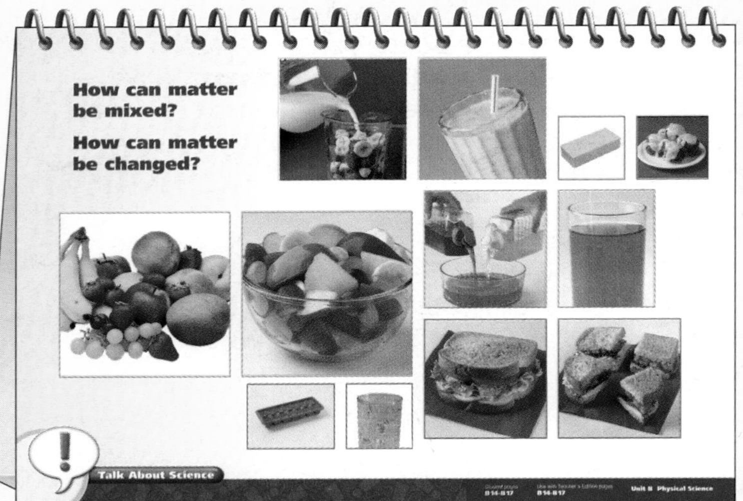

How can matter be changed?

When you mold clay into different shapes, you are changing the way matter looks.

Matter can be changed in many ways. It can change from one state to another. When matter is heated, it can melt. When something melts, it changes from a solid to a liquid. Find something in the picture that is melting.[1]

[1] frozen yog

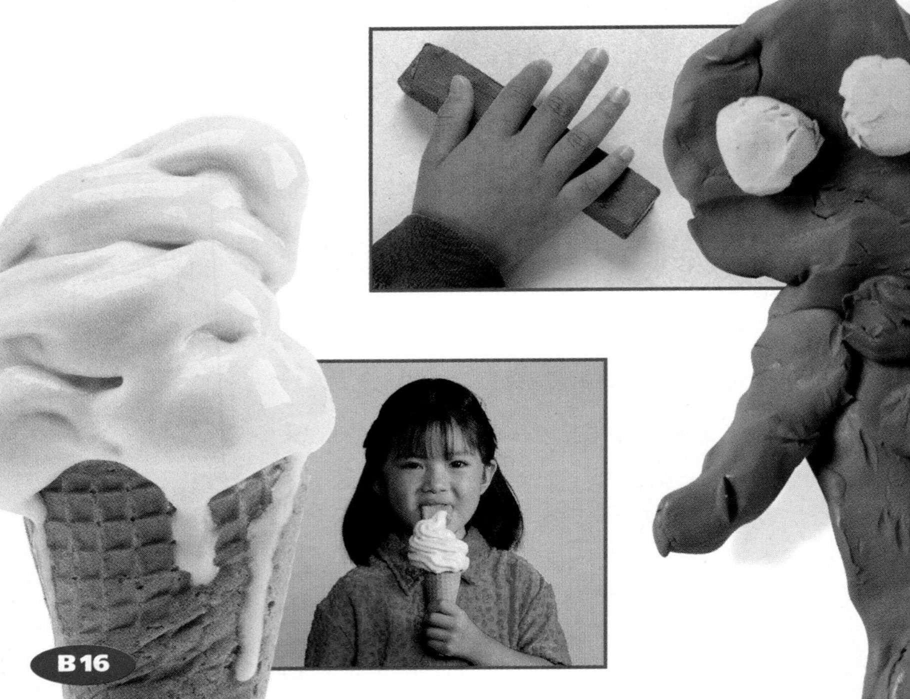

Science Background
- The physical state of matter can be changed by adding or removing heat.
- Many substances have a melting point and a boiling point.
- When most solids are heated to their melting points, they turn into a liquid. When a liquid is cooled to its freezing temperature, it turns into a solid.
- When a liquid is heated to its boiling point, it turns into a gas. When a gas is cooled to its dewpoint, it turns into a liquid.

Possible Misconceptions Some children may think that ice, water, and steam are different substances. Point out that they all are made from the same matter; only the state of the matter has changed.

Matter can be cooled until it freezes. Then it changes from a liquid to a solid. Find something in the picture that is frozen.[2] [2]ice cubes

What are some other ways to change matter?[3] [3]cutting, molding, heating, and so on

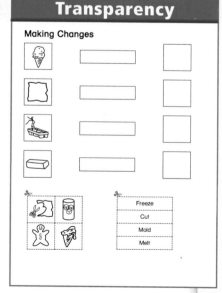

Lesson Review

1. What happens when an object melts?
2. What happens when an object freezes?
3. **Tell** three ways to change matter.

ESL Strategy

Model ways of changing things and describe what you are doing. For example, **I can change the picture on the bulletin board. I can change the shape of this paper by cutting it.** Then ask children to demonstrate ways to *change* things. Encourage them to speak in complete sentences as they describe what they are doing.

Transparency

Making Changes

Freeze

Cut

Mold

Melt

Interactive Transparency Package
Transparency 4

Teach and Apply

Student Pages B 16–B 17

Explain that a change in temperature or a change such as tearing, grinding, or bending is called a *physical change.* Physical changes alter the properties and states of matter, but the substance remains the same. Point out, for example, that a stick of butter is a solid. Ask what happens when the butter is heated. (*It melts into a liquid.*) Then ask what happens to the liquid butter when it is placed in a freezer. (*It freezes into a solid.*)

Reading Assist *Preview and Predict*

Suggest that children read the lesson title and examine the pictures. Have them predict what they will find out about matter in this lesson.

Earth Science

Integrating the Sciences

In this lesson, children learn about ways matter can be changed. In Unit C, Chapter 2, children learn about changes that occur in the water cycle, such as evaporation and condensation.

Assess and Extend

Answers to Lesson Review

1. It changes from a solid to a liquid.
2. It changes from a liquid to a solid.
3. Tell (*Interview*) Children might mention cutting, molding, freezing, and melting.

Check for Understanding

To follow up on the **baseline assessment,** invite children to add other ways the paper might be changed.

Reteach

- Use the Interactive Transparency to reteach Lesson 5 concepts.
- Provide children with clay and encourage them to explore different ways they can change it. Discuss that matter changes because something happens to change it. Ask children to consider what would happen if you left the clay sitting on a table for several days. (*It would dry out and get hard.*)

Activity Organizer

Objective
Identify ways that heat can change the state of matter.

Process Skills predicting, observing

Materials

Kit Items plastic-coated plate

School-Supplied Items ice cube, clock

Time about 20 minutes

Grouping individual or small groups

Additional Resources
- Lab Manual
- Teacher Demonstration Kit

Introduce

The Lesson 6 Investigate Activity, *How fast can you melt an ice cube?,* is on the **Flip Chart.**

Activate Prior Knowledge

Ask children if they know why ice melts. List children's suggestions on the chalkboard.

Language Development *Role-Play*

Have one child pretend to be a clock ticking off the seconds to reach one minute. Ask other children to pretend to jump rope to see how many times they can hop on one foot in that minute. Remind children that a minute is 60 seconds long.

How fast can you melt an ice cube?

Process Skills
- predicting
- observing

Materials

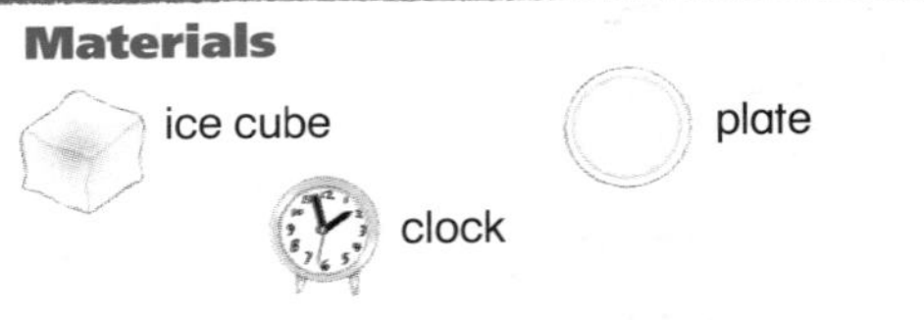

Steps

1. Put your ice cube on your plate.
2. How can you make your ice cube melt fast? Write down your ideas. Pick one way to try.
3. **Predict** how long it will take you to melt your ice cube.

Science Background

- Water conducts heat 200 times faster than air.
- Heat is conducted much faster from water to an ice cube than from air to an ice cube, so, for example, an ice cube in water will melt faster than an ice cube in an empty glass.
- Air is such a poor conductor of heat that it is an excellent insulator. Down quilts and plastic foam cups work by containing many pockets of air.

Technology

Review the demonstration of this Investigate's procedure on the *Physical Science* **Activity Video,** Segment 1.

4. Record the starting time.
5. **Observe** your ice cube as it melts.
6. How long did it take you to melt your ice cube? Record the ending time.
7. Compare your results with your **prediction**.

Think About Your Results

1. What did you do to melt your ice cube?
2. What was the fastest way someone in your class melted his or her ice cube?

Inquire Further

What would be a fast way to melt a large block of ice?

Teach and Apply

- Before children begin the activity, demonstrate how long it takes an ice cube to melt without doing anything to it. This will give children something on which to base their predictions.
- You may want to have children work in cooperative groups of 3. Suggest that one child act as timekeeper, one as recorder, and the third as tester. Children can use Lab Manual page 37.

Safety Note *Caution children not to put ice cubes in their mouths to melt them.*

Reading Assist *Decoding Words*

Remind children that when they see the *vowel-consonant-e* pattern in words such as *time, cube,* and *ice,* the vowel is long and the *e* is silent.

What to Expect

Children will discover that the method producing the most heat will melt the ice cube the fastest.

Assess and Extend

Answers to Think About Your Results

1. Answers may include putting it under their arm, placing it in the sunlight, breathing on it, and so on.
2. Answers may include putting it in the sun, breaking it into pieces and then putting it in the sun.

Inquire Further

Answers may vary but could include breaking it up and then putting it in the sun.

Enrichment

Suggest that children compare the time it takes to melt two ice cubes. One cube is a whole cube and the other cube has been broken into pieces.

Higher Order Thinking *Infer*

Ask: **Which would take longer, freezing water into an ice cube or melting an ice cube into water? Why?** (*Answers will vary based on children's experiences with freezing and melting.*)

Lab Manual

How fast can you melt an ice cube?

Prediction

I predict the ice cube will melt in ____________ minutes.

Plan

To make my ice cube melt, I will ____________

Draw your starting and ending times.

Start End

Results

The ice cube melted in ____________ minutes.

Lab Manual p. 37

Activity Rubric

Use the following activity scoring rubric to assess students' performance.

Scoring Criteria	1	2	3	4
Student followed directions to complete the activity.				
Student predicted how long it would take to melt an ice cube.				
Student developed a plan to facilitate the melting of the ice cube.				
Student compared actual results with prediction.				
Student presented the results of the investigation.				

Scoring Key

4 points correct, complete, detailed
3 points partially correct, complete, detailed
2 points partially correct, partially complete, lacks some detail
1 point incorrect or incomplete, needs assistance

Lab Manual p. T13

Call 1-888-537-4908 with your Activity questions or comments.

Science Center

Flip Chart

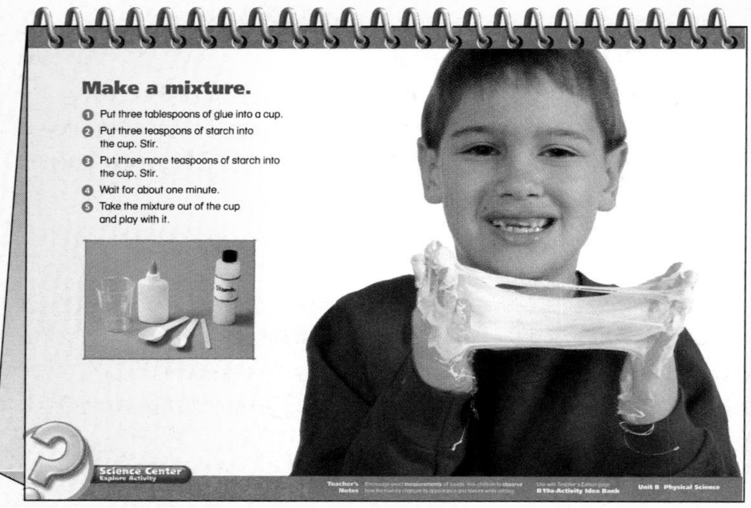

Make a mixture.

Objective

Observe how matter can change when mixing things together.

Process Skills measuring, observing

Materials

Kit Items liquid starch, 10-ounce plastic cup

School-Supplied Items white glue, craft sticks, measuring spoons

Safety Note *Be sure that children wash their hands after the activity.*

Procedure

- Help children **measure** the glue and the starch. Tell them to keep stirring until the mixture thickens.
- Have children **observe** how the mixture changes when they add starch to the glue.
- You can use **Lab Manual** page 38 with this activity.
- ***Teaching Tip*** In order for the mixture to be the right consistency—rubbery but soft—children must follow the steps in order.

Lab Manual

Make a mixture.

Write what each material feels like and looks like.
Draw a picture of each material.

Material	Description	Picture
Glue		
Starch		
Mixture		

Lab Manual, p. 38

Connections

School and Community

Ideas for bringing the school and community together:

Field Trips

- science museum
- cafeteria kitchen
- cement factory
- power plant

Guest Speakers

- pharmacist
- chemist
- bricklayer
- baker or chef

Themes

The activities on these pages can be used with classroom themes such as:

- cooking
- changes
- weather

Books for Children

Children might enjoy these books about matter:

Experiment with Air by Bryan Murphy. Simple experiments that demonstrate the basic principles of air. (Lerner, ISBN 0-8225-2452-X)

Feel the Wind by Arthur Dorros. What causes wind and its effect on our environment. Includes instructions to make a weather vane. (HarperCollins, ISBN 0-06-445095-3)

Cross-Curricular Options

LITERATURE

The Puddle Pail

Use the book to discuss changes in matter.

Materials *The Puddle Pail* by Elisa Kleven. (Dutton, ISBN 0-525-45803-4)

Procedure

- Blue crocodile Ernst dreams of collecting puddles, clouds, and stars. His green brother, Sol, collects feathers and seashells.
- After reading, ask: **Why can't you collect clouds or stars or puddles? If you could collect puddles, how might your collection change? What kinds of solids can you collect?**
- Have children draw conclusions about how liquids take the shape of their containers.

Multiple Intelligences linguistic

Measuring Matter

Demonstrate changes in matter.

Materials plastic bowl, measuring cup, spoon, flour, salt, water, food coloring

Procedure

- Display the recipe for play dough.
- As children measure the ingredients, encourage them to identify the kinds of matter. As they mix, talk about how matter changes.
- When the dough is ready, children can use it to make sculptures.

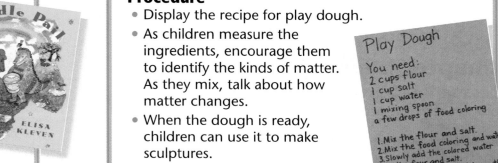

Play Dough
You need:
2 cups flour
1 cup salt
1 cup water
1 mixing spoon
a few drops of food coloring
1. Mix the flour and salt.
2. Mix the food coloring and water.
3. Slowly add the colored water to the four and salt.
4. Knead the dough until smooth.

Multiple Intelligences
logical-mathematical

Gifted and Talented
Ask children to double, then triple the recipe.

Landforms

Write about solid, liquid, and gas in nature.

Materials magazine pictures of outdoor scenes, paper, pencil

Procedure

- Display pictures of landforms, including mountains, plains, beaches, lakes, rivers, and oceans, as well as the sky. Name each one.
- Ask children to write sentences about the forms of matter they see, for example: *A mountain is a solid. The ocean is a liquid.*

Multiple Intelligences linguistic

Paper Fun

Make an origami cup.

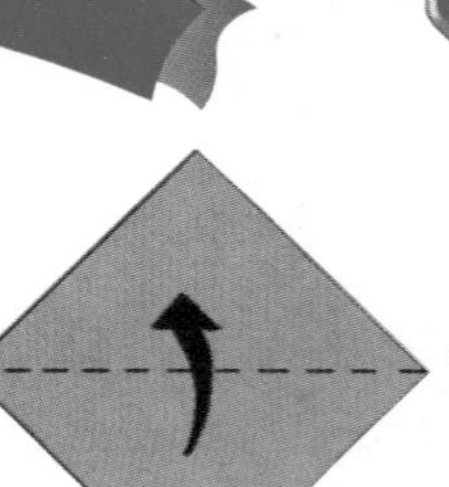

Materials squares of white paper, water

Procedure

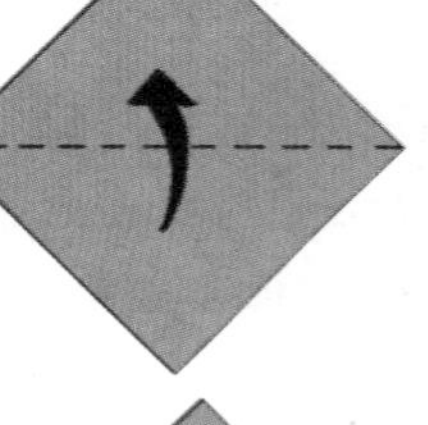

- Help children fold a sheet of square paper in half diagonally.
- Fold the left corner so it touches the right side; fold the right corner so it touches the left side.

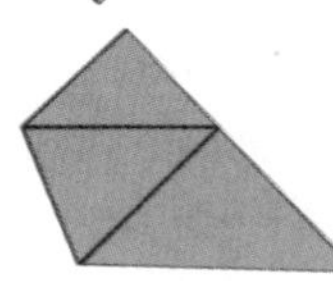

- Fold each of the top flaps over their respective sides.
- Open the cup, fill with water, and drink.

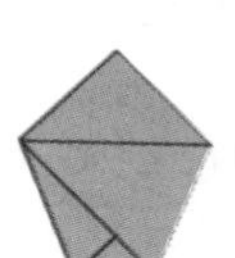

- Encourage children to talk about how the paper changed.

Multiple Intelligences spatial

Special Needs Children with limited physical ability may find it helpful to dictate instructions to a partner who can construct the paper cup.

Review Organizer

Materials

Kit Items none

School-Supplied Items paper, pencil

Time about 30 minutes

Grouping small groups

Additional Resources

- Chapter 1 Assessment: Teacher's Assessment Package

Chapter Main Ideas

Lesson 1 Objects can be sorted according to properties: color, size, shape, weight, texture.

Lesson 2 Matter is anything that takes up space and has weight.

Lesson 3 The states of matter are solid, liquid, and gas. A solid has definite volume and shape. A liquid takes the shape of its container. A gas can change shape and volume.

Lesson 4 Matter can be mixed.

Lesson 5 Matter can change from one state to another.

Lesson 6 Heat melts ice. The more heat that is applied, the faster the ice melts.

Reviewing Science Words

1. A ball is round and can bounce.
2. Matter is anything that takes up space and has weight.
3. The states of matter are solid, liquid, and gas.
4. Possible answers: furniture, books, toys
5. When you pour a liquid into a container, it takes the shape of the container.
6. When you fill a balloon, the gas takes the size and shape of the balloon.

Reviewing Science Ideas

1. Children might mention solids mixed together, as in a salad. They might mention liquids mixed together, as in oil and vinegar. They might mention a solid mixed with a liquid, as in lemonade.
2. Heat can change matter by causing it to melt.

Chapter 1 Review

Reviewing Science Words

1. What are some **properties** of a ball?
2. What is **matter**?
3. What are the **states of matter**?
4. List some things that are **solids**.
5. What happens to a **liquid** when you pour it into a different container?
6. What happens to the shape of a **gas** when you fill a balloon?

Reviewing Science Ideas

1. Give an example of two kinds of matter mixed together.
2. How can heat change matter?

Technology

 Children can review *Matter* with the **Practice & Assessment CD-ROM.**

 Children can use the **Production Studio** to show what they've learned about *Matter.*

 Children can use The KnowZone™ at **www.kz.com** to review and test their science knowledge.

 You can use **TestWorks™** to customize assessment for your children.

Play a guessing game.

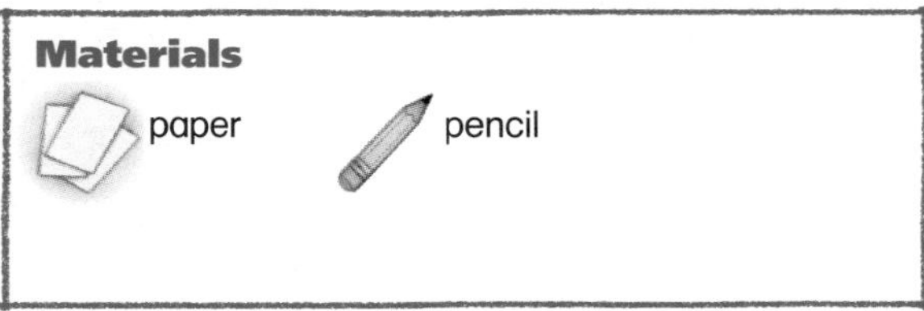

1. Think of an object. Keep it a secret.
2. Write down clues about your object. Your clues should include some properties of your object and its state of matter.
3. Read your clues aloud. Give your group ten tries to guess your object.

Performance Assessment Teaching Tips

- Before children play the guessing game, review the states of matter and properties of objects.
- After children state their clues, ask questions such as the following to cover properties that were not addressed: **What state of matter is your object? What color is your object?**

Enrichment

Post a clue card for a secret object of the day. For example: "My object is a solid. It is purple. It is about 3 paper clips long. It is light. It floats. What is my object?" (*purple crayon*) Have children write their answers on index cards and leave them in an answer box. Near the end of the day, read the clue card. Then read and discuss the answer cards.

Chapter 1 Skills Trace

Process Skills Development	Observing	Predicting
Skill Introduced	xiv	xv
Skill Applied	B 9 B 11 B 15 B 18–B 19	B 11 B 18–B 19
Skill Assessed	End Matter 6–7	End Matter 16–17

Chapter Review pages are also on the **Flip Chart.**

Chapter Assessment

Draw a circle around the object described in the sentence.

1. This object is round and has stripes.

2. This object is large and floats.

Complete each sentence with one of these words: gas, solid, or liquid.

3. A ________ has a size and shape of its own.
4. A ________ can be poured.
5. When a ________ melts, it becomes a liquid.
6. A ________ can change size and shape.

Draw a circle around the picture in each group that is a different state of matter.

7.   

8. 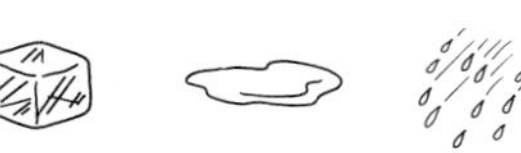

Teacher's Assessment Package pp. 23–24

Assessment Rubric

	Matter
4	Correctly identifies the properties of an object and its state of matter.
3	Makes a few errors in identifying the properties of an object and its state of matter.
2	Has trouble identifying the properties of an object and its state of matter.
1	Cannot identify the properties of an object or its state of matter.

Chapter 2 Planning Guide

Lesson/Activity and Flip Chart	Objectives/Process Skills	Time Options/Activity Materials
Chapter Opener Student Edition pp. B22–B23 and **Flip Chart** *They're All Around*		**Have less time?** Use the Graphic Organizer on Teacher's Assessment Package p. 27 for an overview of the lessons. Use the Flip Chart to teach lesson concepts and science activities. **Have more time?** Use the Flip Chart to reinforce and extend lesson concepts and activities. Use the Cross-Curricular Options in the Activity Idea Bank on Teacher's Edition pp. B27b, B31b, and B39b.
Lesson 1 Student Edition pp. B24–B25 ***How can you make sounds?*** **Explore Activity** ***Make sounds.*** **Flip Chart** ***Talk About Science***	**Objectives** • Learn how to make sounds and change volume. • Learn that sound is produced when objects vibrate. **Process Skills** observing	**Kit Items** none **School-Supplied Items** classroom objects such as pencils, rulers, blocks, crayons
Lesson 2 Student Edition pp. B26–B27 ***What is pitch?*** **Explore Activity** ***Make a pitch finder.*** **Flip Chart** ***Talk About Science***	**Objective** Learn to identify high and low sounds and ways to change pitch. **Process Skills** observing, classifying	**Kit Items** rubber band **School-Supplied Items** safety goggles, book, pencil
Activity Idea Bank Teacher's Edition pp. B27a–B27b **Flip Chart** **Science Center Explore Activity** ***Explore sounds.***	**Objective** Explore ways to change the sound made when a can is tapped by a pencil. **Process Skills** controlling variables	**Kit Items** none **School-Supplied Items** different-size cans; classroom objects such as pencils, cotton, and paper wads
Lesson 3 Student Edition pp. B28–B29 ***What are some sources of heat?*** **Flip Chart** ***Talk About Science***	**Objectives** • Identify sources of heat. • Identify materials that conduct heat.	**Have more time?** Use the following teaching guide option: Interactive Transparency 5, Interactive Transparency Package
Lesson 4 Student Edition pp. B30–B31 and **Flip Chart** **Investigate Activity** ***Which container will warm up fastest?***	**Objective** Determine that some materials conduct heat better than others. **Process Skills** observing, predicting	**Kit Items** foam cup, plastic cup, aluminum-foil pan, 3 thermometers **School-Supplied Items** metal can, water, masking tape (*to cover cut edges of can*), clock **Advance Prep** Prepare recording sheets in advance.
Activity Idea Bank Teacher's Edition pp. B31a–B31b **Flip Chart** **Science Center Explore Activity** ***Measure temperature.***	**Objective** Measure heat. **Process Skills** observing	**Kit Items** thermometer **School-Supplied Items** paper, pencil
Lesson 5 Student Edition pp. B32–B33 ***What are some sources of light?*** **Flip Chart** ***Talk About Science***	**Objectives** • Identify sources of light. • Learn that sources of light also give off heat.	
Reading for Science Student Edition pp. B34–B35 ***Using a Word Web***	**Objective** Use a word web.	
Lesson 6 Student Edition pp. B36–B37 ***How does light move?*** **Explore Activity** ***Go on a scavenger hunt.*** **Flip Chart** ***Talk About Science***	**Objectives** • Learn that light travels in a straight line. • Learn what happens when light strikes an object. **Process Skills** observing	**Kit Items** flashlight, 2 batteries **School-Supplied Items** none **Advance Prep** Make sure you have some of the following items available for the scavenger hunt: mirror or foil, hand lens or eyeglasses, cellophane or other transparent items, books or other solid items.
Lesson 7 Student Edition pp. B38–B39 and **Flip Chart** **Experiment Activity** ***Experiment with shadows.***	**Objective** Experiment to determine how changing an object's distance from a light source changes the size of its shadow. **Process Skills** experimenting, observing (formulative hypotheses, identifying and controlling variables, collecting data)	**Kit Items** flashlight, 2 batteries **School-Supplied Items** small toy or classroom object
Activity Idea Bank Teacher's Edition pp. B39a–B39b **Flip Chart** **Science Center Explore Activity** ***Play a mirror game.***	**Objective** Try to draw a path through a maze by looking at its reflection in a mirror. **Process Skills** observing	**Kit Items** none **School-Supplied Items** simple outline maze of a star, pencil, folder, hand mirror
Chapter Review Student Edition pp. B40–B41 and **Flip Chart**		**Kit Items** none **School-Supplied Items** magazines or catalogs, scissors, glue

Lesson/Activity and Flip Chart	Additional Resources		Technology
Chapter Opener Student Edition pp. B22–B23 and **Flip Chart** ***They're All Around***	**Teacher's Assessment Package** • Graphic Organizer, p. 27 **Instructional Resources** • Family Activity, pp. 33–34 • Vocabulary Preview, p. 35	**Songs & Activities Package** • *They're All Around*, pp. 17–18 **Wall Chart,** p. 23	**Practice & Assessment CD-ROM** **AudioText** **Production Studio** **www.sfscience.com** **Songs & Activities Package** **Teacher's Resource Planner CD-ROM**
Lesson 1 Student Edition pp. B24–B25 ***How can you make sounds?*** **Explore Activity** ***Make sounds.*** **Flip Chart** ***Talk About Science***	**Lab Manual** • Lab Manual, p. 39 • Activity Rubric, p. T14	**Teacher Demonstration Kit**	
Lesson 2 Student Edition pp. B26–B27 ***What is pitch?*** **Explore Activity** ***Make a pitch finder.*** **Flip Chart** ***Talk About Science***	**Lab Manual** • Lab Manual, p. 40 • Activity Rubric, p. T14	**Teacher Demonstration Kit**	
Activity Idea Bank Teacher's Edition pp. B27a–B27b **Flip Chart** **Science Center Explore Activity** ***Explore sounds.***	**Lab Manual** • Lab Manual, p. 41 • Activity Rubric, p. T15		
Lesson 3 Student Edition pp. B28–B29 ***What are some sources of heat?*** **Flip Chart** ***Talk About Science***	**Interactive Transparency Package** • Interactive Transparency 5		
Lesson 4 Student Edition pp. B30–B31 and **Flip Chart** **Investigate Activity** ***Which container will warm up fastest?***	**Lab Manual** • Lab Manual, pp. 43–44 • Activity Rubric, p. T15	**Teacher Demonstration Kit**	*Physical Science* **Activity Video**
Activity Idea Bank Teacher's Edition pp. B31a–B31b **Flip Chart** **Science Center Explore Activity** ***Measure temperature.***	**Lab Manual** • Lab Manual, p. 45 • Activity Rubric, p. T16		
Lesson 5 Student Edition pp. B32–B33 ***What are some sources of light?*** **Flip Chart** ***Talk About Science***		**Wall Chart,** p. 24	
Reading for Science Student Edition pp. B34–B35 ***Using a Word Web***	**Instructional Resources** • Reading for Science, p. 36		
Lesson 6 Student Edition pp. B36–B37 ***How does light move?*** **Explore Activity** ***Go on a scavenger hunt.*** **Flip Chart** ***Talk About Science***	**Lab Manual** • Lab Manual, p. 46 • Activity Rubric, p. T16	**Teacher Demonstration Kit** **Wall Chart,** p. 25	
Lesson 7 Student Edition pp. B38–B39 and **Flip Chart** **Experiment Activity** ***Experiment with shadows.***	**Lab Manual** • Lab Manual, pp. 47–48 • Activity Rubric, p. T17	**Teacher Demonstration Kit** **Wall Chart,** p. 26	*Physical Science* **Activity Video**
Activity Idea Bank Teacher's Edition pp. B39a–B39b **Flip Chart** **Science Center Explore Activity** ***Play a mirror game.***	**Lab Manual** • Lab Manual, p. 49 • Activity Rubric, p. T17		
Chapter Review Student Edition pp. B40–B41 and **Flip Chart**	**Teacher's Assessment Package** • Chapter 2 Assessment, pp. 29–30		**Practice & Assessment CD-ROM** **Production Studio** **The KnowZone™ at www.kz.com** **TestWorks™**

Lab Manual

How can you make sounds?

Draw some ways to make sounds.
Label each way. You can use the word bank to help.

Students' drawings to illustrate ways to make sounds.

Lab Manual
p. 39

Lab Manual

What is pitch?

Draw a pencil and a rubber band on each pitch finder. Show where you plucked to make high and low sounds.

Students' drawings should show a rubber band around the book with a pencil under it. A higher sound is made on the short side of the rubber band. A lower sound is made on the long side.

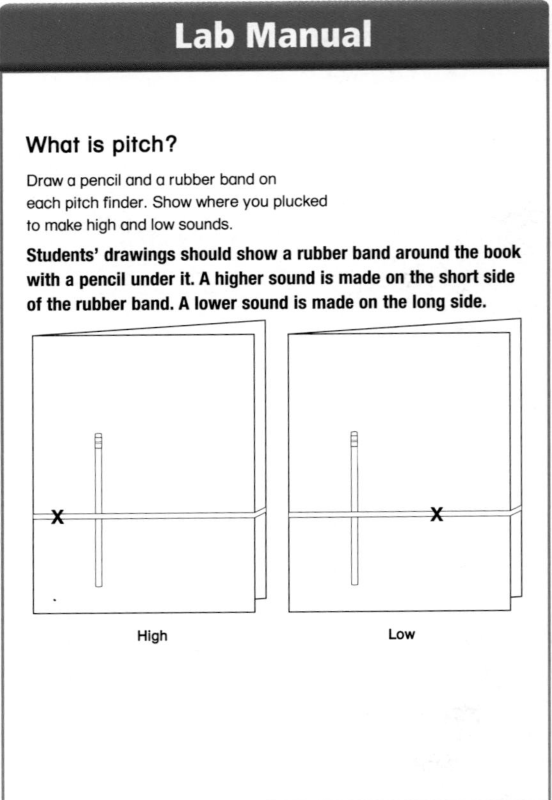

Lab Manual
p. 40

Lab Manual

Explore sounds.

Write what you did to change the sound.
Write what happened each time.

What I did	What happened
The changes students made to their cans will influence the kinds of sounds they described.	

Lab Manual
p. 41

Transparency

Sources of Heat

Interactive Transparency Package
Transparency 5

Lab Manual

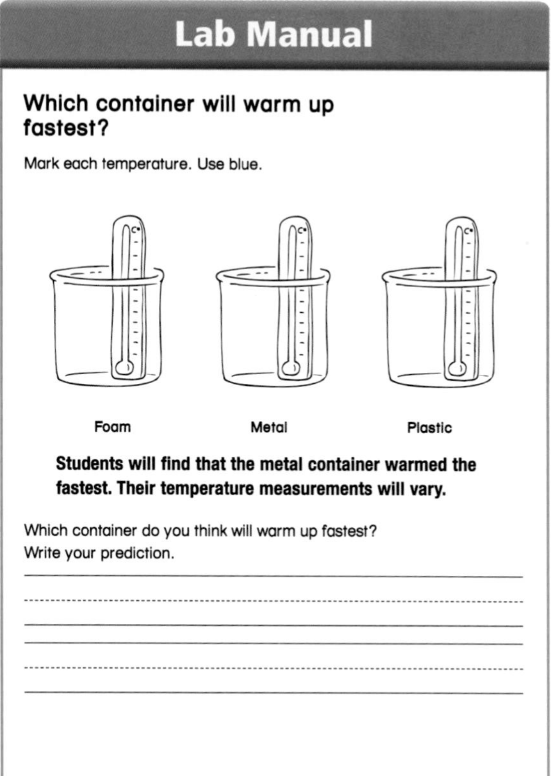
Which container will warm up fastest?

Mark each temperature. Use blue.

Students will find that the metal container warmed the fastest. Their temperature measurements will vary.

Which container do you think will warm up fastest?
Write your prediction.

Lab Manual
p. 43

Lab Manual

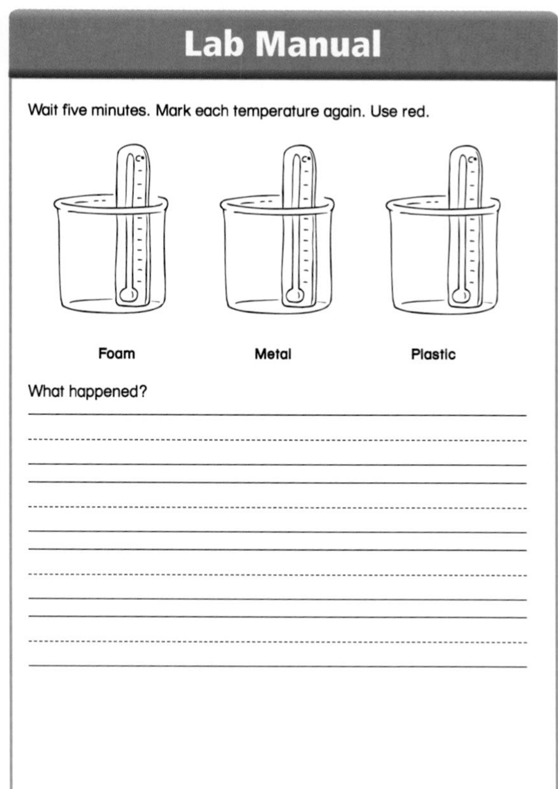
Wait five minutes. Mark each temperature again. Use red.

What happened?

Lab Manual
p. 44

Lab Manual

Measure temperature.

Write ways you changed the temperature.
Write each temperature.

What I did	Temperature
Students' methods for warming the thermometer will vary.	

Lab Manual
p. 45

Reading for Science

Using a Word Web

Complete each word web. **Answers may va**

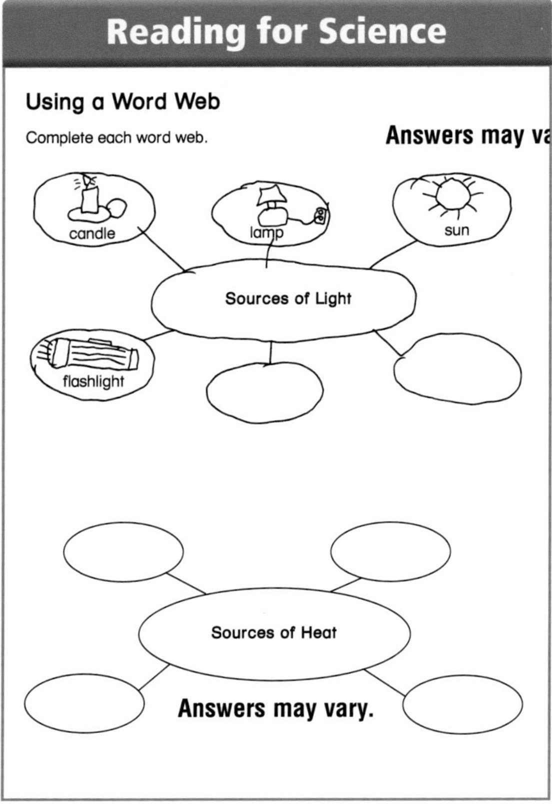

Sources of Heat

Answers may vary.

Instructional Resources
p. 36

Lab Manual

How does light move?

Draw or write the name of each object you found.

Light passes through

Light is blocked by

Movement of light

Light bounces off

Light bends going through

Students' answers will vary. Examples might include: Light passes through a window and glass; light is blocked by solids such as books and buildings; light bounces off mirrors and shiny objects; light bends going through water or a prism.

Lab Manual
p. 46

Lab Manual

Experiment with shadows.

Problem

How can you change the size of a shadow?
Share your ideas with a friend.

Give Your Hypothesis

If you move an object farther from a light, will the shadow get larger or smaller? Write what you think.

Control the Variables

Make sure you keep your flashlight steady.

Test Your Hypothesis

Follow the steps to do the experiment.
Observe both shadows.

Students' hypotheses will vary. Students should conclude that the closer the object is to the light, the larger the shadow. Students can change the size of the shadow by altering the distance of either the object or the light source to each other.

Lab Manual
p. 47

Lab Manual

Collect Your Data

Draw pictures to show the size of each shadow.

Close to the light	Far from the light

Tell Your Conclusion

How can you change the size of a shadow?

Inquire Further

In what other ways can you change the shadow?

Lab Manual
p. 48

Lab Manual

Play a mirror game.

Use a mirror to draw around the maze.
Try not to touch the lines.

Lab Manual
p. 49

Chapter 2 Assessment

Draw a circle around the word that finishes each sentence.

1. **Light** from the sun is made up of many colors.

   Sound Shadows Light

2. **Heat** can be made when you rub objects together.

   Heat Light Shadows

3. When a guitar string vibrates, it makes **sound**.

   heat light sound

Write Yes or No.

Yes 4. Heat passes quickly through metal.

Yes 5. The sun is a source of light.

Yes 6. The pitch of a sound can be high or low.

No 7. Light bends passing through a clear window.

Teacher's Assessment Package p. 29

Chapter 2 Assessment

Look at each picture. Follow the directions.

8. Draw a circle around three things that make light.

9. Draw a circle around three things that make heat.

10. Draw a circle around three things that make sound.

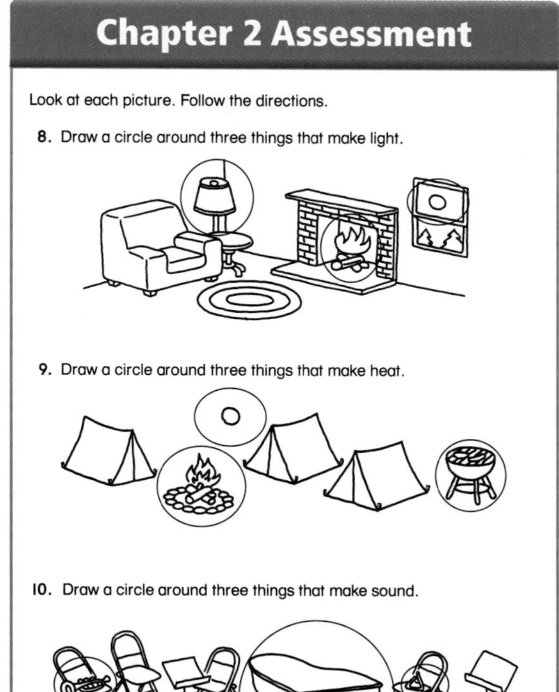

Teacher's Assessment Package p. 30

Table of Contents

Introducing the Chapter

The song *They're All Around* also is on the **Flip Chart.**

- Ask children where they notice sound, heat, and light in their daily lives. Tell children that in this chapter they will learn more about sound, heat, and light.
- Distribute the Family Activity blackline master page.

Singing the Song

Have children sing the song *They're All Around* on side 1 of the CTW cassette. Distribute pages 17–18 from the CTW Song and Activity Book.

Reading Assist *Contractions*

Write the words *they are* and *they're* on the chalkboard. Explain that *they're* is a contraction. A contraction is made by putting two words together. The apostrophe takes the place of the letters that are taken out. Ask children to find other contractions in the song. (*it's, you'll*)

Vocabulary Preview

Use the Vocabulary Preview blackline master to introduce the vocabulary words for this chapter.

Lesson 1 vibrate, volume
Lesson 2 pitch
Lesson 3 source

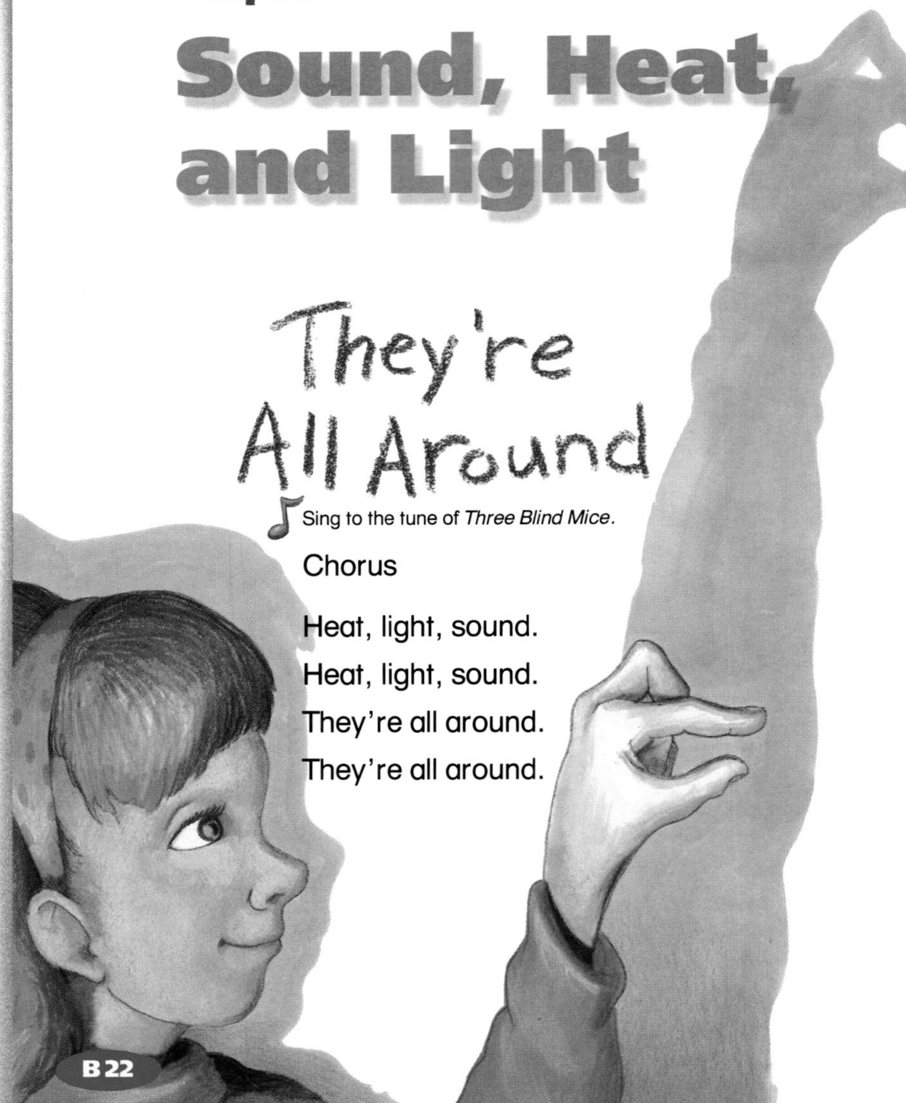

Sing to the tune of *Three Blind Mice*.

Technology

 **Practice & Assessment CD-ROM** 

 **AudioText**

 **Production Studio**

 **www.sfscience.com**

 **Teacher's Resource Planner**

 **Songs & Activities Package**

CTW Song & Activity

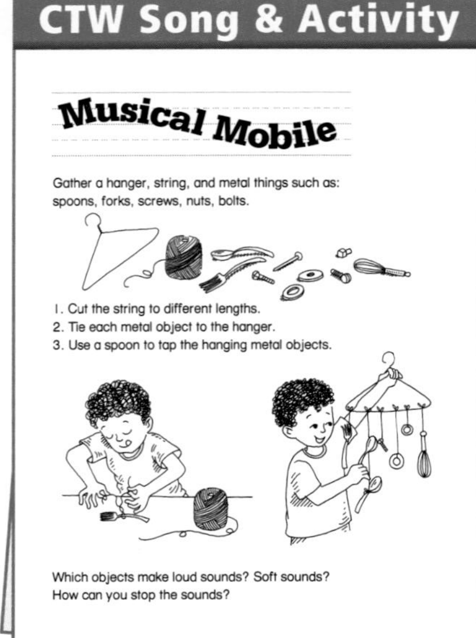

Musical Mobile
Gather a hanger, string, and metal things such as: spoons, forks, screws, nuts, bolts.
1. Cut the string to different lengths.
2. Tie each metal object to the hanger.
3. Use a spoon to tap the hanging metal objects.
Which objects make loud sounds? Soft sounds? How can you stop the sounds?

Songs & Activities Package pp. 17–18

What could you do to make some heat?
Try rubbing your hands as you hear the beat.
Then touch your face, you can feel the heat.

Sing the chorus.

When you block the light what comes into view?
It's something different, it's something new.
It's a special shadow made just by you.

Sing the chorus.

What are some ways you can make a sound?
Tap a glass with a spoon, give a pillow a pound.
Or pluck a string and you'll hear a sound.

Sing the chorus.

Original lyrics by Gerri Brioso and Richard Freitas.
Produced by Children's Television Workshop.

B23

Family Activity

Science at Home

Dear Family:
Our class is starting Chapter 2. We will be learning about sound, heat, and light. These are the main ideas for Chapter 2.
- Sounds are made by vibrating objects.
- The pitch of a sound can be high or low.
- Heat has many sources.
- Objects such as the sun and fire create light.
- Light moves in straight lines.

We will also be learning science vocabulary words for Chapter 2. By the end of Chapter 2, we will be able to read the vocabulary words and tell what they mean.

Word Bank
vibrate
volume
pitch
source

Home Projects

Here are some activities that will help your child understand the main ideas in Chapter 2. The activities are easy, fast, and fun.

Activities

- With your child listen to the radio and identify the pitches of your favorite artists' voices. Have your child identify high and low sounding voices.

Instructional Resources pp. 33–34

Vocabulary Preview

vibrate	volume
pitch	heat source
light source	experiment
rainbow	shadow

Instructional Resources p. 35

INQUIRY

Use a KWL chart at the beginning of each new chapter to encourage inquiry. In the *K* column, record what children already *know* about sound, heat, and light. In the *W* column, help children brainstorm a list of what they *want* to know. Throughout the chapter, ask children what they have *learned* and record their responses in the *L* column. A KWL chart is available in the **Wall Chart** page 23.

Chapter 2 Skills Trace

Process Skills Development	Observing	Classifying	Predicting	Experimenting
Skill Introduced	xiv	xiv	xv	xv
Skill Applied	B25 B27 B30–B31 B37 B38–B39	B27	B30–B31	B38–B39
Skill Assessed	End Matter 6–7	End Matter 10–11	End Matter 16–17	End Matter 28–29

Science Literature Library

Annie's Gifts
by Angela Shelf Medearis.
Everyone in Annie's family loved music. More that anything else, Annie wanted to make music, but no matter how hard she tried, she just couldn't play an instrument. In this story, Annie discovers that different people have different talents; she realizes she has her own special gifts and they are important too. (Just Us Books, ISBN 0-940975-319)

ANNIE'S GIFTS
by Angela Shelf Medearis
Illustrated by Anna Rich

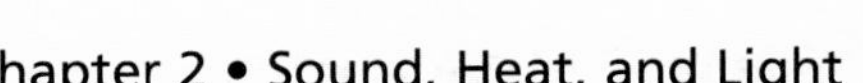

Lesson Organizer

Objectives

- Learn how to make sounds and change volume.
- Learn that sound is produced when objects vibrate.

Process Skills observing

Vocabulary vibrate, volume

Materials

Kit Items none

School-Supplied Items classroom objects such as pencils, rulers, blocks, crayons

Additional Resources

- Lab Manual
- Teacher Demonstration Kit

Introduce

Activate Prior Knowledge

Have children sit quietly and listen to sounds around them. Ask what sounds they hear.

Language Development *Vocabulary*

Point out that the words *vibrate* and *vibration* are in the same word family; *vibrate* is an action word, a verb, *vibration* is a naming word, a noun.

Flip Chart

Name things on the **Flip Chart** that produce sounds. (*birds, train, ambulance, whistle, and so on*)

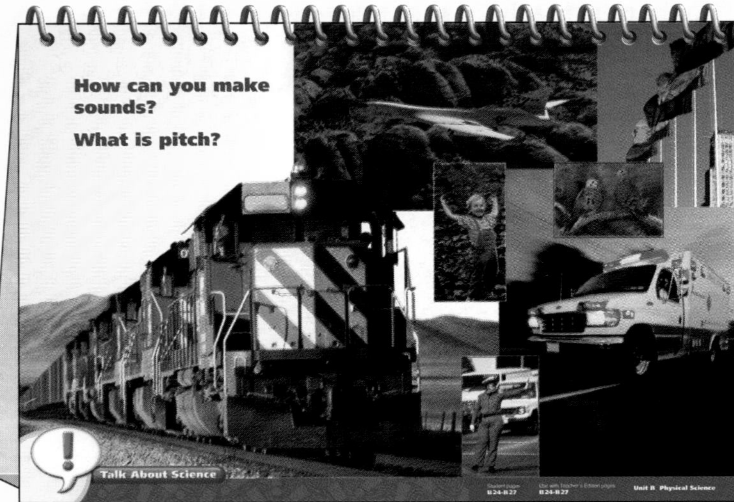

How can you make sounds?

Bang! Whir! What made those sounds? A balloon popped. Someone blew a noisemaker. What a noisy party!

There are many ways to make sounds. Sound is made when an object vibrates. **Vibrate** means to move back and forth. What objects in the picture vibrate to make sound?[1]

Volume is how loud or soft a sound is. What loud and soft sounds have you heard?

Talk about the picture. What other sounds would you hear at a party? How would you describe these sounds?

Science Background

- When matter vibrates, the vibrations produce waves of sound energy. Sound waves travel through matter.
- Applying greater force or energy to matter creates stronger vibrations and therefore stronger sound waves.
- The strength of a sound wave is known as its intensity. A sound wave with high intensity carries more energy than a sound wave with low intensity.

Science Across Cultures Many cultures celebrate birthdays or other important events. Have children tell or write about celebrations that are part of their culture. Ask children what kinds of sounds, such as music, are part of these celebrations.

Explore Activity

Make sounds.

Materials

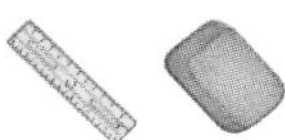  objects from your desk

Process Skills

- observing

Process Skills

Steps

1. Have your partner cover his or her eyes.
2. Use objects from your desk to make a sound. Ask your partner to **observe** by listening.
3. Have your partner guess how you made the sound.
4. Take turns.

Share. Draw some ways to make sounds.

Lesson Review

1. How are sounds made?
2. What is volume?
3. **Tell** how you can change the volume of a sound.

B25

Lab Manual

How can you make sounds?

Draw some ways to make sounds.
Label each way.

Lab Manual
p. 39

Activity Rubric

Use the following activity scoring rubric to assess students' performance.

Scoring Criteria	1	2	3	4
Student followed directions to complete this activity.				
Student used a word bank to identify types of sounds that can be made.				
Student drew four ways he or she could make sounds.				
Student distinguished a variety of sounds that he or she could make.				
Student presented a variety of sound-producing activities in a visual format.				

Scoring Key
4 points correct, complete, detailed
3 points partially correct, complete, detailed
2 points partially correct, partially complete, lacks some detail
1 point incorrect or incomplete, needs assistance

Lab Manual
p. T14

 **Call 1-888-537-4YOU with your Activity questions or comments.**

Teach and Apply

Student Page B24

Demonstrate how to place your fingers on your throat to feel the vibration of your vocal cords as you speak. You might want to have children place their hands on a radio or tape player that is playing in order to feel vibrations, or place a tuning fork in a beaker of water to watch the vibrations.

Reading Assist *Vowel Sounds*

Write the word sound on the chalkboard and review the /ou/ pronunciation. Have children find other words in this lesson with /ou/. (*loud, sounds*)

Student Page B25

Explore Activity

Time about 15 minutes

Grouping cooperative groups of 2

Encourage children to find many different ways to make sounds, such as tapping, rubbing, and shaking. Children can complete Lab Manual page 39 as they do the activity.

Assess and Extend

Answers to Lesson Review

1. Sounds are made when objects vibrate.
2. Volume is how loud or soft a sound is.
3. **Tell** (*Interview*) Children's answers might include shaking with more or less force, or tapping on a harder or softer surface.

Inquire Further

Ask the following question to guide further inquiry:
What are some other ways to make sounds?

Enrichment

Have children try to find the object their partners used in the activity and make the same sound, louder or softer.

Higher Order Thinking *Apply*

Ask: **How can we control the volume in our classroom?** (*Children might answer that they could speak softly, put objects down gently, and so on.*)

Lesson Organizer

Objective

Learn to identify high and low sounds and ways to change pitch.

Process Skills observing, classifying

Vocabulary pitch

Materials

Kit Items rubber band

School-Supplied Items safety goggles, book, pencil

Additional Resources

- Lab Manual
- Teacher Demonstration Kit

Introduce

Activate Prior Knowledge

Recall the story *The Three Bears.* Ask children to speak in a Baby Bear voice and a Papa Bear voice.

Language Development *Homonyms*

Explain that *pitch* describes the different voices of the bears. Remind children that they know another meaning for *pitch*—to throw a ball.

Flip Chart

Discuss things on the **Flip Chart** that produce sound—what sounds they make and if any change pitch. Ask: **What might it sound like if all the things on the Flip Chart produced sounds with the same pitch?**

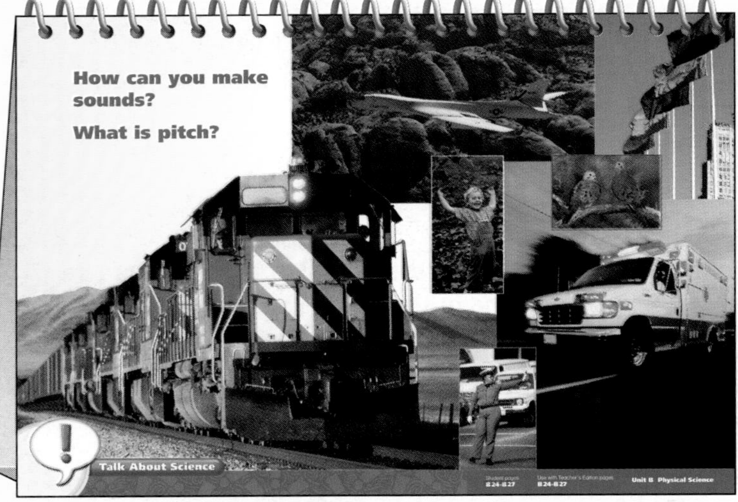
How can you make sounds?
What is pitch?
Talk About Science
Unit B Physical Science

What is pitch?

Sing a song! Hum a tune! Listen to your voice go up and down.

Sounds can be high or low. **Pitch** is how high or low a sound is. What high and low sounds have you heard?

The pitch of a sound can be changed. It can become higher or lower. When you sing, you change the pitch of your voice.

Talk about the sounds these instruments make. How could you change the pitch of each instrument?[1]

[1] Use differe strings, ke and so on

MY SONG BOOK

Science Background

- The pitch of a sound depends on the frequency of the sound waves.
- If an object vibrates more slowly, the sound waves are longer and have a low frequency. They make a sound with a low pitch.
- If an object vibrates more quickly, the sound waves are shorter and have a higher frequency. They make a sound with a higher pitch.

Possible Misconceptions Children may confuse the pitch of a sound with the loudness of a sound. For example, a lion's roar may have a low pitch but a loud sound. An alarm on a watch may have a high pitch but a soft sound.

Make a pitch finder.

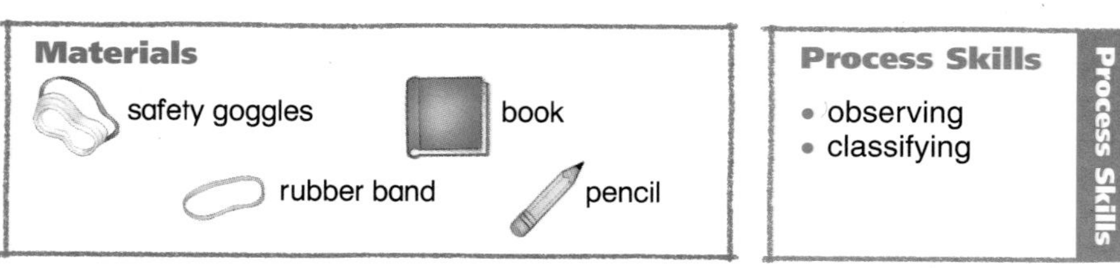

Process Skills

- observing
- classifying

Steps

1. Put on your safety goggles. Make a pitch finder like the one in the picture.
2. Hold the pencil in place. Pluck the rubber band. Observe the sound.
3. Find ways to change the sound. Classify each sound as high or low.

Share. Draw your pitch finder. Show how you made high and low sounds.

Lesson Review

1. What is pitch?
2. How did you change the pitch?
3. **Show** how you can make high and low sounds.

Lab Manual

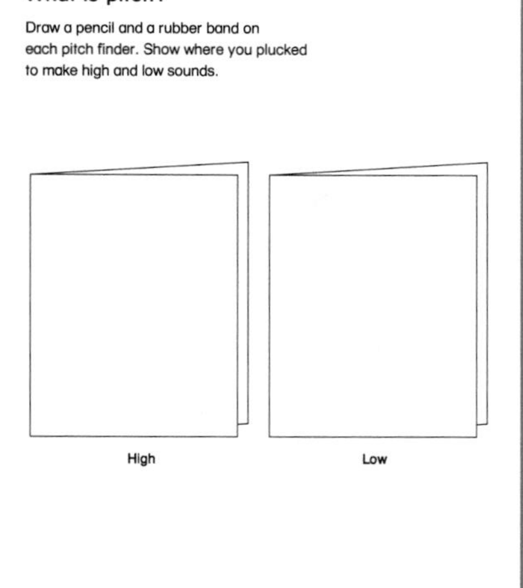
What is pitch?

Draw a pencil and a rubber band on each pitch finder. Show where you plucked to make high and low sounds.

High

Low

Lab Manual
p. 40

Activity Rubric

Use the following activity scoring rubric to assess students' performance.

Scoring Criteria	1	2	3	4
Student followed directions to complete this activity.				
Student drew representations of pitch finders.				
Student observed high and low pitch and learned how to make changes in pitch.				
Student classified sounds according to the quality of high and low.				
Student recorded his or her findings about high and low pitch in a visual representation.				

Scoring Key
4 points correct, complete, detailed
3 points partially correct, complete, detailed
2 points partially correct, partially complete, lacks some detail
1 point incorrect or incomplete, needs assistance

Lab Manual
p. T14

Teach and Apply

Student Page B26

Sing a simple song such as *Twinkle, Twinkle, Little Star.* As children sing, move your hand up and down to reflect high and low pitch.

Reading Assist *Context Clues*
Remind children that they can figure out a new word in their reading by looking at other words and pictures. Ask what clues help them understand the word *instruments* on page B26.

Student Page B27

Explore Activity

Time about 20 minutes

Grouping individual

Children make a simple instrument and change the pitch by moving the pencil and plucking the rubber band. Have children lift the rubber band before moving the pencil. Children can complete Lab Manual page 40.

What to Expect
When children pluck the longer side, the vibrations are slower, so the pitch is lower.

Assess and Extend

Answers to Lesson Review

1. Pitch is how high or low a sound is.
2. Children can change pitch by moving the pencil and plucking the rubber band.
3. **Show** (*Performance Assessment*) Children can pluck the longer side of the rubber band to make a low sound and the shorter side to make a high sound.

Inquire Further

Ask the following question to guide further inquiry: **What would happen if you used a thinner or thicker rubber band?** (*A thinner rubber band will produce a higher sound. A thicker rubber band will produce a lower sound.*)

Higher Order Thinking *Solving Problems*
Ask: **How would you change the pitch on a stringed instrument?** (*Children might answer that they could make the strings longer or shorter, or they could pull the strings tighter.*)

Call 1-888-537-4908 with your Activity questions or comments.

Science Center

Flip Chart

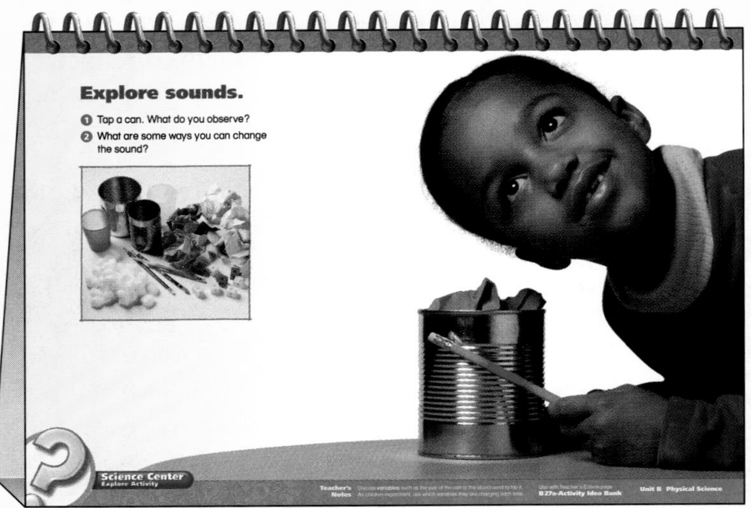

Explore sounds.
1 Tap a can. What do you observe?
2 What are some ways you can change the sound?
Science Center

Explore sounds.

Objective

Explore ways to change the sound made when a can is tapped by a pencil.

Process Skills controlling variables

Materials

Kit Items none

School-Supplied Items different-size cans; classroom objects such as pencils, cotton, paper wads

Safety Note *Cover sharp edges of cans with masking tape.*

Procedure

- Children **control variables,** such as the material they put in the can and the object they tap it with, and observe the sound that results.
- Ask children to record their observations and use them to communicate their discoveries.
- You can use **Lab Manual** page 41 with this activity.

What to Expect

Children discover that putting different objects in the can usually changes the sound and its pitch. The material of the object used to tap the can may change the quality of the sound.

Lab Manual

Explore sounds.

Write what you did to change the sound.
Write what happened each time.

What I did	What happened

Lab Manual, p. 41

Connections

School and Community

Ideas for bringing the school and community together:

Field Trips

- musical performance
- local high school band
- musical instrument store

Guest Speakers

- piano tuner
- musician or band director
- audiologist
- school nurse

Themes

The activities on these pages can be used with classroom themes such as:

- music
- senses
- inventions and inventors

Books for Children

Children might enjoy these books about sound:

Doorbell
by Jan Pienkowski. A pop-up animal kingdom with a button that rings with a "ding-dong" sound of a doorbell. (Price Stern Sloan, ISBN 0-8431-3452-6)

Hearing Sounds With Easy-to-Make Scientific Projects
by Gary Gibson. Hands-on experiments that help explain sound, vibrations, and pitch. (Copper Beech Books, ISBN 1-56294-614-5)

Night Sounds, Morning Colors
by Rosemary Wells. A young boy's experiences as he uses the seasons to explore his senses. (Dial Books, ISBN 0-80371-301-0)

Cross-Curricular Options

LITERATURE

Jonathan Cleaned Up—Then He Heard a Sound

Use the book to explore sound effects.

Materials *Jonathan Cleaned Up—Then He Heard a Sound: Or Blackberry Subway Jam* by Robert N. Munsch. (Annick Press, ISBN 0-920236-20-0)

Procedure

- In this imaginative tale, a young boy is upset because his house has been turned into a subway stop just after cleanup.
- Have children identify all the sounds that Jonathan hears—the people, the subway train, the computer.
- Bring the story to life by having children make sound effects as you read.

Multiple Intelligences linguistic

MUSIC

Making Music

Make a musical instrument.

Materials common objects such as boxes, rubber bands, cardboard tubes, cans, craft sticks, paper plates, plastic bottles, dried beans; safety goggles; scissors

Procedure

- Children make instruments using everyday materials.
- Have children play their instruments and demonstrate how to change the pitch or volume.

Multiple Intelligences musical

Gifted and Talented Challenge children to compose a simple song to perform for the class.

WRITING

Sound Words

Brainstorm sound words and write a story.

Procedure

- Generate a list of sound words with children and classify the words as loud, soft, pleasant, unpleasant, and so on.
- Display the list in the writing center. Encourage children to add words throughout the week.
- Challenge children to write a story using some or all of the words.

Multiple Intelligences linguistic

Special Needs Some children may find it helpful to have the sound words written on cards that they can take to their desks.

LISTENING

Peter and the Wolf

Listen for pitch in a musical recording.

Materials *Peter and the Wolf* recording by Sergei Prokofiev, craft sticks and art supplies

Procedure

- In *Peter and the Wolf,* characters are represented by musical instruments.
- Play the recording. Point out sounds with high and low pitch.
- Ask: **If you could choose an instrument for each animal in the story, which would you choose and why?**
- Children can make stick puppets and act out the story as they listen.

Multiple Intelligences musical, linguistic

Lesson Organizer

Objectives

- Identify sources of heat.
- Identify materials that conduct heat.

Vocabulary source

Additional Resources

- Interactive Transparency

Introduce

Activate Prior Knowledge

Ask children to draw a picture showing one or more things that give off heat. Save their work to use as a **baseline assessment.**

Language Development *Make a List*

Help children brainstorm a list of places where they have felt heat. (*beach, desert, kitchen, and so on*) After completing the lesson, you may want to help children determine the source of heat for each place on the list.

Flip Chart

Have children name sources of heat in the pictures. Ask: **What other heat sources can you think of?** (*candle, hot coals*)

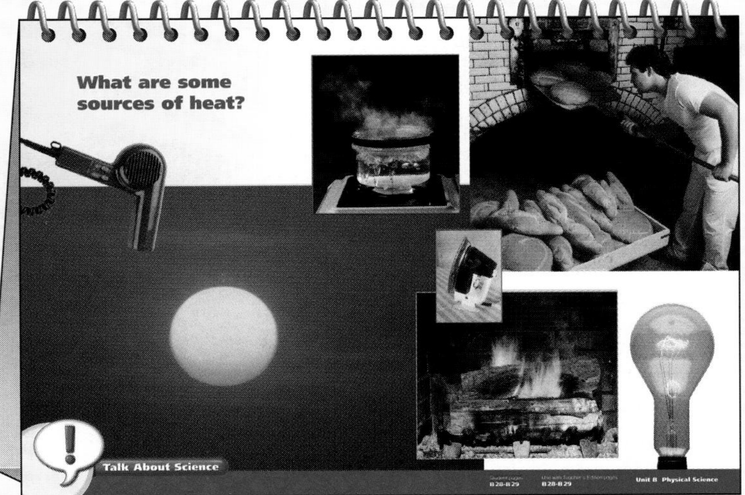

What are some sources of heat?

It is a hot day! Heat comes from the light of the sun. Heat comes from other places too.

Sunlight is a source of heat. A **source** is a place from which something comes. Rubbing things together can produce heat. What heat sources are in the picture?[1] What other heat sources do you know about?

[1] sun, hot c
candle

Science Background

- Heat is the transfer of energy from one substance to another. Matter can be heated by conduction, convection, or radiation.
- During conduction, energy moves from warm objects to the cooler objects that are touching them.
- A moving liquid or gas carries energy during convection. Matter keeps flowing as warm matter rises and cooler matter sinks.
- The sun's energy is a kind of radiation—energy that can move through empty space. Radiation that is absorbed makes an object's particles move faster and become warmer.

You can use heat to cook. Heat moves from warmer places and objects to cooler ones. It moves from the hot fire to the cold food.

Heat moves easily through metal. It does not move easily through wood and cloth. How do the people in the picture protect their hands from the heat?[2]

[2]oven mitt, wooden handle, corn holders

Lesson Review

1. What is a source?
2. What are some sources of heat?
3. **Draw** a picture of food being cooked on a stove. Draw an arrow to show which way the heat moves.

B29

ESL Strategy

Provide sentence frames to help children state questions and answers. For example,
Is _______ a source of heat?
Yes, _______ is a source of heat.

Transparency

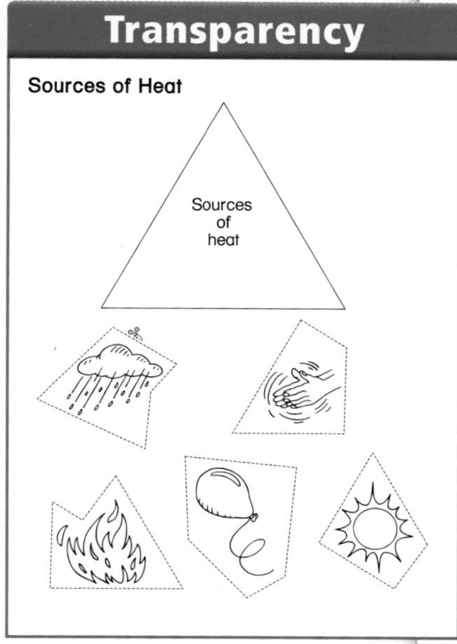

Interactive Transparency Package
Transparency 5

Teach and Apply

Student Pages B28–B29

Discuss sources of heat in children's homes.

Ask children how they have seen people protect themselves from heat in the kitchen. (*Children may mention using pot holders, wooden utensils, and so on.*)

Reading Assist *Vowel Combinations*

Point out the *ou* combination in *source.* Explain that in this word, the letters *our* are pronounced the same as *or.*

Real-World Applications

We use metal pots and pans for cooking, because heat moves easily through metal, thereby heating the food in the pan. Nonmetal materials, such as ceramic, are practical for dishes, as they do not conduct heat as quickly.

Assess and Extend

Answers to Lesson Review

1. A source is a place from which something comes.
2. Some sources of heat are the sun, fire, and rubbing things together.
3. **Draw** (*Portfolio Assessment or Journal*) Children's pictures should show an arrow pointing from the burner up to the pot of food.

Check for Understanding

To follow up on the **baseline assessment,** have children add to their drawings of sources of heat.

Reteach

Use the Interactive Transparency to reteach Lesson 3 concepts.

Activity Organizer

Objective

Determine that some materials conduct heat better than others.

Process Skills observing, predicting

Materials

Kit Items foam cup, plastic cup, aluminum-foil pan, 3 thermometers

School-Supplied Items metal can, water, masking tape (*to cover cut edges of can*), clock

Time about 20 minutes

Grouping cooperative groups of 4

Additional Resources

- Lab Manual
- Teacher Demonstration Kit

Introduce

The Lesson 4 Investigate Activity, *Which container will warm up fastest?*, is also on the **Flip Chart.**

Activate Prior Knowledge

Ask children if they have ever had hot cocoa or other hot drinks. Discuss what kinds of cups they used.

Language Development *Scientific Language*

Explain that a prediction is more than a guess because it is based on what you already know.

Which container will warm up fastest?

Process Skills

Process Skills
- observing
- predicting

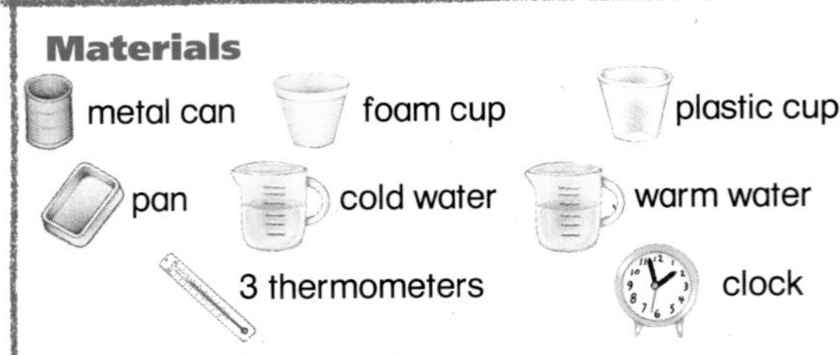

1. Put cold water and a thermometer in each container.
2. Observe each thermometer.
3. Use pictures like the ones shown. Mark the temperature on each picture.

B30

Science Background

Materials through which heat passes easily, such as most metals, are conductors. Materials such as wool, straw, paper, cork, and wood are not good conductors. Poor conductors are insulators.

Teaching Tips Covering the Fahrenheit side will make the thermometer easier to read. Children do not need to read the numbers on the thermometer to mark the temperature. Children should use the same amount of cold water in each container. The cold water in each container should be the same temperature. If children are having difficulty seeing the changes in temperature on the Celsius scale, you may want to have them use the Fahrenheit scale.

Technology

Review the demonstration of this Investigate's procedure on the *Physical Science* **Activity Video,** Segment 2.

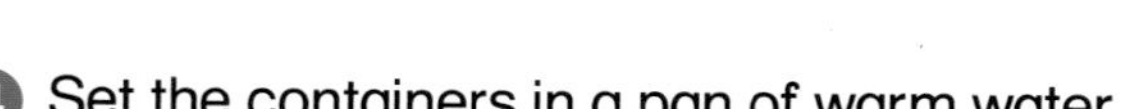

4. Set the containers in a pan of warm water.
5. Which container will warm up fastest? **Predict.**
6. Wait 5 minutes. **Observe** and mark each temperature again.
7. Which container warmed up fastest? Compare your results with your **prediction.**

Think About Your Results

1. Which container warmed up fastest?
2. Does heat move more easily through metal, plastic, or foam? Explain.

Inquire Further

Suppose you wanted to keep ice cubes from melting. What kind of container would you use? Why?

B31

Lab Manual

Which container will warm up fastest?

Mark each temperature. Use blue.

Foam | Metal | Plastic

Which container do you think will warm up fastest?
Write your prediction.

Lab Manual
pp. 43–44

Activity Rubric

Use the following activity scoring rubric to assess students' performance.

Scoring Criteria	1	2	3	4
Student followed directions to complete this activity.				
Student predicted which of three materials would warm up fastest when placed in a pan of warm water.				
Student observed the difference in temperatures over a five-minute period.				
Student measured temperatures and changes for three materials.				
Student explained that heat moves more quickly through some materials than others.				

Scoring Key
4 points correct, complete, detailed
3 points partially correct, complete, detailed
2 points partially correct, partially complete, lacks some detail
1 point incorrect or incomplete, needs assistance

Lab Manual
p. T15

Teach and Apply

- In this activity, children compare foam, metal, and plastic to see which conducts heat best.

Safety Note *Cover cut edges of the cans with masking tape.*

- Children need to have their recording sheets prepared in advance, either in their journals or using Lab Manual pages 43–44.
- Explain that when the line in the thermometer goes up, the temperature is getting warmer.

Reading Assist *Base Words*

Write the word *prediction* on the chalkboard. Show children the base word *predict* and the *-ion* ending.

What to Expect

Children will discover that water in the metal can warms up faster than the water in the cups, because metal conducts heat better than foam or plastic.

Assess and Extend

Answers to Think About Your Results

1. The metal container warmed up fastest.
2. Heat moves more easily through metal than foam or plastic. We know this because the water in the metal can warms up faster than the water in the cups.

Inquire Further

Children might say that they would use a foam cup because the foam cup kept the water coldest.

Enrichment

Try the activity again, using containers of different materials such as paper, ceramic, and glass.

Higher Order Thinking *Apply*

Ask: **If you could have only one cup for both hot and cold drinks, what kind of cup would you use? Why?** (*A foam cup will work well for hot and cold drinks, because heat does not pass through foam easily.*) You may want to point out that foam is not an environmentally friendly product. Have children brainstorm other products that would be a better choice for the environment although not as good an insulator, such as a plastic mug or ceramic mug or paper cup with handle.

Call 1-888-537-4908 with your Activity questions or comments.

Science Center

Flip Chart

Measure temperature.
1 Find ways to make your thermometer get warm.
2 Which way worked the fastest?
3 Which way made the thermometer the warmest?
Science Center

Measure temperature.

Objective

Measure heat.

Process Skills observing

Materials

Kit Items thermometer

School-Supplied Items paper, pencil

Safety Note *Caution children not to squeeze too hard on the thermometer.*

Procedure

- Review with children how to read a thermometer.
- Have children try different ways to make the thermometer get warm.
- Ask children to **observe** the temperature and record the number at which the red line stops.
- You can use **Lab Manual** page 45 with this activity.

What to Expect

Temperatures will rise at varying rates and at different levels, depending on how and where in the classroom the thermometer is handled.

Lab Manual

Measure temperature.

Write ways you changed the temperature.
Write each temperature.

What I did	Temperature

Lab Manual, p. 45

Connections

School and Community

Ideas for bringing the school and community together:

Field Trips

- school cafeteria
- restaurant
- school boiler room
- fire department

Guest Speakers

- fire marshall
- chef
- school cafeteria worker
- school custodian

Themes

The activities on these pages can be used with classroom themes such as:

- foods
- five senses
- inventions
- tools and machines

Books for Children

Children might enjoy these books about heat:

Hot and Cold
by Allan Fowler. This photo essay about hot and cold presents related concepts such as temperature, climates, and changing states of matter. (Childrens Press, ISBN 0-516-06021-X)

Hot or Not?
by Nicola Baxter. Children decide what things are hot, hotter—and not. (Childrens Press, ISBN 0-516-09267-7)

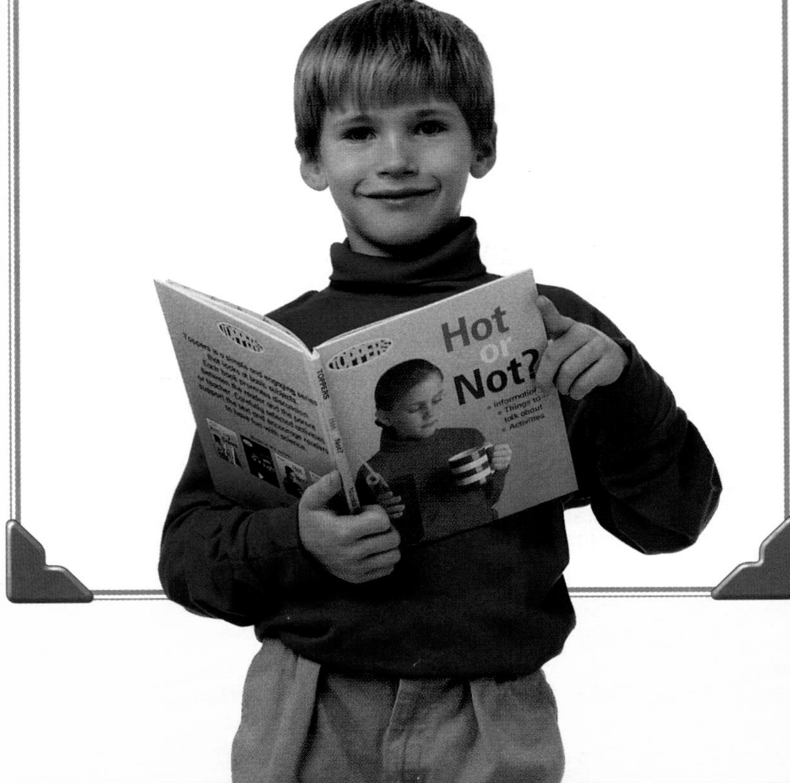

Cross-Curricular Options

LITERATURE

The Magic School Bus Gets Baked in a Cake

Use the book to talk about heat's effects.

Materials *The Magic School Bus Gets Baked in a Cake: A Book About Kitchen Chemistry* by Linda Beech. (Scholastic, ISBN 0-590-22295-3)

Procedure

- Ms. Frizzle's class takes a bus ride inside a birthday cake. They learn about reactions that occur when ingredients are put together and heat is applied.
- Have children describe what happens to the cake mix when the heat is turned on in the oven.
- Have children make up their own story about what happens when heat is applied to something, such as a can of soup or logs in a fireplace.

Multiple Intelligences linguistic

MATH

Outside Temperatures

Measure and record outside temperatures.

Materials Celsius thermometer, large graph grid, pencil

Procedure

- Have children measure the outside air temperature at the same time each day for a week.
- Help them record the information on a bar graph.
- At the end of the week, help children interpret the information on the graph.

Multiple Intelligences logical-mathematical, linguistic

Gifted and Talented Ask children to find the Fahrenheit equivalent of the week's temperatures.

WRITING

Hot Recipes

Write recipes for foods eaten warm.

Materials drawing paper, pencil, crayons

Procedure

- Have children write recipes for their favorite warm foods.
- Remind children to list the ingredients.
- Encourage children to illustrate their recipes.

Multiple Intelligences linguistic

ESL Have children pantomime *mix, pour, stir,* and *measure* to reinforce their understanding of cooking terms.

SOCIAL STUDIES

Let's Eat!

Make a restaurant menu.

Materials drawing paper, crayons

Procedure

- Discuss places people like to eat and foods they eat there.
- Have children focus on foods that are served warm in restaurants. Ask: **How are these foods prepared? Served? Kept warm?**
- Children can create restaurant menus. Have them describe how they would prepare and serve the warm foods.

Multiple Intelligences linguistic

Lesson Organizer

Objectives

- Identify sources of light.
- Learn that sources of light often also give off heat.

Additional Resources

- Wall Chart

Introduce

Activate Prior Knowledge

Ask children to draw or list any sources of light they know about. Save their work to use as a **baseline assessment.**

Language Development *Make a List*

Let children share the lists or drawings they made. Use their ideas to make a big list of "light words" and post it in the classroom.

Flip Chart

Discuss the picture. Ask children to find sources of light.

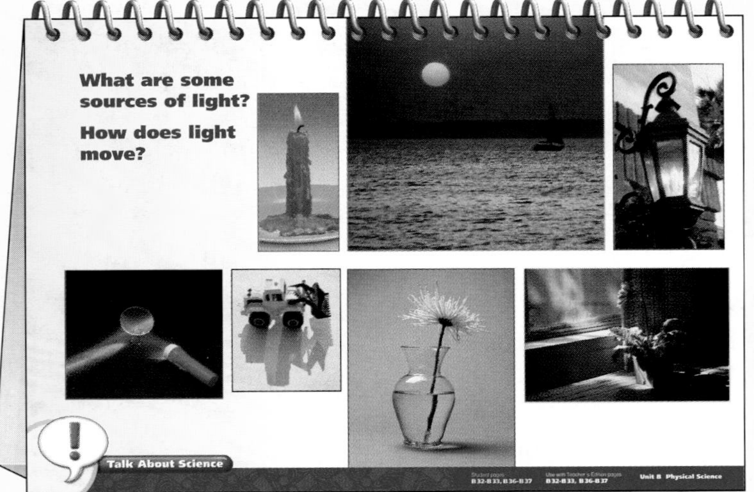

What are some sources of light?

Think about your room at night. What is it like? You probably cannot see very well. You need light in order to see.

Light comes from the sun, fire, and light bulbs. Most light sources also give off heat. What other light sources do you know about?

Talk about these pictures. How are they alike and different?[1] What sources of light do you see?[2]

[1] same sce day and
[2] sun, lam street lig flashligh

B32

Science Background

- Raindrops in the air bend and reflect the light waves coming from the sun. The sunlight is separated into the colors seen in a rainbow.
- The band of colors formed when white light is bent is called the visible spectrum.

Math-Science Connection Have children predict whether there are more light sources in their classroom or in a room at home. Use **Wall Chart** page 24 to tally the light sources in the classroom. Have children tally the light sources in a room at home and write their findings on the chart. Discuss the results.

Technology

Children learn how fireflies make light at **www.sfscience.com**

What does light look like to you? You might be surprised to learn that white light is really made up of many colors.

Sometimes you can see the colors in light after a rainstorm. When sunlight moves through drops of water in the air, the light is separated into the colors of a rainbow. These colors are red, orange, yellow, green, blue, indigo, and violet. What colors do you see in this rainbow?

Lesson Review

1. What are some sources of light?
2. How does a rainbow form?
3. **Draw** a rainbow.

B33

ESL Strategy

Children may be familiar with several meanings of light (*light in weight, light in color, and so on*). Demonstrate light and dark by turning the lights on and off. Have children point to light sources in the room and say, "This ________ is a light source."

Teach and Apply

Student Pages B32–B33

- Discuss the pictures on page B32 and ask children how they are alike and different.
- Point out that colors in a rainbow always appear in the same sequence: red, orange, yellow, green, blue, indigo, violet. Explain that indigo is violet-blue.
- If you have a prism, use it to demonstrate how light is separated into the colors of the rainbow.

Reading Assist *Silent Consonants*

Remind children that when the letters *gh* are in the middle of a word, they are usually silent as in *light.* Help children recall other silent *gh* words, such as *fight, night, bright.*

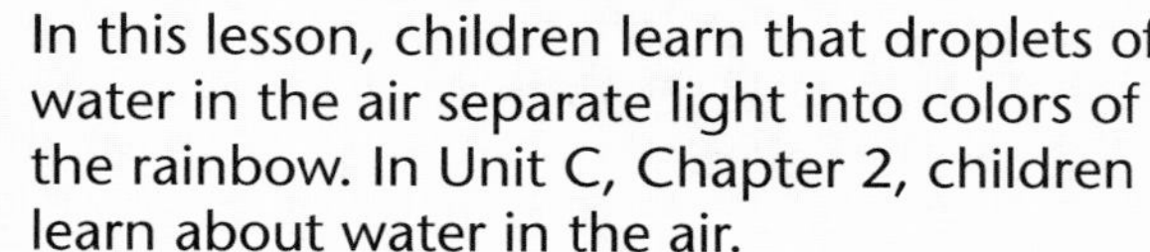

Earth Science

Integrating the Sciences

In this lesson, children learn that droplets of water in the air separate light into colors of the rainbow. In Unit C, Chapter 2, children learn about water in the air.

Assess and Extend

Answers to Lesson Review

1. Some sources of light are the sun, fire, and lightbulbs.
2. A rainbow forms when sunlight moves through drops of water in the air and the light is separated into colors.
3. **Draw** (*Portfolio Assessment or Journal*) Children's pictures should show a rainbow with red, orange, yellow, green, blue, indigo, and violet. Suggest that children use a very dark blue to represent indigo if they do not have an indigo crayon.

Check for Understanding

To follow up on the **baseline assessment,** have children add to their lists or drawings of sources of light.

Reteach

Take a walking tour through school and have children point out sources of light. Ask if any of the sources of light are also sources of heat. Have children draw sources of light they found.

Reading Organizer

Objective
Use a word web.

Additional Resources
- Reading for Science blackline master

Teaching Reading for Science
- On these pages, children learn how to use a word web. This lesson prepares them to complete a word web in the next lesson. It also helps them visually organize the concepts they will be reading about in Lesson 6.
- Word webs and other graphic organizers present information in a visual format. They present facts and concepts and highlight the relationships between them. Other types of graphic organizers include Venn diagrams, time lines, and concept maps.
- Graphic organizers actively engage children in learning. They can be used to introduce material, link prior knowledge to new material, and review content. Graphic organizers can also be used to help children organize their ideas before writing.
- Have children read and complete the Reading for Science lesson and the Reading for Science blackline master.

Student Page B34
- Ask children if they have ever seen or used a word web. Have them give examples and draw some on the chalkboard. Explain that word webs can be used to brainstorm, organize ideas, and communicate information.
- Children might be familiar with the concept of webs from spiderwebs or the World Wide Web.
- Point out that this word web branches out from the center. Others may branch out from the top, or even the side, of a page.

Using a Word Web

This is a word web. You can use a word web to group your ideas. Point to the topic. The topic is what the word web is about. Point to the examples. Each example tells something about the topic.

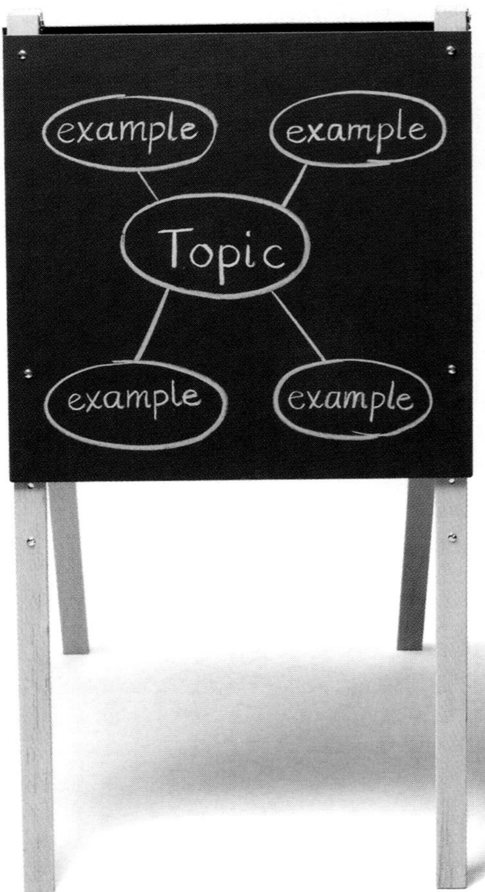

B34

ESL Strategy

Show children several different word webs. Explain that the *topic* of each word web is what the word web is about. The other words tell about the topic. Name the topic of each web and ask children to point to it. Then ask them to point to and name words that tell about the topic.

This word web has been started.
What is the topic? What are the examples?
How would you complete the word web?

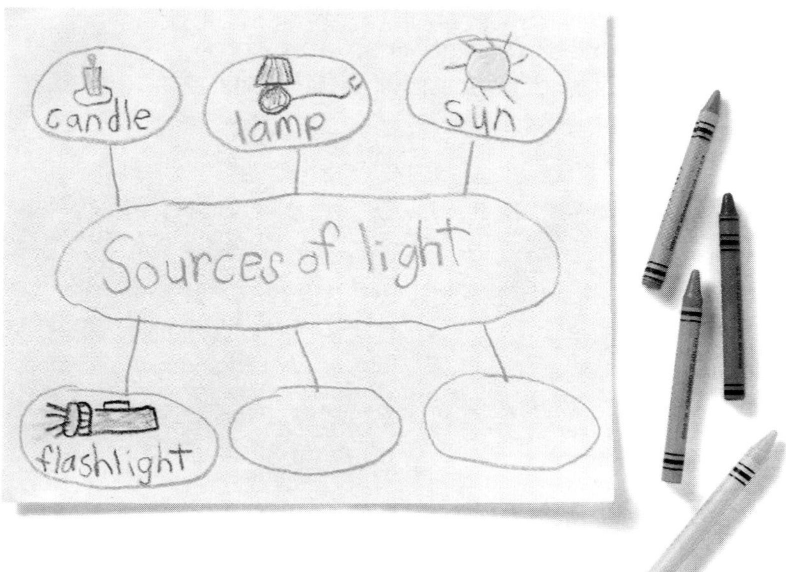

Turn the page to find out how a word web can help you learn more about light.

Reading for Science

Using a Word Web

Here is the word web from page 35. Complete it.

candle
lamp
sun
Sources of Light
flashlight

Now look at this word web about sources of heat. Think about the topic. How would you complete the web?

Sources of Heat

Instructional Resources p. 36

Student Page B35

- Point out that this web is about sources of light. Have children trace the path of each line from the topic to the example.
- Elicit ideas for adding to the web. Possible answers include fire, lightbulbs, car headlights, lighted clockfaces, and exit signs.
- Explain that a word web is not limited to a certain number of examples. Other examples can be added by making circles and connecting them to the web.

Apply Reading for Science to Lesson 6

Children will use what they learned about word webs to complete the next lesson.

Lesson Organizer

Objectives

- Learn that light travels in a straight line.
- Learn what happens when light strikes an object.

Process Skills observing

Materials

Kit Items flashlight, 2 batteries

School-Supplied Items none

Additional Resources

- Lab Manual
- Teacher Demonstration Kit
- Wall Chart

Introduce

Activate Prior Knowledge

Ask children to think about a time they used a flashlight. Ask: **What did you use it for? How did it help you?**

Language Development *Game*

Play "Simon Says," having children move in different ways. Use words from the lesson, such as *straight, bend, bounce,* and *block.* For example, **Simon says walk in a straight line. Now bend your knees.**

Flip Chart

Have children find a shadow in a picture. Ask: **How do you think shadows are made?**

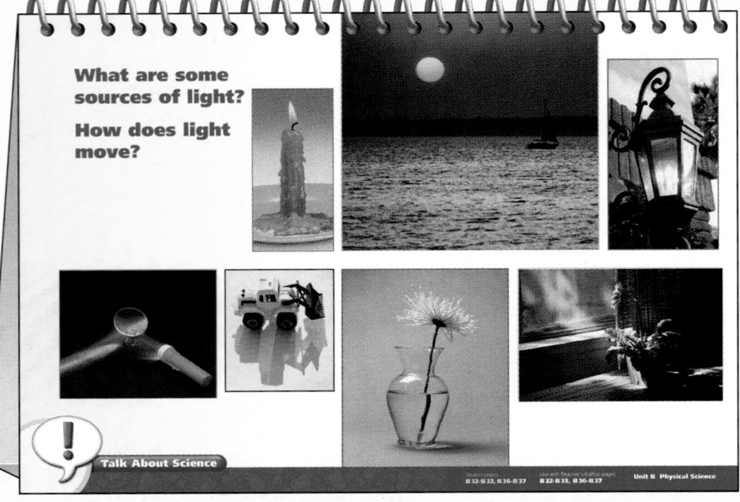

How does light move?

Can you walk in a straight line? Can you walk in a zigzag? How many other ways can you move? Did you know that light moves too?

Light moves in straight lines. This word web shows what happens when light hits different objects.

Light passes through a window.

Light is blocked. A shadow is formed.

Movement of light

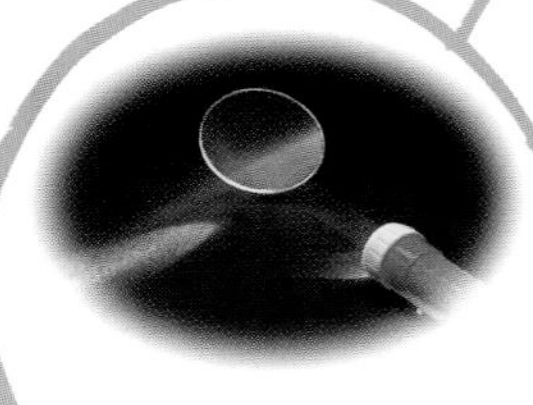

Light bounces off a mirror.

Light bends goi through wate

Science Background

- The bending of light is called refraction. Light bends (*refracts*) as it changes speed while passing from one material to another. The straw in the picture appears to be broken because light waves are refracted as they pass from water into the air.
- An opaque object blocks light, forming a shadow.
- A transparent object allows light to pass through so that whatever is behind can be seen clearly.
- Reflection is the bouncing of a light wave off a surface. When light waves are reflected off very smooth surfaces, such as mirrors, images can be seen on these surfaces.

Teaching Tips You can use a mirror to demonstrate bouncing light. When you shine a flashlight into the mirror, a spot of light will bounce from the mirror onto a surface, such as the wall.

Go on a scavenger hunt.

Materials

flashlight

Process Skills

- observing

Steps

1. Use your flashlight. Find one object in the room that makes light bounce.
2. Find one object that makes light bend.
3. Find one object that light can pass through.
4. Find one object that blocks light.

Share. Make a word web. Draw or write the name of each object you observed.

Lesson Review

1. How does light move?
2. What happens when light hits a mirror?
3. **Show** an object that blocks light.

B37

Teach and Apply

Student Page B36

Point out that the pictures on this page are part of a word web. Have children find the topic and the examples.

Reading Assist *Silent Consonants*

Write the word *straight* on the chalkboard. Remind children that sometimes *gh* is silent. Cover up the *gh* to help children decode the word.

Student Page B37

Explore Activity

Time about 15 minutes

Grouping cooperative groups of 4

Make sure some of the following items are available for the scavenger hunt: mirror or foil (*to bounce light*), hand lens or eyeglasses (*to bend light*), cellophane or other transparent items (*to let light pass through*), books or other solid items (*to block light*). Children can complete Lab Manual page 46. Use **Wall Chart** page 25 to present children with a different type of word web. Have them write the different objects the class found for each category.

Safety Note *Caution children not to shine the light in anyone's eyes.*

Lab Manual

How does light move?

Draw or write the name of each object you found.

Light passes through

Light is blocked by

Movement of light

Light bounces off

Light bends going through

Lab Manual p. 46

Activity Rubric

Use the following activity scoring rubric to assess students' performance.

Scoring Criteria	1	2	3	4
Student followed directions to perform this activity.				
Student identified objects that cause light to pass through, bounce off, block, or bend.				
Student observed how light interacts with a variety of objects.				
Student recorded his or her observations about the movement of light.				
Student created a word web to cluster the various types of light movement.				

Scoring Key

4 points correct, complete, detailed
3 points partially correct, complete, detailed
2 points partially correct, partially complete, lacks some detail
1 point incorrect or incomplete, needs assistance

Lab Manual p. T16

Assess and Extend

Answers to Lesson Review

1. Light moves in straight lines.
2. Light bounces when it hits a mirror.
3. **Show** (*Performance Assessment*) Children should show a solid object, such as a book or a block.

Inquire Further

Ask the following question to guide further inquiry: **How can you make a spot of light on a wall or ceiling? How can you make the spot touch a particular item in the room?**

Higher Order Thinking *Apply*

Ask: **If you wanted to make a room as dark as possible, what kind of curtains would you use? Why?** (*curtains made of thick materials that block light*)

Call 1-888-537-4908 with your Activity questions or comments.

Activity Organizer

Objective
Experiment to determine how changing an object's distance from a light source changes the size of its shadow.

Process Skills experimenting, observing (formulating hypotheses, identifying and controlling variables, collecting and interpreting data)

Materials
Kit Items flashlight, 2 batteries
School-Supplied Items small toy or classroom object

Time about 30 minutes

Grouping cooperative groups of 4

Additional Resources
- Lab Manual
- Teacher Demonstration Kit
- Wall Chart

Introduce

Activity Summary
The Lesson 7 Experiment Activity, *Experiment with Shadows,* is also on the **Flip Chart.** In this activity, children use scientific methods to determine how an object's distance from a light source affects the size of its shadow. Children will find that when the object is closer to the light, the shadow will be larger because the object blocks more light. When the object is farther from the light, the shadow will be smaller.

Activate Prior Knowledge
Ask children to think about a time they made a shadow. Ask them to describe the shadow and tell how they made it.

Using Scientific Language
Review the vocabulary of scientific methods on pages xii–xiii.

Reading Assist *Decoding*
In this experiment, it is helpful to review such words as *experiment, hypothesis, prediction,* and *conclusion* to make sure children can read and pronounce them. Use syllabication when necessary.

Experiment with shadows.

Process Skills
- experimenting
- observing

Materials

flashlight

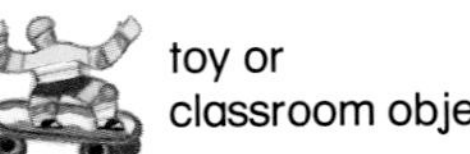
toy or classroom object

Problem
How can you change the size of a shadow?

Give Your Hypothesis
If you move an object farther from a light, will the shadow get larger or smaller? Tell what you think.

Control the Variables
Make sure you keep your flashlight steady.

Test Your Hypothesis
Follow these steps to do the experiment.

1. Shine the flashlight on a wall.
2. Put the object close to the light. Observe the shadow.
3. Now put the object far from the light. Observe the shadow again.

B38

Science Background
When an object blocks light, it casts a shadow. The more light an object blocks, the larger the shadow will be.

Math-Science Connection Have children measure the size of the shadows, as well as the distances from the light to the object to the wall. Have children record their measurements on the **Wall Chart** page 26. Discuss the findings.

Technology

Review the demonstration of this Experiment's procedure on the *Physical Science* **Activity Video,** Segment 3.

Children extend their investigation of light and shadows at **www.sfscience.com.**

Collect Your Data

Use a chart like this one. Draw pictures to show the size of each shadow.

far from the light
close to the light

Tell Your Conclusion

Compare your results and hypothesis. How can you change the size of a shadow?

Inquire Further

In what other ways can you change the shadow?

B39

Lab Manual

Experiment with shadows.

Problem

How can you change the size of a shadow?
Share your ideas with a friend.

Give Your Hypothesis

If you move an object farther from a light, will the shadow get larger or smaller? Write what you think.

Control the Variables

Make sure you keep your flashlight steady.

Test Your Hypothesis

Follow the steps to do the experiment.
Observe both shadows.

Lab Manual
pp. 47–48

Activity Rubric

Use the following activity scoring rubric to assess students' performance.

Scoring Criteria	1	2	3	4
Student followed directions to perform this experiment.				
Student stated a hypothesis about the relationship of light and distance on the size of shadows.				
Student controlled the variable of light in conducting the experiment.				
Student recorded the data he or she collected.				
Student explained his or her conclusion based on the data that was collected.				

Scoring Key
4 points correct, complete, detailed
3 points partially correct, complete, detailed
2 points partially correct, partially complete, lacks some detail
1 point incorrect or incomplete, needs assistance

Lab Manual
p. T17

Call 1-888-537-4908 with your Activity questions or comments.

Teach and Apply

Problem

Ask children to share their ideas about ways they might change the size of a shadow.

Give Your Hypothesis

Point out to children that hypotheses can be worded in *if . . . then* statements. Have children record their hypotheses on Lab Manual page 47.

Control the Variables

To keep the flashlight steady, have children place it on a desk, the floor, or a stack of books.

Safety Note *Caution children not to shine the light in anyone's eyes.*

Test Your Hypothesis

Have children take turns moving the object closer to and farther from the light.

Collect Your Data

Tell children to draw only the shadow and not to include other details they see on the object itself.

Assess and Extend

Tell Your Conclusion

Have children reread their hypothesis and compare it with their results. Children should conclude that they can change the size of a shadow by moving the object closer to or farther from a light.

Inquire Further

Have children work in small groups to discuss other ways to change the shadow. Have children record their ideas on Lab Manual page 48.

Higher Order Thinking *Hypothesize*

Ask: **How can you make your object cast shadows that have different shapes?** (*turn the object in different directions*)

Science Center

Flip Chart

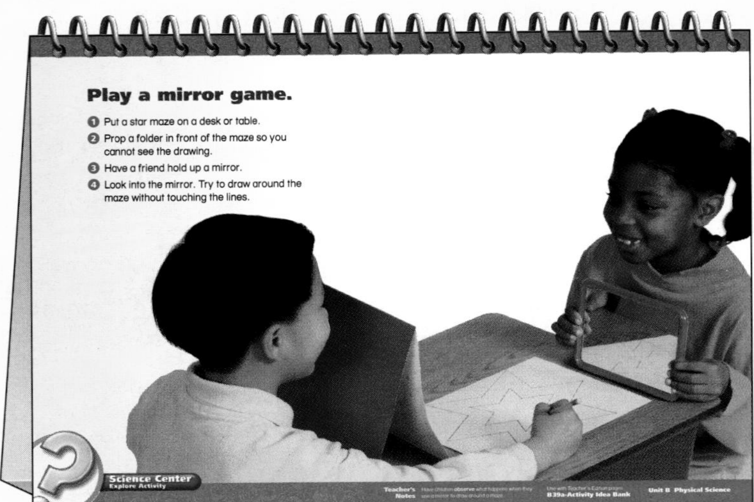

Play a mirror game.

Objective

Try to draw a path through a maze by looking at its reflection in a mirror.

Process Skills observing

Materials

Kit Items none

School-Supplied Items simple outline maze of a star, pencil, folder, hand mirror

Safety Note *Caution children to be careful with the mirror.*

Procedure

- You may want to tape the folder to the desk to keep it in place.
- The child holding the mirror must make sure that it is angled so that the other child can see the entire maze clearly.
- Children **observe** what happens when they use a mirror to draw around a maze.
- You can use **Lab Manual** page 49 with this activity.

What to Expect

Children discover that the mirror reverses the image of the maze, making it difficult to draw around the maze.

Lab Manual

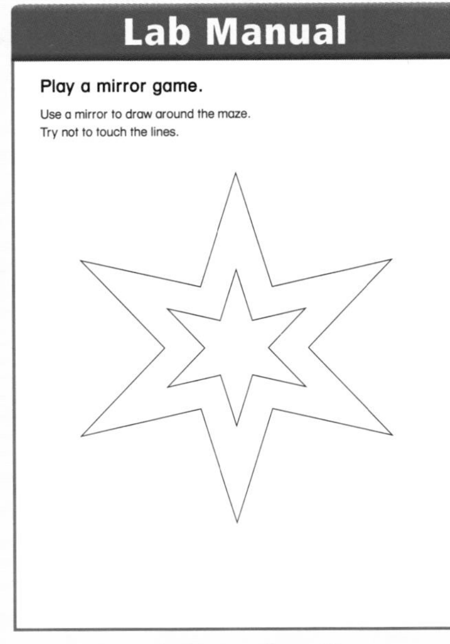
Play a mirror game.

Use a mirror to draw around the maze.
Try not to touch the lines.

Lab Manual, p. 49

Connections

School and Community

Ideas for bringing the school and community together:

Field Trips

- planetarium
- shadow walk
- retail lighting store
- high school theater

Guest Speakers

- artist
- photographer
- interior designer
- member of theater light crew

Themes

The activities on these pages can be used with classroom themes such as:

- astronomy
- outdoors
- weather
- color
- shadows
- inventions and inventors

Books for Children

Children might enjoy these books about light:

Day Light, Night Light: Where Light Comes From
by Franklyn Mansfield Branley.
While exploring the properties of light, this book combines hands-on activities with fun facts.
(HarperCollins, ISBN 0-06-445171-2)

What Makes a Shadow?
by Clyde Robert Bulla.
What shadows are and how they are formed. Includes suggestions to make shadow puppets.
(HarperCollins, ISBN 0-69470-081-9)

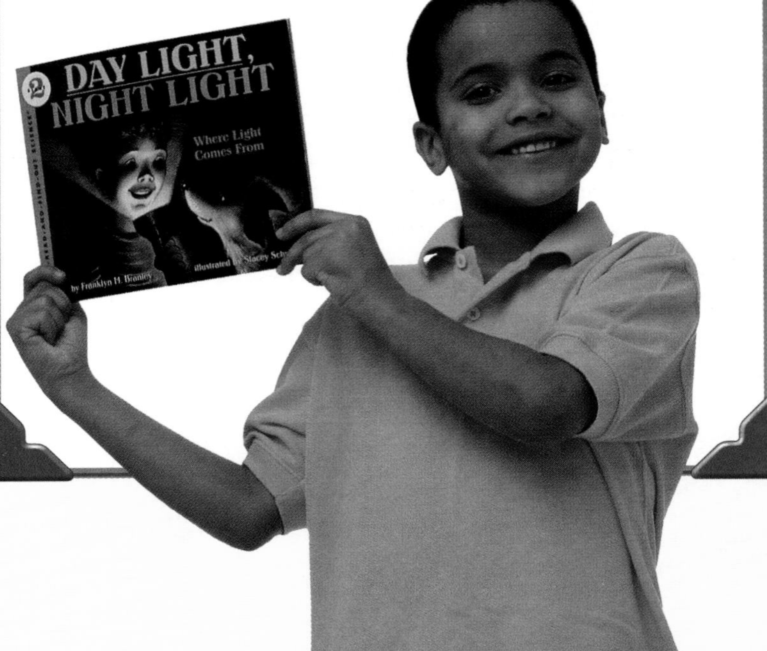

Cross-Curricular Options

LITERATURE

My Shadow

Use the book to talk about shadows.

Materials *My Shadow* by Robert Louis Stevenson. (Paper Star, ISBN 0-698-11365-9)

Procedure

- Read this illustrated version of Stevenson's poem about a child and the child's shadow.
- Encourage children to talk about the child's shadow. Ask: **How did the child's shadow change? Why did the child say the shadow was lazy and still in bed?**
- Have children write and illustrate a poem about a time when they made a shadow.

Multiple Intelligences linguistic

MATH

Measuring Shadows

Measure shadows at different times of day.

Materials chalk, measuring tape

Procedure

- Partners take turns drawing around each other's shadow at different times of day.
- They measure their shadows from head to toe and record the measurements.
- They compare the size of the shadow at different times of the day.

Multiple Intelligences logical-mathematical, linguistic

ESL Place three pieces of string in varying lengths on a table. Ask children to point to the shortest string. Then have them point to the longest string.

WRITING

Secret Shadow Riddles

Write riddles and make shadows.

Materials overhead projector, paper, pencil

Procedure

- Children secretly select several classroom objects and write clues describing them.
- Children take turns placing their objects on a shielded overhead projector and reading their clues.
- Classmates guess the object based on its shadow and the clues read.

It is mostly straight.
It is skinny.
It is pointy at one end.

Multiple Intelligences linguistic, spatial

PHYSICAL EDUCATION

Shadow Tag

Play shadow tag.

Procedure

- The child chosen to be it tries to step on the shadow of another child.
- Ask: **If you don't want to get caught, is it better to run toward the sun or away? Why?** (*It is better to run away from the sun because your shadow will be in front of you and more easily hidden.*)

Multiple Intelligences bodily-kinesthetic, logical-mathematical

Special Needs Children with physical disabilities may enjoy flashlight tag. Players shine flashlights on a wall and try to "tag" each other's lights.

Review Organizer

Materials

Kit Items none

School-Supplied Items magazines or catalogs, scissors, glue

Time about 30 minutes

Grouping cooperative groups of 4

Additional Resources

- Chapter 2 Assessment: Teacher's Assessment Package

Chapter Main Ideas

Lesson 1 Sounds are made when objects vibrate. The volume of a sound can change.

Lesson 2 The pitch of a sound can change.

Lesson 3 Heat comes from various sources, such as sunlight and fire. Heat moves from warmer objects and places to cooler ones.

Lesson 4 Heat moves through metal more easily than it moves through foam or plastic.

Lesson 5 Some sources of light also give off heat. Light is made up of many colors.

Lesson 6 Light moves in straight lines. When light hits different objects, it can pass through, bounce, bend, or be blocked.

Lesson 7 The shadow of an object becomes smaller as the object is moved farther from a light source.

Reviewing Science Words

1. Children's answers might include a radio, TV, musical instrument, voice, barking dog, machinery.
2. Children might suggest a voice, musical instrument, songbird.
3. Answers might include tapping, shaking, dropping.
4. Sources of light in the room might include sunlight, lightbulbs, lamp, flashlight, overhead projector.

Reviewing Science Ideas

1. Sounds are made when objects vibrate.
2. The sun and fire are two sources of heat.
3. Heat moves more easily through metal than wood.
4. A shadow is formed when an object blocks light.

Chapter 2 Review

Reviewing Science Words

1. What are some things that can change **volume**?
2. What are some things that can change **pitch**?
3. How can you make an object **vibrate**?
4. What **sources** of light do you see in the room?

Reviewing Science Ideas

1. How are sounds made?
2. Name two sources of heat.
3. Does heat move more easily through metal or wood?
4. How does a shadow form?

B40

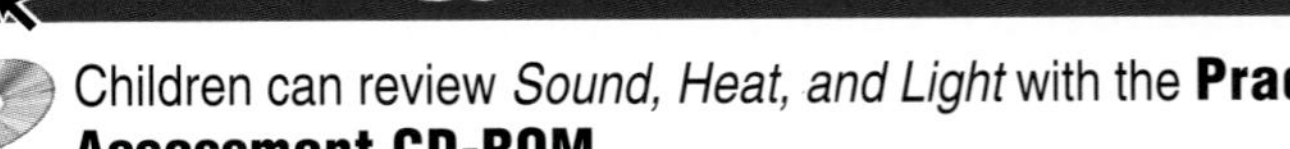

Technology

Children can review *Sound, Heat, and Light* with the **Practice & Assessment CD-ROM.**

Children can use the **Production Studio** to show what they've learned about *Sound, Heat, and Light.*

Children can use The KnowZone™ at **www.kz.com** to review and test their science knowledge.

You can use **TestWorks™** to customize assessment for your children.

Make a collage.

Materials

magazines or catalogs | scissors | glue

1. Work with a group.
2. Find pictures that show sound, heat, and light.
3. Tell about your pictures.
4. Glue your pictures onto a collage.

Chapter Assessment

Draw a circle around the word that finishes each sentence.

1. ________ from the sun is made up of many colors.
   Sound Shadows Light
2. ________ can be made when you rub objects together.
   Heat Light Shadows
3. When a guitar string vibrates, it makes ________.
   heat light sound

Write Yes or No.

________ 4. Heat passes quickly through metal.

________ 5. The sun is a source of light.

________ 6. The pitch of a sound can be high or low.

________ 7. Light bends passing through a clear window.

Teacher's Assessment Package pp. 29–30

Assessment Rubric

	Sound, Heat, and Light
4	Correctly identifies sources of sound, heat, and light.
3	Makes a few errors in identifying sources of sound, heat, and light.
2	Has difficulty identifying sources of sound, heat, and light.
1	Cannot identify sources of sound, heat, and light.

Performance Assessment Teaching Tips

- Before beginning the activity, help children brainstorm a list of pictures to look for that show sound, heat, and light.
- Department store catalogs and home decorating magazines are good sources of pictures.
- Have children tell about the pictures they found. Ask questions such as: **Were there pictures that could go in more than one group? How did you decide where to put them?**
- Children can use extra pictures to create booklets to take home.

Enrichment

When the collage is finished, have children choose a picture from each of the three categories and use their pictures to write a story.

Chapter 2 Skills Trace

Process Skills Development

	Observing	Classifying	Predicting	Experimenting
Skill Introduced	xiv	xiv	xv	xv
Skill Applied	B25 B27 B30–B31 B37 B38–B39	B27	B30–B31	B38–B39
Skill Assessed	End Matter 6–7	End Matter 10–11	End Matter 16–17	End Matter 28–29

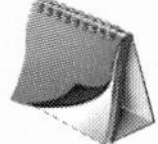
Chapter Review pages are also on the **Flip Chart.**

Lesson/Activity and Flip Chart	Objectives/Process Skills	Time Options/Activity Materials
Chapter Opener Student Edition pp. B42–B43 and **Flip Chart** ***Go, Train, Go***		**Have less time?** Use the Graphic Organizer on Teacher's Assessment Package p. 33 for an overview of the lessons. Use the Flip Chart to teach lesson concepts and science activities. **Have more time?** Use the Flip Chart to reinforce and extend lesson concepts and activities. Use the Cross-Curricular Options in the Activity Idea Bank on Teacher's Edition pp. B49b, B55b, and B59b.
Reading for Science Student Edition pp. B44–B45 ***Cause and Effect***	**Objective** Communicate cause and effect relationships.	
Lesson 1 Student Edition pp. B46–B47 ***What makes objects move?*** **Explore Activity** ***Make an object move.*** **Flip Chart** ***Talk About Science***	**Objective** Identify ways to make objects move. **Process Skills** predicting, estimating and measuring	**Kit Items** none **School-Supplied Items** metric ruler, common classroom objects
Lesson 2 Student Edition pp. B48–B49 ***What is gravity?*** **Explore Activity** ***Explore gravity.*** **Flip Chart** ***Talk About Science***	**Objective** Describe how gravity affects objects. **Process Skills** predicting	**Kit Items** none **School-Supplied Items** common classroom objects
Activity Idea Bank Teacher's Edition pp. B49a–B49b **Flip Chart** **Science Center Explore Activity** ***Move an object.***	**Objective** Make an object move in different ways. **Process Skills** observing	**Kit Items** none **School-Supplied Items** classroom objects such as ball of paper, eraser, pencil, book
Lesson 3 Student Edition pp. B50–B51 ***What is a magnet?*** **Explore Activity** ***Push and pull magnets.*** **Flip Chart** ***Talk About Science***	**Objective** Identify when magnets attract and repel each other. **Process Skills** observing	**Kit Items** 3-cm donut magnets **School-Supplied Items** unsharpened pencils
Lesson 4 Student Edition pp. B52–B53 ***What can a magnet attract?*** **Explore Activity** ***Go fishing with a magnet.*** **Flip Chart** ***Talk About Science***	**Objective** Identify some objects a magnet will attract. **Process Skills** predicting, observing	**Kit Items** 3-cm donut magnets, string **School-Supplied Items** common classroom objects, unsharpened pencils **Advance Prep** Collect a good mixture of magnetic and nonmagnetic items.
Lesson 5 Student Edition pp. B54–B55 and **Flip Chart** **Investigate Activity** ***How many paper clips will a magnet pick up?***	**Objective** Use a magnet to pick up paper clips. **Process Skills** predicting, observing	**Kit Items** 3-cm donut magnets **School-Supplied Items** large paper clips
Activity Idea Bank Teacher's Edition pp. B55a–B55b **Flip Chart** **Science Center Explore Activity** ***Use a magnet.***	**Objective** Identify objects through which a magnet will attract a paper clip. **Process Skills** predicting, collecting data	**Kit Items** 3-cm donut magnet **School-Supplied Items** items, some of which are magnetic
Lesson 6 Student Edition pp. B56–B57 ***How does electricity move?*** **Explore Activity** ***Light a bulb.*** **Flip Chart** ***Talk About Science***	**Objective** Explain how electricity moves. **Process Skills** observing, communicating	**Kit Items** light bulb, 1.3 volts; insulated 22-gauge wire; D battery, 1.5 volts **School-Supplied Item** safety goggles **Advance Prep** Cut the insulated wire and strip the ends for contact.
Lesson 7 Student Edition pp. B58–B59 ***How do you use electricity safely?*** **Flip Chart** ***Talk About Science***	**Objectives** • Name some ways to use electricity safely. • Name some uses of electricity.	**Have more time?** Use the following teaching guide option: Interactive Transparency 6, Interactive Transparency Package
Activity Idea Bank Teacher's Edition pp. B59a–B59b **Flip Chart** **Science Center Explore Activity** ***Explore electricity.***	**Objective** Identify which objects are good conductors of electricity. **Process Skills** observing, classifying	**Kit Items** 22-gauge insulated wire, #14 miniature lamp, D battery **School-Supplied Items** masking tape, metallic and non-metallic items
Chapter Review Student Edition pp. B60–B61 and **Flip Chart**		**Kit Items** 3-cm donut magnet **School-Supplied Items** string, cardboard, tape, paper, scissors, crayons or markers

Lesson/Activity and Flip Chart	Additional Resources		Technology
Chapter Opener Student Edition pp. B42–B43 and **Flip Chart** *Go, Train, Go*	**Teacher Assessment Package** • Graphic Organizer, p. 33 **Instructional Resources** • Family Activity, pp. 41–42 • Vocabulary Preview, p. 43	**Songs & Activities Package** • *Go, Train, Go*, pp. 19–20 **Wall Chart,** p. 27	**Practice & Assessment CD-ROM** **AudioText** **Production Studio** **www.sfscience.com** **Songs & Activities Package** **Teacher's Resource Planner CD-ROM**
Reading for Science Student Edition pp. B44–B 45 ***Cause and Effect***	**Instructional Resources** • Reading for Science, p. 44		
Lesson 1 Student Edition pp. B46–B47 ***What makes objects move?*** **Explore Activity** ***Make an object move.*** **Flip Chart** ***Talk About Science***	**Lab Manual** • Lab Manual, p. 51 • Activity Rubric p. T18	**Teacher Demonstration Kit** **Wall Chart,** p. 28	
Lesson 2 Student Edition pp. B48–B49 ***What is gravity?*** **Explore Activity** ***Explore gravity.*** **Flip Chart** ***Talk About Science***	**Lab Manual** • Lab Manual, p. 52 • Activity Rubric, p. T18	**Teacher Demonstration Kit**	
Activity Idea Bank Teacher's Edition pp. B49a–B49b **Flip Chart** **Science Center Explore Activity** ***Move an object.***	**Lab Manual** • Lab Manual, p. 53 • Activity Rubric, p. T19		
Lesson 3 Student Edition pp. B50–B51 ***What is a magnet?*** **Explore Activity** ***Push and pull magnets.*** **Flip Chart** ***Talk About Science***	**Lab Manual** • Lab Manual, p. 54 • Activity Rubric, p. T19	**Teacher Demonstration Kit**	
Lesson 4 Student Edition pp. B52–B53 ***What can a magnet attract?*** **Explore Activity** ***Go fishing with a magnet.*** **Flip Chart** ***Talk About Science***	**Lab Manual** • Lab Manual, p. 55 • Activity Rubric, p. T20	**Teacher Demonstration Kit** **Wall Chart,** p. 29	
Lesson 5 Student Edition pp. B54–B55 and **Flip Chart** **Investigate Activity** ***How many paper clips will a magnet pick up?***	**Lab Manual** • Lab Manual, p. 56 • Activity Rubric, p. T20	**Teacher Demonstration Kit**	*Physical Science* **Activity Video**
Activity Idea Bank Teacher's Edition pp. B55a–B55b **Flip Chart** **Science Center Explore Activity** ***Use a magnet.***	**Lab Manual** • Lab Manual, p. 57 • Activity Rubric, p. T21		
Lesson 6 Student Edition pp. B56–B57 ***How does electricity move?*** **Explore Activity** ***Light a bulb.*** **Flip Chart** ***Talk About Science***	**Lab Manual** • Lab Manual, pp. 58 • Activity Rubric, p. T21	**Teacher Demonstration Kit** **Wall Chart,** p. 30	
Lesson 7 Student Edition pp. B58–B59 ***How do you use electricity safely?*** **Flip Chart** ***Talk About Science***	**Interactive Transparency Package** • Interactive Transparency 6	**Wall Chart,** p. 31	
Activity Idea Bank Teacher's Edition pp. B59a–B59b **Flip Chart** **Science Center Explore Activity** ***Explore electricity.***	**Lab Manual** • Lab Manual, p. 59 • Activity Rubric, p. T22		
Chapter Review Student Edition pp. B60–B61 and **Flip Chart**	**Teachers Assessment Package** • Chapter 3 Assessment, pp. 35–36		**Practice & Assessment CD-ROM** **Production Studio** **The KnowZone™ at www.kz.com** **TestWorks™**

Reading for Science

Cause and Effect

Look at each cause. Draw a circle around the picture that shows what happens. Draw a picture in the last box to show what happens to the ice cream.

Cause	Effect
	Children should draw a picture of a melted ice cream cone in the blank box.

Instructional Resources
p. 44

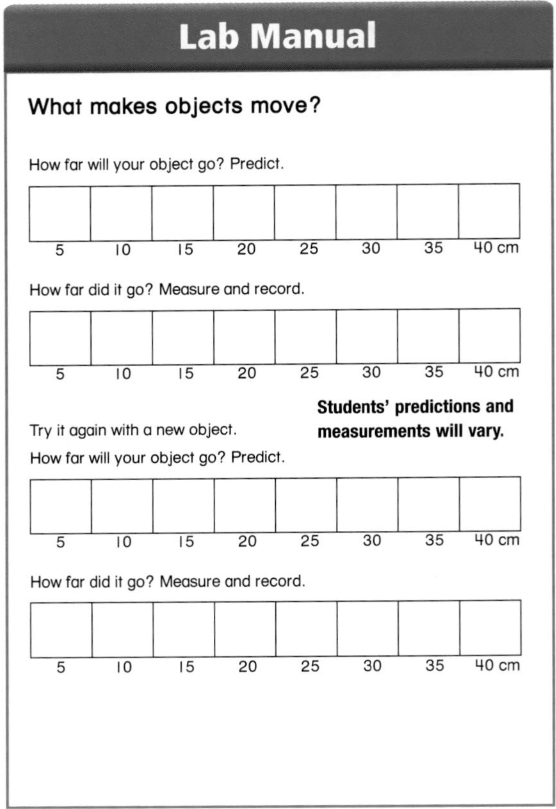

Lab Manual

What makes objects move?

How far will your object go? Predict.

5 10 15 20 25 30 35 40 cm

How far did it go? Measure and record.

5 10 15 20 25 30 35 40 cm

Try it again with a new object.

Students' predictions and measurements will vary.

How far will your object go? Predict.

5 10 15 20 25 30 35 40 cm

How far did it go? Measure and record.

5 10 15 20 25 30 35 40 cm

Lab Manual
p. 51

Lab Manual

What is gravity?

Draw the objects you are testing.

Which object will hit the floor first? Predict.

Write what happened.

Students' selection of objects will vary. They may predict that heavier objects will hit the floor first, but will find that objects with the least air resistance will hit the floor first, regardless of weight.

Lab Manual
p. 52

Lab Manual

Move an object.

What object did you choose? Draw it.

Students' choices and responses will vary.

Draw ways you moved your object.

Lab Manual
p. 53

Lab Manual

What is a magnet?

Draw what you see when you add one magnet.

Students will learn that opposite poles of the magnet will attract, or pull toward, each other, while like poles will push away, or repel, each other.

Draw what you see when you flip the top magnet over.

Draw what you see when you add another magnet.

Lab Manual
p. 54

Lab Manual

What can a magnet attract?

Draw objects you tested.

Objects a magnet will attract.

Objects a magnet will not attract.

Students' responses will depend on the objects they selected.

A magnet will attract

All objects that contain iron will be attracted to the magnet.

A magnet will not attract

Lab Manual
p. 55

Lab Manual

How many paper clips will a magnet pick up?

Use the graph to show your prediction and your results.

Students' predictions will vary as will their actual results.

15
14
13
12
11
10
9
8
7
6
5
4
3
2
1
0

Prediction Results

Lab Manual
p. 56

Lab Manual

Use a magnet.

Will a magnet attract a paper clip through an object?

Object	Prediction	Results
		Results will vary depending on objects chosen.

Lab Manual
p. 57

Lab Manual

How does electricity move?

Draw your battery and other materials.
Draw how you made the circuit to light the bulb.

Students' drawings should indicate that the electrical circuit is closed when the metal cap of the battery touched the metal receptor of the light.

Lab Manual
p. 58

Transparency

Using Electricity Safely

Interactive Transparency Package
Transparency 6

Lab Manual

Explore electricity.

Draw things that made the bulb light.
Draw things that did not light the bulb.

These things made the bulb light.
Students' choice of objects and their results will vary.

These things did not light the bulb.

Lab Manual
p. 59

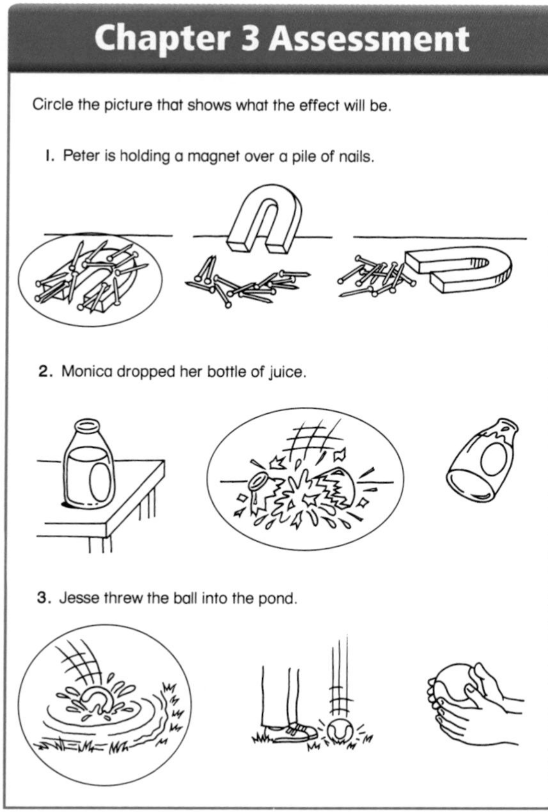

Chapter 3 Assessment

Circle the picture that shows what the effect will be.

1. Peter is holding a magnet over a pile of nails.

2. Monica dropped her bottle of juice.

3. Jesse threw the ball into the pond.

Teacher's Assessment Package
p. 35

Chapter 3 Assessment

Write the word that finishes each sentence.

4. A ______________ is the place on the magnet that has the strongest push or pull.

   lodestone pole gravity

5. The opposite ends of two magnets will ______________ .

   attract fall repel

6. When you drop your pencil, ______________ causes it to fall.

   lodestone gravity electricity fall

7. ______________ makes a computer work.

   Electricity Gravity Force

8. It is ______________ to use a toaster with a broken cord.

   okay safe unsafe

Draw an X on the picture that answers the question.

9. Which picture shows something that a magnet will attract?

10. Which picture shows a complete circuit?

Teacher's Assessment Package
p. 36

Table of Contents

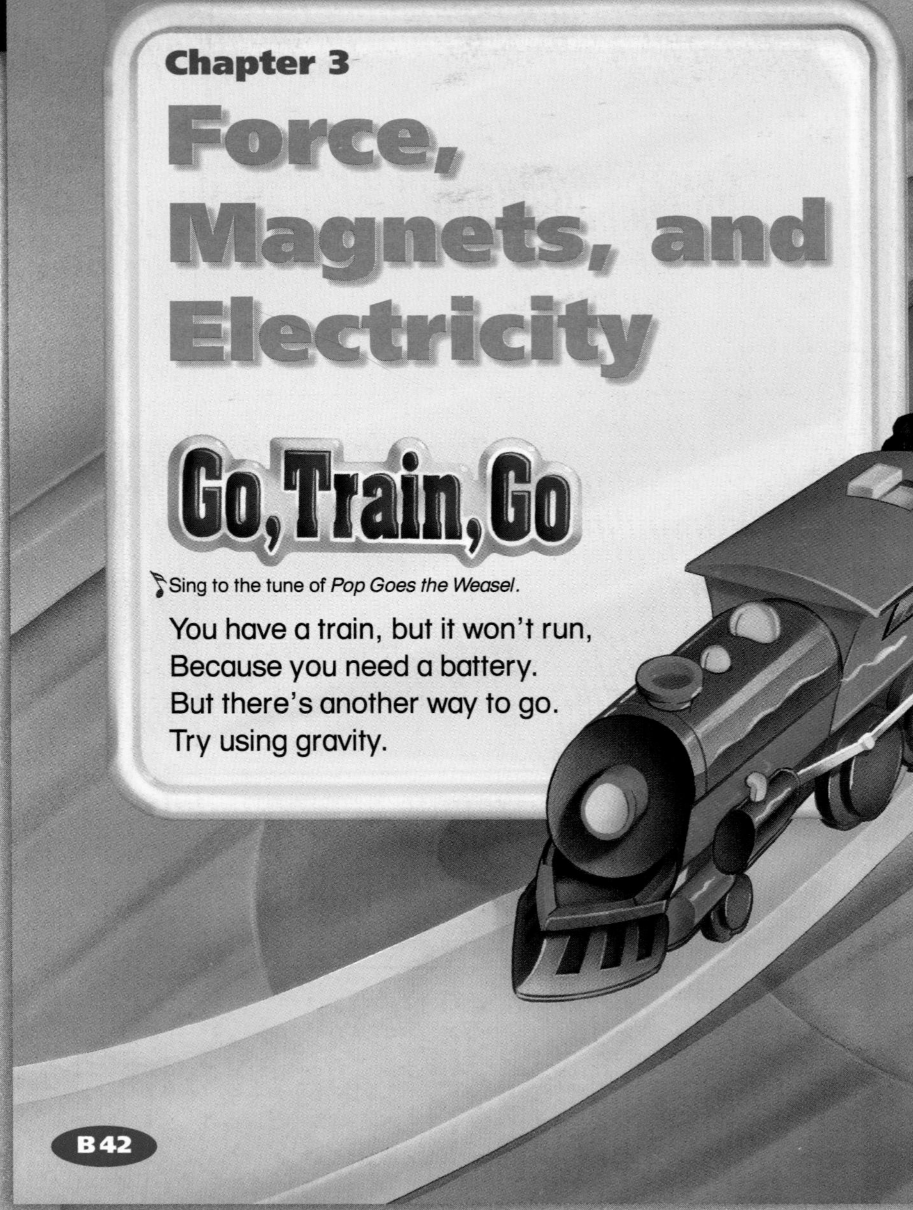

Chapter 3

Force, Magnets, and Electricity

Go, Train, Go

Sing to the tune of *Pop Goes the Weasel.*

You have a train, but it won't run,
Because you need a battery.
But there's another way to go.
Try using gravity.

B42

Introducing the Chapter

The song *Go, Train, Go* is on the **Flip Chart.**

- Have children follow your directions as you say: **Push your chair forward. Pull up a sock**. Point out that each time children push or pull an object, they are using a force to make it move. Tell children that in this chapter they will learn more about force, magnets, and electricity.
- Distribute the Family Activity blackline master page.

Singing the Song

Have children sing the song *Go, Train, Go* on side 1 of the CTW cassette. Distribute pages 19–20 from the CTW Song Activity Book.

Reading Assist *Use Reading Clues*

Encourage children to use reading clues to discover how gravity, a magnet, and a battery can all make a train move. (*Gravity pulls the train down the hill; a magnet pulls it to you; and a battery makes it go on its own.*)

Vocabulary Preview

Use the Vocabulary Preview blackline to introduce the vocabulary words for this chapter.

Lesson 1 force
Lesson 2 gravity
Lesson 3 pole, attract, repel
Lesson 6 circuit

Technology

Practice & Assessment CD-ROM

AudioText

Production Studio

www.sfscience.com

Teacher's Resource Planner

Songs & Activities Package

CTW Song & Activity

What Is It?

See if you can guess the answer to this riddle.

It is made of glass.
It needs electricity to work.
It helps you see.
What is it?

Now, make up riddles of your own.
1. Pick an object.
2. Draw it on a piece of paper.
3. Write clues about the object on the back of the paper.
4. Have someone guess the answer to your riddle. Then show your picture. Did your friend guess the riddle?
5. Take turns making up more riddles.

Songs & Activities Package pp. 19–20

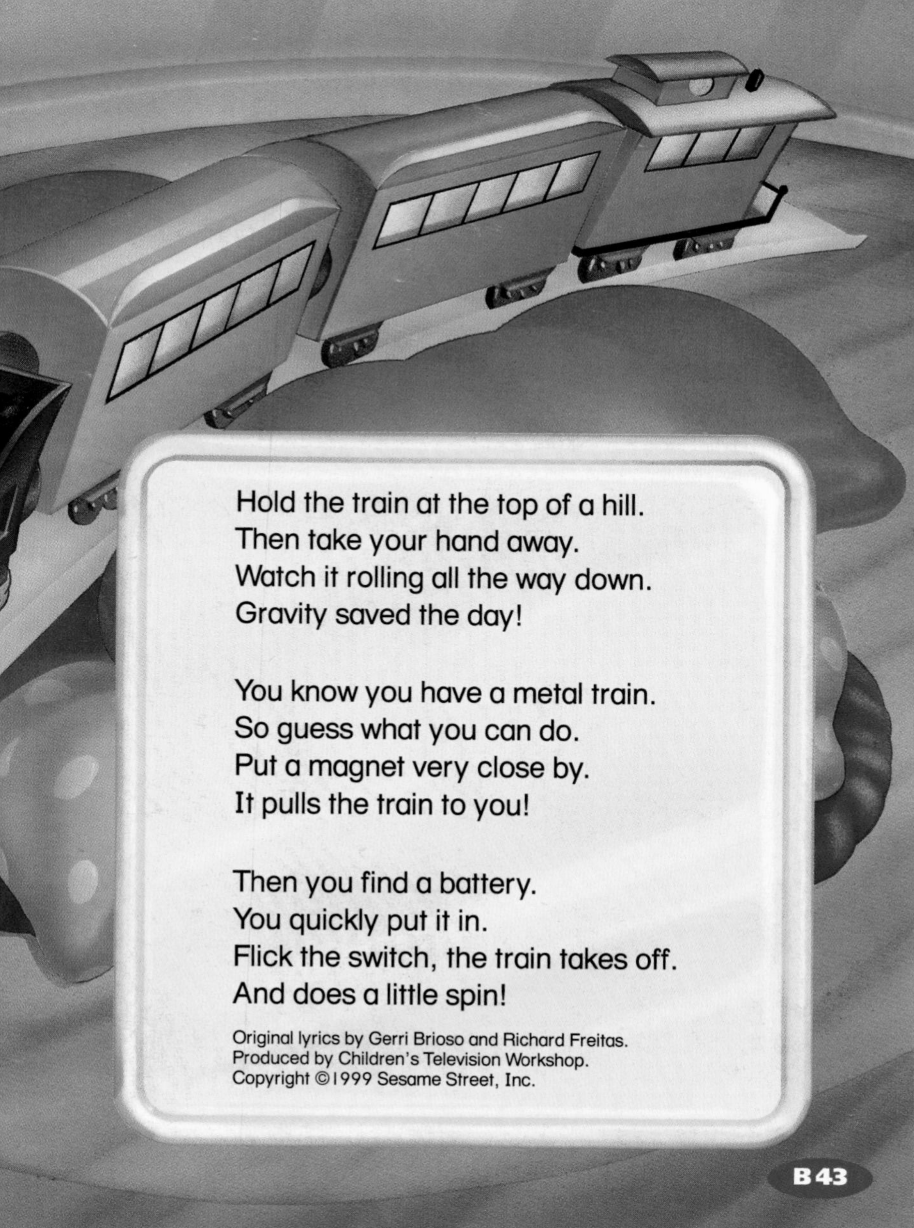

Hold the train at the top of a hill.
Then take your hand away.
Watch it rolling all the way down.
Gravity saved the day!

You know you have a metal train.
So guess what you can do.
Put a magnet very close by.
It pulls the train to you!

Then you find a battery.
You quickly put it in.
Flick the switch, the train takes off.
And does a little spin!

Original lyrics by Gerri Brioso and Richard Freitas.
Produced by Children's Television Workshop.
Copyright ©1999 Sesame Street, Inc.
B43

Family Activity

Science at Home

Dear Family:
Our class is starting Chapter 3. We will be learning about force, magnets, and electricity. These are the main ideas for Chapter 3.

- Force is a push or pull that makes something move.
- Gravity is the force that pulls things down.
- Magnets can push or pull certain metal objects.
- Electricity moves through a path called a circuit and powers certain objects such as lights.

We will also be learning science vocabulary words for Chapter 3. By the end of Chapter 3, we will be able to read the vocabulary words and tell what they mean.

Word Bank
force
gravity
pole
attract
repel
circuit

Home Projects
Here are some activities that will help your child understand the main ideas in Chapter 3. The activities are easy, fast, and fun.

Activities
- Help your child study the concept of force by rolling cans across the kitchen floor. Choose a few cans of the same size from your pantry. Take turns rolling the cans, making sure that you use a different amount of force each time. Discuss how the force affects how far each can rolls.

Instructional Resources
pp. 41–42

Vocabulary Preview

force	gravity
pole	attract
repel	circuit
magnet	push

Instructional Resources
p. 43

INQUIRY

Use a KWL chart at the beginning of each new chapter to encourage inquiry. In the *K* column, record what children already *know* about force, magnets, and electricity. In the *W* column, help children brainstorm a list of what they *want* to know about force, magnets, and electricity. Throughout the chapter, ask children what they have *learned* about force, magnets, and electricity and record their responses in the *L* column. A KWL chart is available on **Wall Chart** page 27.

Chapter 3 Skills Trace

Process Skills Development

	Predicting	Estimating and Measuring	Observing	Communicating
Skill Introduced	xv	xiv	xiv	xiv
Skill Applied	B47 B49 B53 B54–B55	B47	B51 B53 B54–B55 B57	B57
Skill Assessed	End Matter 16–17	End Matter 12–13	End Matter 6–7	End Matter 8–9

Science Literature Library

Riding the Ferry with Captain Cruz
by Alice K. Flanagan, photographs by Christine Osinski. With simple text and photographs, this book describes the duties and responsibilities of a ferryboat captain who takes people back and forth across the bay from Staten Island to Manhattan. (Children's Press, ISBN 0-516-26059-6)

Reading Organizer

Objective
Communicate cause-and-effect relationships.

Additional Resources
- Reading for Science blackline master

Teaching Reading for Science

- In science, cause and effect are identified as variables. The effect is the responding variable. The cause is the manipulated variable, and it is something that can change. Both variables can be measured. In the next lesson, understanding cause-and-effect relationships will help children communicate what causes objects to move.
- Communicating cause-and-effect relationships also helps children build understanding of events in their daily lives.
- Have children read and complete the Reading for Science lesson and the Reading for Science blackline master.

Student Page B44

- Before beginning the page, write the words *cause* and *effect* on the chalkboard. Define *cause* as a person, thing, or event that makes something happen. The *effect* is what happens as a result. Then turn off the classroom lights and ask: **What happened?** (*The lights went off.*) Record the response under *effect.* Ask: **What caused the lights to go off?** (*You pushed the switch.*) Record the response under *cause.* Then say: **The lights went out because I pushed the switch.**
- Continue modeling and discussing other cause-and-effect relationships such as the following:

  The plant is healthy because I planted it in soil, gave it water, and placed it in sunlight.

  The erasers are dusty because they were used to erase the chalkboard.
- Direct attention to the picture on page B44. Ask: **What is the child doing?** (*kicking the ball*) Record the response in the *cause* column on the chalkboard.
- After discussing the picture, have children tell what the effect will be and record their responses in the *effect* column.

Cause and Effect

Talk about the picture.

A **cause** is what makes something happen.
The **effect** is what happens.

The boy is going to kick the ball. What will the effect be?

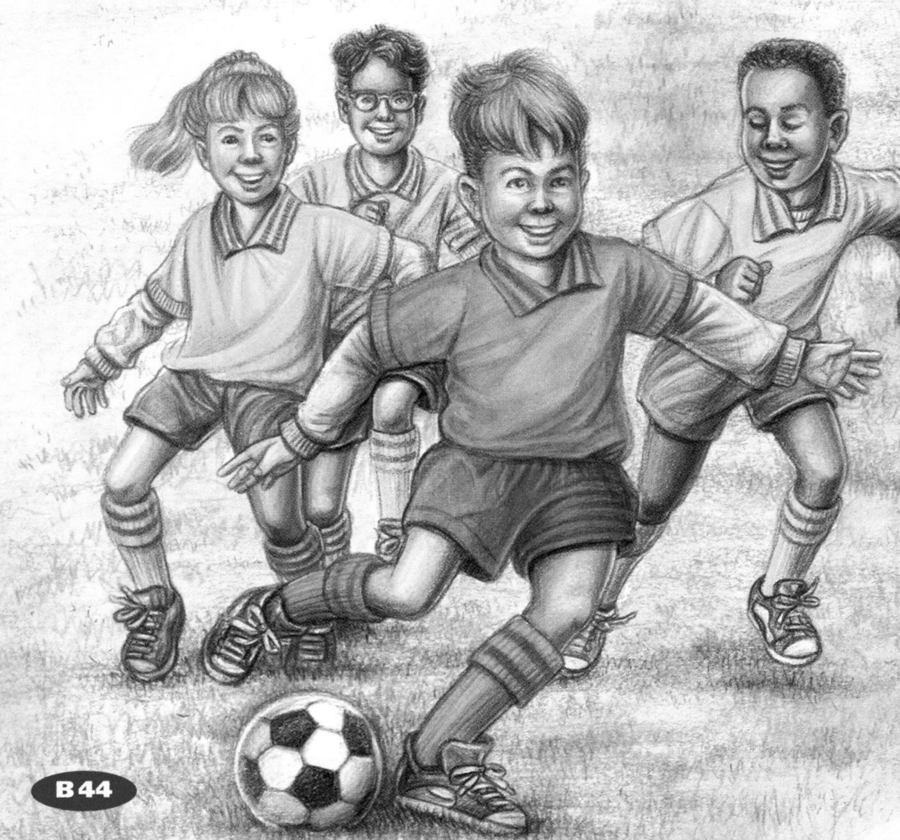

ESL Strategy

Model and discuss cause-and-effect relationships such as these: Press hard on a pencil point and ask: **What happened?** Open the door and ask: **What caused the door to open?**

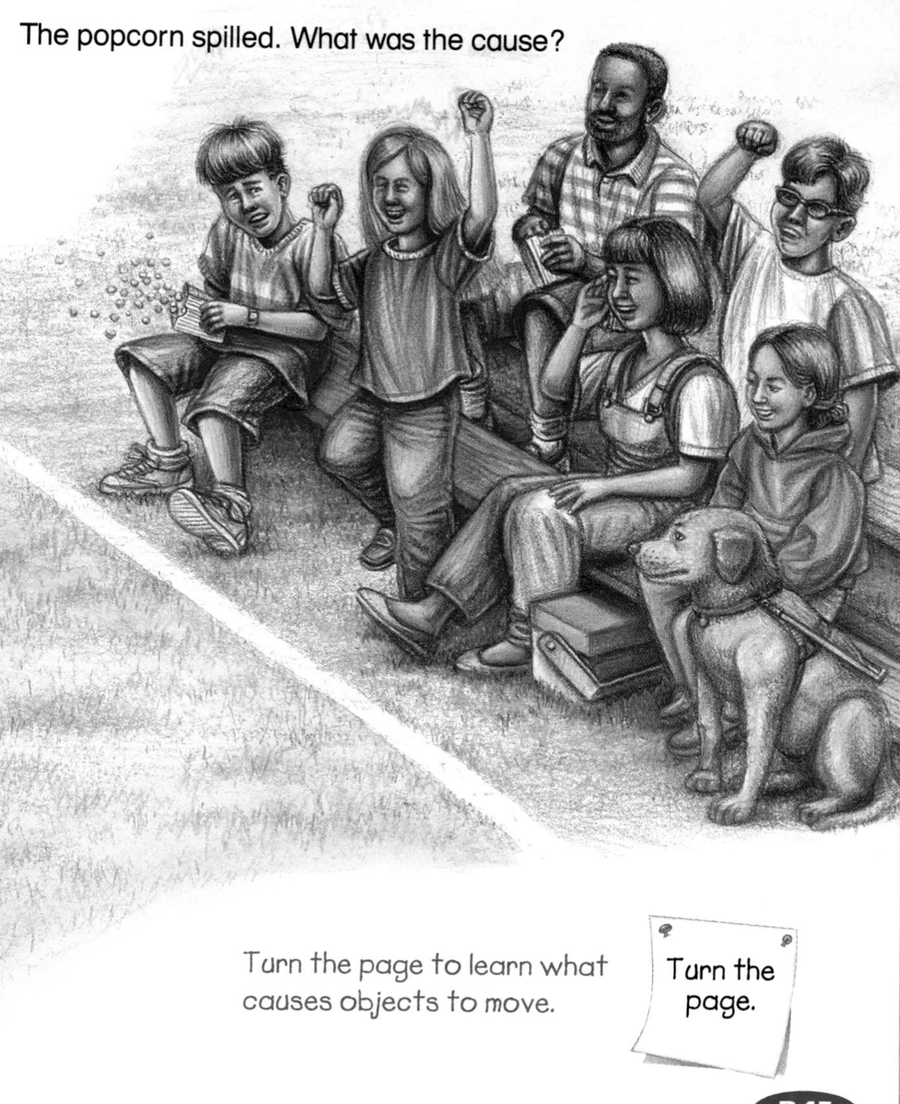

The popcorn spilled. What was the cause?
Turn the page to learn what causes objects to move.
Turn the page.
B45

Student Page B45

- Read aloud the sentences on page B45.
- Have children look at the picture, and ask: **What happened to the popcorn?** (*It spilled.*) Record the response in the *effect* column on the chalkboard.
- Have children answer the question "What was the cause?" by completing the following sentence starter: "The popcorn spilled because . . ." Record their responses in the *cause* column on the chalkboard.
- For each scenario, be sure children understand the direct relationship between the effect and its cause.

Apply Reading for Science to Lesson 1

Children will use what they learned about cause and effect to complete the next lesson.

Reading for Science

Cause and Effect

Look at each cause. Draw a circle around the picture that shows what happens. Draw a picture in the last box to show what happens to the ice cream.

Cause	Effect

Instructional Resources p. 44

Lesson Organizer

Objective
Identify ways to make objects move.

Vocabulary force
Process Skills predicting, estimating and measuring

Materials
Kit Items none

School-Supplied Items metric ruler, common classroom objects

Additional Resources
- Lab Manual
- Teacher Demonstration Kit
- Wall Chart

Introduce

Activate Prior Knowledge
Ask children to think about the things they moved today and whether they pushed or pulled. List their responses and save for use as a **baseline assessment.**

Language Development *Vocabulary*
Write words that describe movements, such as *hop, fly, swing, roll, push, pull, slide, skate, jog,* and *run.* Then invite children to select a word and act it out.

Flip Chart
Discuss what causes the objects in the picture to move—pushing, pulling, dropping. Ask children to name other ways they can move objects.

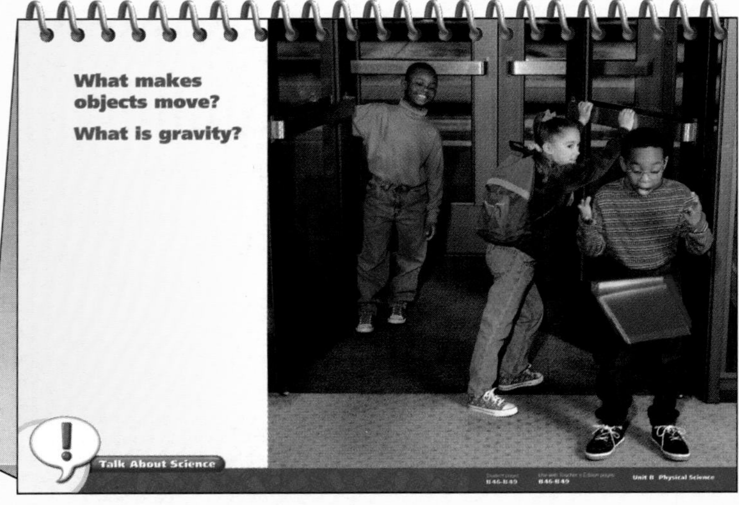
What makes objects move?
What is gravity?
Talk About Science
Unit B Physical Science

What makes objects move?

Whoosh! Crack! The ball flies through the air. What caused the ball to move?

The batter caused the ball to move. An object moves when it is pushed or pulled. **Force** is the push or pull that makes something move. The more force you use, the more the object moves.

You can use force to move an object up, down, right, or left. You can make it move in a straight line, a curve, or even a zigzag. How do you use force to move objects every day?[1]

[1] Answers r... include pi... up and pu... objects, o... and closin... door, and...

Science Background
- A bat is a simple machine called a lever. A simple machine has few or no moving parts and makes work easier.
- You exert a smaller force over a greater distance as you move the handle of a claw hammer—a lever—to pull out a nail. In return, the claw exerts a relatively large force as it pulls out the nail a short distance.

Math-Science Connection
Draw or write the names of four items that all children tested, one in each column at the bottom of **Wall Chart** page 28. Ask children to color in a square above whichever item went farthest for them. Discuss the results of the graph.

Make an object move.

Materials

ruler — common classroom objects

Process Skills

- predicting
- estimating and measuring

Steps

1. Choose one object.
2. If you blow on it, how far will it go? Predict.
3. Blow on your object. Measure how far it goes.
4. How can you make it go farther?
5. Choose a new object. Do the activity again.

Share. Compare your results with a friend's results.

Lesson Review

1. What is force?
2. When you use a lot of force to move an object, what happens?
3. **Tell** how you can make an object move.

B47

Lab Manual

What makes objects move?

How far will your object go? Predict.

5	10	15	20	25	30	35	40 cm

How far did it go? Measure and record.

5	10	15	20	25	30	35	40 cm

Try it again with a new object.
How far will your object go? Predict.

5	10	15	20	25	30	35	40 cm

How far did it go? Measure and record.

5	10	15	20	25	30	35	40 cm

Lab Manual
p. 51

Activity Rubric

Use the following activity scoring rubric to assess students' performance.

Scoring Criteria	1	2	3	4
Student followed directions to complete this activity.				
Student predicted the distance an object would move when blown.				
Student measured the distance each object moved.				
Student recorded the actual distance moved by various objects when blown.				
Student summarized the results of the data he or she collected.				

Scoring Key
4 points correct, complete, detailed
3 points partially correct, complete, detailed
2 points partially correct, partially complete, lacks some detail
1 point incorrect or incomplete, needs assistance

Lab Manual
p. T18

Teach and Apply

Student Page B46

Ask children whether the batter pushed or pulled the ball to make it move.

Reading Assist *Vocabulary*
Have children demonstrate their understanding of the word *force* by alternately pushing and pulling a box across the room. Encourage them to say "I am forcing the box to move by pushing it."

Student Page B47

Explore Activity

Time about 10 minutes

Grouping cooperative groups of 2

Children can complete Lab Manual page 51 as they do the activity. Help children realize that they may be able to make their objects go farther by blowing with more force.

What to Expect
Children's results will depend on the weight of the objects as well as the force with which they blow.

Assess and Extend

Answers to Lesson Review

1. Force is the push or pull that makes something move.
2. The object goes faster or farther than when you use less force.
3. **Tell** (*Interview*) Answers may include pushing, pulling, blowing, and so on.

Check for Understanding
As a follow-up to the **baseline assessment,** invite children to review the list they made in Activate Prior Knowledge and make any changes needed.

Inquire Further

Ask the following questions to guide further inquiry:
How are your results like your friends' results? How are they different?

Higher Order Thinking *Draw Conclusions*
Ask children to explain if an object, such as a ball, could ever move by itself.

Call 1-888-537-4908 with your Activity questions or comments.

Lesson Organizer

Objective
Describe how gravity affects objects.

Vocabulary gravity

Process Skills predicting

Materials
Kit Items none

School-Supplied Items common classroom objects

Additional Resources
- Lab Manual
- Teacher Demonstration Kit

Introduce

Activate Prior Knowledge
Toss a piece of crumpled paper straight up into the air, drop the paper from shoulder level, and toss the paper into a basket. Ask: **What makes the paper fall to the ground each time?**

Language Development *Poetry*
Have children make up a poem using a word that suggests movement, such as *up, down, near,* or *far.*

Flip Chart
Ask what happened to the books in the picture when they were dropped. Ask: **Why did the books fall?** (*Gravity pulled them down.*)

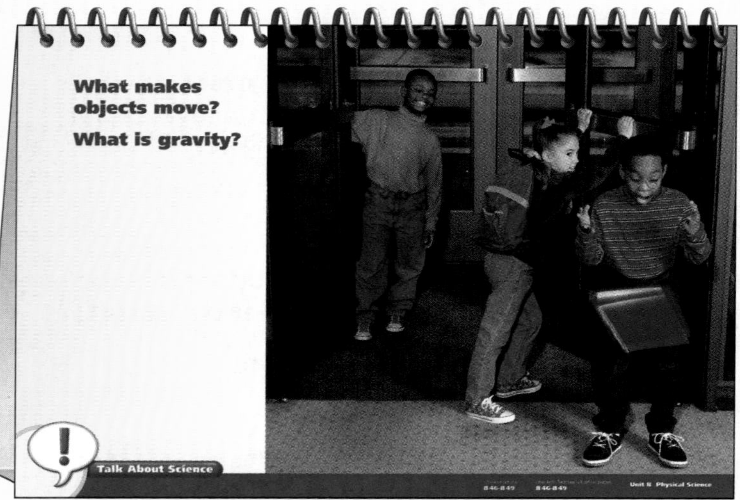
What makes objects move?
What is gravity?
Talk About Science
Unit B Physical Science

What is gravity?

It is a fun day at the park! What force is making the boy slide down the slide?

The boy slides down because of gravity. **Gravity** is the force that pulls things down.

When you jump into the air, gravity pulls you back down. If you let go of an object, gravity makes it fall. If you lose your balance, you will fall too.

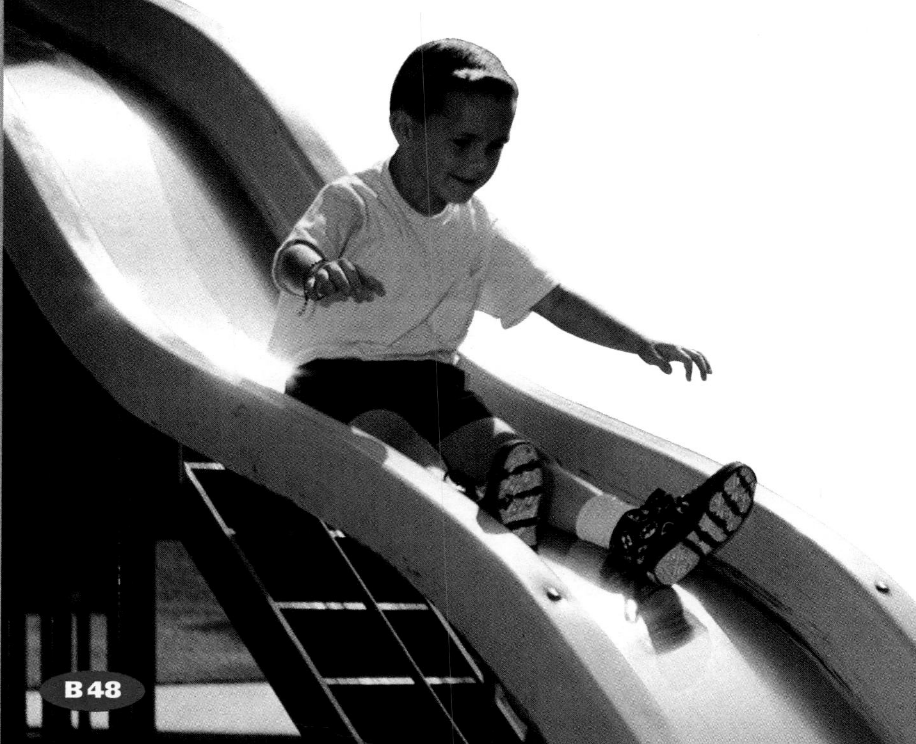

B48

Science Background

- Gravity is a force of attraction between all masses in the universe. The attractive force of one object is equal to and opposite that of the other. When a ball drops to the ground, the pull of the ball on the earth is equal to and opposite the pull of the earth on the ball.
- Galileo, seventeenth-century astronomer and physicist, discovered that when gravity is the only force acting, all objects fall toward the earth at the same rate of acceleration, regardless of their weight, size, or shape.

Possible Misconceptions Although all objects do fall at the same rate of acceleration, wind resistance sometimes affects an object because of its shape or size. This slows its rate when compared with an object that has a different shape or size.

Explore gravity.

Materials

common classroom objects

Process Skills

- predicting

Steps

1. If you drop two objects at the same time, which will hit the floor first? Predict.
2. Hold two objects at the same height and drop them at the same time.
3. Which hit the floor first?
4. Try it again with two new objects.

Share. Compare your predictions with your results.

Lesson Review

1. What is gravity?
2. What happens if you let go of an object?
3. **Show** what happens when you drop two objects from the same height at the same time.

Lab Manual

What is gravity?

Draw the objects you are testing.

Which object will hit the floor first? Predict.

Write what happened.

Lab Manual
p. 52

Activity Rubric

Use the following activity scoring rubric to assess students' performance.

Scoring Criteria	1	2	3	4
Student drew objects involved in this activity.				
Student predicted which of two objects would hit the floor first when dropped.				
Student controlled the height of the falling objects.				
Student recorded the actual results of the comparisons.				
Student demonstrated the force of gravity.				

Scoring Key
4 points correct, complete, detailed
3 points partially correct, complete, detailed
2 points partially correct, partially complete, lacks some detail
1 point incorrect or incomplete, needs assistance

Lab Manual
p. T18

Teach and Apply

Student Page B48

Remind children that in the previous activity they discovered ways to move an object. In each case the object eventually stopped moving. Help children realize that the force of gravity was one factor that caused the object to stop moving.

Reading Assist ***Word Meanings***
Have children find the word *slide* on the page. Point out that the first reference is a verb—it shows action. The second is a noun—it names an object.

Student Page B49

Explore Activity

Time about 10 minutes
Grouping cooperative groups of 2

 ***Safety Note*** *Provide only unbreakable objects for this activity.*

Provide items of different weights so children can experiment with dropping light items versus heavy items. Children can complete Lab Manual page 52.

Assess and Extend

Answers to Lesson Review

1. Gravity is the force that pulls things down.
2. If you let go of an object, it falls.
3. **Show** (*Performance Assessment*) The objects will probably hit the floor at the same time.

Inquire Further

Ask the following questions to guide further inquiry: **Did your prediction match your results? What did you learn from this activity?** (*Answers will vary.*)

Enrichment
Suggest that children try the activity by dropping one item from a greater height than the other.

Higher Order Thinking *Infer*
Ask: **What would happen to things on the earth if gravity did not exist?** (*Everything would float away into space.*)

 **Call 1-888-537-4908 with your Activity questions or comments.**

Science Center

Flip Chart

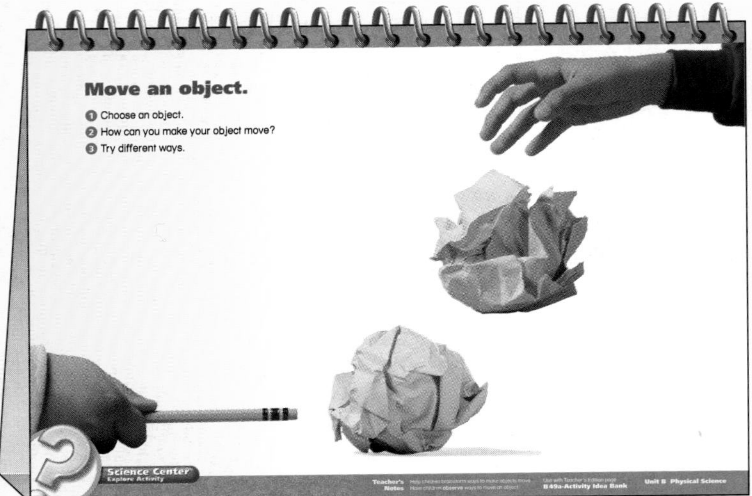

Move an object.
1 Choose an object.
2 How can you make your object move?
3 Try different ways.
Science Center

Move an object.

Objective

Make an object move in different ways.

Process Skills observing

Materials

Kit Items none

School-Supplied Items classroom objects, such as ball of paper, eraser, pencil, book

Procedure

- Brainstorm a list of ways to make objects move. Post the list so children can refer to it.
- Children **observe** different ways they can move an object.
- Ask children to record their observations and use them to communicate their discoveries.
- You can use **Lab Manual** page 53 with this activity.

What to Expect

Children discover that objects are moved with a push or a pull. The object's weight and the strength of the push or pull are two variables that can affect how far the object moves.

Lab Manual

Move an object.

What object did you choose? Draw it.

Draw ways you moved your object.

Lab Manual, p. 53

Connections

School and Community

Ideas for bringing the school and community together:

Field Trips

- science museum
- construction site
- farm

Guest Speakers

- engineer
- heavy-equipment operator

Themes

The activities on these pages can be used with classroom themes such as:

- machines and tools
- space
- energy

Books for Children

Children might enjoy these books about machines:

Whizz! Click! by Diana Noonan. Rose's bedroom is full of toys that whizz, spin, and winch—until they break. Uncle Max has a unique way of fixing Rose's broken toys. (Celebration Press, ISBN 0-478-20527-9)

The Inventors' Diary by Jane Buxton. A week-long project to make a track for marbles. (Celebration Press, ISBN 0-478-20520-1)

Mike Mulligan and His Steam Shovel by Virginia Lee Burton. Mike and his steam shovel, Mary Anne, dig canals, cut through mountains, and hollow out cellars for skyscrapers. (Houghton Mifflin, ISBN 0-395-25939-8)

Cross-Curricular Options

LITERATURE

The Magic School Bus Plays Ball: A Book About Forces

Explore friction and the forces of push and pull.

Materials *The Magic School Bus Plays Ball: A Book About Forces* by Joanna Cole. (Scholastic, ISBN 0-590-92240-8)

Procedure

- A Magic School Bus trip inside a ball teaches friction and the forces of push and pull.
- Clarify for children the facts and fantasy parts of the story.
- Have children demonstrate friction by pushing an object across a desk and a rug. Discuss how different surfaces, such as grass, cement, carpet, ice, and so on, affect friction.

Multiple Intelligences linguistic

ART

Defy Gravity

Make a glider.

Materials paper, crayons, markers

Procedure

- Challenge children to design and make paper airplanes.
- Have them test the planes to see which stay in the air the longest or fly farthest.
- Analyze together why particular gliders stayed in the air longer than others.

Multiple Intelligences spatial

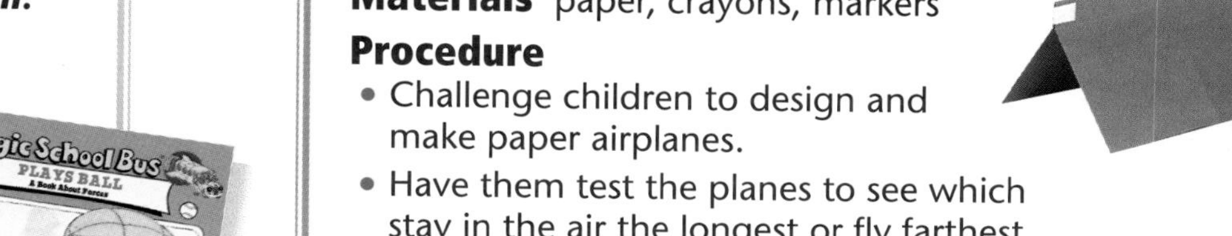

WRITING

No Gravity?

Write a story.

Procedure

- Ask children to imagine what the world would be like if there were no gravity.
- Have them work in groups to write and illustrate a story about what might happen at different places, such as the grocery store or a restaurant, without gravity.

Multiple Intelligences linguistic

PHYSICAL EDUCATION

Playground Forces

Understand what forces are used on the playground.

Materials playground equipment, ball, rope, chalk, toys

Procedure

- Ask children to choose some equipment or a toy to play with.
- Ask each child to identify the kind of force he or she is using.
- Have children explain how force is helping them play.

Multiple Intelligences bodily-kinesthetic, linguistic

Special Needs Children with physical limitations may describe the forces being used by other children.

Lesson Organizer

Objective
Identify when magnets attract and repel each other.

Vocabulary
pole, attract, repel

Process Skills observing

Materials
Kit Items 3-cm donut magnets

School-Supplied Items unsharpened pencils

Additional Resources
- Lab Manual
- Teacher Demonstration Kit

Introduce

Activate Prior Knowledge
Ask children to tell about magnets, such as refrigerator magnets, they may have at home.

Language Development *Vocabulary*
Remind children that forces can make things move. Have children demonstrate how forces work by pulling something, then pushing it away.

Flip Chart
Discuss what magnets can do. Ask which poles on the magnets in the drawing attract each other (*opposite poles*) and which poles repel each other (*like poles*).

What is a magnet?

Have you ever seen objects stick to a rock? Certain metal objects will stick to a rock called a lodestone. Lodestone is a natural magnet.

lodestone

Magnets can push or pull certain metal objects. A **pole** is the place on a magnet that has the strongest push or pull.

Find the north and south poles on the magnets in the picture. Opposite poles attract each other. **Attract** means to pull toward. Like poles repel each other. **Repel** means to push away.

What do you think would happen if two south poles were put together?[1]

[1] They would repel each oth

Science Background

- The pull of a magnet is the result of a magnetic field that surrounds the magnet. This field can pass through many materials, including air, water, and paper.
- The force field of a magnet weakens as the distance from the magnet increases. It is strongest at the poles.

Science Across Cultures Natural magnets, or lodestones, are a type of iron ore called magnetite. Ancient Greeks knew that magnetite had magnetic properties. Sailors from ancient China used lodestone compasses to help guide their ships.

Teaching Tips Be sure to use ring magnets like those provided in the kit. It is important that children use unsharpened pencils.

Push and pull magnets.

Materials
3 magnets
unsharpened pencil

Process Skills
- observing

Steps
1. Hold your pencil like the one in the picture.
2. Put a magnet onto your pencil.
3. Put another magnet on the pencil. Observe.
4. Flip the top magnet over. Observe.
5. Put a third magnet on the pencil. Observe.

Share. Draw your pencil. Show how it looks before you flip the top magnet over and then after you flip the magnet.

Lesson Review
1. What does a magnet do?
2. What happens when opposite poles of two magnets are put together?
3. **Tell** what happens when you flip the top magnet over. Explain why.

B51

Lab Manual

What is a magnet?

Draw what you see when you add one magnet.

Draw what you see when you flip the top magnet over.

Draw what you see when you add another magnet.

Lab Manual p. 54

Activity Rubric

Use the following activity scoring rubric to assess students' performance.

Scoring Criteria	1	2	3	4
Student followed the directions to complete this activity.				
Student observed what happens when opposite poles of magnets are put together.				
Student observed what happens when similar poles of magnets are put together.				
Student recorded his or her observations in a series of drawings.				
Student explained what happened when magnets attract and repel each other.				

Scoring Key
4 points correct, complete, detailed
3 points partially correct, complete, detailed
2 points partially correct, partially complete, lacks some detail
1 point incorrect or incomplete, needs assistance

Lab Manual p. T19

Teach and Apply

Student Page B50

Point out that the bird sticking to the lodestone in the picture is made of metal. Explain that the north and south poles of a magnet are often labeled *N* and *S*. The poles are the strongest part of a magnet.

Reading Assist *Multiple Meanings*
Children may think of other meanings for the word *pole,* such as a long, slender piece of metal or a wooden flagpole. Tell children that here the word *pole* means a place on a magnet that has the strongest push or pull.

Student Page B51

Explore Activity

Time about 10 minutes

Grouping cooperative groups of 4

Have children show how the magnets react to each other. Lead children to discover that like poles of two magnets repel each other, and different poles attract each other. Children can complete Lab Manual page 54.

Safety Note Remind children to keep magnets away from computers, cassettes, and software.

Assess and Extend

Answers to Lesson Review
1. A magnet pushes or pulls certain metal objects.
2. When opposite poles of two magnets are put together, they attract each other.
3. **Tell** (*Interview*) Children's explanations should include the idea that like poles repel each other while opposite poles attract each other.

Inquire Further

Ask the following question to guide further inquiry: **What would happen if you tried the activity with different kinds of magnets?** (*Like poles would repel and unlike poles would attract.*)

Higher Order Thinking *Apply*
Ask: **What would happen if you slid a bar magnet through a path lined with other magnets?** (*Some magnets would attach to one end and some would be pushed away from the path.*)

Call 1-888-537-4908 with your Activity questions or comments.

Lesson Organizer

Objective

Identify some objects a magnet will attract.

Process Skills predicting, observing

Materials

Kit Items 3-cm donut magnets, string

School-Supplied Items common classroom objects, unsharpened pencils

Additional Resources

- Lab Manual
- Teacher Demonstration Kit
- Wall Chart

Introduce

Activate Prior Knowledge

Ask children to draw a picture showing a magnet and label its poles as north and south.

Language Development *Word Web*

Display **Wall Chart** page 29. Invite children to predict what objects might be attracted to magnets and what objects might not be. Record their responses on the **Wall Chart** and save for use as a **baseline assessment.**

Flip Chart

Discuss which objects in the picture a magnet will pick up. Explain that magnets will attract objects that contain iron.

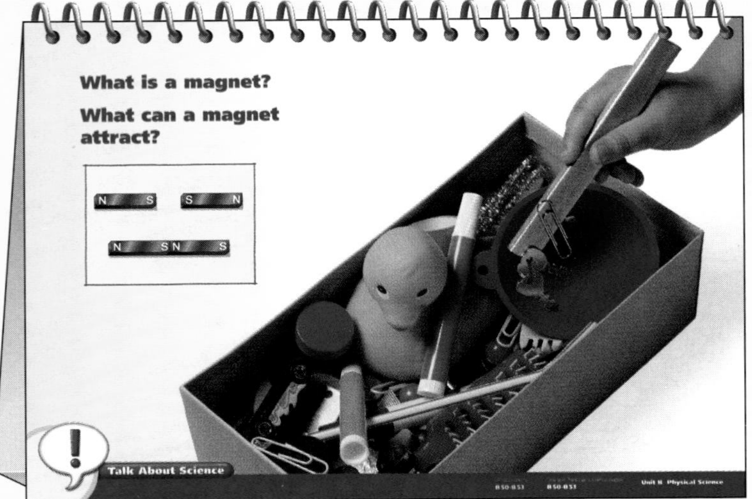

What can a magnet attract?

Wow! This big magnet looks strong! Can it pull all these things toward it? What can a magnet attract?

A magnet attracts certain metal objects. You can use a magnet to find out which kinds of metal objects it will attract.

Talk about the objects in the picture. Which ones do you think the magnet will attract? Why?[1]

[1] Accept all answers that refer to objects that contain iron.

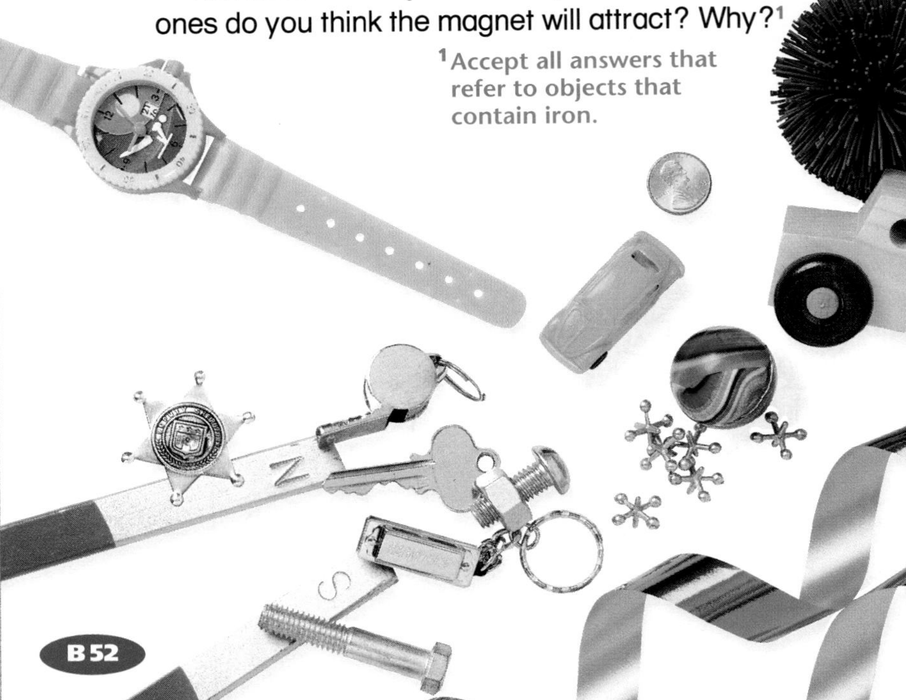

B52

Science Background

All substances have magnetic properties. Some are more magnetic than others.

Science Across Cultures Some countries, including Japan and Germany, have developed trains that use magnetism to move. These trains do not have wheels. An electromagnet—a piece of iron with wire around it—is located on the bottom of the train, allowing it to float above the magnet on the track.

Teaching Tips Remind children to keep the magnets away from computers, cassettes, and computer disks.

Go fishing with a magnet.

Materials

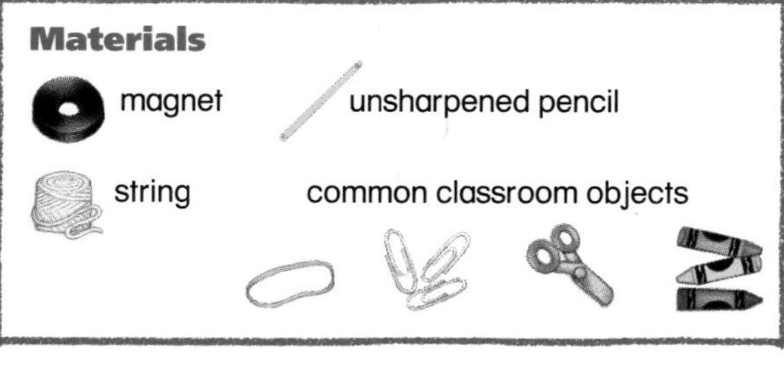

Process Skills

- predicting
- observing

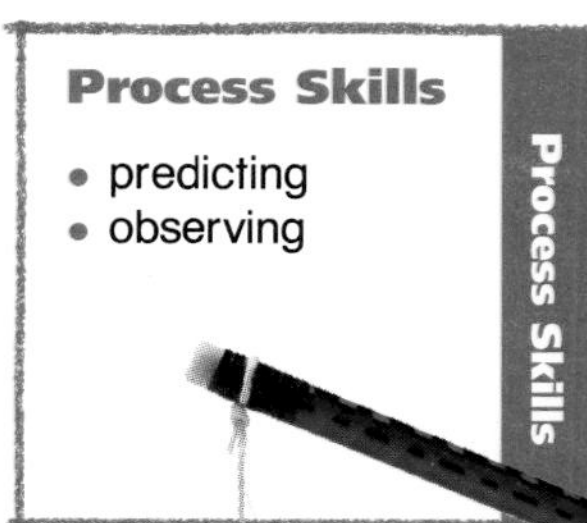

Steps

1. Tie one end of your string to a magnet.
2. Tie the other end to a pencil.
3. Which objects will your magnet attract? Predict.
4. Dip your magnet into a group of objects.
5. Which objects does your magnet attract? Observe.

Share. Make a list of objects a magnet will attract.

Lesson Review

1. What does a magnet attract?
2. Name some things a magnet does not attract.
3. **Tell** how you can predict whether a magnet will attract an object.

B53

Lab Manual

What can a magnet attract?

Draw objects you tested.

Objects a magnet will attract.	Objects a magnet will not attract.

A magnet will attract ______

A magnet will not attract ______

Lab Manual
p. 55

Activity Rubric

Use the following activity scoring rubric to assess students' performance.

Scoring Criteria	1	2	3	4
Student drew common objects to complete this activity.				
Student predicted which objects would be attracted to the magnet.				
Student observed objects that were attracted or not attracted to a magnet.				
Student recorded his or her observations in drawings.				
Student classified objects in terms of those that were attracted to a magnet and those that were not.				

Scoring Key
4 points correct, complete, detailed
3 points partially correct, complete, detailed
2 points partially correct, partially complete, lacks some detail
1 point incorrect or incomplete, needs assistance

Lab Manual
p. T20

Call 1-888-537-4908 with your Activity questions or comments.

Teach and Apply

Student Page B 52

Explain that even the strongest magnets will have little effect on objects that do not contain iron. Point out that magnets attract objects that contain iron.

Reading Assist *Preview and Predict*
Using the lesson title and the pictures, have children predict what they will learn about magnets in this lesson.

Student Page B 53

Explore Activity

Time about 15 minutes

Grouping cooperative groups of 2

- Be sure that children have a good mixture of magnetic and nonmagnetic items.
- Encourage children to move the magnet to different distances to see how far the magnetic effects are evident. Point out that the pull of a magnet diminishes as the magnet moves away from the objects. Children can complete Lab Manual page 55.

Assess and Extend

Answers to Lesson Review

1. A magnet attracts objects with iron.
2. A magnet does not attract something that is not metal, such as wood or paper, or some types of metals, such as aluminum cans.
3. **Tell** (*Interview*) Many, but not all, metal items are magnetic; nonmetal items are not magnetic.

Check for Understanding

To follow up on the **baseline assessment,** have children add to the chart about magnets.

Inquire Further

Ask the following question to guide further inquiry: **What are some other objects the magnet will attract?** (*It will attract any other objects that contain iron.*)

Higher Order Thinking *Compare and Contrast*

Ask children to tell how the objects that are attracted to magnets are alike and different.

Activity Organizer

Objective
Use a magnet to pick up paper clips.

Process Skills predicting, observing

Materials
Kit Items 3-cm donut magnets

School-Supplied Items large paper clips

Time about 5 minutes

Grouping cooperative groups of 3

Additional Resources
- Lab Manual
- Teacher Demonstration Kit

Introduce

The Lesson 5 Investigate Activity, *How many paper clips will a magnet pick up?,* is on the **Flip Chart.**

Activate Prior Knowledge
Have children watch as you place several metallic and nonmetallic items in a bag. Ask what would happen if you placed a magnet in the bag and shook it. Have a volunteer try it and then slowly lift the magnet out of the bag to see the results.

Language Development *Scientific Language*
Remind children that a prediction is more than a guess because they are using information they already know. Ask children to tell what they already know about magnets that will help them predict how many paper clips a magnet will pick up.

Investigate Activity

How many paper clips will a magnet pick up?

Process Skills
- predicting
- observing

Materials

 magnet

 paper clips

Steps
1. Use a chart like the one in the picture.
2. How many paper clips will your magnet pick up? Record your **prediction** by coloring in the chart.
3. Put your magnet into a pile of paper clips.
4. Lift the magnet out. **Observe.**
5. How many paper clips did your magnet pick up? Record your results.

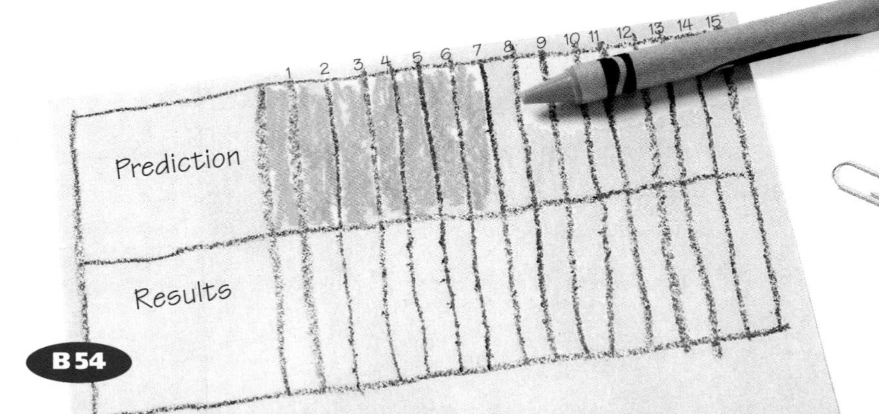

B54

Science Background
- The difference between a piece of iron and an iron magnet is that the electrons in the atoms of the iron are randomly distributed whereas the electrons in the atoms of the magnet are aligned.
- The magnetic effect of the magnet can be destroyed by striking or heating the magnet sufficiently to cause the electrons' positions to become random.
- The electrons in the atoms of the paper clip line up while it is attached to the magnet. The paper clip becomes a temporary magnet and is able to attract other clips.

Technology

Review the demonstration of this Investigate's procedure on the *Physical Science* **Activity Video,** Segment 4.

Think About Your Results

1. How many paper clips did your magnet pick up?
2. When one paper clip was picked up, what happened to the paper clips near it?

Inquire Further

How would your magnet need to change to pick up more paper clips?

Lab Manual

How many paper clips will a magnet pick up?

Use the graph to show your prediction and your results.

15
14
13
12
11
10
9
8
7
6
5
4
3
2
1
0

Prediction | Results

Lab Manual
p. 56

Activity Rubric

Use the following activity scoring rubric to assess students' performance.

Scoring Criteria	1	2	3	4
Student assembled the materials to perform this activity.				
Student predicted the number of paper clips that a magnet would pick up.				
Student observed the actual number of paper clips that a magnet attracted.				
Student recorded the actual results of the activity.				
Student presented the results of the investigation in the form of a chart.				

Scoring Key

4 points correct, complete, detailed
3 points partially correct, complete, detailed
2 points partially correct, partially complete, lacks some detail
1 point incorrect or incomplete, needs assistance

Lab Manual
p. T20

Call 1-888-537-4908 with your Activity questions or comments.

Teach and Apply

- In this activity, children discover how many paper clips they can pick up with a magnet.
- Have children predict how many paper clips their magnets will pick up and record their predictions.
- After children put their magnets into the pile of paper clips, have them remove the clips one at a time to count how many were held by the magnet.
- Have children try attaching paper clips to the magnet in other ways. Ask children which way enabled the magnet to pick up more clips.
- Children can complete Lab Manual page 56.

Reading Assist *Use Picture Clues*

Encourage children to look at the pictured chart to help them determine how to complete their own charts.

What to Expect

Children will discover that not only does the magnet pick up the paper clips directly, but the clips directly attached to the magnet also help hold other clips to it.

Assess and Extend

Answers to Think About Your Results

1. Answers will vary.
2. When one paper clip was picked up, many of the nearby clips were also picked up.

Inquire Further

Children could use a stronger magnet, a bigger or different-shaped magnet, or hold their magnet in a different position. Encourage them to try many ways.

Higher Order Thinking *Apply*

Ask: **What objects might you be able to pick up while holding a sheet of paper under the magnet?** (*Children might apply their knowledge by answering paper fasteners, safety pins, metal washers, large nails, and jar lids.*)

Science Center

Flip Chart

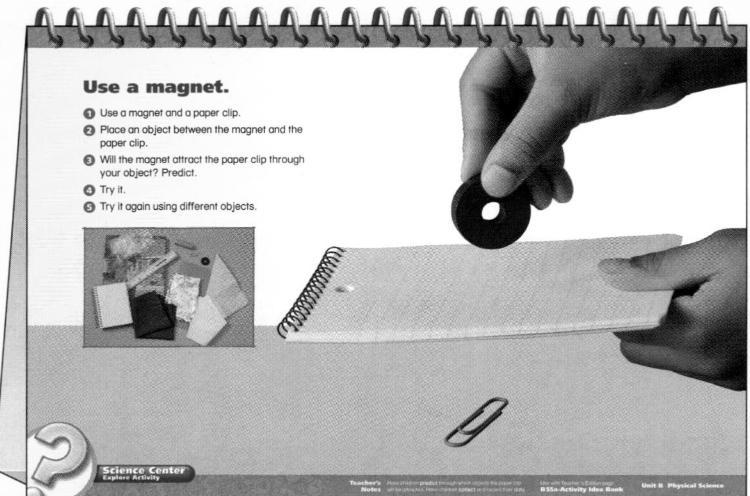

Use a magnet.

Objective

Identify objects through which a magnet will attract a paper clip.

Process Skills predicting, collecting data

Materials

Kit Items 3 cm donut magnet

School-Supplied Items items, some of which are magnetic

Procedure

- Have each child choose an object and **predict** if the magnet will attract the paper clip through the object.
- Invite children to **collect data** as they record what happens with each object.
- Encourage children to try different objects.
- You can use **Lab Manual** page 57 with this activity.

What to Expect

Children discover that the force of a magnet will travel through some objects and not others, depending on an object's thickness.

Lab Manual

Use a magnet.

Will a magnet attract a paper clip through your object?

Object	Prediction	Results

Lab Manual, p. 57

Connections

School and Community

Ideas for bringing the school and community together:

Field Trips

- science museum
- salvage yard
- construction site

Guest Speakers

- power plant worker
- mechanical engineer
- MRI technician

Themes

The activities on these pages can be used with classroom themes such as:

- magnets
- machines
- tools

Books for Children

Children might enjoy these books about magnets and electricity:

What Magnets Can Do by Allan Fowler. What a magnet is, what it is made of, how it works, and how to make magnets. (Childrens Press, ISBN 0-516-46034-X)

The Tricky Sticky Problem by Diana Noonan. When Mr. Martin's key falls down the drain, some children try a variety of ways to retrieve it. (Celebration Press, ISBN 0-478-20514-7)

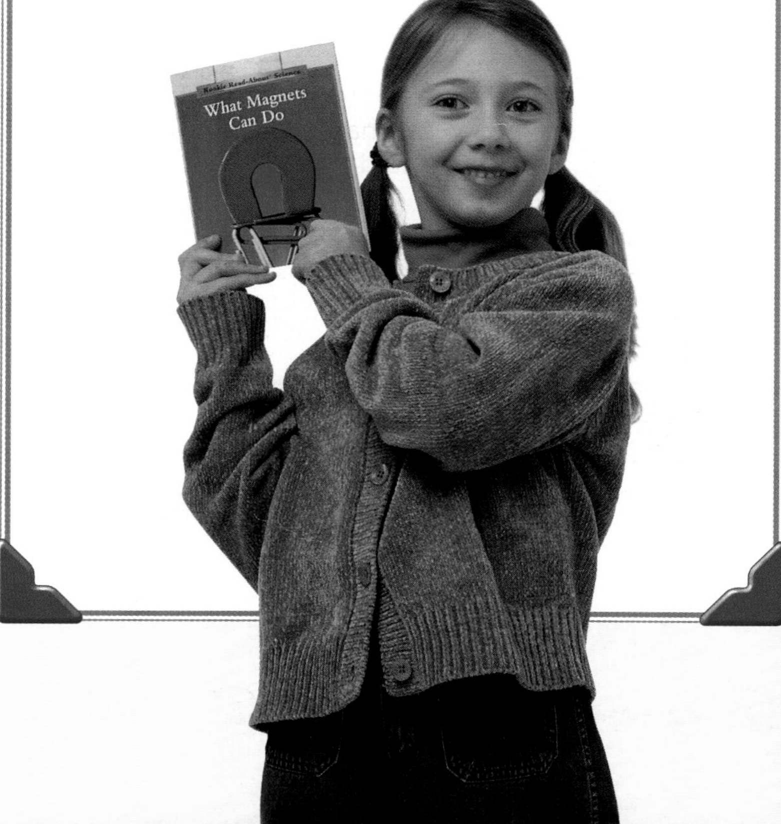

Cross-Curricular Options

LITERATURE

What Makes a Magnet?

Use the book to explore magnets.

Materials *What Makes a Magnet?* by Franklyn M. Branley. (HarperCollins, ISBN 0-06-445148-8), darning needles, corks, large bowl, water, marker, safety goggles

Procedure

- This book describes how magnets work and provides instructions for making a magnet and a compass.
- Have children magnetize a needle as explained in the book. Supply darning needles or other dull needles for children to use. Make sure children wear safety goggles.
- Lead children to understand that magnetism is one kind of force.

Multiple Intelligences linguistic

Amazing

Make a magnet maze.

Materials pencil, ruler, magnet, paper clip

Procedure

- Have children create mazes.
- Encourage them to draw pictures to indicate the beginning and the end of the maze and to give the maze a title.
- Then have children use a paper clip on top of the paper and a magnet on the bottom to move the clip through the maze.

Multiple Intelligences logical-mathematical

Gifted and Talented Challenge children to discover what other materials a magnet's force can pass through.

Helpful Magnets

Make refrigerator magnets.

Materials cardboard or tagboard, crayons, glue, small bar and circle magnets, scissors

Procedure

- Explain that refrigerators have metal doors that magnets are attracted to.
- Have children choose a magnet and a cardboard or tagboard shape about one-half inch larger than the magnet all around.
- Have them draw a picture on the paper shape and glue the magnet to the back.
- Ask children what their refrigerator magnets might hold.

Multiple Intelligences spatial

SOCIAL STUDIES

Electromagnets at Work

Learn how electromagnets work in the community.

Materials pictures of electromagnetic machines

Procedure

- Invite a guest from a salvage/recycling yard, construction site, or hospital to explain how electromagnets are used to do work in the community.
- Show children pictures of electromagnetic machines at work.

Multiple Intelligences spatial

ESL Let children write worker names in English and their first language on cards and practice saying the names.

Lesson Organizer

Objective
Explain how electricity moves.

Vocabulary circuit

Process Skills observing, communicating

Materials

Kit Items lightbulb, 1.3 volts; insulated 22-gauge wire; D battery, 1.5 volts

School-Supplied Items safety goggles

Additional Resources
- Lab Manual
- Teacher Demonstration Kit
- Wall Chart

Introduce

Activate Prior Knowledge
List electrical appliances on the chalkboard. Ask children to choose one and write what they think makes it work. Save their ideas as a **baseline assessment.**

Language Development *Make a List*
Invite children to complete **Wall Chart** page 30. The items listed in the right column are useful electrical objects. Have children list items we could use to do the same thing if we did not have electricity.

Flip Chart
Ask what makes the light in the picture work. (*electricity*) Point to the drawing of the circuit. Have a volunteer trace the path electricity takes.

How does electricity move?
How do you use electricity safely?
Talk About Science

How does electricity move?

Turn on a light. What happens? Electricity makes the light work.

Electricity travels in a path called a **circuit**. If you want to turn on a light, a complete circuit must be made.

Electricity can be stored in a battery. Look at the pictures. Which bulb is lit? Why?[1]

[1]the bulb on the bott[om] because a complete c[ircuit] is made

+
-

incomplete circuit

+
-

complete circuit

B56

Science Background
- The movement of electricity is called *current.* The strength of the current is determined by the force being applied at the source.
- Electricity must flow in a complete circuit from its source. A switch to the off position breaks the circuit.

Teaching Tips In advance, cut the insulated wire and strip the ends for contact. Suggest that children explore different ways to connect the battery, the light, and the wire so that the bulb will light up. Point out that some devices can be used either with batteries or with an electrical outlet. The source of electricity can be through the outlet or the battery, which stores electricity.

Light a bulb.

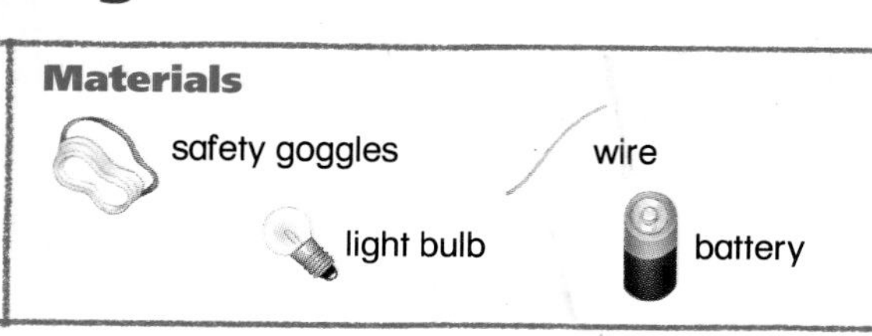

Materials
safety goggles
wire
light bulb
battery

Process Skills
- observing

Steps

1. Put on your safety goggles.
2. Put your materials together to make a complete circuit.
3. How can you make the bulb light up? **Observe.**

Share. Tell how to make a complete circuit.

Lesson Review

1. What is a circuit?
2. Where can electricity be stored?
3. **Show** how you lit your bulb.

B57

Lab Manual

How does electricity move?

Draw your battery and other materials.
Draw how you made the circuit to light the bulb.

Lab Manual
p. 58

Activity Rubric

Use the following activity scoring rubric to assess students' performance.

Scoring Criteria	1	2	3	4
Student followed directions to complete this activity.				
Student drew an electrical circuit to light a bulb.				
Student conducted the activity following proper safety procedures.				
Student observed the results of a completed electrical circuit.				
Student presented his or her observations in a drawing.				

Scoring Key
4 points correct, complete, detailed
3 points partially correct, complete, detailed
2 points partially correct, partially complete, lacks some detail
1 point incorrect or incomplete, needs assistance

Lab Manual
p. T21

Teach and Apply

Student Page B 56

Explain that when the parts of something, like a machine or appliance, are separated, the machine often does not work. But when the parts are put together, they can do things that they cannot do on their own.

Reading Assist *Word Meanings*
Explain that a *circuit* is a path that makes a complete *circle.* Call attention to the similarities of the words.

Student Page B 57

Explore Activity

Time about 15 minutes

Grouping cooperative groups of 4

Refer children to the picture of the complete circuit on page B 56 to help them make their own circuit. Ask why wire was used for this activity. (*It conducts electricity.*) Children can complete Lab Manual page 58.

Safety Note *Tell children not to leave the wires attached to the battery; the wires will heat up.*

Assess and Extend

Answers to Lesson Review

1. A circuit is a path that makes a complete circle.
2. Electricity can be stored in a battery.
3. **Show** (*Performance Assessment*) Children should show that one end of the wire is wrapped around the metal part of the bulb; the other end is taped to the bottom of the battery; the bottom of the bulb is being touched to the top of the battery.

Check for Understanding

To follow up on the **baseline assessment,** ask children to evaluate their ideas about how the appliance worked.

Inquire Further

Ask the following question to guide further inquiry: **Why is it important to cover or insulate the outside of electrical wire?** (*to prevent shock*)

Higher Order Thinking *Apply*

Ask children what they think is used to complete the circuit between an electrical power plant and the light in their bedroom.

Call 1-888-537-4908 with your Activity questions or comments.

Lesson Organizer

Objectives

- Name some ways to use electricity safely.
- Name some uses of electricity.

Additional Resources

- Wall Chart
- Interactive Transparency

Introduce

Activate Prior Knowledge

Ask children to make a list of things they use every day that need electricity. Save children's work for use as a **baseline assessment.**

Language Development *Venn Diagram*

Ask children to name some devices they use at home that can be used either with batteries, an electrical outlet, or both. Record their answers on **Wall Chart** page 31. Point out that in both cases the power needs to be turned on for the object to work.

Flip Chart

Discuss things in the picture that use electricity. Have children name ways to use electricity safely.

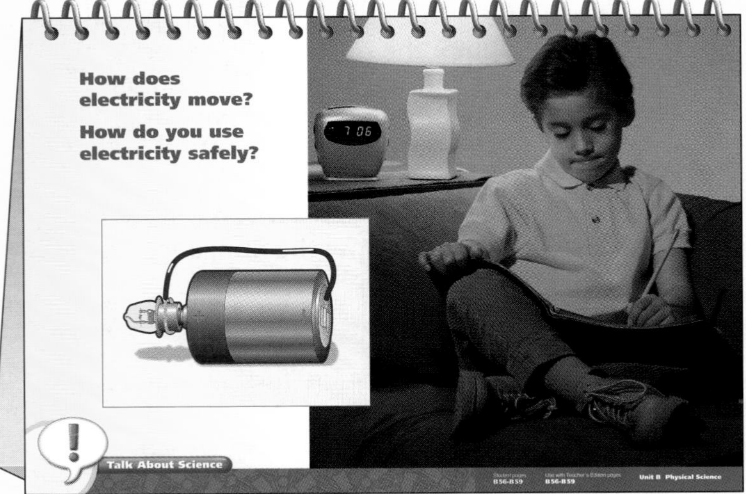
How does electricity move?
How do you use electricity safely?
Talk About Science

How do you use electricity safely?

Listen to music. Look at books. Work on the computer. There is so much to do at the library! [1]possible answers: lights, appliances, and so on.

Electricity makes many things at the library work. It makes the lights work, so you can see and read. It makes the CD player work, so you can listen to music or stories.

What things in your school use electricity? What things at home use electricity?[1]

B58

Science Background

- A magnetic field surrounds an electric current. Wire can be looped around an iron bar to form an electromagnet. An electromagnet works as a magnet only when electricity is flowing through it.
- Electromagnets are the bases of electric motors, automobile starters, thermostats, and telephones.

Possible Misconceptions Children may think that electricity comes from the appliance rather than from a power station. Discuss how electricity travels from the power station into our homes and from the wall plug to a lamp or other electrical appliance.

List Mania!!!

Look around your home and find out 5 electrical appliances which use mains electricity or batteries or both. Write them down in the table below.

Uses Main electricity	Uses Batteries	Uses both

You need to be careful when you use electricity. Do not touch wires or electrical outlets. Do not use anything with a broken cord or wire. Use electricity only in a dry place and keep your hands dry.

Lesson Review

1. What are some ways you use electricity?
2. Name some ways to stay safe when you are using electricity.
3. **Draw** an object that uses electricity.

B59

ESL Strategy

Focus children's attention on the pictures. Ask them to use complete sentences to tell about things in the library that use electricity.

Transparency

Using Electricity Safely

ABCDEFGHIJK

X X X

Interactive Transparency Package
Transparency 6

Teach and Apply

Student Pages B58–B59

Ask children to point out things at the library that need electricity. Explain that electricity is used to produce light, heat, sound, sparks, and magnetic effects.

Reading Assist *Word Meaning*

Explain that the word *electrical* means having to do with *electricity.* In this case, electrical outlets are used to connect to the electricity. Ask children to name other words in this word family. (*electric, electrician, electrify*)

Assess and Extend

Answers to Lesson Review

1. Answers may include using lights and tape players.
2. Do not touch outlets; do not use anything with broken cords or wires; stay dry and use electricity in a dry place.
3. **Draw** (*Portfolio Assessment or Journal*) Accept any object that plugs in or uses a battery.

Check for Understanding

To follow up on the **baseline assessment,** ask children to add to their lists of electrical items they use every day. Remind them that batteries also provide electrical current.

Reteach

- Use the Interactive Transparency to reteach Lesson 7 concepts.
- Have children move around the classroom and point out items that need electricity to work.

Science Center

Flip Chart

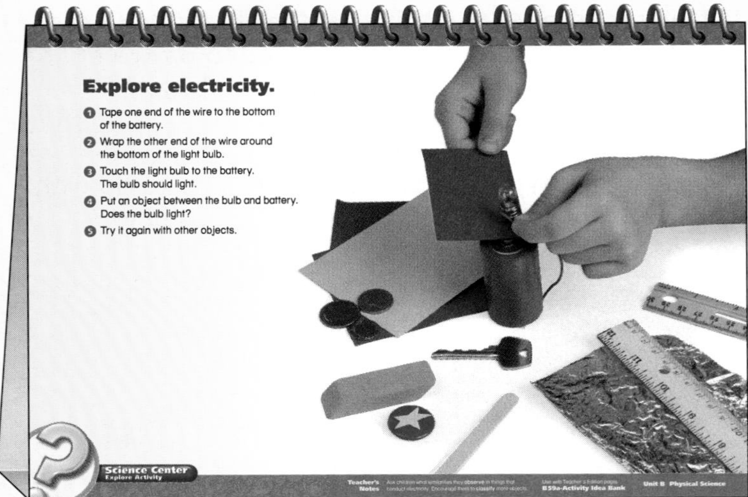

Explore electricity.
1 Tape one end of the wire to the bottom of the battery.
2 Wrap the other end of the wire around the bottom of the light bulb.
3 Touch the light bulb to the battery. The bulb should light.
4 Put an object between the bulb and battery. Does the bulb light?
5 Try it again with other objects.
Science Center

Explore electricity.

Objective

Identify which objects are good conductors of electricity.

Process Skills observing, classifying

Materials

Kit Items 22-gauge insulated wire, #14 miniature lamp, D battery

School-Supplied Items masking tape, metallic and nonmetallic items

Safety Note Remind children that the ends of the wire are sharp. Caution them not to put the wire into a plug or wall outlet.

Procedure

- In advance, cut the wire into strips and strip the ends.
- Invite children to **observe** what happens to the bulb as they try various objects.
- Ask children to **classify** the objects into two groups based on whether the lightbulb lights.
- You can use **Lab Manual** page 59 with this activity.

What to Expect

Children discover that most metallic materials conduct electricity while most nonmetallic materials do not.

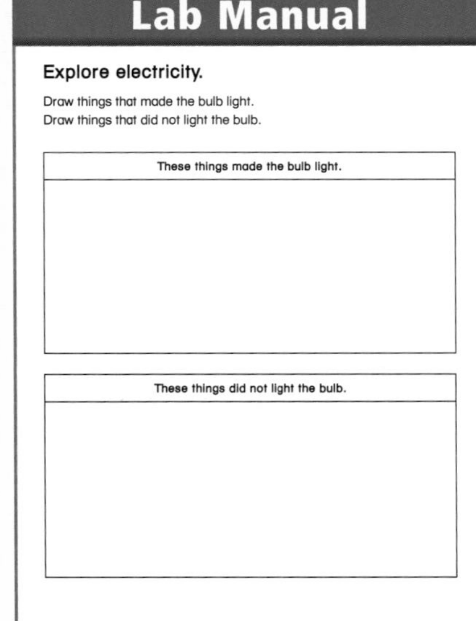

Lab Manual

Explore electricity.

Draw things that made the bulb light.
Draw things that did not light the bulb.

These things made the bulb light.

These things did not light the bulb.

Lab Manual, p. 59

Connections

School and Community

Ideas for bringing the school and community together:

Field Trips

- science museum
- power plant

Guest Speakers

- electrician
- local power plant representative

Themes

The activities on these pages can be used with classroom themes such as:

- inventions
- safety
- energy

Books for Children

Children might enjoy these books about electricity:

The Magic School Bus and the Electric Field Trip by Joanna Cole and Bruce Degen. Ms. Frizzle's class explores electricity by traveling through the town's power lines. (Scholastic, ISBN 0-590-44682-7)

Electricity: Mind-Boggling Experiments You Can Turn Into Science Fair Projects by Janice VanCleave. Twenty hands-on electricity activities. (Wiley, ISBN 0-471-31010-7)

Understanding Electricity with easy to make scientific projects by Gary Gibson. Interactive experiments that cover electrical power, circuits, conductors, insulators, battery power, and more. (Aladdin, ISBN 0-7613-04622)

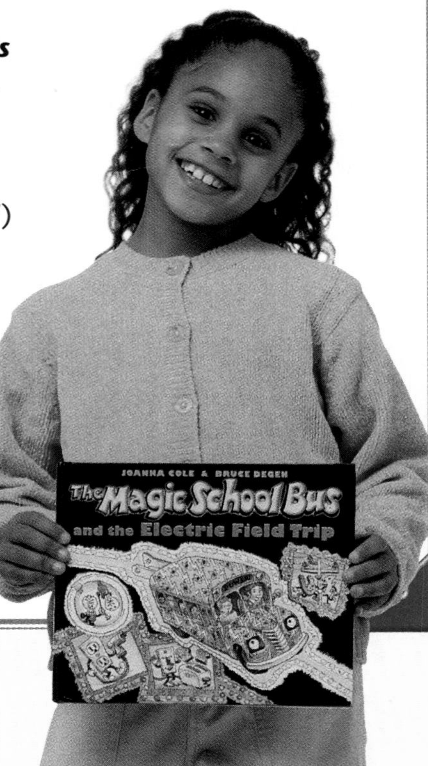

Cross-Curricular Options

LITERATURE

Keep the Lights Burning, Abbie

Share a true story about a young lighthouse keeper.

Materials *Keep the Lights Burning, Abbie* by Peter and Connie Roop. (Carolrhoda, ISBN 0-87614-454-7)

Procedure

- This is a true story about a girl and her family who lived in a lighthouse on the coast of Maine in 1856, before electricity.
- Discuss Abbie's bravery and how she kept the lights burning during a long storm.
- Talk about lighting before electricity. Generate a picture time line of old-fashioned lights, such as candles, torches, and kerosene lamps.

Multiple Intelligences linguistic

MATH

Poll and Tally

Take a poll and graph the results.

Materials paper, crayons, ruler

Procedure

- Generate a list of common appliances.
- Have children poll their homes or school to see how many of each appliance they have.
- Tally the results and make a class bar graph.
- Help children interpret the graph to determine the most and least common appliances.

How We Use Electricity

Appliances: Television, Toaster, Hair Dryer, Video Games, Stereo, Radio, Blender

1 2 3 4 5 6 7

Multiple Intelligences logical-mathematical

ESL To make sure children understand what an appliance is, have them point to and name different appliances in a catalog.

WRITING

Electric Inventions

Write about an invention that uses electricity.

Materials paper, pencil, crayons

Procedure

- Ask children to think of things they do "by hand" that they would like an electric machine to help them do.
- Have children write sentences describing what their invention would do. Encourage them to give it a name.
- Children can draw pictures of the invention doing its job.

Multiple Intelligences linguistic, spatial

Gifted and Talented Children can use crafts supplies and found materials to build a model of their helper—a nonelectric version.

SOCIAL STUDIES

Energy Savers

Make posters about saving electricity.

Materials paper, crayons, markers

Procedure

- Help children create a class list of ways electricity is used in many households.
- Discuss how family members can use electricity wisely and conserve energy, such as by turning off lights when leaving a room, or keeping air conditioners and heaters at reasonable temperatures.
- Encourage children to refer to the list and create posters to describe energy-saving tips.

Multiple Intelligences linguistic

Review Organizer

Materials

Kit Items 3-cm donut magnet

School-Supplied Item string, cardboard, tape, paper, scissors, crayons or markers

Time about 30 minutes

Grouping cooperative groups of 4

Additional Resources

- Chapter 3 Assessment: Teacher's Assessment Package

Chapter Main Ideas

Lesson 1 Force is the push or pull that makes something move.

Lesson 2 Gravity is the force between the earth and objects. Gravity pulls objects to the earth.

Lesson 3 Magnets push or pull certain metal objects. Opposite poles attract; like poles repel.

Lesson 4 Magnets can attract certain metal objects. You can test objects to see if magnets will attract them.

Lesson 5 Magnets attract metal paper clips. The number of paper clips a magnet can hold depends on the size of the paper clips and the type of magnet.

Lesson 6 Electricity travels in a path called a circuit.

Lesson 7 Electricity is a part of our daily lives. It is important to follow safety rules when using electricity.

Reviewing Science Words

1. Children may mention pushing or pulling.
2. Gravity pulls objects down.
3. Two like magnetic poles repel each other.
4. A circuit is a path that makes a complete circle.

Reviewing Science Ideas

1. Objects can move up, down, right, left, in a straight line, in a curve, or in a zigzag.
2. Children may mention paper clips, staples, and other items that contain iron.
3. Electricity moves in a circuit.
4. Do not use objects with broken or frayed cords, use electricity only with dry hands, do not touch outlets.

Chapter 3 Review

Reviewing Science Words

1. How can you use **force** to make an object move?
2. What does **gravity** do?
3. If two **poles** that are alike come together, do they **attract** or **repel** each other?
4. What is a **circuit**?

Reviewing Science Ideas

1. What are some ways objects can move?
2. Name three things a magnet will attract.
3. How does electricity move?
4. How can you use electricity safely?

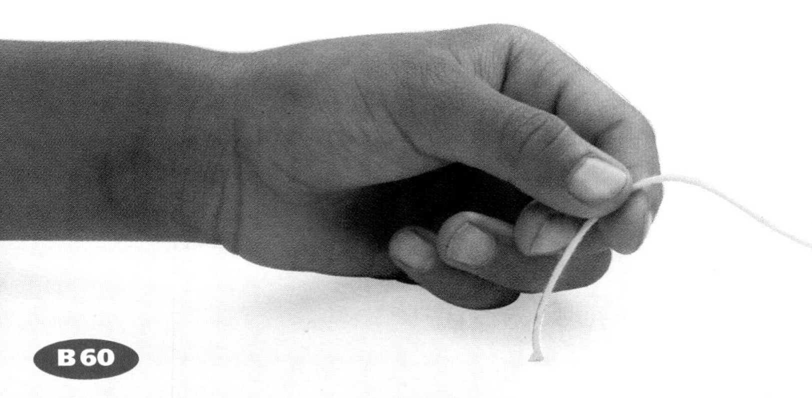

B60

Technology

 Children can review *Force, Magnets, and Electricity* with the **Practice & Assessment CD-ROM.**

 Children can use the **Production Studio** to show what they've learned about *Force, Magnets, and Electricity.*

 Children can use The KnowZone™ at **www.kz.com** to review and test their science knowledge.

 You can use **TestWorks™** to customize assessment for your children.

Build a toy that moves.

Materials

magnets common classroom objects

1. Work with a group.
2. Design a toy.
3. Talk about different ways you can make your toy move.
4. Build your toy and decorate it.

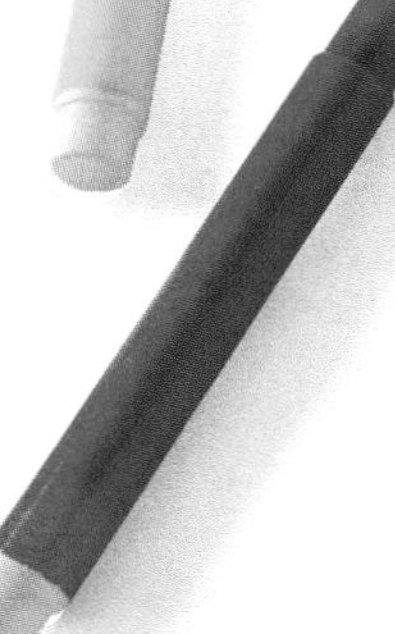

B 61

Chapter Assessment

Circle the picture that shows what the effect will be.

1. Peter is holding a magnet over a pile of nails.

2. Monica dropped her bottle of juice.

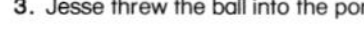

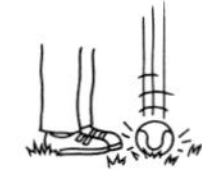

3. Jesse threw the ball into the pond.

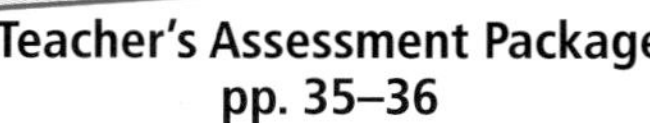

Teacher's Assessment Package pp. 35–36

Assessment Rubric

	Movement
4	Demonstrates a good understanding of ways an object can move.
3	Demonstrates a partial understanding of ways an object can move.
2	Has difficulty demonstrating an understanding of the ways an object can move.
1	Is unable to demonstrate an understanding of the ways an object can move.

Performance Assessment Teaching Tips

- Have children brainstorm a list of ways toys move, such as rolling, falling, zigzagging, up, down, left, and right.
- Be sure children understand that their toys must include ideas about force and about magnets from the chapter. Children may want to create a magnetic toy, a push toy, or a toy they pull with a string. Remind children that they can look at the pictures in the chapter for ideas.
- Children can draw and label pictures of their toys before building them. Remind them to use their drawings to determine what materials to gather.
- Have children tell about the toy they invented. Ask questions such as: **How does your toy move? Do you push it or pull it? What happens if you push your toy harder? Softer? Does your toy have a magnet? What does the magnet do?**

Enrichment

Have each group member draw a picture of the group toy. Challenge them to make one change to the design that will affect the way the toy moves. Have children label their pictures.

Chapter 3 Skills Trace

Process Skills Development

	Predicting	Estimating and Measuring	Observing	Communicating
Skill Introduced	xv	xiv	xiv	xiv
Skill Applied	B 47 B 49 B 53 B 54–B 55	B 47	B 51 B 53 B 54–B 55 B 57	B 57
Skill Assessed	End Matter 16–17	End Matter 12–13	End Matter 6–7	End Matter 8–9

Chapter Review pages are also on the **Flip Chart.**

Review Organizer

Using Multiple Intelligences

The following activities can be used to assess children's understanding of Unit B concepts. Assign the activities based on each child's strongest learning modality. The following chart shows which intelligences are developed in each assessment option.

Activity	Intelligence
Make a chart.	logical-mathematical, spatial
Design a playground ride.	spatial
Write a song.	linguistic, musical

Plan your festival.

Unit Performance Review pages are also on the **Flip Chart.**

Have individuals or groups of children choose one or more of the following activities in which to participate. You may want to set aside a portion of one or more days when children can work on their projects and then present them to classmates.

Design a playground ride.

Before children begin, have them share experiences with rides at playgrounds and at county fairs. Discuss how the rides use force, magnets, and electricity to make them work. As children draw their playground ride, have them think about how a magnet or electricity could make the ride work. Hang a long sheet of craft paper at children's eye level. Invite children to attach their pictures to the paper to make a class playground picture.

Make a chart.

Before children begin their charts, encourage them to explain how they can tell whether something is a solid, a liquid, or a gas. You may want to duplicate blank charts for children on drawing paper with the labels "Solids," "Liquids," "Gases." Suggest that children share their completed charts with partners. Encourage them to ask questions such as the following as they look at partners' charts: "How do you know that this object is a solid? What are some other gases that you might have written?"

Write a song.

Invite children to work in small groups to write and sing songs. Children may want to write an original song, or write new words for a common tune such as *Twinkle, Twinkle Little Star,* or *If You're Happy and You Know It.*

Unit B Performance Review

How can you show what you have learned about force? You can write, draw, or act things out. Choose one thing to show your friends. Have a festival to show what you have learned.

Plan your festival.

1. Pick a project you would like to do.
2. Get what you need for your project.
3. Plan how to show your project to others.

Design a playground ride.

Think about things you see in a playground. Use what you know about force, magnets, and electricity to design a ride for your playground. Draw a picture of your ride. Make a class playground. Glue your picture along with classmates' pictures on a large sheet of paper. Take turns telling about your rides.

Make a chart.

Make a chart with three columns. Label the columns solids, liquids, and gases. Write words or draw pictures in the columns to show solids, liquids, or gases.

Write a song.

Write a song about sound, light, or heat. Make part of your song soft. Make part of your song loud. Use high and low sounds. Give your song a name and sing it to the class.

B63

Assessment Rubric

	Make a chart.	Design a playground ride.	Write a song.
4	Shows a good understanding of the difference among solids, liquids, and gases.	Demonstrates a good understanding of force and magnets or electricity.	Shows a good understanding of pitch and volume, and sound, light, or heat.
3	Shows a fair understanding of the difference among solids, liquids, and gases.	Demonstrates a fair understanding of force and magnets or electricity.	Shows a fair understanding of the concepts of pitch and volume, and sound, light, or heat.
2	Has difficulty showing an understanding of the difference among solids, liquids, and gases.	Has difficulty showing an understanding of force and magnets or electricity.	Has difficulty showing an understanding of pitch and volume, and sound, light, or heat.
1	Is unable to show an understanding of the difference among solids, liquids, and gases.	Is unable to show an understanding of force and magnets or electricity.	Is unable to show an understanding of pitch and volume, and sound, light, or heat.

Portfolio Assessment

Suggested items from this unit to include in children's portfolios are listed on the following pages in the Teacher's Assessment Package:

- Chapter 1: page 19
- Chapter 2: page 25
- Chapter 3: page 31

Unit B Performance Assessment

- The formal Performance Assessment for this unit is on pages 60 A–60 B of the Lab Manual Teacher's Edition.
- The student recording sheet for the formal Performance Assessment for this unit is on pages 61–62 of the Lab Manual, both in the Teacher's Edition and the Student Edition.

Writing Organizer

Objective
Write explanatory sentences to give directions.

Teaching Writing for Science

The Writing for Science page is also on the **Flip Chart.**

Explain to children that their purpose is to write sentences that give directions. Point out that they will share their writing with classmates.

Writing Directions

Guide children through the steps of the writing process.

1. **Prewrite** Think of a noisemaker. Draw a picture of it.
   Encourage children to describe different noisemakers they have seen and used. You may want to bring in some noisemakers for children to explore. Have children draw pictures of a noisemaker that they would like to make. Then encourage them to think about how they could make the noisemakers.
2. **Draft** List the materials you want to use. Write the steps to make a noisemaker.
   You can model this step by having children help you work through the thinking process. Let them hear how you might explain how to make a simple noisemaker. Encourage children to visualize making their noisemaker as they write the steps. Have them number each step to show the order.
3. **Revise** Read the steps. Do they make sense? Read the list of materials. Did you forget anything? Make changes if you need to.
   Have children read through their explanations to see if someone could follow the directions to make a noisemaker. Encourage children to share their drafts and discuss whether the instructions make sense.
4. **Edit** Check your writing to make sure it is correct. Make a neat copy.
   Children can correct errors in capitalization, spelling, and so on during this step. Encourage them to read their writing carefully to make sure others will be able to read it.
5. **Publish** Show your picture and directions to others. Now they can make the noisemaker.
   Suggest that children form small groups and take turns reading their explanations aloud to each other. Encourage listeners to tell if they think they could make the noisemaker by following the directions.

Writing Directions

When you explain how to do something, you are giving directions. You can draw pictures and write sentences to give directions for how to make something. Be sure to put the steps in the right order.

1. **Prewrite** Think of a noisemaker. Draw a picture of it.
2. **Draft** List the materials you want to use. Write the steps to make a noisemaker.
3. **Revise** Read the steps. Do they make sense? Read the list of materials. Did you forget anything? Make changes if you need to.
4. **Edit** Check your writing to make sure it is correct. Make a neat copy.
5. **Publish** Show your picture and directions to others. Now they can make the noisemaker.

B 64

Writing Rubric

	4	3	2	1
Follows steps of writing process in order				
Communicates specific details and information				
Includes ideas related to topic				
Writes clear sentences				
Uses correct capitalization				

Scoring Key **Total Score** ______

4 points correct, complete, detailed
3 points partially correct, complete, detailed
2 points partially correct, partially complete, lacks some detail
1 point incorrect or incomplete, needs assistance

Technology

Children can share their explanatory sentences at **www.sfscience.com.**

C1

Science Background

What Is Earth Science? Earth science is the study of what makes up the earth and the things that effect the earth. For young children this means studying rocks, soil, volcanoes, temperature, rainfall, and the moon. Earth science can help answer questions such as these: How do rocks become soil? Why do the seasons change? What causes day and night?

About the Photograph The photograph on this page shows a pinwheel. Ask children to tell what they know about pinwheels and in what kind of weather a pinwheel is likely to spin. Tell children they will learn more about weather and seasons in Chapter 2, "Weather and Seasons."

Technology

You can use the **Teacher's Resource Planner** to plan and organize your curriculum.

In This Unit

In this unit, children learn about the earth, weather, seasons, and the solar system. They study what makes up rocks and soil, volcanoes and earthquakes, and the resources we get from the earth. They experiment with temperature and measure rain. They discover what causes night and day, study the phases of the moon, and find out what is in our solar system.

Books for Teachers

Chapter 1

Education Goes Outdoors by Frank A. Johns, Kurt Allen Liske, and Amy L. Evans. Community resources are used to develop children's awareness of their environment. (Scott Foresman - Addison Wesley, ISBN 0-201-20471-1)

Earth Book for Kids: Activities to Help Heal the Environment by Linda Schwartz. Arts and crafts projects, experiments, and activities that encourage children to enjoy and protect the environment. (The Learning Works, ISBN 0-88160-195-0)

Chapter 2

Weather Watch by Valerie Wyatt. Explanations of what makes weather, why it changes, and how it affects people and animals, along with activities for weather-related projects. (Kids Can Press, ISBN 0-201-15404)

Usborne Book of Weather Facts by Anita Ganeri. Fascinating facts about the world's weather and climate. (EDC Publishing, ISBN 0-86020-975-X)

Chapter 3

Moon Journals: Writing, Art, and Inquiry Through Focused Nature Study by Joni Cancer and Gina Rester-Zodrow. The authors recount how their students observed the moon for 28 days and recorded their impressions. Ideas for creating and using similar journals. (Heinemann, ISBN 0-435-07221-8)

How Come? by Kathy Wollard. Detailed answers to frequently asked questions about our world. (Workman Publishing Company, ISBN 1-56305-324-1)

	Chapter Concepts/ National Science Education Standards	Lessons/Vocabulary
Chapter 1	**The Earth** p. C4 **Concepts** Features of the earth include mountains, hills, valleys, oceans, rivers, and lakes. Rocks are made from minerals, and come in many shapes, sizes, textures, and colors. Erosion of land happens when soil or rock are carried away. Volcanoes and earthquakes are natural events that change the earth. Natural resources are useful materials from the earth. Recycling and reusing objects can help protect the earth and keep it clean. Many everyday items can be recycled. **National Science Education Standards**  Content Standard D, p. 130 • **Properties of earth materials** • **Changes in earth and sky**	**Lesson 1** *What are some features of the earth? p. C6* **Reading for Science** *Using Descriptive Words p. C8* **Lesson 2** *What are rocks like? p. C10* **Lesson 3** *How can rocks and soil be changed? p. C12* **Vocabulary** erosion **Lesson 4** *How do volcanoes and earthquakes change the earth? p. C14* **Vocabulary** lava **Lesson 5** *How can you make a model of a volcano? p. C16* **Lesson 6** *What resources do we get from the earth? p. C18* **Vocabulary** natural resources **Lesson 7** *How can you help protect the earth? p. C20* **Vocabulary** recycling **Lesson 8** *What can be recycled? p. C22*
Chapter 2	**Weather and Seasons** p. C26 **Concepts** Scientists use thermometers and anemometers to measure the weather. Changes in temperature can be measured and recorded. Weather and seasonal changes in spring, summer, fall, and winter affect plants and animals. The movement of water from clouds to the earth and back again is called the water cycle. **National Science Education Standards**  Content Standard D, p. 130 • **Changes in earth and sky**	**Lesson 1** *What can you tell about the weather? p. C28* **Vocabulary** thermometer, anemometer **Math in Science** *Using Measurement Tools p. C30* **Lesson 2** *Experiment with temperature. p. C32* **Lesson 3** *What happens in spring and summer? p. C34* **Lesson 4** *What happens in fall and winter? p. C36* **Lesson 5** *Is there water in air? p. C38* **Vocabulary** evaporates, condenses, water cycle **Lesson 6** *How does water vapor condense? p. C40* **Lesson 7** *What are some kinds of bad weather? p. C42* **Vocabulary** tornado, drought
Chapter 3	**The Solar System** p. C46 **Concepts** Day and night happen because the earth rotates. The sun only appears to move across the sky because the earth moves. The moon is not like the earth because it has no air nor living things. The moon seems to change shape because we see only the part of the moon with sunlight shining on it. The phases of the moon can be recorded. The sun is a star at the center of our solar system about which all the planets in our solar system orbit. Scientists gain information about our solar system through a variety of means. **National Science Education Standards**  Content Standard D, p. 130 • **Objects in the sky** • **Changes in earth and sky**	**Lesson 1** *What causes day and night? p. C48* **Lesson 2** *What do we know about the moon? p. C50* **Vocabulary** craters, phases **Lesson 3** *How can you record the phases of the moon? p. C52* **Reading for Science** *Using Picture Clues p. C54* **Lesson 4** *What is in our solar system? p. C56* **Vocabulary** orbit **Lesson 5** *How do we learn about the solar system? p. C58* **Vocabulary** telescope
Unit C Assessment	**Unit Performance Review** pp. C62–C63 **Writing for Science** p. C64	

Activity Opportunities

Student Edition
- Explore Activity ***Make a model of features of the earth.*** p. C7
- Explore Activity ***Show erosion.*** p. C13
- Investigate Activity ***How can you make a model of a volcano?*** pp. C16–C17
- Explore Activity ***Make compost.*** p. C21

Flip Chart
- Science Center Explore Activity *Match rocks with clues.*
- Science Center Explore Activity *Make a model of an earthquake.*
- Science Center Explore Activity *Protect the earth.*

Teacher's Edition
- Activity Idea Bank, pp. C13a–C13b, C17a–C17b, C23a–C23b

Additional Resources
- Family Activity, Instructional Resources Package, pp. 49–50
- Vocabulary Preview, Instructional Resources Package, p. 51
- Graphic Organizer, Teacher's Assessment Package, p. 39
- Lab Manual, pp. 63, 65, 66, 67, 68, 69, 71
- Interactive Transparency 7, Interactive Transparency Package
- Wall Chart, pp. 32, 33, 34, 35, 36, 37

Technology
- *Earth Science* National Lab **www.sfscience.com**

Assessment Opportunities

Student Edition
- Lesson 1 Review, p. C7
- Lesson 2 Review, p. C11
- Lesson 3 Review, p. C13
- Lesson 4 Review, p. C15
- Lesson 6 Review, p. C19
- Lesson 7 Review, p. C21
- Lesson 8 Review, p. C23
- Chapter 1 Review, pp. C24–C25

Teacher's Edition
- Process Skills Development, pp. C5 & C25
- Assessment Rubric, p. C25

Teacher's Assessment Package
- Chapter 1 Review, p. 40
- Chapter 1 Assessment, pp. 41–42
- Portfolio Ideas, p. 37

Lab Manual
- Activity Rubric, pp. T23, T24, T25, T26

Technology
- **Practice & Assessment CD-ROM**
- **Production Studio**
- **The KnowZone™ at www.kz.com**
- **TestWorks™**

Student Edition
- Explore Activity ***Make an anemometer.*** p. C29
- Experiment Activity ***Experiment with temperature.*** pp. C32–C33
- Explore Activity ***Observe the water cycle.*** p. C39
- Investigate Activity ***How does water vapor condense?*** pp. C40–C41

Flip Chart
- Science Center Explore Activity *Observe wind.*
- Science Center Explore Activity *Explore evaporation.*

Teacher's Edition
- Activity Idea Bank, pp. C37a–C37b, C43a–C43b

Additional Resources
- Family Activity, Instructional Resources Package, pp. 57–58
- Vocabulary Preview, Instructional Resources Package, p. 59
- Graphic Organizer, Teacher's Assessment Package, p. 45
- Lab Manual, pp. 73, 75–76, 77, 78, 79, 80
- Interactive Transparency 8, Interactive Transparency Package
- Wall Chart, pp. 38, 39, 40, 41, 42

Technology
- *Earth Science* National Lab **www.sfscience.com**

Student Edition
- Lesson 1 Review, p. C29
- Lesson 3 Review, p. C35
- Lesson 4 Review, p. C37
- Lesson 5 Review, p. C39
- Lesson 7 Review, p. C43
- Chapter 2 Review, pp. C44–C45

Teacher's Edition
- Process Skills Development, pp. C27 & C45
- Assessment Rubric, p. C45

Teacher's Assessment Package
- Chapter 2 Review, p. 46
- Chapter 2 Assessment, pp. 47–48
- Portfolio Ideas, p. 43

Lab Manual
- Activity Rubric, pp. T26, T27, T28, T29

Technology
- **Practice & Assessment CD-ROM**
- **Production Studio**
- **The KnowZone™ at www.kz.com**
- **TestWorks™**

Student Edition
- Explore Activity ***Show how the earth rotates.*** p. C49
- Investigate Activity ***How can you record the phases of the moon?*** pp. C52–C53

Flip Chart
- Science Center Explore Activity *Make a moon project.*
- Science Center Explore Activity *Make a model of a rocket.*

Teacher's Edition
- Activity Idea Bank, pp. C53a–C53b, C59a–C59b

Additional Resources
- Family Activity, Instructional Resources Package, pp. 65–66
- Vocabulary Preview, Instructional Resources Package, p. 67
- Graphic Organizer, Teacher's Assessment Package, p. 51
- Lab Manual, pp. 81, 83, 85, 87
- Interactive Transparency 9, Interactive Transparency Package
- Wall Chart, pp. 43, 44, 45, 46, 47, 48

Technology
- *Earth Science* National Lab **www.sfscience.com**

Student Edition
- Lesson 1 Review, p. C49
- Lesson 2 Review, p. C51
- Lesson 4 Review, p. C57
- Lesson 5 Review, p. C59
- Chapter 3 Review, pp. C60–C61

Teacher's Edition
- Process Skills Development, pp. C47 & C61
- Assessment Rubric, p. C61

Teacher's Assessment Package
- Chapter 3 Review, p. 52
- Chapter 3 Assessment, pp. 53–54
- Portfolio Ideas, p. 49

Lab Manual
- Activity Rubric, pp. T29, T30, T31

Technology
- **Practice & Assessment CD-ROM**
- **Production Studio**
- **The KnowZone™ at www.kz.com**
- **TestWorks™**

Student Edition
- Unit C Performance Review, pp. C62–C63

Teacher's Edition
- Assessment Rubric, p. C63

Technology
- *Writing for Science* **www.sfscience.com**

Activity Organizer

Objective
Experiment to find out how to use toothpicks and clay to build a structure that will hold a block.

Process Skills predicting, observing

Parallel Student Book Lesson
Chapter 2, Lesson 1

Materials toothpicks, modeling clay, wooden block

EXTENDED INQUIRY

What can you build to hold a block?

The following activity is a model of an inquiry-based science fair project for you to do with the class. A list suggesting individual science projects follows the activity. Use these steps of scientific inquiry.

Steps

1 Ask a question about objects, organisms, and events in the environment.

- Pose the following question to children: **How can you use toothpicks and clay to build a structure that will hold a block?**
- Discuss the idea that buildings and other structures are designed to withstand changes in the land, such as changes that might occur in an earthquake.
- Provide children with toothpicks, modeling clay, and a wooden block. Ask them predict how they might design their structures to make them sturdy enough to hold the wooden block. Children will use the toothpicks and clay to build a structure.

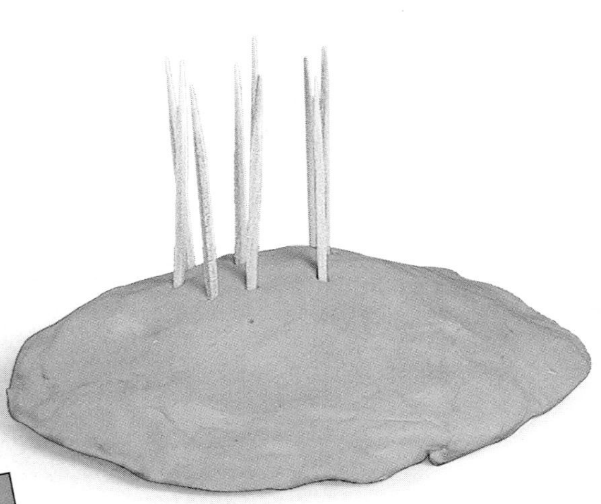

This activity follows methods of scientific inquiry suggested in the National Science Education Standards.

2 Plan and conduct a simple investigation.

- Have each child or group design and build structures.
- Children might use a trial and error method to refine their designs.
- Encourage children to talk about what they are doing and why.

3 Employ simple equipment and tools to gather data and extend the senses.

To show what they can build to hold a block, children may want to:

- draw a picture of the structure
- make a tape recording describing their process and results

4 Use data to construct a reasonable explanation.

- Ask: **Why did some structures hold a block better than others?** (*Possible answers: They had a wider base; two or more toothpicks were placed side by side instead of individually.*)

5 Communicate investigations and explanations.

- Have children discuss their observations. Children should describe similarities in the structures that were able to hold the block.

Inquire Further

Ask children how they could build a structure strong enough to hold two blocks or a heavier object.

Science Fair Projects

Chapter 1 Landform Models
Display picture postcards that depict different landforms. Then have children use clay, sand, water, and other materials to create a large model of a landform.

Chapter 2 Tornado in a Bottle
Invite children to create a tornado, using 2 two-liter bottles, duct tape, and water. They fill one bottle with water to the neck. Then they place the empty bottle on top of the other one, securing the bottles with duct tape. Children invert the bottles to create a whirling, funnel-shaped tornado.

Chapter 3 Solar Oven Have children explore how the sun provides solar energy. Have them tape foil, shiny side up, to the inside of a shoe box. Children put a small piece of a potato in the box, cover the box with plastic wrap, and place the box in the sun for most of a day to "cook." Invite children to experiment with other foods.

Technology

Children can participate in the Earth Science extended inquiry *National Lab* at **www.sfscience.com.**

Unit Overview

Teaching Science and Technology

Unit C Earth Science pages are also on the **Flip Chart.**

Have children look at the pictures. Talk about ways these pictures show examples of technology.

- The shaking table was designed to support civil engineers working to prevent major earthquake disasters. It can effectively simulate an earthquake, giving researchers increased flexibility and control over their experiments.
- Several types of weather satellites exist. Geostationary satellites operate in high orbit at the same speed as the earth's rotation. They track weather patterns for an entire hemisphere. Polar-orbiting satellites operate in low-orbit and pass over the entire atmosphere of the earth every 24 hours as the earth rotates beneath it. They monitor atmospheric temperature, moisture level, and ozone layer integrity.
- These jetpacks are safety devices for astronauts. When working outside the space shuttle, astronauts can sometimes drift away. They use the jetpack to push themselves back in place.

Science and Technology In Your World!

What happens during an earthquake?

An earthquake simulator is a special shaking table. It can help scientists learn more about earthquakes. People can use this information to design buildings and bridges that are safer.

Chapter 1
The Earth

What does a weather satellite do?

It takes pictures that help scientists learn about clouds, temperature, and amounts of water in the air. The pictures help scientists predict the weather.

Chapter 2
Weather and Seasons

C2

Writing for Science

Descriptive

Write a Weather Report

Invite children to write a weather report. Suggest that they describe what it is like outside today, or have them select their favorite type of weather to describe. Remind children to follow the steps of the writing process: prewrite, draft, revise, edit, publish.

The Writing Process

The Writing Process

1. Prewrite
   - Talk with another person about things you can write about.
   - Choose one thing and draw a picture of it.
2. Draft
   Write sentences about your picture.
3. Revise
   Read what you wrote. Do you like it? Make changes if you want to.
4. Edit
   Check your writing to make sure it is correct. Make a neat copy.
5. Publish
   Share your picture and your writing with others.

Instructional Resources p. xi

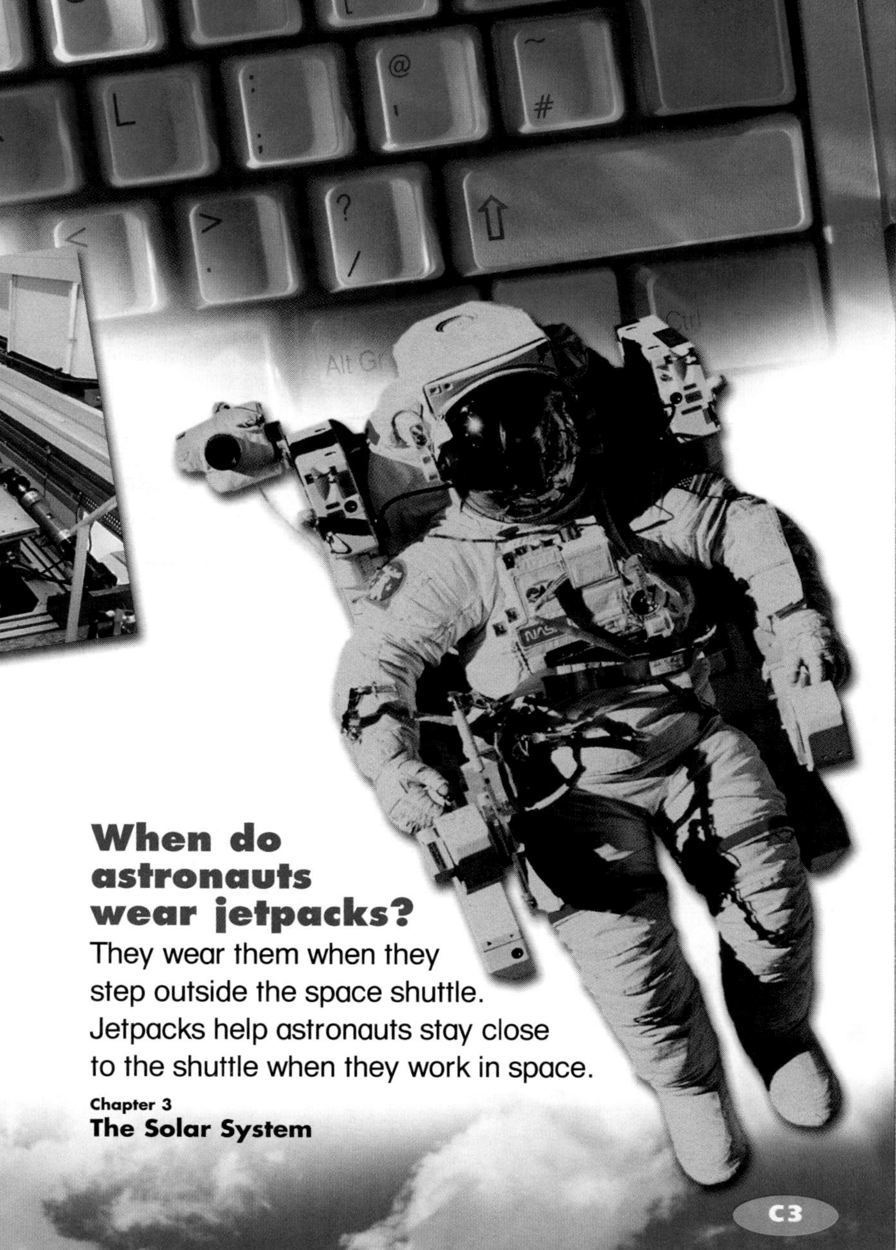

When do astronauts wear jetpacks?
They wear them when they step outside the space shuttle. Jetpacks help astronauts stay close to the shuttle when they work in space.
Chapter 3
The Solar System
C3

INQUIRY

One aspect of inquiry involves asking questions. Give each child three index cards, one for each chapter in this unit. After they read the Science and Technology pages, have children write one question about each chapter. Throughout each chapter, children should use their text and other resources to look for the answer to their question. At the conclusion of each chapter, children should share the answer to their question with the class.

Math-Science Connection

Calculating

Tell children that a jetpack travels about 3 meters per second. Use this information to present word problems such as the following: **An astronaut is wearing a jetpack that travels 3 meters per second. How far can the astronaut travel in 2 seconds? In 3 seconds?**

Lesson/Activity and Flip Chart	Objectives/Process Skills	Time Options/Activity Materials
Chapter Opener Student Edition pp. C4–C5 and **Flip Chart** ***Mountains and Rocks***		**Have less time?** Use the Graphic Organizer on Teacher's Assessment Package p. 39 for an overview of the lessons. Use the Flip Chart to teach lesson concepts and science activities. **Have more time?** Use the Flip Chart to reinforce and extend lesson concepts and activities. Use the Cross-Curricular Options in the Activity Idea Bank on Teacher's Edition pp. C13b, C17b, and C23b.
Lesson 1 Student Edition pp. C6–C7 ***What are some features of the earth?*** **Explore Activity** ***Make a model of features of the earth.*** **Flip Chart** ***Talk About Science***	**Objective** Identify features of the earth such as mountains and lakes. **Process Skills** making and using models	**Kit Items** modeling clay, sand **School-Supplied Items** rocks, blue construction paper
Reading for Science Student Edition pp. C8–C9 ***Using Descriptive Words***	**Objective** Use descriptive words.	
Lesson 2 Student Edition pp. C10–C11 ***What are rocks like?*** **Flip Chart** ***Talk About Science***	**Objective** Identify types of rocks.	**Have more time?** Use the following teaching guide option: Interactive Transparency 7, Interactive Transparency Package
Lesson 3 Student Edition pp. C12–C13 ***How can rocks and soil be changed?*** **Explore Activity** ***Show erosion.*** **Flip Chart** ***Talk About Science***	**Objective** Identify ways rocks and soil can be changed. **Process Skills** observing, predicting, making and using models	**Kit Items** soil, cup, pan **School-Supplied Items** water, safety goggles **Advance Prep** Make a small hole in the bottom of each cup with the tip of a pencil.
Activity Idea Bank Teacher's Edition pp. C13a–C13b **Flip Chart** **Science Center Explore Activity** ***Match rocks with clues.***	**Objective** Identify the properties of different rocks. **Process Skills** observing, communicating	**Kit Items** rock specimen pack **School-Supplied Items** 3 index cards, paper, pencil
Lesson 4 Student Edition pp. C14–C15 ***How do volcanoes and earthquakes change the earth?*** **Flip Chart** ***Talk About Science***	**Objective** Identify ways that volcanoes and earthquakes change the earth.	
Lesson 5 Student Edition pp. C16–C17 and **Flip Chart** **Investigate Activity** ***How can you make a model of a volcano?***	**Objective** Make a model of a volcano. **Process Skills** making and using models, estimating and measuring, observing	**Kit Items** modeling clay, vinegar, plastic vial, baking soda, pan **School-Supplied Items** safety goggles, spoon, dishwashing soap, red food coloring, craft stick
Activity Idea Bank Teacher's Edition pp. C17a–C17b **Flip Chart** **Science Center Explore Activity** ***Make a model of an earthquake.***	**Objective** Demonstrate effects of earthquakes. **Process Skills** predicting	**Kit Items** none **School-Supplied Items** paper, wood or plastic blocks
Lesson 6 Student Edition pp. C18–C19 ***What resources do we get from the earth?*** **Flip Chart** ***Talk About Science***	**Objective** Identify natural resources and their uses.	
Lesson 7 Student Edition pp. C20–C21 ***How can you help protect the earth?*** **Explore Activity** ***Make compost.*** **Flip Chart** ***Talk About Science***	**Objective** Identify some effects of pollution and ways people can protect natural resources. **Process Skills** observing, making definitions	**Kit Items** soil **School-Supplied Items** food scraps, leaves, grass, water, craft stick, plastic jar with lid **Advance Prep** If you use clear, plastic bottles, cut the tops off.
Lesson 8 Student Edition pp. C22–C23 ***What can be recycled?*** **Flip Chart** ***Talk About Science***	**Objective** Identify some items that can be recycled.	
Activity Idea Bank Teacher's Edition pp. C23a–C23b **Flip Chart** **Science Center Explore Activity** ***Protect the earth.***	**Objective** Identify ways to protect the earth. **Process Skills** classifying	**Kit Items** none **School-Supplied Items** tape, paper, crayons or markers
Chapter Review Student Edition pp. C24–C25 and **Flip Chart**		**Kit Items** none **School-Supplied Items** magazines, books

Lesson/Activity and Flip Chart	Additional Resources		Technology
Chapter Opener Student Edition pp. C4–C5 and **Flip Chart** ***Mountains and Rocks***	**Teacher's Assessment Package** • Graphic Organizer, p. 39 **Instructional Resources** • Family Activity, pp. 49–50 • Vocabulary Preview, p. 51	**Songs & Activities Package** • *Mountains and Rocks*, pp. 21–22 **Wall Chart,** p. 32	**Practice & Assessment CD-ROM** **AudioText** **Production Studio** **www.sfscience.com** **Songs & Activities Package** **Teacher's Resource Planner CD-ROM**
Lesson 1 Student Edition pp. C6–C7 ***What are some features of the earth?*** **Explore Activity** ***Make a model of features of the earth.*** **Flip Chart** ***Talk About Science***	**Lab Manual** • Lab Manual, p. 63 • Activity Rubric, p. T23	**Teacher Demonstration Kit**	
Reading for Science Student Edition pp. C8–C9 ***Using Descriptive Words***	**Instructional Resources** • Reading for Science, p. 52		
Lesson 2 Student Edition pp. C10–C11 ***What are rocks like?*** **Flip Chart** ***Talk About Science***	**Interactive Transparency Package** • Interactive Transparency 7	**Wall Chart,** p. 33	
Lesson 3 Student Edition pp. C12–C13 ***How can rocks and soil be changed?*** **Explore Activity** ***Show erosion.*** **Flip Chart** ***Talk About Science***	**Lab Manual** • Lab Manual, p. 65 • Activity Rubric, p. T23	**Teacher Demonstration Kit**	
Activity Idea Bank Teacher's Edition pp. C13a–C13b **Flip Chart** **Science Center Explore Activity** ***Match rocks with clues.***	**Lab Manual** • Lab Manual, p. 66 • Activity Rubric, p. T24		
Lesson 4 Student Edition pp. C14–C15 ***How do volcanoes and earthquakes change the earth?*** **Flip Chart** ***Talk About Science***			
Lesson 5 Student Edition pp. C16–C17 and **Flip Chart** **Investigate Activity** ***How can you make a model of a volcano?***	**Lab Manual** • Lab Manual, p. 67 • Activity Rubric, p. T24	**Teacher Demonstration Kit** **Wall Chart,** p. 34	*Earth Science* **Activity Video**
Activity Idea Bank Teacher's Edition pp. C17a–C17b **Flip Chart** **Science Center Explore Activity** ***Make a model of an earthquake.***	**Lab Manual** • Lab Manual, p. 68 • Activity Rubric, p. T25		
Lesson 6 Student Edition pp. C18–C19 ***What resources do we get from the earth?*** **Flip Chart** ***Talk About Science***		**Wall Chart,** p. 35	
Lesson 7 Student Edition pp. C20–C21 ***How can you help protect the earth?*** **Explore Activity** ***Make compost.*** **Flip Chart** ***Talk About Science***	**Lab Manual** • Lab Manual, p. 69 • Activity Rubric, p. T25	**Teacher Demonstration Kit** **Wall Chart,** p. 36	
Lesson 8 Student Edition pp. C22–C23 ***What can be recycled?*** **Flip Chart** ***Talk About Science***		**Wall Chart,** p. 37	
Activity Idea Bank Teacher's Edition pp. C23a–C23b **Flip Chart** **Science Center Explore Activity** ***Protect the earth.***	**Lab Manual** • Lab Manual, p. 71 • Activity Rubric, p. T26		
Chapter Review Student Edition pp. C24–C25 and **Flip Chart**	**Teacher's Assessment Package** • Chapter 1 Assessment, pp. 41–42		**Practice & Assessment CD-ROM** **Production Studio** **The KnowZone™ at www.kz.com** **TestWorks™**

Lab Manual

What are some features of the earth?

Label each feature of the earth shown in the picture.
You can use the labels at the bottom of the page.
Cut them out and glue them to the picture.

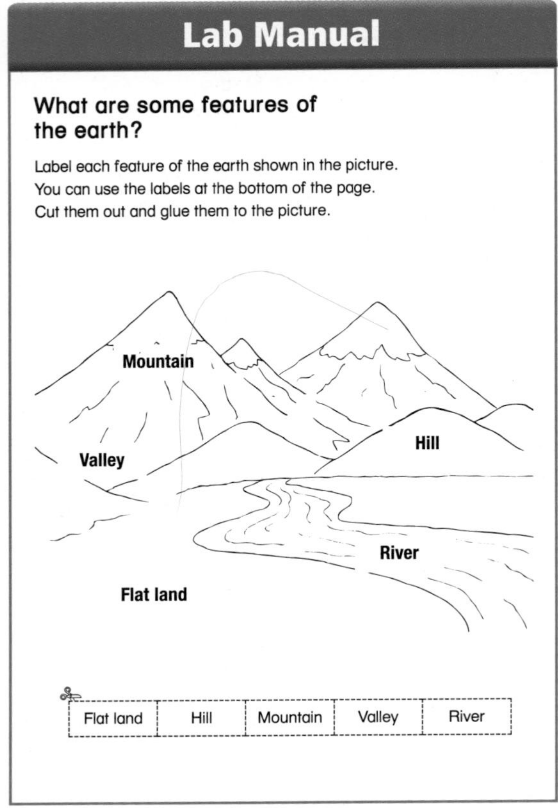

Flat land	Hill	Mountain	Valley	River

Lab Manual
p. 63

Reading in Science

Using Descriptive Words

Write two words from the box to describe each picture.

big	long	white	black	soft	smooth	thin	wet

big, black	white, soft
long, thin	smooth, wet

Draw a picture of something round. Color it.
Describe your picture to a friend.

Children should draw something round.

Instructional Resources
p. 52

Transparency

Describing Rocks

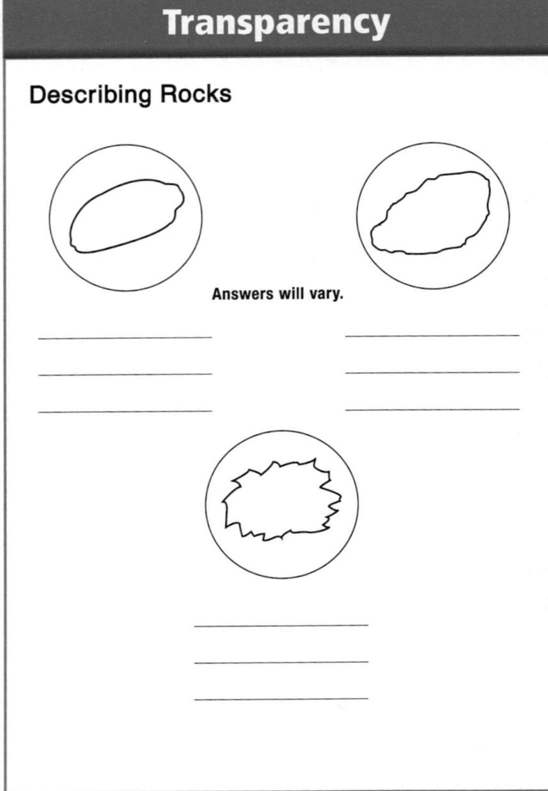

Interactive Transparency Package
Transparency 7

Lab Manual

How can rocks and soil be changed?

Draw how your soil mountain looked before and after you poured water on it.

Students' drawings of their soil "mountain" will vary as will their depictions of the erosion caused by the running water.

Before

After

Lab Manual
p. 65

Lab Manual

Match rocks with clues.

Draw your rocks. Write clues about the color, size, and texture of each rock.

Students' descriptions of the rocks they selected will vary. Comments about color, size, and texture will also vary.	Color: ______ Size: ______ Texture: ______
	Color: ______ Size: ______ Texture: ______
	Color: ______ Size: ______ Texture: ______

Lab Manual
p. 66

Lab Manual

How can you make a model of a volcano?

Draw the things you used to make your volcano.

Students should identify the materials suggested in their text, which include clay, dishwashing soap, baking soda, vinegar, and red food coloring. Their drawings will vary.

Draw what happened.

Lab Manual p. 67

Lab Manual

Make a model of an earthquake.

What will happen when you move the paper?

Draw your prediction.

Students' predictions should indicate that one or both "buildings" will fall in the earthquake. Their drawings will vary.

Draw what happened.

Lab Manual p. 68

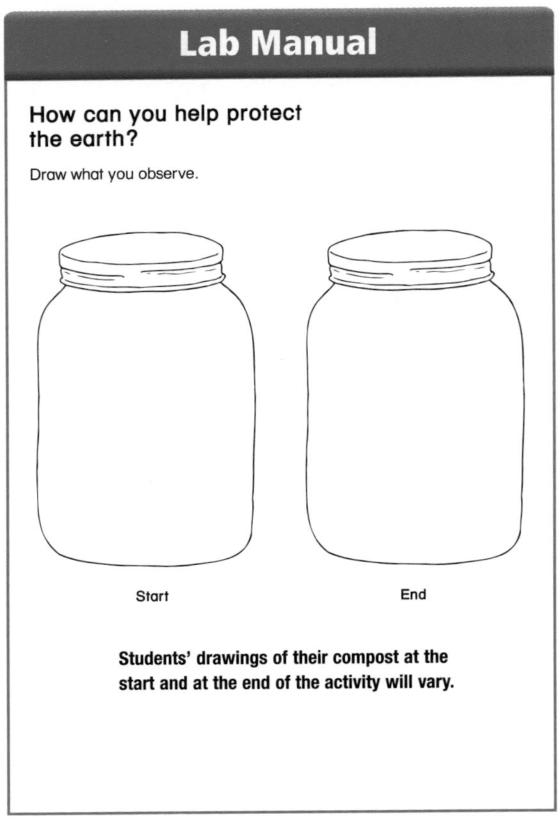

Lab Manual

How can you help protect the earth?

Draw what you observe.

Start

End

Students' drawings of their compost at the start and at the end of the activity will vary.

Lab Manual
p. 69

Lab Manual

Protect the earth.

Write or draw a way to conserve paper, water, and fuel.

Paper	**Students' ideas for saving paper, water, and fuel will vary.**
Water	
Fuel	

Lab Manual
p. 71

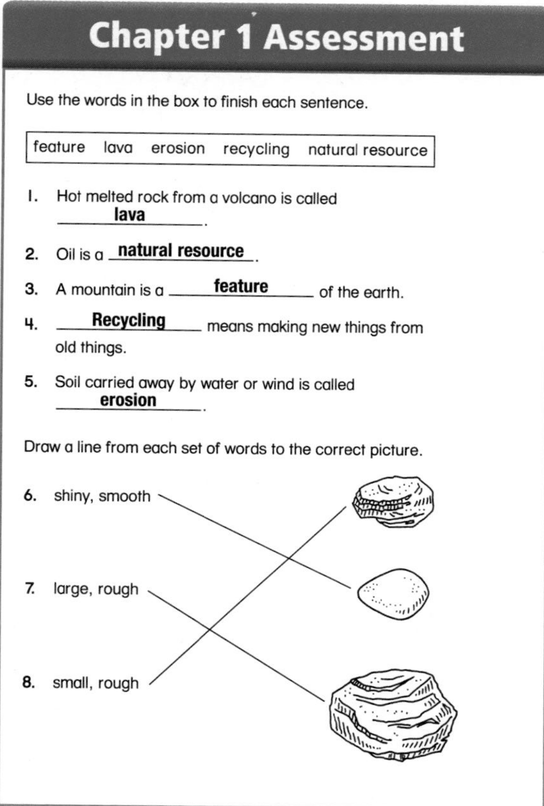

Chapter 1 Assessment

Use the words in the box to finish each sentence.

feature	lava	erosion	recycling	natural resource

1. Hot melted rock from a volcano is called **lava**.
2. Oil is a **natural resource**.
3. A mountain is a **feature** of the earth.
4. **Recycling** means making new things from old things.
5. Soil carried away by water or wind is called **erosion**.

Draw a line from each set of words to the correct picture.

6. shiny, smooth
7. large, rough
8. small, rough

Teacher's Assessment Package
p. 41

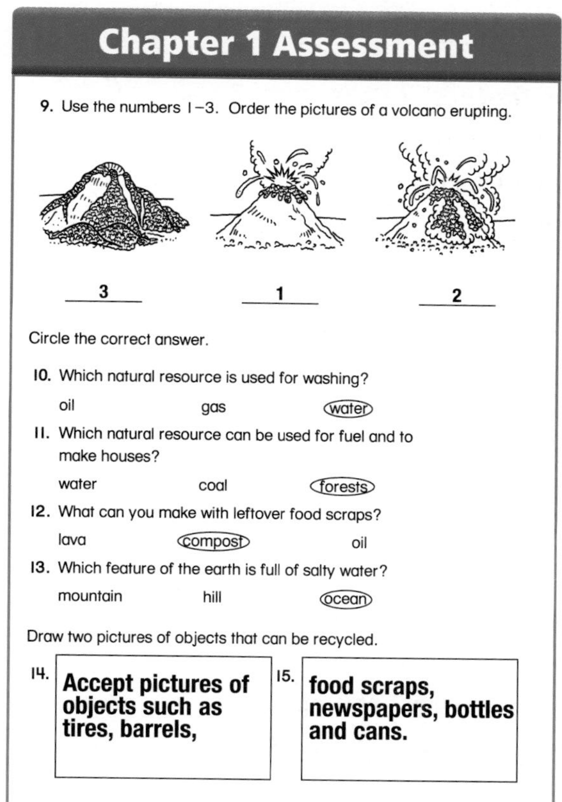

Chapter 1 Assessment

9. Use the numbers 1–3. Order the pictures of a volcano erupting.

3 **1** **2**

Circle the correct answer.

10. Which natural resource is used for washing?
oil gas (water)
11. Which natural resource can be used for fuel and to make houses?
water coal (forests)
12. What can you make with leftover food scraps?
lava (compost) oil
13. Which feature of the earth is full of salty water?
mountain hill (ocean)

Draw two pictures of objects that can be recycled.

14. **Accept pictures of objects such as tires, barrels,**
15. **food scraps, newspapers, bottles and cans.**

Teacher's Assessment Package
p. 42

Table of Contents

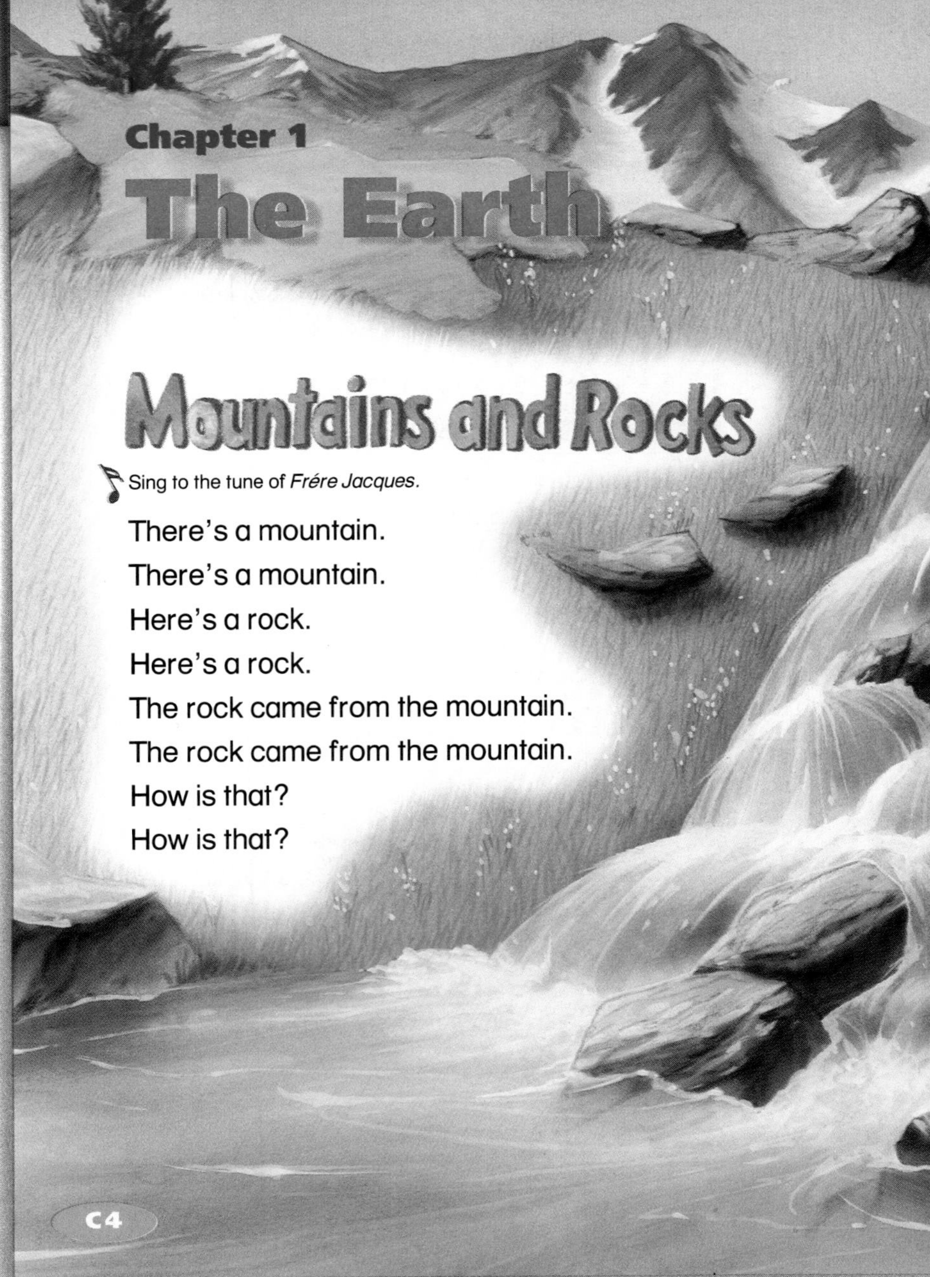
Chapter 1

The Earth

Mountains and Rocks

Sing to the tune of *Frére Jacques.*

There's a mountain.
There's a mountain.
Here's a rock.
Here's a rock.
The rock came from the mountain.
The rock came from the mountain.
How is that?
How is that?

C4

Introducing the Chapter

The song *Mountains and Rocks* is on the **Flip Chart.**

- Ask children to describe the earth.
- Distribute the Family Activity blackline master page.

Singing the Song

Have children sing the song *Mountains and Rocks* on side 2 of the CTW cassette. Distribute pages 21–22 from the CTW Song Activity Book.

Reading Assist *Decode Words*

Write *rush* and *rushing* on the board. Call attention to the *-ing* ending. Have children find other words in the song with *-ing.* (*wearing, breaking, making*)

Technology

 **Practice & Assessment CD-ROM** 

 **AudioText**

 **Production Studio**

 **www.sfscience.com**

 **Teacher's Resource Planner**

 **Songs & Activities Package** 

CTW Song & Activity

Save The Planet Poll

Living things need clean air, soil and water.
1. Ask your family, friends and neighbors to do these things.
2. Fill in a square for each one they have done in the last week.

Recycle the trash.
Use less electricity.
Do not let water run when it is not needed.
Do not litter.

Songs & Activities Package
pp. 21–22

Vocabulary Preview

Use the Vocabulary Preview blackline master to introduce the vocabulary words for this chapter.

Lesson 3 erosion
Lesson 4 lava
Lesson 6 natural resources
Lesson 7 recycling

There's a river,
By the mountain.
Rushing by,
Rushing by.
Wearing down the mountain,
Breaking off some pieces.
Making rocks.
Making rocks.

Just like mountains,
Just like mountains,
Rocks change too.
Rocks change too.
Wind and water change their
Size and shape and texture.
Day by day.
Day by day.

Original lyrics by Gerri Brioso and Richard Freitas.
Produced by Children's Television Workshop.

INQUIRY

Use a KWL chart at the beginning of each chapter. In the *K* column, record what children *know* about the earth. In the *W* column, list what they *want* to know. Throughout the chapter, ask children what they have *learned.* Record their responses in the *L* column. A KWL chart is on **Wall Chart** page 32.

Chapter 1 Skills Trace

Process Skills Development

	Making and Using Models	Observing	Predicting	Estimating and Measuring	Making Definitions
Skill Introduced	xv	xiv	xv	xiv	xv
Skill Applied	C7 C13 C16–C17	C13 C16–C17 C21	C13	C16–C17	C21
Skill Assessed	End Matter 20–21	End Matter 6–7	End Matter 16–17	End Matter 12–13	End Matter 18–19

Family Activity — Science at Home

Dear Family:
Our class is starting Chapter 1. We will be learning about the earth. These are the main ideas for Chapter 1.
- The earth has features such as rivers, mountains, and oceans.
- Rocks come in many sizes, shapes, and colors.
- Erosion, volcanoes, and earthquakes change the earth.
- The earth has many natural resources.
- Recycling can help to protect the earth.

We will also be learning science vocabulary words for Chapter 1. By the end of Chapter 1, we will be able to read the vocabulary words and tell what they mean.

Word Bank
erosion
lava
natural resources
recycling

Home Projects
Here are some activities that will help your child understand the main ideas in Chapter 1. The activities are easy, fast, and fun.

Activities
- Take your child on a neighborhood rock hunt. Start by making a list of descriptive words that include colors, shapes, sizes, and textures. Put these descriptive words together into different combinations to create a list of rock descriptions. Then search your neighborhood or backyard for the rocks that fill your list.

Instructional Resources pp. 49–50

Vocabulary Preview

erosion	lava
natural resources	recycling
fuel	erupt
feature	model

Instructional Resources p. 51

SF Science Literature Library

The Sun, the Wind and the Rain
by Lisa Westberg Peters.
The story of two mountains—one made by the earth; the other made by a girl on the beach.
(Henry Holt,
ISBN 0-8050-1481-0)

Lesson Organizer

Objective

Identify features of the earth such as mountains and lakes.

Process Skills making and using models

Materials

Kit Items modeling clay, sand

School-Supplied Items rocks, blue construction paper

Additional Resources

- Lab Manual
- Teacher Demonstration Kit

Introduce

Activate Prior Knowledge

Ask children to describe what the land looks like at their favorite outdoor place. Lead them to mention any land or bodies of water they recall.

Language Development *Sing a Song*

Invite children to sing songs that mention different types of land, such as *This Land Is Your Land* or *America the Beautiful.*

Flip Chart

Discuss the features of the earth in the pictures. Have children tell about places they have seen that have those features.

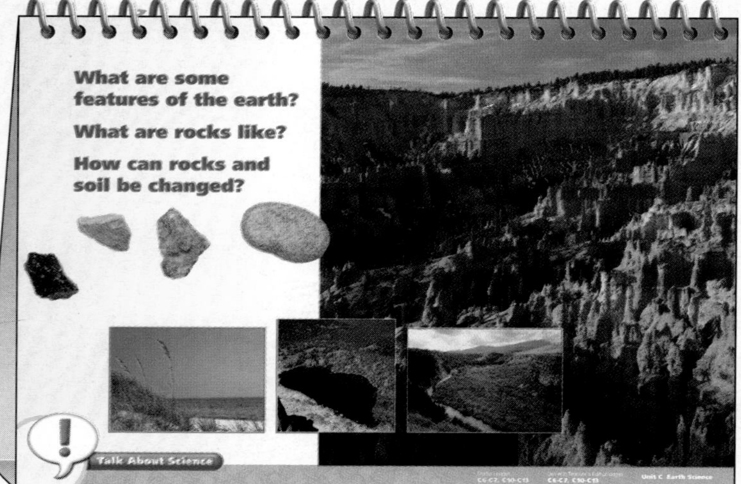
What are some features of the earth?
What are rocks like?
How can rocks and soil be changed?
Talk About Science

What are some features of the earth?

What will you see if you look down from an airplane or a very high hill? You will probably see land and water.

The earth has mountains, hills, and valleys. It also has oceans, rivers, and lakes. These are all called features of the earth.

Ocean water is salty. Lakes, ponds, rivers, and streams are filled with fresh water.

What features of the earth can you see in this picture?

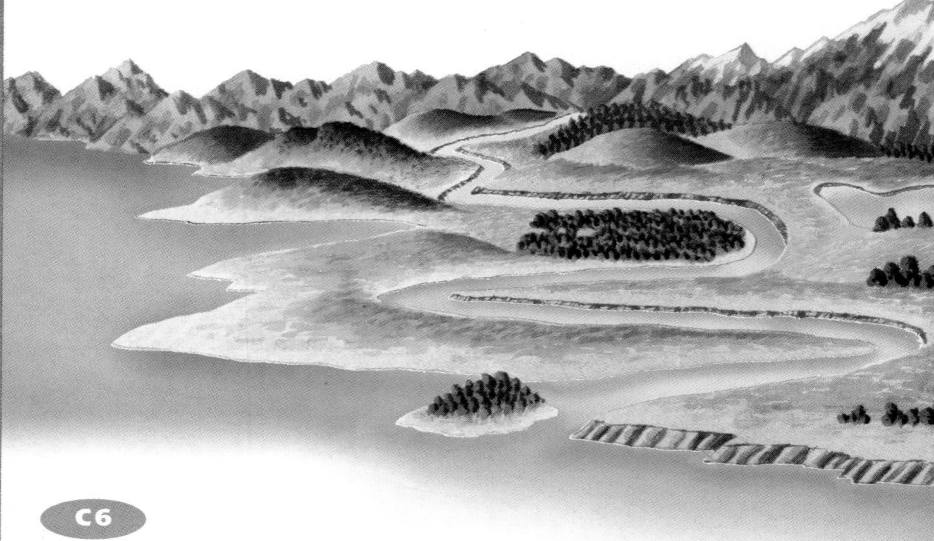

C6

Science Background

- About three-quarters of the surface of the earth is covered by oceans.
- The continental landmasses are floating on the semisolid or partially molten layer of the earth's mantle. They move about one-half inch per year.
- Mountains are formed when one landmass presses into another.
- About 10 percent of the earth's surface is covered by glacial ice, but glaciers contain about 70 percent of the world's fresh water.

Teaching Tips Use brown and green modeling clay to represent colors in nature. Provide books or a variety of pictures showing different

Make a model of features of the earth.

Materials

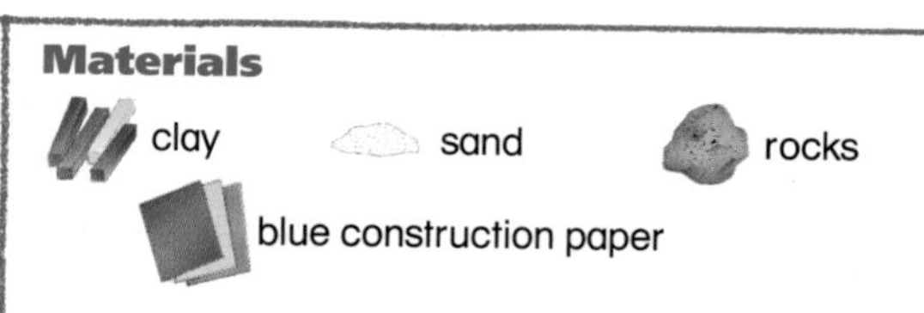

Process Skills

- making and using models

Steps

1. Use your clay to make a model of land. Include hills, mountains, and valleys.
2. Add sand and rocks to your model.
3. Use blue paper to show water.

Share. Name the features of the earth shown in your model.

Lesson Review

1. What are some features of the earth?
2. Where can you find fresh water?
3. **Draw** a picture of some features of the earth.

Teach and Apply

Student Page C6

Invite children to take turns pointing out features of the earth they see in the picture. Then ask them which features are land and which are water.

Reading Assist *Word Meanings*
Explain that the word *features,* as used in the lesson, means "parts." All of the land and water mentioned in the text are parts of the earth.

Student Page C7

Explore Activity

Time about 30 minutes
Grouping cooperative groups of 2
Before children start their models, suggest that they draw pictures of what they want to make. Children can complete Lab Manual page 63.

Assess and Extend

Answers to Lesson Review

1. Answers may include mountains, hills, valleys, oceans, rivers, and lakes.
2. Fresh water can be found in lakes, ponds, rivers, and streams.
3. **Draw** (*Journal*) Drawings may include mountains, hills, valleys, oceans, rivers, lakes, ponds, and streams.

Inquire Further

Ask the following question to guide further inquiry:
What land and water features would you see from an airplane flying above your community?

Enrichment

Invite children to **make** a clay **model** that includes local or regional landforms. If possible, provide children with an aerial photo of your community.

Higher Order Thinking *Evaluate*

Ask: **Why do you think it is important that we have different types of land?** (*Children might evaluate the uses of familiar land features and conclude that they are important because they are pretty or because they provide food, shelter, water, or products.*)

Lab Manual

What are some features of the earth?

Label each feature of the earth shown in the picture. You can use the labels at the bottom of the page. Cut them out and glue them to the picture.

Flat land | Hill | Mountain | Valley | River

Lab Manual
p. 63

Activity Rubric

Use the following activity scoring rubric to assess students' performance.

Scoring Criteria	1	2	3	4
Student followed directions to complete this activity.				
Student used a visual model of the earth's features.				
Student distinguished various landforms.				
Student recognized and labeled various features of the earth.				
Student completed a visual representation of features of the earth.				

Scoring Key
4 points correct, complete, detailed
3 points partially correct, complete, detailed
2 points partially correct, partially complete, lacks some detail
1 point incorrect or incomplete, needs assistance

Lab Manual
p. T23

Call 1-888-537-4908 with your Activity questions or comments.

Reading Organizer

Objective

Use descriptive words.

Additional Resources

- Reading for Science blackline master

Teaching Reading for Science

- Using descriptive words is an important part of communicating science ideas. Descriptive words provide details about an object's properties. Scientists use descriptive words to help them classify objects. Once a scientist knows the descriptive words associated with a particular bird, rock, or flower, he or she can use that information to help identify other objects that belong to the same group.
- Children can use descriptive words to help them classify objects too, because descriptive words help children sort objects as alike or different. For example, once children use descriptive words to describe rocks, they can sort the rocks according to like attributes, such as rough and shiny. As children use descriptive words to describe an object's properties, they gain experience in communicating science ideas.
- Have children read and complete the Reading for Science lesson and the Reading for Science blackline master.

Student Page C8

- Have children work with partners to choose and describe an object. Have partners guess the objects being described. Discuss who was able to guess the objects and why.
- Explain that color, shape, size, and texture are properties and that children can use descriptive words to tell more about these properties.
- Make a four-column chart on the chalkboard titled "Descriptive Words." Write these column titles: "Color," "Shape," "Size," "Texture." Have children brainstorm descriptive words for each property. Record their responses in the appropriate column.
- Add other descriptive words children use as they describe the pictures on page C8.

Using Descriptive Words

You use descriptive words to tell about objects. Descriptive words tell about an object's properties. They tell about an object's color, shape, size, and texture.

Describe one of the objects in each section.

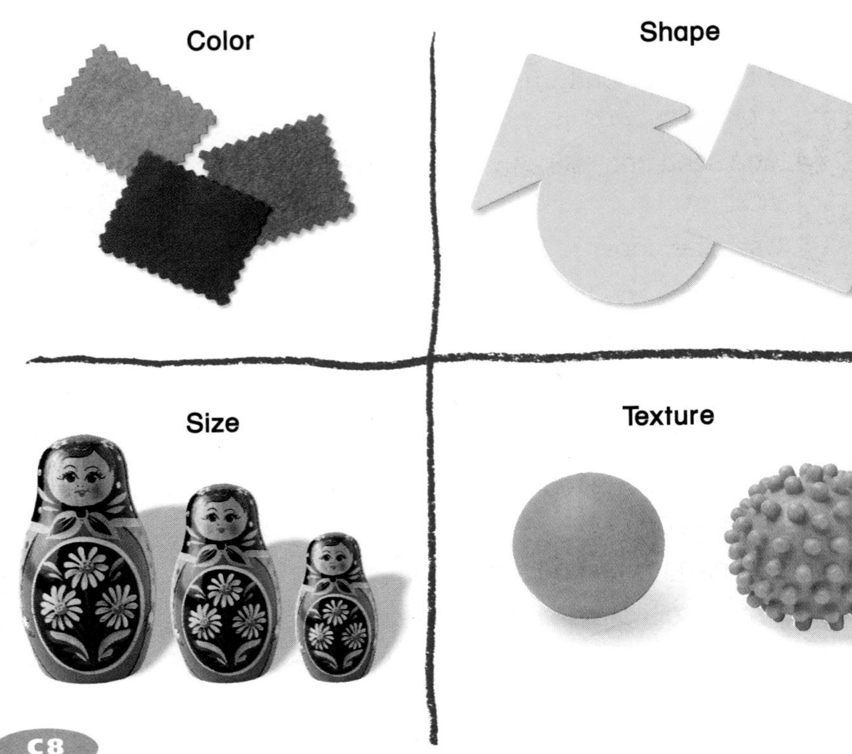

C8

ESL Strategy

Say each of the describing words on page C9 and ask children to point to something on the page and something in the classroom that matches the description. Encourage children to speak in complete sentences. For example: *Here is a rectangle on the page. This book is a rectangle.*

Read each of these sentences.
Can you picture this object?

1. It is a rectangle. 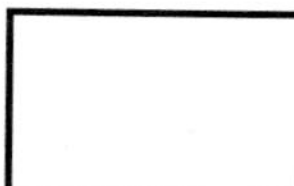

2. It is a rectangle. It is red, white, and blue.

3. It is a rectangle. It is red, white, and blue. It has stars and stripes.

4. It is a rectangle. It is red, white, and blue. It has stars and stripes. You might see it hanging from a pole.

Draw the object.

Which descriptive words helped you the most? Why?

Turn the page to find out how you can use descriptive words to tell about rocks.

Reading for Science

Using Descriptive Words

Write two words from the box to describe each picture.

big long white black soft smooth thin wet

big, black	white, soft
long, thin	smooth, wet

Draw a picture of something round. Color it.
Describe your picture to a friend.

Children should draw something round.

Instructional Resources p. 52

Student Page C9

- Have children listen as you read aloud the descriptions. Pause after each description and say: **Raise your hand if you know what object I am describing.** If children raise their hands after hearing any of the first three descriptions, ask them to share their guesses.
- After reading all the descriptions, have children draw the object that is being described. (*American flag*)
- Discuss how children knew what to draw.
- Children should recognize that the last description of the object was the most helpful because it provided the most information.
- Point out that each description provides more details about the object. Ask: **Which words tell about color?** (*red, white, blue*) **Which words tell about shape?** (*rectangle, stars, stripes*)

Apply Reading for Science to Lesson 2

Children will use what they learned about using descriptive words to complete the next lesson.

Lesson Organizer

Objective
Identify types of rocks.

Additional Resources
- Wall Chart
- Interactive Transparency

Introduce

Activate Prior Knowledge
Provide a collection of rocks for children to examine. Ask children to describe ways the rocks are alike and different. Record their responses on **Wall Chart** page 33. Save the chart for use as a **baseline assessment.**

Language Development *Scientific Language*
Diamonds, emeralds, rubies, gold, talc, calcite, salt, iron, and quartz are all minerals. Explain that minerals are nonliving, useful materials that come from the earth. Except for magma, all rocks are combinations of minerals.

Flip Chart
Have children compare the rocks in the pictures with the rocks in your classroom collection. Have children describe the rocks that are alike.

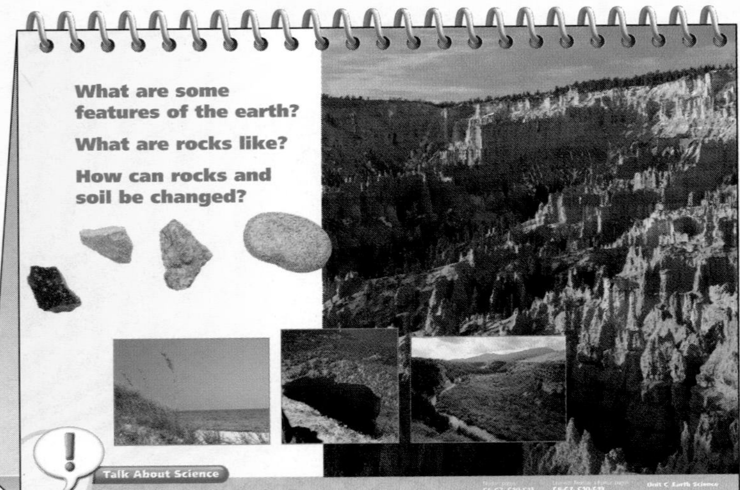

What are some features of the earth?
What are rocks like?
How can rocks and soil be changed?
Talk About Science

What are rocks like?

What a beautiful rock collection! How would you describe the rocks in this picture?

Rocks come in many sizes, shapes, and colors. Some rocks are shiny and smooth. Others are dull and rough. Some rocks are small enough to fit in your hand. Others are as big as a tree.

C10

Science Background

- *Igneous* rocks are formed from magma and lava, hot molten masses of minerals. Magma works its way upward through the earth's hard crust and cools, forming igneous rock.
- *Sedimentary* rocks are formed from sediments—sand, clay, and so on. The sediments become compacted and cemented together to form rock.
- *Metamorphic* rocks are formed when existing rocks are subjected to heat and pressure.

Science Across Cultures In China and Japan, rocks are used to create gardens. If possible, provide pictures of some of these gardens. Invite children to make rock gardens with sand, rocks, and greenery in a shoe box lid.

Rocks are made of minerals. If you look closely at some of these rocks, you might see different colors. Each color is a mineral that is part of the rock.

Lesson Review

1. What are rocks made of?
2. How can rocks be different from each other?
3. **Write** about one of the rocks in the picture. Use descriptive words.

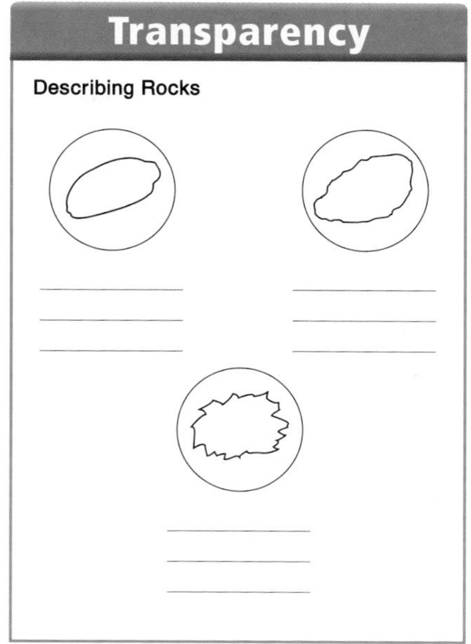

Interactive Transparency Package
Transparency 7

Teach and Apply

Student Pages C10–C11

- Let children again examine the rocks. Have chil[dren] view the rocks through a hand lens. Point out h[ow] the rocks are made up of smaller materials.
- Encourage children to use as many descriptive w[ords] as possible to tell about the rocks pictured.

Reading Assist *Plurals*

Tell children that we often add *s* to a word to show more that one. Write *rocks* on the chalkboard and have children find it on the page. Then have children find other words on the pages that name more than one. (*sizes, shapes, colors, others, minerals, words*)

Real-World Applications

Rocks are used to build homes, walls, bridges, streets, floors, tools, statues, and monuments. Artists make sculptures using different kinds of stone, such as marble and granite. Certain kinds of stones and minerals found in rocks are used to make jewelry.

Assess and Extend

Answers to Lesson Review

1. Rocks are made of minerals.
2. Answers may include size, shape, color, and texture.
3. **Write** (*Portfolio Assessment*) Children should use descriptive words, such as *rough, smooth, big, small, round, flat, bumpy.*

Check for Understanding

To follow up on the **baseline assessment,** have children revisit **Wall Chart** page 33. Encourage them to revise the lists as needed.

Reteach

- Use the Interactive Transparency to reteach Lesson 2 concepts.
- Provide children with a collection of rocks. Then have them group the rocks in different ways, such as by size, shape, color, weight, or texture. Ask them to describe how the groups are alike and different.

Lesson Organizer

Objective
Identify ways rocks and soil can be changed.

Vocabulary erosion
Process Skills observing, predicting, making and using models

Materials
Kit Items soil, cup, pan

School-Supplied Item water, safety goggles

Additional Resources
- Lab Manual
- Teacher Demonstration Kit

Introduce

Activate Prior Knowledge
Invite children to answer the question, **What is the earth made of?** (*Children may mention things like mountains, lakes, streams, rocks, minerals, and soil.*)

Language Development *Vocabulary*
Discuss what children know about soil—what it's made of and how it is used.

Flip Chart
Discuss how water, wind, or pieces of rocks may have changed the rocks and soil in the pictures. Ask: **How do you think the scenes might have looked before erosion took place?**

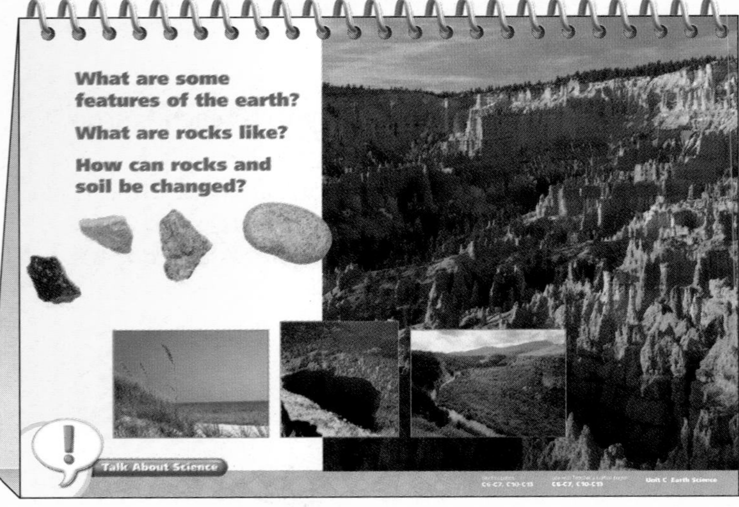

What are some features of the earth?
What are rocks like?
How can rocks and soil be changed?
Talk About Science
Unit C Earth Science

How can rocks and soil be changed?

Can you find the path in this picture? The path was made by water. What happened to the soil that used to be there?

The soil may have been slowly washed away by the water. The soil may also have been worn away by small pieces of rock that were carried in the water.

When soil or rock are carried away by water, wind, or other rocks, it is called **erosion**. Plant roots help prevent erosion by keeping the soil in place.

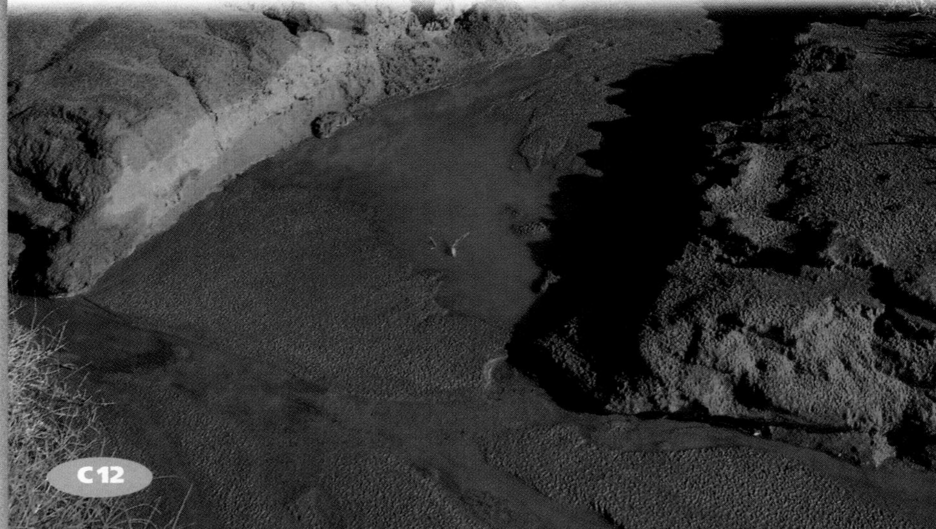

Science Background

- Erosion is the movement of soil and rocks by wind, water, and pieces of rock.
- Weathering is the wearing down or breaking apart of rocks. Most rocks weather slowly over many years.

Teaching Tips You can create funnels from foam cups. Make a small hole in the bottom of each cup with the tip of a pencil. Be careful not to make the hole too large. As children work, advise them to pack the soil to make mountains. Have them hold their cups about 15 centimeters above the mountains and slowly pour the water.

Show erosion.

Materials

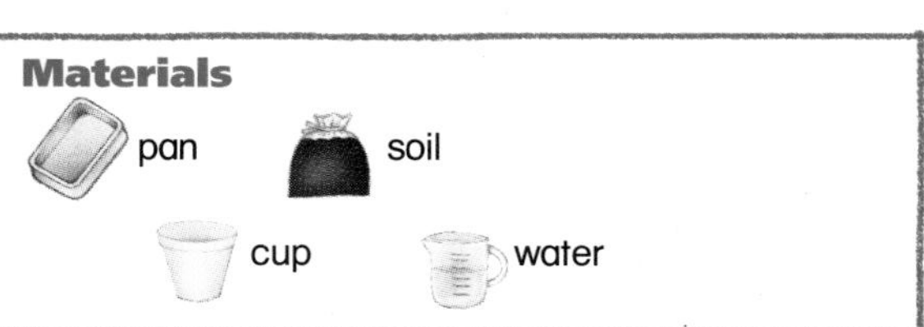

Process Skills

- observing
- predicting
- making and using models

Process Skills

Steps

1. Put some soil in your pan. Make a model of a mountain.
2. Predict what will happen if you pour water onto the soil.
3. Hold the cup over the soil.
4. Have a partner slowly pour some water into the cup. Observe.

Share. Tell how you showed erosion.

Lesson Review

1. What is erosion?
2. How do plants help the soil?
3. **Draw** your soil before and after you poured the water.

C13

Lab Manual

How can rocks and soil be changed?

Draw how your soil mountain looked before and after you poured water on it.

Before

After

Lab Manual p. 65

Activity Rubric

Use the following activity scoring rubric to assess students' performance.

Scoring Criteria	1	2	3	4
Student followed directions to complete this activity.				
Student observed the effects of erosion on soil.				
Student established a cause and effect relationship between running water on soil and the process of erosion.				
Student observed a process of change.				
Student drew a representation of soil before and after an erosion process.				

Scoring Key
4 points correct, complete, detailed
3 points partially correct, complete, detailed
2 points partially correct, partially complete, lacks some detail
1 point incorrect or incomplete, needs assistance

Lab Manual p. T23

Teach and Apply

Student Page C12

Encourage children to talk about the possible causes of erosion described.

Reading Assist *Word Meaning*
Have children preview the page to spot unfamiliar words, such as *erosion* or *prevent.* Help children with the meanings.

Student Page C13

Explore Activity

Time 15 minutes

Grouping cooperative groups of 4

As children watch what happens when water is poured through the hole in the cup onto the soil, help them notice that the water flows downhill. Ask children why they think water flows downhill. Lead them to realize that gravity plays a part in erosion. Children can complete Lab Manual page 65.

Safety Note *Suggest that children wear safety goggles to keep water and soil from splattering into their eyes.*

Assess and Extend

Answers to Lesson Review

1. Erosion is when soil or rock is carried away by water, wind, or other rocks.
2. Plants help the soil by preventing erosion. Their roots keep the soil in place.
3. **Draw** (*Portfolio Assessment or Journal*) "Before" pictures should show a pile of soil in the shape of a mountain. "After" pictures might show displaced soil, broken-down soil, and streams of water.

Inquire Further

Ask the following question to guide further inquiry: **How could you prevent erosion in your model of a mountain?** (*Children might suggest putting something in the way, such as rocks or trees.*)

Higher Order Thinking *Infer*
Ask: **Why might we need to slow erosion?** (*Children might infer that we need the soil to grow food, and we want our houses and streets to stay on solid ground.*)

Call 1-888-537-4908 with your Activity questions or comments.

Science Center

Flip Chart

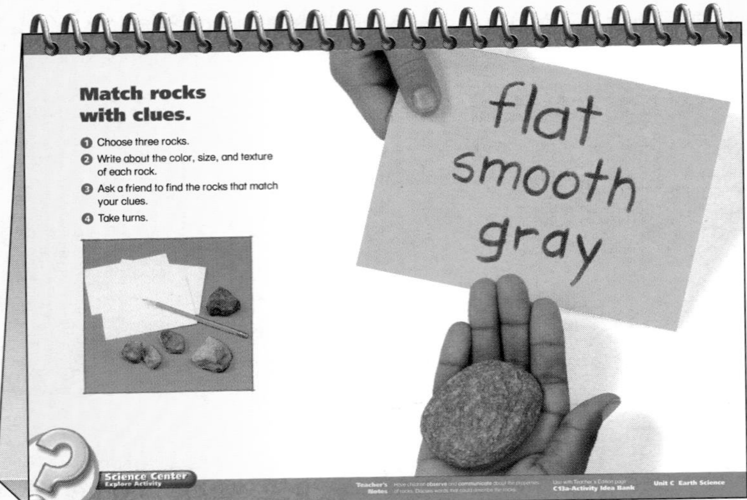

Match rocks with clues.

Objective

Identify the properties of different rocks.

Process Skills observing, communicating

Materials

Kit Items rock specimen pack

School-Supplied Items 3 index cards, paper, pencil

Safety Note *Caution children not to throw rocks because they may hurt someone.*

Procedure

- Children **observe** the properties of various rocks.
- Children **communicate** by recording their observations on separate pieces of paper or index cards. You can use **Lab Manual** page 66.
- Invite pairs of children to use their index cards to play a game. One child picks and displays a card, the other child uses the clues to find the matching rock.

What to Expect

Children observe rocks' similarities and differences.

Lab Manual

Match rocks with clues.

Draw your rocks. Write clues about the color, size, and texture of each rock.

	Color: ______ Size: ______ Texture: ______
	Color: ______ Size: ______ Texture: ______
	Color: ______ Size: ______ Texture: ______

Lab Manual, p. 66

Connections

School and Community

Ideas for bringing the school and community together:

Field Trips

- nature center
- local pond, stream, or lake
- terraced farm

Guest Speakers

- geologist
- environmentalist
- representative from the Army Corps of Engineers

Themes

The activities on these pages can be used with classroom themes such as:

- habitats
- natural resources
- geography
- vacation destinations

Books for Children

Children might enjoy these books about landforms and rocks:

Around and About: The Ground Below Us by Kate Petty and Jakki Wood. Harry and his dog, Ralph, make many discoveries about the earth while flying around the globe in a hot-air balloon. (Barron's, ISBN 0-8120-1232-1)

Rocks & Minerals at Your Fingertips by Judy Nayer. Where rocks and minerals come from, what they are made of, and how they are important. (McClanahan, ISBN 1-56293-547-X)

Cross-Curricular Options

LITERATURE

Welcome to the Sea of Sand

Use the book to discuss what deserts are like.

Materials *Welcome to the Sea of Sand* by Jane Yolen. (Putnam, ISBN 0-399-22765-2)

Procedure

- This book portrays the desert with dramatic paintings of land, plants, and animals.
- After reading the story aloud to children, help them locate deserts on a map.
- Discuss animals and plants of the desert as well as the features of the land.
- Afterward, encourage children to draw or paint desert scenes for a bulletin board display.

Multiple Intelligences linguistic

MATH

Pattern Game

Play a guessing game.

Materials a variety of rocks in different colors, types, sizes, textures

Procedure

- One child places rocks in a simple pattern that is different in one way, such as large, small, large. The partner guesses the pattern.
- Then one child places rocks in a pattern that is different in two ways, such as large and brown, small and black, large and brown. The partner guesses the pattern.
- Partners continue to switch roles.

Multiple Intelligences spatial, linguistic

Gifted and Talented Challenge partners to make more complex patterns.

SOCIAL STUDIES

Postcards

Design a postcard.

Materials large index cards, crayons

Procedure

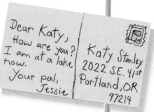

- Have children think of places that they have visited or would like to visit.
- Invite them to draw a picture of one of the place's natural features, such as a lake, river, or mountain, on one side of the postcard. Let them use an encyclopedia or atlas if they need help. On the other side, have them write a note to a friend, telling about their experiences.

Multiple Intelligences spatial, linguistic

Special Needs Visually impaired children might dictate messages into a tape recorder.

ART

Field Scientist

Draw signs of erosion and weathering.

Materials drawing pad, pencil, hand lens

Procedure

- Discuss how weathering has an effect on rocks, buildings, playground equipment, and cars.
- Invite children to become field scientists by walking around the schoolyard or their neighborhood to look for signs of weathering or erosion. Have them draw pictures to show their findings.

Multiple Intelligences spatial

Lesson Organizer

Objective
Identify ways that volcanoes and earthquakes change the earth.

Vocabulary lava

Introduce

Activate Prior Knowledge

Ask children to think of ways that an area of land can be changed. Have them list their ideas and save them for use as a **baseline assessment.**

Language Development *Drama*

Ask children what they would do if the earth suddenly started moving and shaking. Stamp your feet on the floor and have children pretend they can feel an earthquake. Invite children to act out what they would do. Discuss what they did.

Flip Chart

Have children describe what is happening in the pictures. Ask: **How does the earth change when a volcano erupts or an earthquake happens?**

How do volcanoes and earthquakes change the earth?

Fountains of red-hot liquid squirt high into the air. This volcano is erupting!

When a volcano erupts, lava is pushed out. **Lava** is melted rock that comes from inside the earth. Hot lava that flows from a volcano can hurt people and animals and harm the land.

When lava cools, it hardens into solid rock. Over time, the cooled lava can build up into a mountain.

C14

Science Background

- Earthquakes and volcanoes are most common near the boundaries of tectonic plates—large sections of the earth's crust that slowly move over partially melted rock in the upper mantle.
- Earthquakes and volcanoes occur when two tectonic plates move into each other, away from each other, or past each other.
- Undersea volcanoes can rise above the surface of the water, forming islands like Hawaii.

Possible Misconceptions Some children may think that, during an earthquake, all the cracks that open up in the ground are huge, swallowing people, cars, and houses. Point out that most cracks caused by the shaking during an earthquake are only a few meters or yards deep.

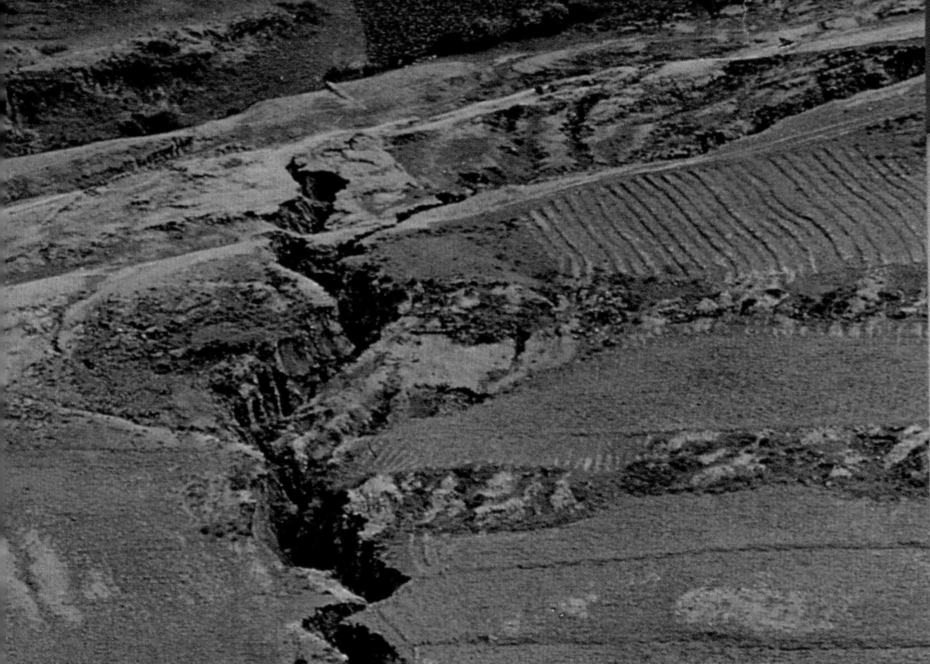

When an earthquake happens, the earth shakes back and forth. Roads, bridges, and buildings can be ruined.

An earthquake can change the land quickly. How did an earthquake change the land in this picture?[1]

[1] It cracked open the land.

Lesson Review

1. What is lava?
2. What happens when a volcano erupts?
3. **Tell** how volcanoes and earthquakes change the earth.

C15

ESL Strategy

Invite children to pretend that their hands are the earth and pantomime what happens in a volcano and then what happens in an earthquake.

Teach and Apply

Student Pages C14–C15

- Point out that in the 1980 eruption of Mount St. Helens in Washington, huge amounts of volcanic ash were thrown into the air. In violent eruptions like this, the ash fills the air and covers vegetation, homes, and towns for miles. Explain that since then, scientists who study volcanoes have developed more effective techniques to predict when eruptions will occur.
- Discuss safety precautions to take during an earthquake, such as these: Indoors, stay away from windows and heavy furniture that could fall; outdoors, stay away from high buildings or objects that could fall.

Reading Assist *Use Picture Clues*

Suggest that children look at the picture of the volcano to help them figure out what the word *squirt* means.

Assess and Extend

Answers to Lesson Review

1. Lava is melted rock on the earth's surface that comes from inside the earth.
2. When a volcano erupts, lava is pushed out.
3. **Tell** (*Interview*) Answers may vary slightly. Lava from volcanoes changes the earth by creating new mountains. Earthquakes change the earth by damaging roads, bridges, buildings, and the ground.

Check for Understanding

To follow up on the **baseline assessment,** ask children to add to their list ways an earthquake and a volcano might change the land.

Reteach

Invite children to build a block city on a piece of cardboard. Then have them gently shake the cardboard to see what happens. Discuss how an earthquake is similar to the activity.

Activity Organizer

Objective
Make a model of a volcano.

Process Skills making and using models, estimating and measuring, observing

Materials

Kit Items modeling clay, vinegar, plastic vial, baking soda, pan

School-Supplied Items safety goggles, spoon, dishwashing soap, red food coloring, craft stick

Time about 30 minutes

Grouping cooperative groups of 2

Additional Resources
- Lab Manual
- Teacher Demonstration Kit
- Wall Chart

Introduce

The Lesson 5 Investigate Activity, *How can you make a model of a volcano?,* is on the **Flip Chart.**

Activate Prior Knowledge

Invite children to share experiences with volcanoes and earthquakes. Use the Venn diagram on **Wall Chart** page 34 to help children compare volcanoes and earthquakes.

Language Development *Song*

Invite children to use what they know about volcanoes to make up a song. Suggest they use the tune *The Bear Went Over the Mountain.*

How can you make a model of a volcano?

Process Skills
- making and using models
- estimating and measuring
- observing

Materials
safety goggles, clay, container, pan, teaspoon, craft stick, dishwashing soap, baking soda, vinegar, red food coloring

Steps
1. Put on your safety goggles.
2. **Make a model.** Mold the clay around the container in the shape of a volcano. Put your model in the pan.
3. **Measure.** Put 3 teaspoons of baking soda into the container. Add 2 teaspoons of dishwashing soap. Stir with the craft stick.

C16

Science Background

Hot, melted rock, called magma, is deep inside the earth. Heat energy can cause the magma to be squeezed up through the earth's crust. If magma is forced up through the volcano, the volcano erupts. Magma that comes out of a volcano is called lava.

Science Across Cultures Display a world map and use pushpins to identify where famous volcanoes are located. Include Mount St. Helens, the Hawaiian Islands, Mount Vesuvius in Italy, Mount Pinatubo in the Philippines, and Mount Unzen in Japan. Invite children to research other volcanoes on the Internet.

Technology

Review the demonstration of this Investigate's procedure on the *Earth Science* **Activity Video,** Segment 1.

4 Add red food coloring.

5 Fill the rest of the container with vinegar.

6 Observe.

Think About Your Results

1. How is this model like a real volcano?
2. How is this model different from a real volcano?

How could you make your volcano erupt with more force?

Lab Manual

How can you make a model of a volcano?

Draw the things you used to make your volcano.

Draw what happened.

Lab Manual p. 67

Activity Rubric

Use the following activity scoring rubric to assess students' performance.

Scoring Criteria	1	2	3	4
Student assembled materials to make a model of a volcano.				
Student made a model of a volcano.				
Student drew materials used to make a volcano.				
Student followed proper safety procedures.				
Student drew a visual representation of his or her volcano model.				

Scoring Key
4 points correct, complete, detailed
3 points partially correct, complete, detailed
2 points partially correct, partially complete, lacks some detail
1 point incorrect or incomplete, needs assistance

Lab Manual p. T24

Teach and Apply

- In this activity, children use clay to make a model of a volcano.

Safety Note *Be sure children wear their safety goggles during the activity.*

- Children simulate an eruption using dishwashing soap, baking soda, vinegar, and red food coloring.
- After the activity, discuss how the model is similar to and different from a real volcano. Help children understand that the vinegar eruption looks somewhat like a volcanic eruption but is actually very different.
- Children can complete Lab Manual page 67.

Reading Assist *Compound Words*

Ask children what smaller words make up the word *dishwashing*. Help children realize that finding a word made from two words they already know will help them pronounce the new word.

Assess and Extend

Answers to Think About Your Results

1. Answers may include that both have liquid flowing and both have a cone shape.
2. Answers may include that there is no heat, the size is much smaller, the smell is different, it does not come from inside the earth, and so on.

Inquire Further

Children's answers may include using more or less of some of the ingredients.

Enrichment

Challenge children to make a cut-away diagram showing the inside of a volcano. Provide books on the subject to help them do this. Suggest that they label the parts and then use the diagram to explain what a volcano is and how and why it erupts.

Higher Order Thinking *Infer*

Ask: **What might be the effect of a volcano on trees, other plants, and buildings?** (*The lava could cover and kill plants and trees and knock over buildings.*)

Call 1-888-537-4908 with your Activity questions or comments.

Science Center

Flip Chart

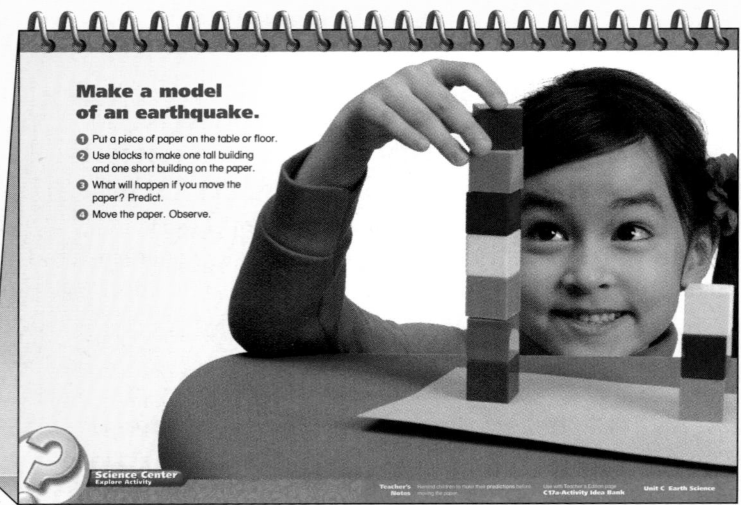

Make a model of an earthquake.
1 Put a piece of paper on the table or floor.
2 Use blocks to make one tall building and one short building on the paper.
3 What will happen if you move the paper? Predict.
4 Move the paper. Observe.
Science Center

Make a model of an earthquake.

Objective

Demonstrate effects of earthquakes.

Process Skills predicting

Materials

Kit Items none

School-Supplied Items paper, wood or plastic blocks

Procedure

- Invite children to stack blocks on a piece of paper to make models of buildings.
- Ask children to **predict** what will happen when they move the paper under the models.
- Children use their models to simulate an earthquake and observe the results.
- You can use **Lab Manual** page 68 with this activity.

What to Expect

Children observe that their models may fall down or fall on each other when they move the paper.

Lab Manual

Make a model of an earthquake.

What will happen when you move the paper?

Draw your prediction.

Draw what happened.

Lab Manual, p. 68

Connections

School and Community

Ideas for bringing the school and community together:

Field Trips

- nature center
- seismology center
- natural disaster center
- TV weather station

Guest Speakers

- geologist
- meteorologist
- Red Cross representative

Themes

The activities on these pages can be used with classroom themes such as:

- natural disasters
- landforms
- habitats
- change

Books for Children

Children might enjoy these books about landforms:

How Mountains Are Made by Kathleen Weidner Zoehfeld. Facts about mountains and their development. (HarperCollins, ISBN 0-06-445128-3)

Fire on the Mountain by Jane Kurtz. An Ethiopian folk story retold with watercolor paintings. (Aladdin, ISBN 0-689-81896-3)

Cross-Curricular Options

LITERATURE

The Rattlebang Picnic

Use the book for a look at how an erupting volcano can spoil a family picnic.

Materials *The Rattlebang Picnic* by Margaret Mahy. (Dial, ISBN 0-8037-1318-5)

Procedure

- This witty story is about a family who unknowingly goes for a picnic atop an erupting volcano.
- Discuss the clever way the McTavishes solved their problem.
- Discuss the meaning of fantasy and reality. Encourage children to tell why the events of this story could not happen in real life.

Multiple Intelligences linguistic

ART

Forces of Nature

Make a diorama.

Materials shoe box, clay, paper, twigs, grass, rocks

Procedure

- Have children construct dioramas to illustrate a particular natural event such as a volcano or an earthquake.
- Invite children to share their dioramas and talk about how the event depicted affects living and nonliving things.

Multiple Intelligences spatial

Gifted and Talented Challenge children to locate materials about real earthquakes and volcanoes in the school library and report to the class about them.

WRITING

News Report

Write a radio announcement.

Procedure

- Have children write a "live" radio news report about an earthquake or a volcano in your area.
- Encourage children to act out their reports and include interviews with people on the scene.
- Have children include facts about the earthquake or volcano in their reports.

Multiple Intelligences linguistic

ESL Provide sentence frames to help children write their reports:
A _______ erupted today.
You can see hot _______ being pushed high into the air.

LANGUAGE ARTS

Be Prepared!

Make a poster.

Materials construction paper, paints, crayons, disaster reference materials

Procedure

- Discuss natural events, such as earthquakes, landslides, or tornadoes, that occur in your area.
- Generate a list of safety precautions for one or more of these events. Refer children to reference books as needed.
- Have children create posters that feature these precautions.
- Display children's work on corridor bulletin boards.

Multiple Intelligences spatial, linguistic

Lesson Organizer

Objective
Identify natural resources and their uses.

Vocabulary natural resources

Additional Resources
- Wall Chart

Introduce

Activate Prior Knowledge

Display pictures of the following objects: a bottle of water, a piece of coal, natural gas, a stick of wood, a can of oil, solar energy, a windmill. Ask children to tell what each thing is and one way it can be used. Record children's ideas on the chalkboard and save them for use as a **baseline assessment.**

Language Development *Word Web*

Display **Wall Chart** page 35. Ask children to name as many things as they can that come from the earth. Point out that useful materials that come from the earth are called natural resources.

Flip Chart

Discuss the natural resources shown in the pictures. Ask: **How do we use these natural resources?**

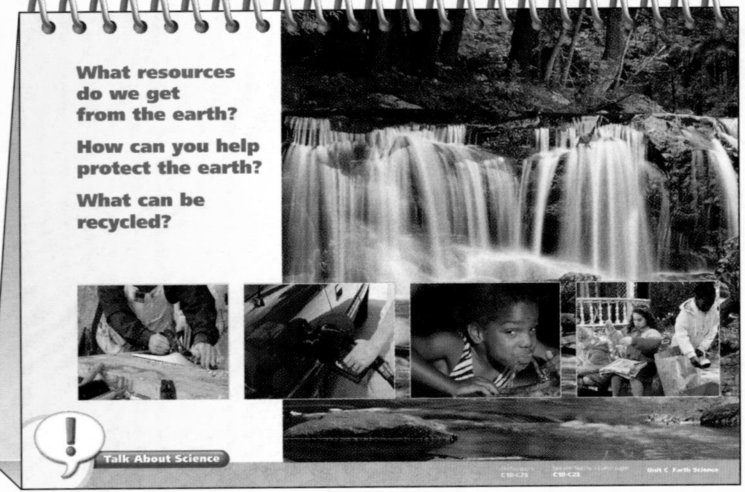
What resources do we get from the earth?
How can you help protect the earth?
What can be recycled?
Talk About Science

What resources do we get from the earth?

You have probably seen sprinklers used for watering lawns. The sprinklers in this picture are used for watering large fields.

Water is used in many ways. You can use water for drinking, cooking, and washing. Water is a natural resource. **Natural resources** are useful materials that come from the earth.

Oil, coal, and gas are also natural resources. They are used for fuel. Fuel heats homes and other buildings. It helps run factories and machines. Oil is also made into gasoline for cars and trucks.

C18

Science Background

- An inexhaustible resource is always available, regardless of how we use it. An example is the sun.
- A renewable resource can be depleted but if used wisely, it will replace itself as it is used. An example is wood.
- A nonrenewable resource exists in a fixed amount on the earth and is not replenished by natural processes. An example is oil.

Possible Misconceptions Tell children that clear water is not always safe to drink. Explain that water must go through a purification process to be safe to drink. Water from their faucet is clean.

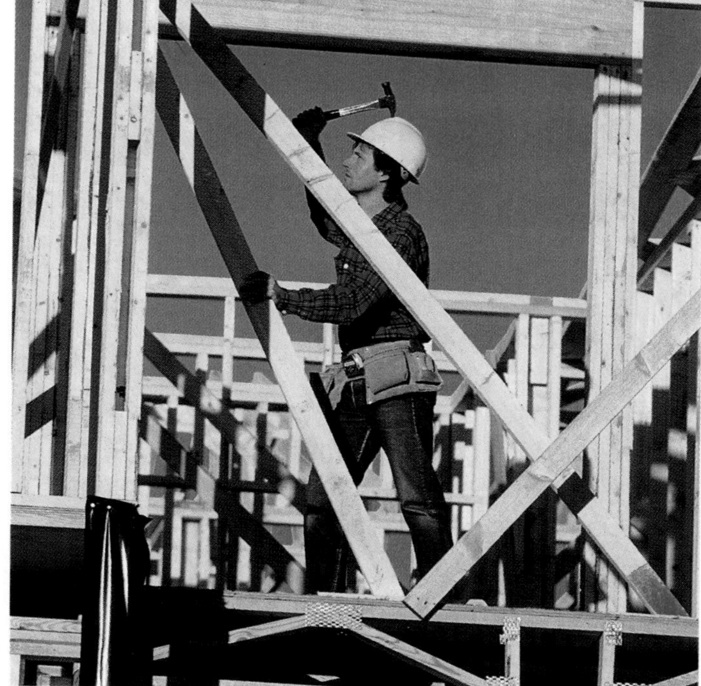

Forests are another natural resource. Trees are cut into lumber to build homes. Wood also can be burned for fuel.

How are natural resources being used in the pictures?[1]

Lesson Review

1. Name some natural resources.
2. What are some ways fuel is used?
3. **Draw** two ways you use water every day.

[1] Water is used to water the plants; lumber is used to build a building.

C19

ESL Strategy

Invite children to act out the different ways people use water, such as drinking a glass of water and watering a lawn.

Teach and Apply

Student Pages C18–C19

- Invite children to name ways other than those listed on the page that people use water every day. Then point out that we use oil, coal, and gas to heat water, to make electricity, and to heat stoves for cooking.
- Ask children to think of ways that they are using trees in their classroom right now. Then challenge them to name other natural resources they use, such as the sun, rocks, minerals, and soil, and at least one way we use each one.

Reading Assist *Parts of Speech*

Discuss different ways the word *water* can be used: as a noun (*Water is a natural resource*), as a verb (*I will water the lawn*), and as an adjective (*I enjoy water sports, such as swimming and skiing*).

Real-World Applications

Petroleum accounts for more than half of the world's total supply of energy. It is used to make gasoline, kerosene, diesel oil, fuel oil, and natural gas. Other products in which petroleum plays a key role are plastics, paints, soaps, and synthetic fibers.

Assess and Extend

Answers to Lesson Review

1. Water, oil, coal, gas, and trees are some natural resources.
2. Fuel is used for heating homes and buildings, running factories and machines, and making gasoline for cars and trucks.
3. **Draw** (*Portfolio Assessment or Journal*) Drawings may include washing, drinking, and cooking.

Check for Understanding

To follow up on the **baseline assessment,** encourage children to make any necessary revisions to the lists created earlier and to add ways each item can be used.

Reteach

Invite each child to select a resource and search through magazines to find pictures showing ways that resource can be used. Then have children write the name of their resources on drawing paper and create collages.

Lesson Organizer

Objective
Identify some effects of pollution and ways people can protect natural resources.

Vocabulary recycling

Process Skills observing, making definitions

Materials

Kit Items soil

School-Supplied Items food scraps, leaves, grass, water, craft stick, plastic jar with lid

Additional Resources
- Lab Manual
- Teacher Demonstration Kit
- Wall Chart

Introduce

Activate Prior Knowledge
Ask: **Why is it important for us to help take care of the earth?**

Language Development *Scientific Language*
Explain that many people help their gardens by making compost; grass clippings, vegetable peelings, and other plant parts that are placed in the soil. The material makes the soil rich with nutrients.

Flip Chart
Draw children's attention to the picture of the recycling container. Ask what recycling means and why it is important.

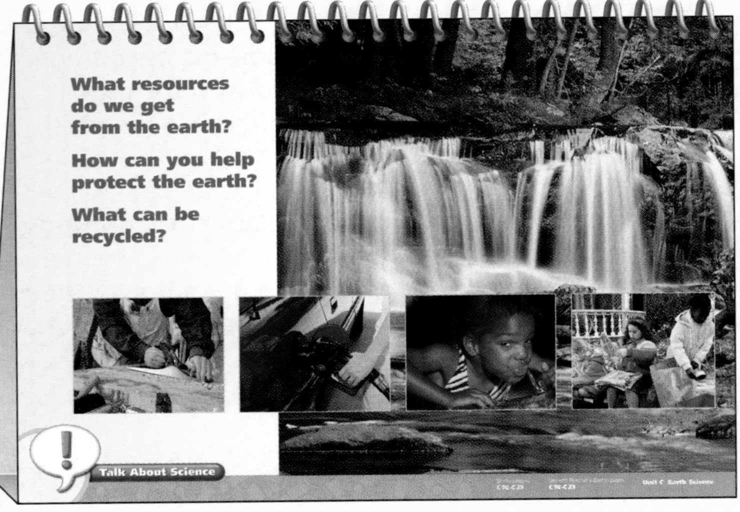
What resources do we get from the earth?
How can you help protect the earth?
What can be recycled?
Talk About Science

How can you help protect the earth?

Think about the last time you threw something away. What was it? Could you have used it again instead of throwing it away?

When trash piles up, the earth gets dirty. Dirty air, water, and land can be harmful to people and animals. You can help protect the earth by keeping it clean. Don't litter. Use things over and over instead of throwing them away.

You can help by recycling too. **Recycling** means making new things from old things. You can recycle cans, bottles, and newspapers.

You can even recycle your leftover food scraps! Use them to make compost, and add the compost to your soil to help your plants grow.

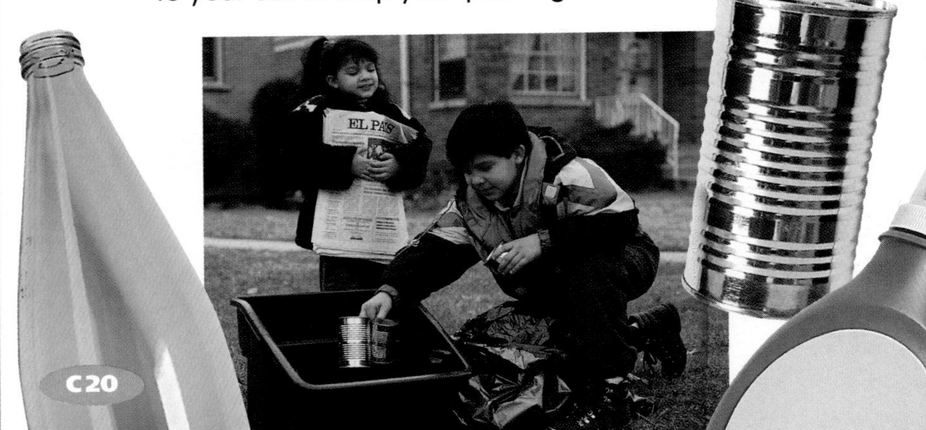
EL PAÍS

C20

Science Background
- Some nonrenewable resources can be replaced with inexhaustible resources. Instead of using oil, wind, water, or solar power might be used.
- People can reduce consumption by changing their habits. Wearing a sweater indoors in cold weather allows people to lower their thermostats.

Teaching Tips You may want to use 1- or 2-liter soda bottles. Cut the tops off and have children cover the bottle with foil, securing with a rubber band.

Math-Science Connection
Have children use the facts on **Wall Chart** page 36 to create a bar graph. Ask questions about the graph such as: **Which uses more water, brushing your teeth or washing the dishes?**

Make compost.

Materials

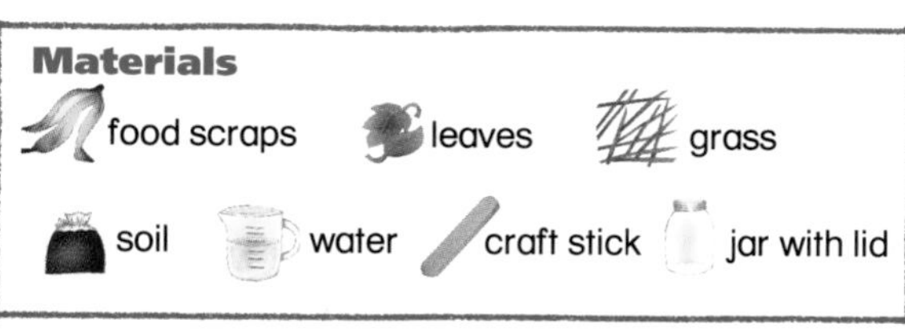

food scraps, leaves, grass, soil, water, craft stick, jar with lid

Process Skills

- observing
- making definitions

Steps

1. Put food scraps, leaves, grass, and soil into the jar.
2. Add a little water. Stir with the craft stick. Cover the jar.
3. Observe the jar every day.
4. Make a definition. Tell what compost means.

Share. Describe your compost.

Lesson Review

1. How can you help protect the earth?
2. What is recycling?
3. **Draw** your compost after five days.

C21

Lab Manual

How can you help protect the earth?

Draw what you observe.

Start | End

Lab Manual p. 69

Activity Rubric

Use the following activity scoring rubric to assess students' performance.

Scoring Criteria	1	2	3	4
Student assembled the materials to create compost to complete this activity.				
Student followed proper procedures to represent a sample of recycling.				
Student observed the compost mixture over a period of time.				
Student drew a representation of the compost at the beginning and after one week and compared them.				
Student explained that composting plant waste is one example of recycling.				

Scoring Key

4 points correct, complete, detailed
3 points partially correct, complete, detailed
2 points partially correct, partially complete, lacks some detail
1 point incorrect or incomplete, needs assistance

Lab Manual p. T25

Teach and Apply

Student Page C20

Help children brainstorm ways they can help take care of the earth.

Reading Assist *Word Meaning*

Point out that *recycle* means to make new things from old so that objects are used again. The prefix *re-* means "again," and *cycle* suggests a circle.

Student Page C21

Explore Activity

Time about 15 minutes

Grouping cooperative groups of 2

Advise children to use plant—not meat—scraps and to keep the compost mixture moist. Children should also open the jars occasionally to ventilate and stir. The compost can become smelly, so children may want to keep their jars outdoors. Children can complete Lab Manual page 69. Encourage children to share their **definitions** of *compost.*

Safety Note *Be sure children wash their hands with soap and water after handling the compost.*

What to Expect

The compost will start to look like a rich soil mixture; the complete process may take about six months.

Assess and Extend

Answers to Lesson Review

1. You can help protect the earth by not littering, using things over and over, and recycling.
2. Recycling is making new things from old things.
3. **Draw** (*Portfolio Assessment or Journal*) Drawings should include the jar, the soil, and organic material at some stage of decay.

Inquire Further

Ask the following questions to guide further inquiry: **How is your compost like your friend's? How is it different? Why is it different?**

Higher Order Thinking *Draw Conclusions*

Ask children why they think it might be important to find new ways to use trash.

Call 1-888-537-4908 with your Activity questions or comments.

Lesson Organizer

Objective
Identify some items that can be recycled.

Additional Resources
- Wall Chart

Introduce

Activate Prior Knowledge
Remind children that in the last lesson they learned about how food scraps can be recycled and used to enrich soil for plant growth. Ask children to brainstorm a list of other items that can be recycled and to tell how they can be used. Record their ideas on chart paper and save for use as a **baseline assessment.**

Language Development *Write a Slogan*
Invite children to make up slogans about recycling, such as "Do Your Part—Reduce, Reuse, Recycle." Tell children that a slogan encourages people to do something.

Flip Chart
Discuss the objects in the picture that are being put into the recycling container. Have children name other things that can be recycled.

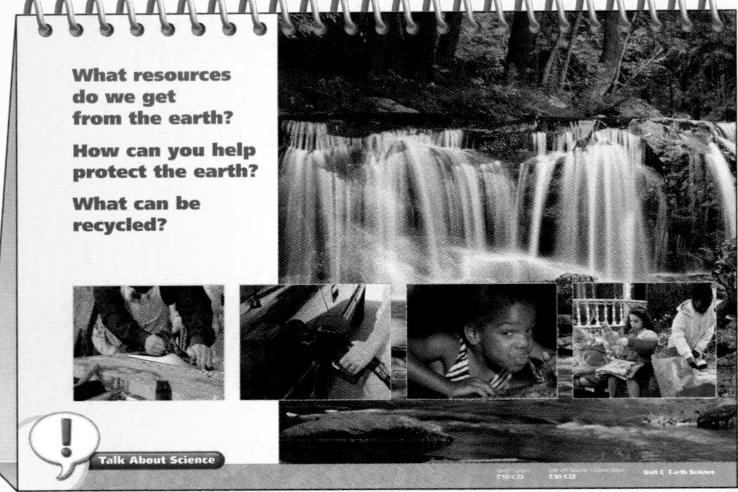
What resources do we get from the earth?
How can you help protect the earth?
What can be recycled?
Talk About Science

What can be recycled?

This playground may look like an ordinary playground. It is actually made completely from reused and recycled objects!

Reused objects are things that are used again and again. How are tires being reused in this playground?[1]

[1] Children are playing on them.

Science Background

- Mineral resources can be recycled, but fossil fuels cannot.
- Minerals such as iron ore, aluminum ore, tin, and manganese are nonrenewable, but discoveries of new deposits have kept up with depletion.
- Coal, oil, and natural gas—fossil fuels—are nonrenewable. The earth's oil resources are estimated to be able to supply sufficient oil for 25 to 200 years.

Teaching Tips You may want to allow time for children to make posters using the slogans they created in Language Development. If you do not already have one, allow children to set up their own recycling center. Find local recycling centers and distribute information about them to children and families.

Many of the things you use every day can be recycled. Cans, bottles, and newspapers can all be recycled to create new products. What did you use today that can be recycled?

Lesson Review

1. What does reuse mean?
2. What is special about the playground in the picture?
3. **Write** a list of some things that can be reused or recycled.

ESL Strategy

Suggest that children make a book of items that can be recycled. Have them draw or cut out pictures and paste them on drawing paper. Then help children label each item. Have children read their books to a friend.

Teach and Apply

Student Pages C22–C23

Point out that recycling allows us to conserve, or save, our natural resources and to reduce the amount of trash that we make. The most commonly recycled materials are paper, plastic, glass, and metal. Ask children to look for labels that indicate recycled products in the classroom or when they are shopping with family members. Most manufactured items that can be recycled can also be made from recycled materials.

Reading Assist *Verb Tenses*

Point out that the words *recycle, recycled,* and *recycling* are all tenses of the same verb. Have children write sentences using each form of the word.

Assess and Extend

Answers to Lesson Review

1. Reuse means to use again and again.
2. It is made from reused or recycled things.
3. **Write** (*Portfolio Assessment or Journal*) Answers may include cans, bottles, and newspapers.

Check for Understanding

To follow up on the **baseline assessment,** ask children to review the list they made of items that can be recycled and how they can be reused. Have children add to or delete items from the list as needed.

Reteach

Ask children to cut out and paste pictures of things that can be recycled on **Wall Chart** page 37. Point out the recycling symbol on the chart.

Science Center

Flip Chart

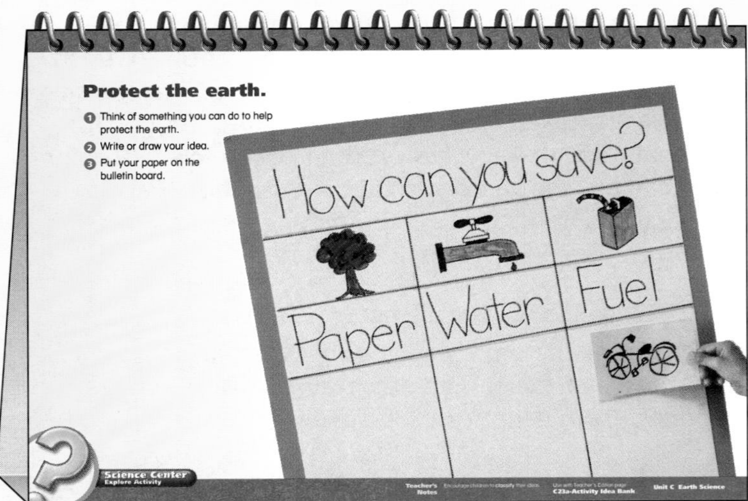

Protect the earth.
1 Think of something you can do to help protect the earth.
2 Write or draw your idea.
3 Put your paper on the bulletin board.
How can you save?
Paper
Water
Fuel
Science Center
Explore Activity

Protect the earth.

Objective

Identify ways to protect the earth.

Process Skills classifying

Materials

Kit Items none

School-Supplied Items tape, paper, crayons or markers

Procedure

- Prepare a classroom bulletin board with title and headings as shown on the **Flip Chart.**
- Invite children to brainstorm different ways they can help protect the earth.
- Have each child choose an idea and record it on paper.
- Children **classify** their ideas by taping the papers under the bulletin board headings.
- You can use **Lab Manual** page 71 with this activity.

What to Expect

Children will find many different ways to protect the earth.

Lab Manual

Protect the earth.

Write or draw a way to conserve paper, water, and fuel.

Paper	
Water	
Fuel	

Lab Manual, p. 71

Connections

School and Community

Ideas for bringing the school and community together:

Field Trips

- landfill/garbage dump
- recycling center

Guest Speakers

- sanitation worker
- ecologist
- environmentalist
- worker from recycling center

Themes

The activities on these pages can be used with classroom themes such as:

- recycling
- the environment
- resources
- conservation
- water
- your community

Books for Children

Children might enjoy these books about the environment:

New Paper, Everyone! by Pat Quinn. Recycle old paper into new paper. (Learning Media, ISBN 0-478-20513-9)

A New True Book: Oil Spills by Darlene R. Stille. The benefits of oil as well as the dangers of oil spills. (Childrens Press, ISBN 0-516-01116-2)

Where Does the Garbage Go? by Paul Showers. Schoolchildren visit a landfill to see what happens to trash. (HarperCollins, ISBN 0-06-445114-3)

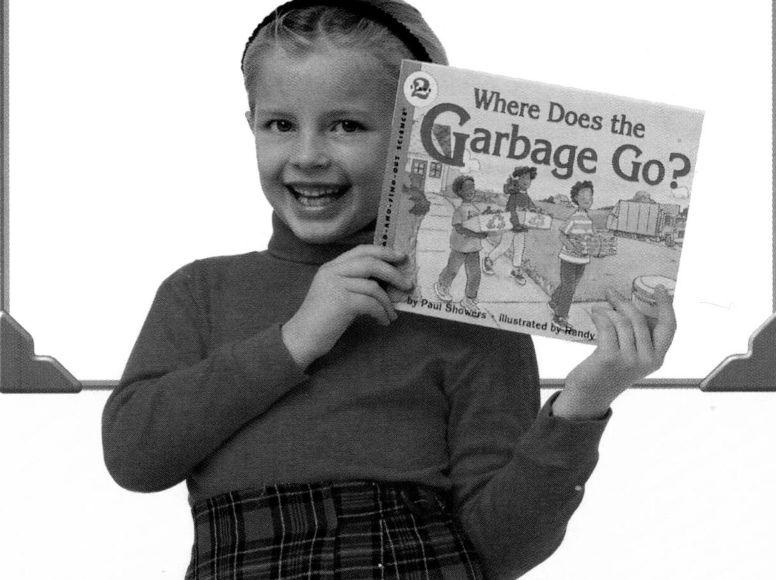

Cross-Curricular Options

LITERATURE

The Lorax

Use the book to talk about the environment.

Materials *The Lorax* by Dr. Seuss. (Random House, ISBN 0-394-82337-0)

Procedure

- The book conveys an important message about the environment but maintains the fun and fanciful language associated with Dr. Seuss.
- Read the story aloud and ask children for their reactions to the Lorax's pleas.
- Ask children to think of how what happened in the story compares to what is happening in today's environment.

Multiple Intelligences linguistic, spatial, natural

MATH

So Much Trash!

Add or multiply to find weekly amount of trash.

Materials calculators, paper

Procedure

- Ask the school custodian how many bags of school trash are thrown away each day of the week.
- Have children determine how many bags would be thrown out in one week, two weeks, one month.
- Encourage children to use calculators to figure the amounts.

Multiple Intelligences logical-mathematical

Gifted and Talented Challenge children to figure out how much trash is disposed of during the school year.

WRITING

Save the Environment

Write a letter.

Materials paper, pencil, envelopes, postage stamps

Procedure

- Invite children to write a class letter to the U.S. Environmental Protection Agency or another environmental organization, asking for information about protecting the environment.

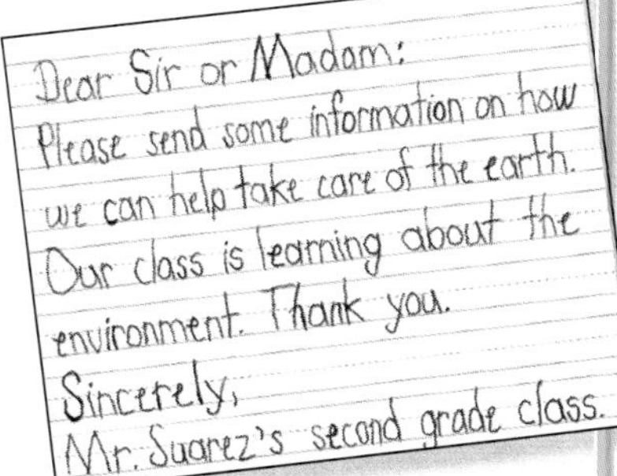

Dear Sir or Madam:
Please send some information on how we can help take care of the earth. Our class is learning about the environment. Thank you.
Sincerely,
Mr. Suarez's second grade class.

- Some children might write a letter asking a local recycling or environmental professional to come speak to the class about saving the environment.

Multiple Intellgences linguistic

ART

Reuse and Recycle!

Create a sculpture with recyclable materials.

Materials paper rolls, newspaper, old greeting cards, clean plastic bottles or containers and other clean recyclables, glue, scissors, masking or other tape

Procedure

- Have children create sculptures with materials that can be recycled.
- When they are finished, have them list all the recyclable materials they used.

Multiple Intelligences spatial

ESL Say the following sentence: **I can recycle a(n) ________.** Have children point to an object and say the object's name to fill in the blank.

Review Organizer

Materials

Kit Items none

School-Supplied Items magazines, books

Time about 30 minutes

Grouping individual

Additional Resources

- Chapter 1 Assessment: Teacher's Assessment Package

Chapter Main Ideas

Lesson 1 Features of the earth include mountains, hills, valleys, oceans, rivers, and lakes.

Lesson 2 Rocks come in many shapes, sizes, textures, and colors. Rocks are made of minerals.

Lesson 3 Erosion of land happens when soil or rock are carried away by water, wind, or other rocks.

Lesson 4 Volcanoes and earthquakes are natural events that change the earth.

Lesson 5 Clay, dishwashing soap, baking soda, and vinegar can simulate an erupting volcano.

Lesson 6 Natural resources are useful materials from the earth, including water, oil, coal, gas, and trees.

Lesson 7 Recycling and reusing objects can help protect the earth and keep it clean.

Lesson 8 Many everyday items can be recycled.

Reviewing Science Words

1. Plant roots help keep the soil in place.
2. Lava is melted rock that comes from inside the earth.
3. Answers might include water, oil, coal, gas, and wood.
4. Recycling protects the earth by keeping it clean and preventing pollution.

Reviewing Science Ideas

1. Mountains, valleys, oceans, rivers, lakes
2. Soft, hard, smooth, bumpy, rough, big, small, shiny
3. During an earthquake, the earth shakes. Sometimes roads, buildings, and bridges are destroyed.
4. Possible answers: Don't litter, use things over and over, recycle, make compost.

Chapter 1 Review

Reviewing Science Words

1. How do plant roots help prevent **erosion**?
2. What is **lava**?
3. Name three **natural resources**.
4. How does **recycling** protect the earth?

Reviewing Science Ideas

1. Name three features of the earth.
2. What words can you use to describe rocks?
3. What happens during an earthquake?
4. What can you do to help protect the earth?

Technology

 Children can review *The Earth* with the **Practice & Assessment CD-ROM.**

 Children can use the **Production Studio** to show what they've learned about *The Earth.*

 Children can use The KnowZone™ at **www.kz.com** to review and test their science knowledge.

 You can use **TestWorks™** to customize assessment for your children.

Tell about the earth.

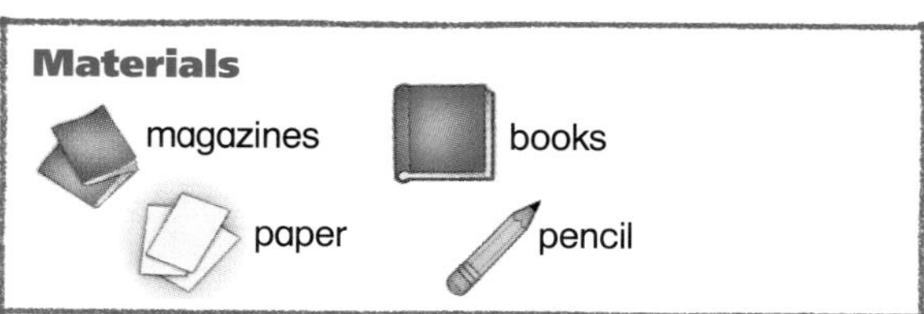

1. Find a picture that shows some features of the earth.
2. Write some sentences that tell about your picture.
3. Display your picture with classmates' pictures.
4. Take turns reading your sentences aloud.
5. Match the sentences and pictures.

C25

Chapter Assessment

Use the words in the box to finish each sentence.

feature lava erosion recycling natural resource

1. Hot melted rock from a volcano is called ____________.
2. Oil is a ____________.
3. A mountain is a ____________ of the earth.
4. Using an old can as a pencil holder is an example of ____________.
5. Soil carried away by water or wind is called ____________.

Draw a line from each set of words to the correct picture.

6. shiny, smooth
7. large, rough
8. small, rough

Teacher's Assessment Package pp. 41–42

Assessment Rubric

	The Earth
4	Correctly identifies and describes features of the earth.
3	Makes a few errors in identifying and describing the features of the earth.
2	Has difficulty identifying and describing the features of the earth.
1	Is unable to identify and describe the features of the earth.

Performance Assessment Teaching Tips

- Before beginning the activity, have children brainstorm a list of the earth's features. Record their responses on the chalkboard.
- Provide travel magazines and brochures, and books about geography and earth science for children to use.
- Be sure children understand that they are to find a picture they can use to talk about the features of the earth. Explain that they are also to talk about ways to protect the environments shown in their pictures.
- If resources are limited, have children work with partners. Together partners can find a picture to share with the class. Then one child can describe the picture focusing on the earth's features, and the partner can describe ways to protect the environment shown in the picture.

Enrichment

After sharing their pictures, have children make posters to show ways to protect the earth's features. Display the completed posters.

Chapter 1 Skills Trace

Process Skills Development

	Making and Using Models	Observing	Predicting	Estimating and Measuring	Making Definitions
Skill Introduced	xv	xiv	xv	xiv	xv
Skill Applied	C7 C13 C16–C17	C13 C16–C17 C21	C13	C16–C17	C21
Skill Assessed	End Matter 20–21	End Matter 6–7	End Matter 16–17	End Matter 12–13	End Matter 18–19

Chapter Review pages are also on the **Flip Chart.**

Lesson/Activity and Flip Chart	Objectives/Process Skills	Time Options/Activity Materials
Chapter Opener Student Edition pp. C26–C27 and **Flip Chart** ***Then I'll Know***		**Have less time?** Use the Graphic Organizer on Teacher's Assessment Package p. 45 for an overview of the lessons. Use the Flip Chart to teach lesson concepts and science activities. **Have more time?** Use the Flip Chart to reinforce and extend lesson concepts and activities. Use the Cross-Curricular Options in the Activity Idea Bank on Teacher's Edition pp. C37b and C43b.
Lesson 1 Student Edition pp. C28–C29 ***What can you tell about the weather?*** **Explore Activity** ***Make an anemometer.*** **Flip Chart** ***Talk About Science***	**Objective** Identify weather measuring instruments. **Process Skills** estimating and measuring	**Kit Items** 2 3-ounce paper cups, straw **School-Supplied Items** safety goggles, push pin, unsharpened pencil with eraser
Math in Science Student Edition pp. C30–C31 ***Using Measurement Tools***	**Objective** Use measurement tools.	
Lesson 2 Student Edition pp. C32–C33 and **Flip Chart** **Experiment Activity** ***Experiment with temperature.***	**Objective** Determine how sunlight affects soil, water, and air temperatures. **Process Skills** experimenting, estimating and measuring (*formulating hypotheses, identifying and controlling variables, and collecting data*)	**Kit Items** 3 9-ounce plastic cups, 3 thermometers, soil **School-Supplied Items** water, clock
Lesson 3 Student Edition pp. C34–C35 ***What happens in spring and summer?*** **Flip Chart** ***Talk About Science***	**Objective** Identify seasonal weather conditions and their effects on plants and animals.	**Have more time?** Use the following teaching guide option: Interactive Transparency 8, Interactive Transparency Package
Lesson 4 Student Edition pp. C36–C37 ***What happens in fall and winter?*** **Flip Chart** ***Talk About Science***	**Objective** Identify seasonal weather conditions and their effects on plants and animals.	**Have more time?** Use the following teaching guide option: Interactive Transparency 8, Interactive Transparency Package
Activity Idea Bank Teacher's Edition pp. C37a–C37b **Flip Chart** **Science Center Explore Activity** ***Observe wind.***	**Objective** Observe wind speed. **Process Skills** observing, communicating	**Kit Items** none **School-Supplied Items** scissors, safety goggles, paper, pushpin, unsharpened pencil with eraser
Lesson 5 Student Edition pp. C38–C39 ***Is there water in air?*** **Explore Activity** ***Observe the water cycle.*** **Flip Chart** ***Talk About Science***	**Objective** Describe the water cycle. **Process Skills** observing	**Kit Items** plastic wrap, 9-ounce plastic cup **School-Supplied Items** warm water, tape, clock
Lesson 6 Student Edition pp. C40–C41 and **Flip Chart** **Investigate Activity** ***How does water vapor condense?***	**Objective** Learn that air contains water. **Process Skills** observing	**Kit Items** food coloring **School-Supplied Items** 2 cans, ice water, warm water, clock
Lesson 7 Student Edition pp. C42–C43 ***What are some kinds of bad weather?*** **Flip Chart** ***Talk About Science***	**Objective** Describe severe weather conditions and ways to stay safe in severe weather.	
Activity Idea Bank Teacher's Edition pp. C43a–C43b **Flip Chart** **Science Center Explore Activity** ***Explore evaporation.***	**Objective** Observe and describe the results of evaporation. **Process Skills** observing	**Kit Items** eye dropper, cup **School-Supplied Items** paper towel, water, cardboard
Chapter Review Student Edition pp. C44–C45 and **Flip Chart**		**Kit Items** none **School-Supplied Items** paper, markers or crayons

Lesson/Activity and Flip Chart	Additional Resources		Technology
Chapter Opener Student Edition pp. C26–C27 and **Flip Chart** ***Then I'll Know***	**Teacher's Assessment Package** • Graphic Organizer, p. 45 **Instructional Resources** • Family Activity, pp. 57–58 • Vocabulary Preview, p. 59	**Songs & Activities Package** • *Then I'll Know*, pp. 23–24 **Wall Chart,** p. 38	**Practice & Assessment CD-ROM** **AudioText** **Production Studio** **www.sfscience.com** **Songs & Activities Package** **Teacher's Resource Planner CD-ROM**
Lesson 1 Student Edition pp. C28–C29 ***What can you tell about the weather?*** **Explore Activity** ***Make an anemometer.*** **Flip Chart** ***Talk About Science***	**Lab Manual** • Lab Manual, p. 73 • Activity Rubric, p. T26	**Teacher Demonstration Kit**	
Math in Science Student Edition pp. C30–C31 ***Using Measurement Tools***	**Instructional Resources** • Math in Science, p. 60		
Lesson 2 Student Edition pp. C32–C33 and **Flip Chart** **Experiment Activity** ***Experiment with temperature.***	**Lab Manual** • Lab Manual, pp. 75–76 • Activity Rubric, p. T27	**Teacher Demonstration Kit**	*Earth Science* **Activity Video**
Lesson 3 Student Edition pp. C34–C35 ***What happens in spring and summer?*** **Flip Chart** ***Talk About Science***	**Interactive Transparency Package** • Interactive Transparency 8	**Wall Chart,** p. 39	
Lesson 4 Student Edition pp. C36–C37 ***What happens in fall and winter?*** **Flip Chart** ***Talk About Science***	**Interactive Transparency Package** • Interactive Transparency 8	**Wall Chart,** p. 40	
Activity Idea Bank Teacher's Edition pp. C37a–C37b **Flip Chart** **Science Center Explore Activity** ***Observe wind.***	**Lab Manual** • Lab Manual, p. 77 • Activity Rubric, p. T27		
Lesson 5 Student Edition pp. C38–C39 ***Is there water in air?*** **Explore Activity** ***Observe the water cycle.*** **Flip Chart** ***Talk About Science***	**Lab Manual** • Lab Manual, p. 78 • Activity Rubric, p. T28	**Teacher Demonstration Kit** **Wall Chart,** p. 41	
Lesson 6 Student Edition pp. C40–C41 and **Flip Chart** **Investigate Activity** ***How does water vapor condense?***	**Lab Manual** • Lab Manual, p. 79 • Activity Rubric, p. T28	**Teacher Demonstration Kit**	*Earth Science* **Activity Video**
Lesson 7 Student Edition pp. C42–C43 ***What are some kinds of bad weather?*** **Flip Chart** ***Talk About Science***		**Wall Chart,** p. 42	
Activity Idea Bank Teacher's Edition pp. C43a–C43b **Flip Chart** **Science Center Explore Activity** ***Explore evaporation.***	**Lab Manual** • Lab Manual, p. 80 • Activity Rubric, p. T29		
Chapter Review Student Edition pp. C44–C45 and **Flip Chart**	**Teacher's Assessment Package** • Chapter 2 Assessment, pp. 47–48		**Practice & Assessment CD-ROM** **Production Studio** **The KnowZone™ at www.kz.com** **TestWorks™**

Lab Manual

What can you tell about the weather?

Draw your anemometer.

Students' drawings of their anemometers will vary as will their descriptions of its use to measure the wind.

How did you use your anemometer to measure the wind?

Lab Manual
p. 73

Math in Science

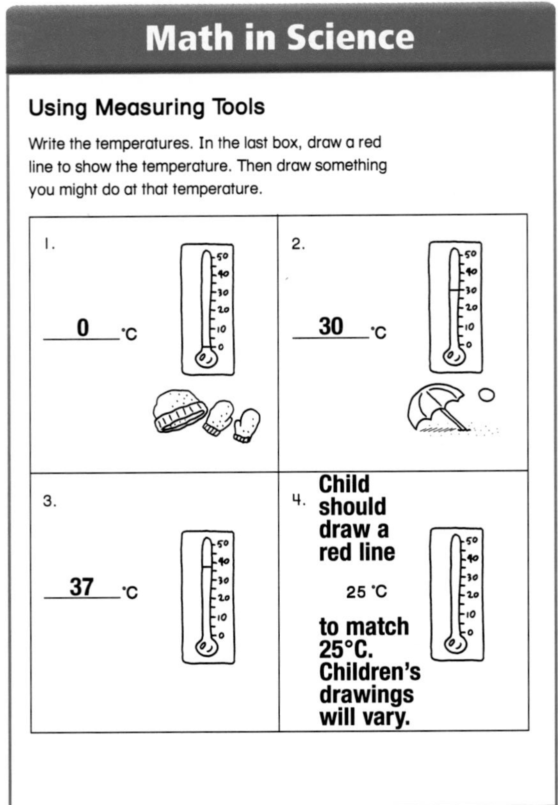

Using Measuring Tools

Write the temperatures. In the last box, draw a red line to show the temperature. Then draw something you might do at that temperature.

1. **0** °C	2. **30** °C
3. **37** °C	4. **Child should draw a red line** 25 °C **to match 25°C. Children's drawings will vary.**

Instructional Resources
p. 60

Lab Manual

Experiment with temperature.

Problem

How do the temperatures of soil, water, and air change after being placed in the sunlight?

Give Your Hypothesis

If you put soil, water, and air in sunlight, will their temperatures go up or down? Write what you think.

Control the Variables

Make sure that each cup is placed in the same amount of sunlight for the same amount of time.

Test Your Hypothesis

Measure the temperatures.

Students' hypotheses will vary but should express the concept that the temperatures of soil, water, and air will go up when placed in sunlight. Students' conclusions should reflect their data.

Lab Manual
p. 75

Lab Manual

Collect Your Data

Record the starting temperatures and the temperatures after 30 minutes.

	Starting temperature	Temperature after 30 minutes
Soil		
Water		
Air		

Tell Your Conclusion

Compare your results and hypotheses. How do the temperatures of soil, water, and air change after being placed in the sunlight?

Inquire Further

What would happen to the temperatures if you put the cups in a shady place?

Lab Manual
p. 76

Transparency

Seasons

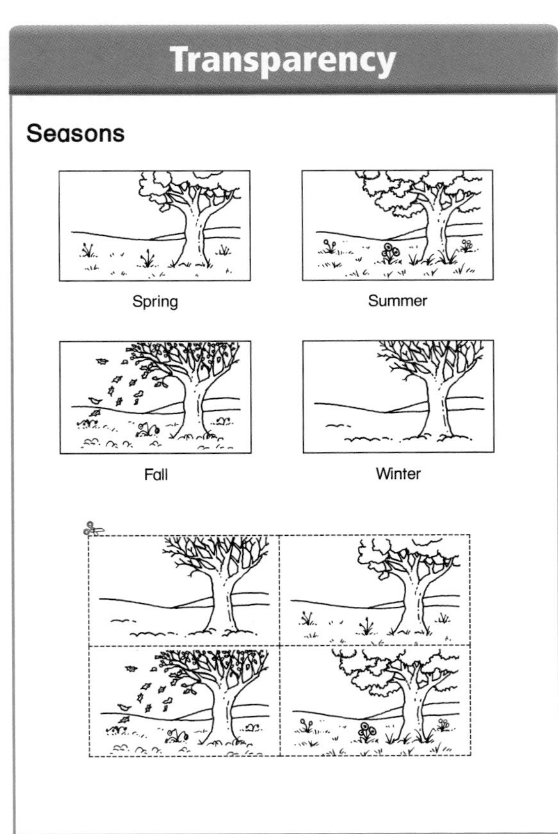

Interactive Transparency Package
Transparency 8

Lab Manual

Observe wind.

Draw a picture to show how you made your pinwheel move.

Students' drawings of their pinwheels and how they moved will vary.

Lab Manual
p. 77

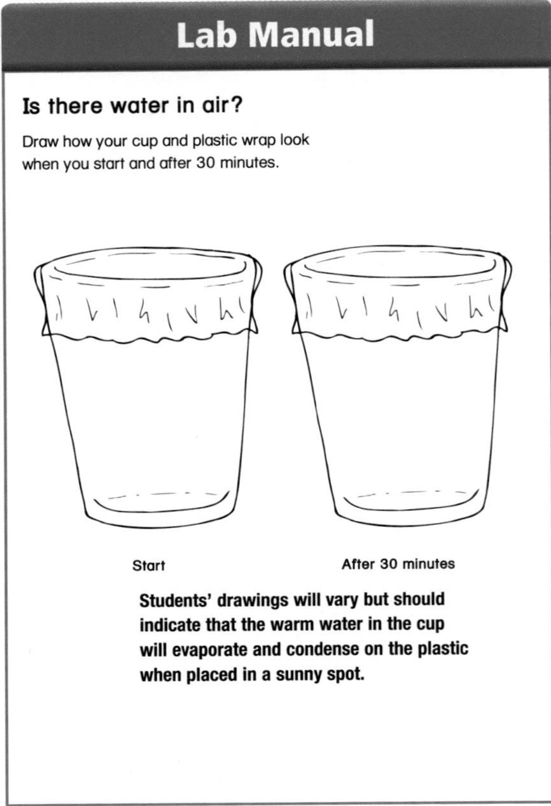

Lab Manual

Is there water in air?

Draw how your cup and plastic wrap look when you start and after 30 minutes.

Start

After 30 minutes

Students' drawings will vary but should indicate that the warm water in the cup will evaporate and condense on the plastic when placed in a sunny spot.

Lab Manual
p. 78

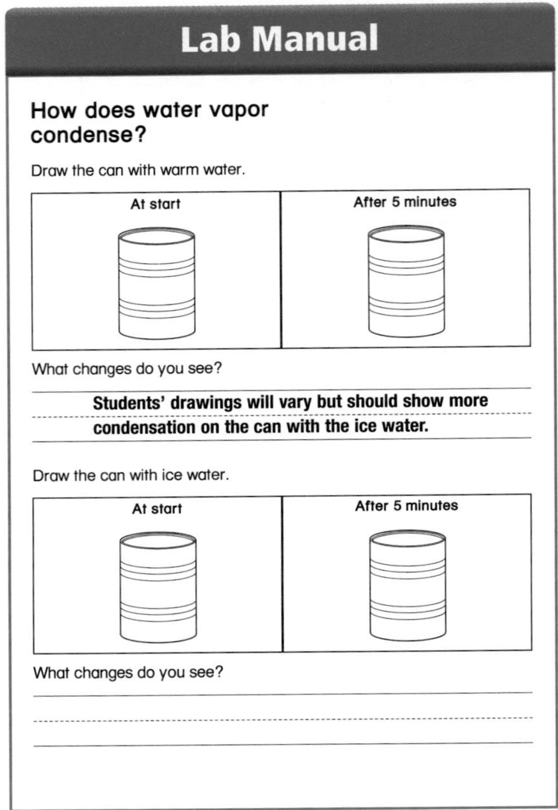

Lab Manual

How does water vapor condense?

Draw the can with warm water.

At start	After 5 minutes

What changes do you see?

Students' drawings will vary but should show more condensation on the can with the ice water.

Draw the can with ice water.

At start	After 5 minutes

What changes do you see?

Lab Manual
p. 79

Lab Manual

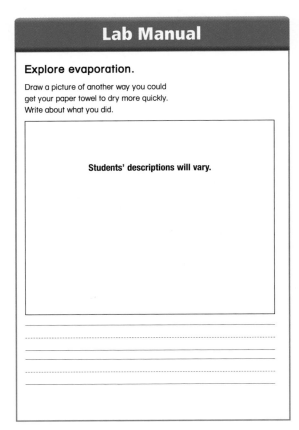

Explore evaporation.

Draw a picture of another way you could get your paper towel to dry more quickly. Write about what you did.

Students' descriptions will vary.

Lab Manual
p. 80

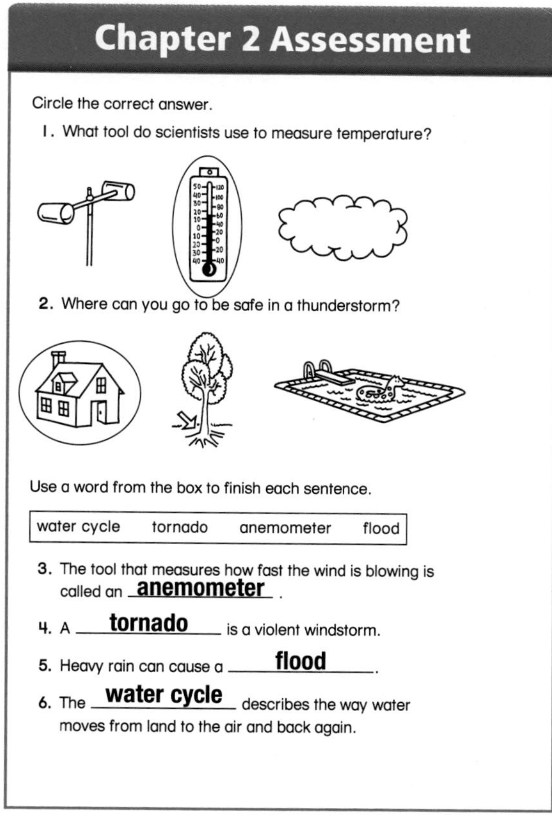

Teacher's Assessment Package
p. 47

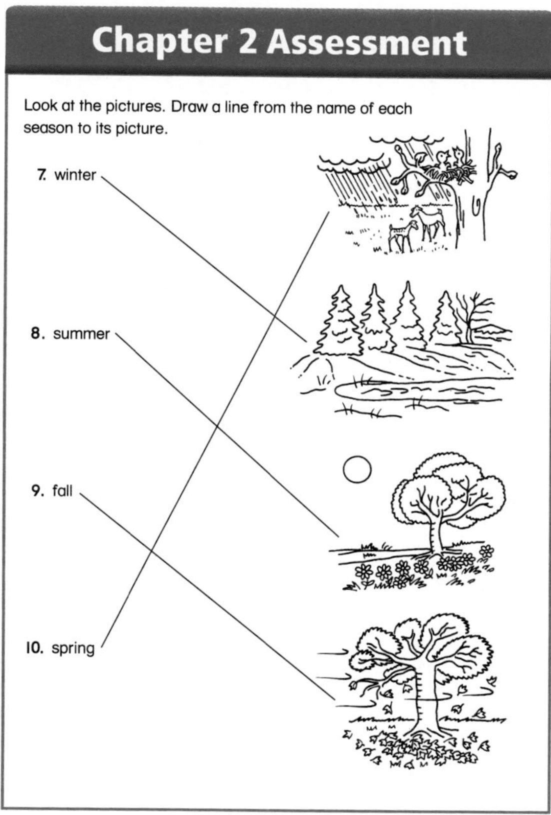

Teacher's Assessment Package
p. 48

Table of Contents

Introducing the Chapter

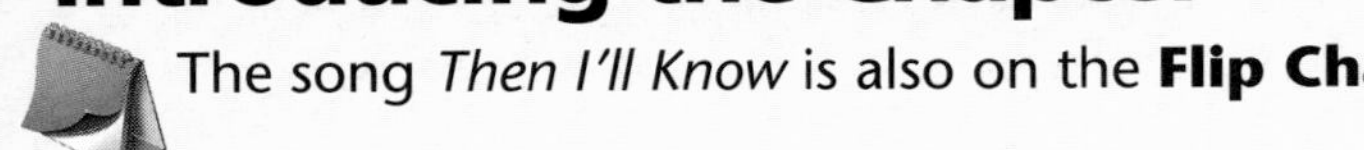

The song *Then I'll Know* is also on the **Flip Chart.**

- Ask questions such as: **Is it cloudy or sunny?** Then discuss why it is important to know about the weather.
- Distribute the Family Activity blackline master page.

Singing the Song

Have children sing the song *Then I'll Know* on side 2 of the CTW cassette. Distribute pages 23–24 from the CTW Song Activity Book.

Reading Assist *Antonyms*

Write the words *high* and *low* on the chalkboard and say them aloud. Ask children to find these words in the song. Talk about the idea that these words have opposite meanings; they are called antonyms.

Vocabulary Preview

Use the Vocabulary Preview blackline master to introduce the vocabulary words for this chapter.

Lesson 1 thermometer, anemometer
Lesson 5 evaporates, condenses, water cycle
Lesson 7 tornado, drought

Chapter 2

Weather and Seasons

Then I'll Know

Sing to the tune of *Picking Up Pawpaws*.

Is the temperature high or low?
Up or down, which way will it go?
I'll check a thermometer and then I'll know.
The temperature is part of the weather.

Is the wind blowing fast or slow?
And what direction does it blow?
I'll check the windsock and then I'll know.
The wind is part of the weather.

Technology

Practice & Assessment CD-ROM

AudioText

Production Studio

www.sfscience.com

Teacher's Resource Planner

Songs & Activities Package

CTW Song & Activity

Tracking the Weather

How does the forecast compare to what really happens? Find out.
1. Read the weather report in the newspaper every day for a week.
2. Record the predictions on the chart.
3. The next day, read the report again. Find out what really happened.

	Predicted High Temperature	Actual High Temperature	Predicted Rain or snow	Did it rain or snow?
Monday				
Tuesday				
Wednesday				
Thursday				
Friday				
Saturday				
Sunday				

At the end of the week, look at this chart. Did the newspaper get it right? How close was it?

Songs & Activities Package
pp. 23–24

Up in the sky I see a rainbow,
It must have rained, not long ago.
I'll check the rain gauge and then I'll know.
The rain is part of the weather.

Family Activity — Science at Home

Dear Family:
Our class is starting Chapter 2. We will be learning about weather and seasons. These are the main ideas for Chapter 2.

- Scientists use tools such as thermometers to measure weather.
- Weather is different during each of the four seasons.
- Water changes form as it moves from the earth to the clouds and back to the earth again.
- People can learn to stay safe in dangerous weather.

We will also be learning science vocabulary words for Chapter 2. By the end of Chapter 2, we will be able to read the vocabulary words and tell what they mean.

Word Bank
thermometer
anemometer
evaporate
condense
water cycle
tornado
drought

Home Projects
Here are some activities that will help your child understand the main ideas in Chapter 2. The activities are easy, fast, and fun.

Activities
- Compare your local weather to other places. Watch a weather report on television or read one in the newspaper. Then discuss how your weather is different from places farther north or south.

Instructional Resources pp. 57–58

Vocabulary Preview

thermometer	anemometer
evaporate	condense
water cycle	tornado
drought	thunderstorm

Instructional Resources p. 59

INQUIRY

Use a KWL chart at the beginning of each chapter. In the *K* column, record what children *know* about weather and the seasons. In the *W* column, list what they *want* to know. Throughout the chapter, ask children what they have *learned.* Record their responses in the *L* column. A KWL chart is available on **Wall Chart** page 38.

Chapter 2 Skills Trace

Process Skills Development	Estimating and Measuring	Experimenting	Observing
Skill Introduced	xiv	xv	xiv
Skill Applied	C29 C32–C33	C32–C33	C39 C40–C41
Skill Assessed	End Matter 12–13	End Matter 28–29	End Matter 6–7

Science Literature Library

What Will the Weather Be?
by Lynda DeWitt.
The basic characteristics of weather—temperature, humidity, wind speed and direction, air pressure—are presented in clear illustrations and text. Children will also learn about how meteorologists gather data for weather forecasts. (HarperTrophy, ISBN 0-06-445113-5)

Lesson Organizer

Objective
Identify weather measuring instruments.

Vocabulary
thermometer, anemometer

Process Skills estimating and measuring

Materials
Kit Items 2 3-ounce paper cups, straw

School-Supplied Items safety goggles, pushpin, unsharpened pencil with eraser

Additional Resources
- Lab Manual
- Teacher Demonstration Kit

Introduce

Activate Prior Knowledge
Ask children how they know when it is windy outside. Have them take turns describing what happens when it is windy.

Language Development *Poetry*
Read aloud a poem about the wind, such as "The Wind" by Robert Louis Stevenson. Invite children to tell what they think the poem means.

Flip Chart
Discuss what the weather is like in each picture. Ask: **What are some clues that help you tell about the weather?**

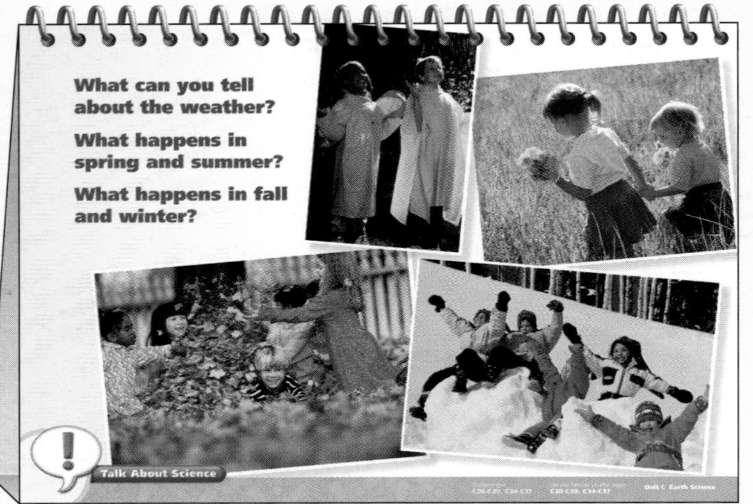

What can you tell about the weather?
What happens in spring and summer?
What happens in fall and winter?
Talk About Science

What can you tell about the weather?

Look outside. What is the weather like today? It may be hot or cold, or sunny or cloudy. Does the picture below show a windy or calm day?

You can tell a lot about the weather just by looking outside. Scientists use tools to measure things about the weather. A **thermometer** measures the temperature of the air. An **anemometer** like the one at the right measures how fast the wind is blowing.

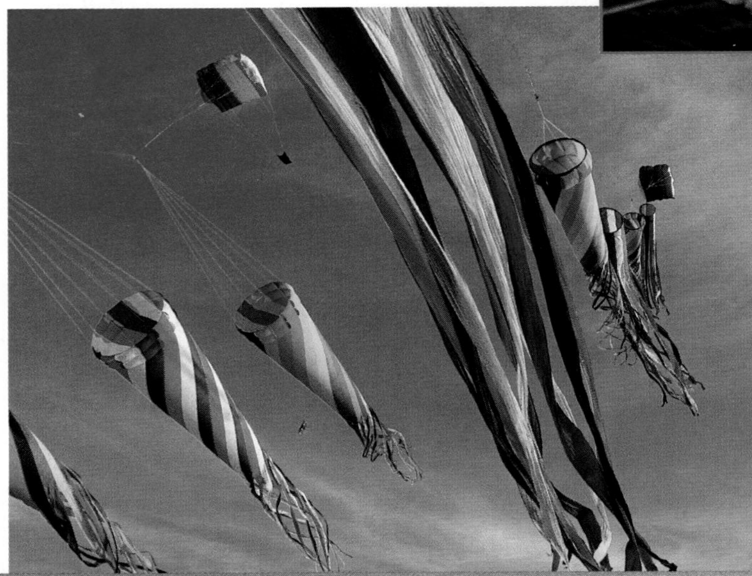

C28

Science Background

- The elements of weather are sunlight, temperature, humidity and precipitation, and winds.
- Atmospheric pressure determines the direction and speed of the wind, and it is the wind that moves air masses of different temperatures and moisture from one locality to another.

Science Across Cultures Explain that weather is different in other parts of the world. Locate areas close to the North and South poles. Ask children why they think areas near the poles have snow and areas near the equator have none. Have children share what they know about the weather in different places.

Make an anemometer.

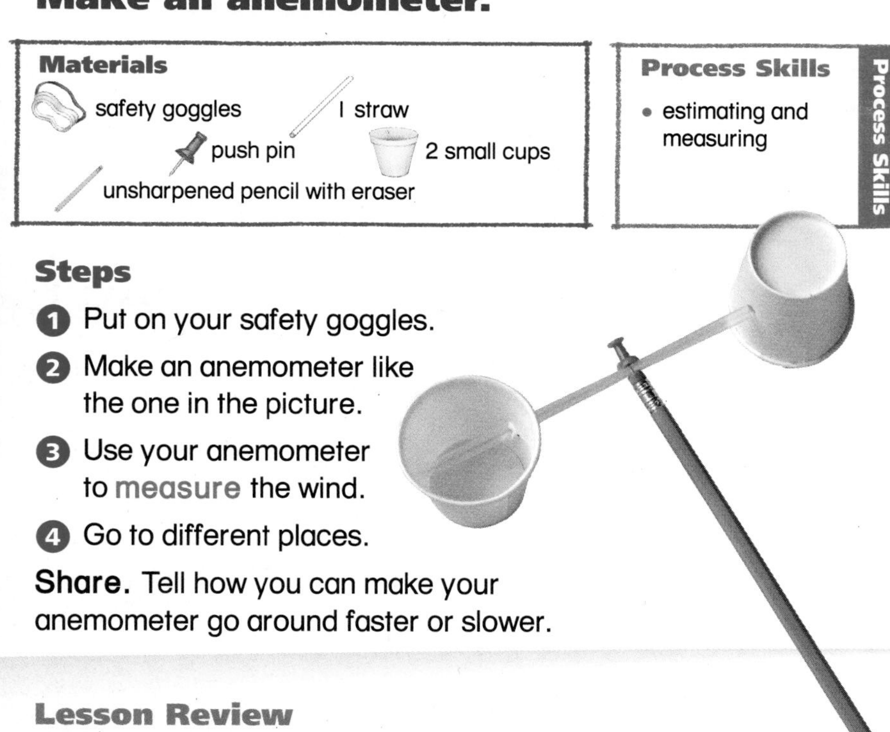

Process Skills

- estimating and measuring

Steps

1. Put on your safety goggles.
2. Make an anemometer like the one in the picture.
3. Use your anemometer to measure the wind.
4. Go to different places.

Share. Tell how you can make your anemometer go around faster or slower.

Lesson Review

1. How can scientists measure the temperature of the air?
2. How can scientists measure how fast the wind is blowing?
3. **Show** how an anemometer can measure the wind.

C29

Lab Manual

What can you tell about the weather?

Draw your anemometer.

How did you use your anemometer to measure the wind?

Lab Manual p. 73

Activity Rubric

Use the following activity scoring rubric to assess students' performance.

Scoring Criteria	1	2	3	4
Student followed directions to complete this activity.				
Student drew an anemometer used to measure the wind.				
Student conducted the activity following proper safety procedures.				
Student reported on how he or she used the anemometer to measure wind.				
Student drew a representation of his or her anemometer.				

Scoring Key
4 points correct, complete, detailed
3 points partially correct, complete, detailed
2 points partially correct, partially complete, lacks some detail
1 point incorrect or incomplete, needs assistance

Lab Manual p. T26

Call 1-888-537-4908 with your Activity questions or comments.

Teach and Apply

Student Page C28

- Point out that thermometers can be used to measure things other than air temperature, such as body temperature, how hot the oven is, water temperature.

Reading Assist *Study Skills*
Have children look up the word *anemometer* in their dictionaries and read the definition. Suggest that they use the pronunciation key to pronounce the word.

Student Page C29

Explore Activity

Time about 30 minutes
Grouping cooperative groups of 4

Safety Note *Show children how to use the pushpins so they do not stick themselves.*

- Make sure the cups are facing the same direction.
- Mark one of the cups with an X. Children can take measurements by counting how many times the X goes around within a given period of time, such as 10 seconds.
- Children can complete Lab Manual page 73 as they do the activity.

Assess and Extend

Answers to Lesson Review

1. Scientists can use a thermometer to measure the temperature of the air.
2. Scientists can use an anemometer to measure how fast the wind is blowing.
3. **Show** (*Performance Assessment*) Children may blow on their anemometers or hold them in a windy place to show how they work.

Inquire Further

Ask the following question to guide further inquiry: **What kind of weather might make your anemometer go faster?** (*Children might mention windstorms, hurricanes, tornadoes, and other windy conditions.*)

Higher Order Thinking *Draw Conclusions*
Ask children to tell why they think it is important to measure the wind or the air temperature.

Math Organizer

Objective

Use measurement tools.

Additional Resources

- Math in Science blackline master

Teaching Math in Science

- **Measuring** is an important science process skill used to collect data. As children learn to use measurement tools, they must develop accuracy and precision. Accuracy depends on the measurement tool itself and on how that measurement tool is used. Precision depends on the accuracy with which the measurement tool is used.
- Have children read and complete the Math in Science lesson and the Math in Science blackline master.

Student Page C30

- Before beginning the page, discuss thermometers. Have children share what they know about these measuring tools. Children might be familiar with thermometers from personal experience such as having their body temperatures taken at home or at the doctor's office.
- Explain that there are two kinds of thermometers. On a Fahrenheit thermometer, the boiling point of water is 212° and the freezing point is 32° above zero. On a Celsius thermometer, the boiling point of water is 100° and the freezing point is 0°.
- Ask: **Why are thermometers used? Who uses thermometers? What does a thermometer look like?**
- Read aloud the explanatory information on page C30. Have children point to the parts of the thermometer as you read about them.

Using Measurement Tools

You can use a thermometer to measure temperature. When the red line goes up, that means it is getting warmer. When the red line goes down, it is getting colder.

The number next to the top of the red line is the temperature. These numbers are called degrees.

When you write the temperature, you can use a small circle to stand for degrees.

This thermometer shows that it is 30° Celsius.

ESL Strategy

Display several pictures of thermometers showing temperatures that range from very cold to very hot. Also display pictures of people dressed for different temperatures. Have children read a thermometer, then select a picture that shows someone dressed for that temperature. Encourage children to discuss their choices.

How many degrees does this thermometer show?[1]

[1] 10° Celcius

Turn the page to do an activity using a thermometer.

Math in Science

Write the temperatures. In the last box, draw a red line to show the temperature. Then draw something you might do at that temperature.

1. ______ °C
2. ______ °C
3. ______ °C
4. 25 °C

Instructional Resources p. 60

Student Page C31

- Ask: **What temperature is shown on the thermometer for the summer scene on page C30?** (*30° Celsius*) **How do we know what the temperature is?** (*The colored line shows the temperature. The number next to the top of the line is the temperature.*)
- Have a similar discussion regarding the thermometer next to the autumn scene.
- Provide additional practice reading a thermometer by calling out temperatures such as 15° Celsius and having children point to where the line would stop if that was the temperature shown on the thermometer.

Apply Math in Science to Lesson 2

Children will use what they learned about using the thermometer, which is one measurement tool, to complete the next lesson.

Activity Organizer

Objective
Determine how sunlight affects soil, water, and air temperatures.

Process Skills experimenting, estimating and measuring (*formulating hypotheses, identifying and controlling variables, and collecting and interpreting data*)

Materials
Kit Items 3 9-ounce plastic cups, 3 thermometers, soil

School-Supplied Items water, clock

Time about 40 minutes

Grouping cooperative groups of 4

Additional Resources
- Lab Manual
- Teacher Demonstration Kit

Introduce

Activity Summary
The Experiment Activity is also on the **Flip Chart.** In this activity, children use scientific methods to compare the temperatures of soil, water, and air before and after the materials have been placed in sunlight. Children will find that the soil heats faster than air or water and therefore has the highest temperature. The water heats the slowest and therefore has the lowest temperature.

Activate Prior Knowledge
Ask children to recall being outdoors on a sunny day. Ask: **How does the sun feel on your skin? How does it feel different on a cloudy day?**

Using Scientific Language
Review the vocabulary of scientific methods on pages xii–xiii.

Reading Assist *Decoding*
In this experiment, it is helpful to review such words as *experiment, hypotheses, variables,* and *conclusion* to be sure children can read and pronounce them. Use syllabication when necessary.

Experiment Activity

Experiment with temperature.

Process Skills
- experimenting
- estimating and measuring

Materials

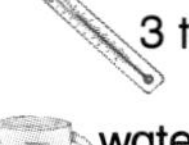

3 cups, 3 thermometers, soil, water, clock

Problem
How do the temperatures of soil, water, and air change after being placed in the sunlight?

Give Your Hypothesis
If you put soil, water, and air in sunlight, will their temperatures go up or down? Tell what you think.

Control the Variables
Make sure that each cup is placed in the same amount of sunlight for the same amount of time.

Test Your Hypothesis
Follow these steps to do the experiment.

1. Fill one cup with soil, one with water, and leave one for air.
2. Measure the temperature inside each cup.

C32

Science Background
- Some of the radiation from the sun can be seen as sunlight. Most sunlight is absorbed by the earth. The earth becomes warm and gives off heat. Those parts of the earth that receive a lot of sunlight, the lower latitudes or tropics, are warm. Those parts of the earth that receive little sunlight, the higher latitudes or polar regions, are cold.
- Sunlight is also absorbed by the water. The water becomes warm more slowly than land. Thus, the ocean temperatures are cooler than those of nearby land in the summer and warmer in the winter.

Technology

Review the demonstration of this Experiment's procedure on the *Earth Science* **Activity Video,** Segment 2.

3. Put all three cups in direct sunlight.
4. **Measure** the temperature inside each cup after 30 minutes.

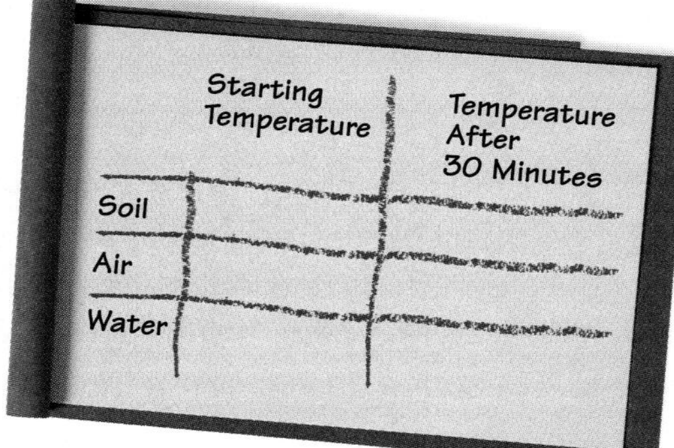

Collect Your Data

Use a chart like this one. Record the starting temperatures and the temperatures after 30 minutes.

Tell Your Conclusion

Compare your results and hypothesis. How do the temperatures of soil, water, and air change after being placed in the sunlight?

Inquire Further

What would happen to the temperatures if you put the cups in a shady place?

C33

Lab Manual

Experiment with temperature.

Problem

How do the temperatures of soil, water, and air change after being placed in the sunlight?

Give Your Hypothesis

If you put soil, water, and air in sunlight, will their temperatures go up or down? Write what you think.

Control the Variables

Make sure that each cup is placed in the same amount of sunlight for the same amount of time.

Test Your Hypothesis

Measure the temperatures.

Lab Manual
pp. 75–76

Activity Rubric

Use the following activity scoring rubric to assess students' performance.

Scoring Criteria	1	2	3	4
Student followed directions to complete this activity.				
Student expressed a hypothesis about the effect of sunlight on the temperature of soil, water, and air.				
Student controlled the variables in the experiment.				
Student collected and recorded data to test the hypothesis.				
Student used a chart to state his or her conclusion about the experiment.				

Scoring Key
4 points correct, complete, detailed
3 points partially correct, complete, detailed
2 points partially correct, partially complete, lacks some detail
1 point incorrect or incomplete, needs assistance

Lab Manual
p. T27

Teach and Apply

Problem

Ask children to share their ideas about how the temperatures of soil, water, and air change after being placed outdoors.

Give Your Hypothesis

To give their hypothesis, have children complete this sentence: "If I put soil, water, and air in sunlight, their temperatures will ______."

Control the Variables

Point out that soil, water, and air are the variables in this experiment.

Test Your Hypothesis

Have each child observe and read the thermometers.

Collect Your Data

Suggest that one child read the temperature while another records it. Children can record their data on Lab Manual page 76.

Assess and Extend

Tell Your Conclusion

Have children reread their hypothesis and compare it with their results. Children should conclude that they can change the temperatures of soil, water, and air by placing them in different locations.

Inquire Further

Have children guess what would happen if they put the cups in a shady place. Have children record their guesses and discoveries on Lab Manual pages 75–76.

Enrichment

Children can try the activity at different times of the day to see how the temperature changes. Encourage them to predict what will happen and then to tell why the temperature may have changed.

Higher Order Thinking *Infer*

Ask children to explain why the temperatures of the soil, water, and air might be different on different days.

Call 1-888-537-4908 with your Activity questions or comments.

Lesson Organizer

Objective

Identify seasonal weather conditions and their effects on plants and animals.

Additional Resources

- Wall Chart
- Interactive Transparency

Introduce

Activate Prior Knowledge

Invite children to tell whether each statement on **Wall Chart** page 39 is true or false. Save their answers for use as a **baseline assessment.**

Language Development *Sequence*

To prepare children for the order of the seasons, have them think about and discuss what happens to a tree during the year—from the first buds and tiny leaves that appear until the leaves drop off.

Flip Chart

Have children identify the pictures that show spring and summer. Ask children to name signs of spring and summer.

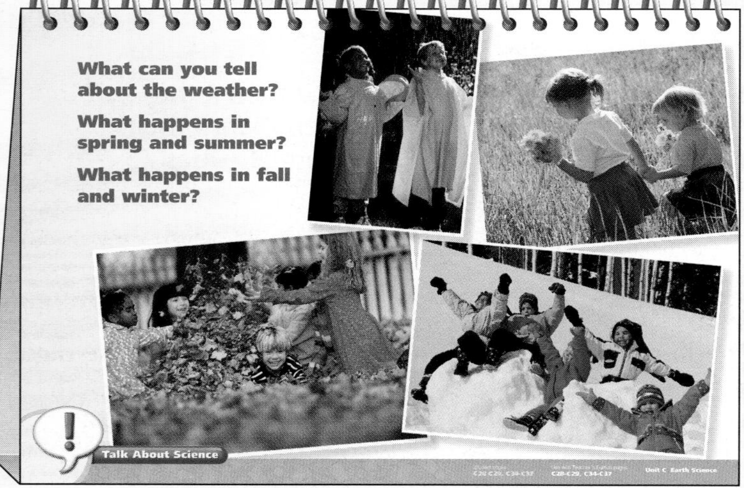

What can you tell about the weather?
What happens in spring and summer?
What happens in fall and winter?
Talk About Science
Unit C Earth Science

What happens in spring and summer?

The four seasons are spring, summer, fall, and winter. Which season do you like best?

In the spring, the air may be cool or warm. In many places, spring is the rainiest season of the year. Buds and leaves begin to grow on plants. Birds and other animals have babies. What signs of spring do you see in these pictures?[1]

[1] buds on trees; baby birds

Spring in New Jersey

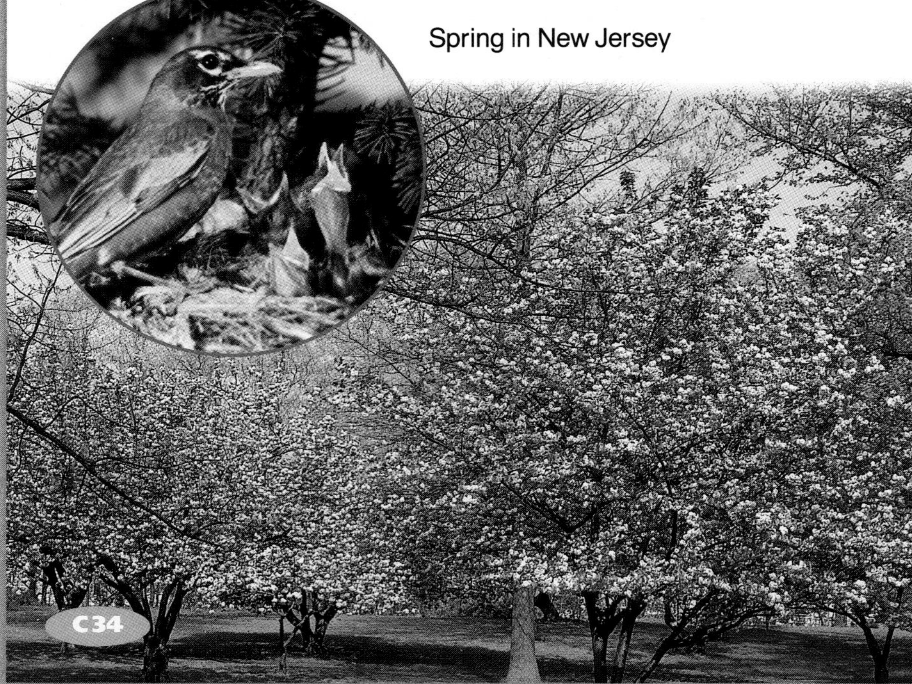

C34

Science Background

- Around March 21, the vernal equinox, the sun is directly over the equator. Day and night are of equal length. The direct solar radiation then moves into the Northern Hemisphere, reaching its most northerly position on or about June 21, the summer solstice. Daytime is at its longest and nighttime at its shortest in the Northern Hemisphere.

Science Across Cultures Encourage children to share spring or summer celebrations they have participated in or know about. For example, many Japanese American communities in the United States celebrate spring cherry blossom festivals.

Summer in Florida

In many places, summer is the hottest season of the year. Trees and other plants have lots of green leaves. Flowers bloom and many fruits and vegetables grow. It is summer in these pictures.

What are spring and summer like where you live?

Lesson Review

1. What happens in spring?
2. What happens in summer?
3. **Draw** a picture of how your neighborhood looks in spring or summer.

C35

ESL Strategy

Have children answer questions about each season, such as: **When is the air usually cooler—spring or summer? Which season is the hottest one of the year? In which season do many plants begin to grow?** Encourage them to answer in complete sentences.

Transparency

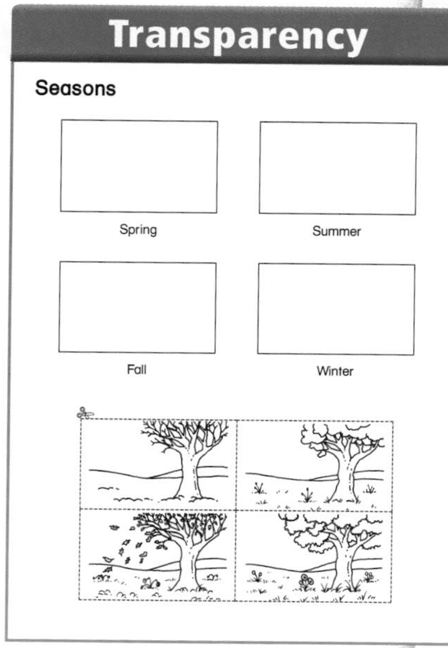

Interactive Transparency Package
Transparency 8

Teach and Apply

Student Pages C34–C35

- Ask children what kinds of clothing they wear during each season. Point out that people often wear different colors in different seasons. Light-colored clothing keeps a person cooler in hot weather, and dark-colored clothing keeps a person warmer in cold weather.
- Help children understand that warm weather and long hours of sunlight during summer months enable plants to grow. This provides food for the animals. Most animals have their babies in the spring so the young can grow when there is the most food.

Reading Assist *Decode Words*

Point out that the word *spring* begins with the *spr* blend. Have children name other words that begin with *spr.* (*spray, sprout, spread*)

Assess and Extend

Answers to Lesson Review

1. The air may be cool or warm, it may be rainy, buds and leaves grow on plants, and birds and other animals have babies.
2. The air is hot, trees have leaves, flowers bloom, and fruits and vegetables grow.
3. **Draw** (*Portfolio Assessment or Journal*) Drawings should include at least one or two signs of spring or summer mentioned in the lesson.

Check for Understanding

To follow up on the **baseline assessment,** have children review their answers to the true and false questions. Allow them to change answers as necessary. Then invite volunteers to rewrite the false statements to make them true.

Reteach

- Use the Interactive Transparency to reteach Lesson 3 concepts.
- Have children draw a line down the center of a sheet of drawing paper. Have them draw a picture showing spring on one side of the page and a picture showing summer on the other side. Then ask them to tell a partner how spring is different from summer.

Lesson Organizer

Objective
Identify seasonal weather conditions and their effects on plants and animals.

Additional Resources
- Wall Chart
- Interactive Transparency

Introduce

Activate Prior Knowledge
Invite children to tell whether each statement on **Wall Chart** page 40 is true or false. Save their answers for use as a **baseline assessment.**

Language Development *Scientific Language*
Explain that when animals *hibernate,* their body processes slow. This enables them to spend the winter when food is scarce in a kind of sleep. They sense when to hibernate when the days begin to get shorter.

Flip Chart
Have children identify the pictures that show fall and winter. Ask children to name signs of fall and winter.

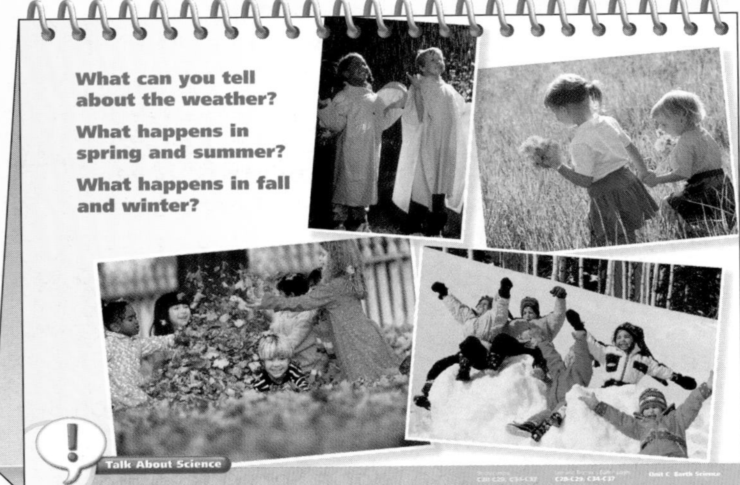

What can you tell about the weather?
What happens in spring and summer?
What happens in fall and winter?
Talk About Science

What happens in fall and winter?

Are days and nights chilly? Do crisp leaves crunch under your feet? What are some signs of fall near your home?

In many places, fall starts out warm and grows cooler. Many plants stop growing. Leaves change colors and drop from the trees. Many animals store food to prepare for the coming winter. What are some signs of fall in these pictures?[1]

[1] leaves char colors; squ collecting f

Fall in Michigan

Science Background

After the summer solstice, direct solar radiation moves south until it reaches the equator on or about September 21, the autumnal equinox. Day and night are of equal length all around the earth. The solar radiation reaches its most southerly position about December 21, the winter solstice. Daytime is at its shortest and nighttime at its longest in the Northern Hemisphere.

Teaching Tips You may want to have children list each season and the changes or lack of changes they have seen take place where they live. Ask children to compare the changes they have seen with the changes mentioned in Lessons 3 and 4.

Winter in Illinois

In many places, winter brings cold air and snow. Water in ponds or lakes can freeze. Many trees have no leaves at all. Some animals hibernate, or sleep, all winter long. How can you tell it is winter in these pictures?[2]

What are fall and winter like where you live?

[2] Trees have no leaves; there is snow; dormouse is hibernating.

Lesson Review

1. What do many animals do in the fall?
2. What is the weather like in the winter?
3. **Tell** how fall and winter are different.

C37

ESL Strategy

Have children answer questions about each season, such as: **Can you hear the crunch of leaves under your feet in fall or in the spring? When do animals store food? When do animals hibernate?** Encourage children to answer in complete sentences.

Transparency

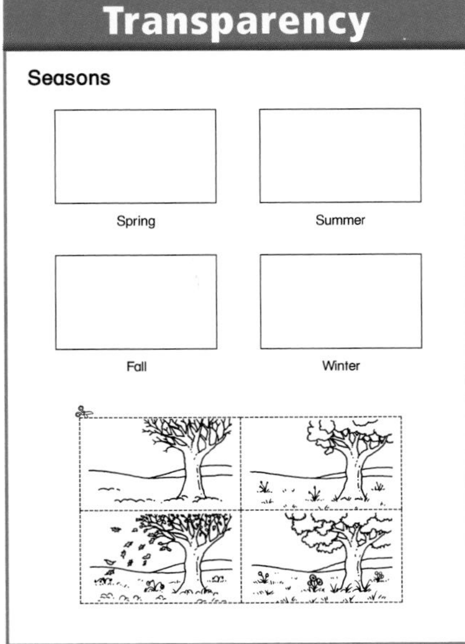

Interactive Transparency Package Transparency 8

Teach and Apply

Student Pages C36–C37

- Tell children that animals that do not store food in the fall for winter must survive on food left over from the previous summer. Some animals also survive winter by growing warm coats of fur that they will lose in the spring. Many birds fly south to warmer areas for the winter and return in the spring.
- Point out that not only do some animals sleep during the winter, but that most plants stop growing.

Reading Assist *Pronunciation*

Point out that the word *fall* is a one-syllable word and *winter* is a two-syllable word. Help children realize that identifying and saying each syllable of a word can help them pronounce it. Have children identify the two syllables in *winter.* Then have them identify other words in the text that have two syllables.

Assess and Extend

Answers to Lesson Review

1. In fall, many animals store food for the winter.
2. The air is cold, snow can fall, and water in ponds or lakes can freeze.
3. **Tell** (*Interview*) Winter is colder than fall; in fall the leaves begin to drop and in winter some trees have no leaves at all.

Check for Understanding

To follow up on the **baseline assessment,** have children review their answers to the true and false questions. Encourage them to change answers as necessary. Invite volunteers to rewrite the false statements to make them true.

Reteach

- Use the Interactive Transparency to reteach Lesson 4 concepts.
- Invite children to look through seasonal magazines to find pictures that show fall and winter and use the pictures to make two collages. Encourage them to include pictures of what the plants and animals look like during each season.

Science Center

Flip Chart

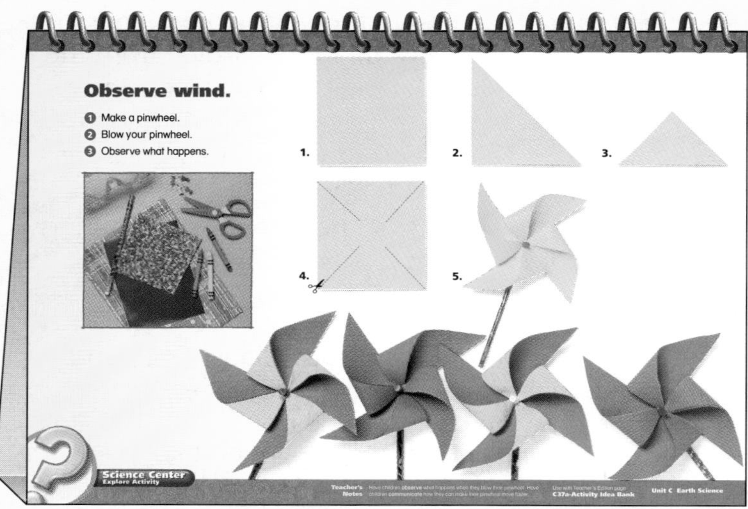

Observe wind.

Objective

Observe wind speed.

Process Skills observing, communicating

Materials

Kit Items none

School-Supplied Items scissors, safety goggles, paper, pushpin, unsharpened pencil with eraser

Safety Note *Tell children to be careful when they push the pin in the eraser.*

Procedure

- Ask children to fold a square of paper as shown.
- Have children cut along the fold lines to 1" of the center.
- Ask children to bend one point of each section to touch the center, and then push a pin through the center into the side of a pencil eraser.
- Children **communicate** what they **observe** when they blow on the pinwheels.
- You can use **Lab Manual** page 77 with this activity.

What to Expect

Children should leave enough space between the pinwheel and the eraser to allow it to move freely.

Lab Manual
Observe wind.
Draw a picture to show how you made your pinwheel move.

Lab Manual, p. 77

Connections

School and Community

Ideas for bringing the school and community together:

Field Trips

- local newspaper
- TV or radio station

Guest Speakers

- meteorologist
- TV weather person
- zoologist or botanist

Themes

The activities on these pages can be used with classroom themes such as:

- weather
- seasons
- change
- habitats
- patterns

Books for Children

Children might enjoy these books about weather and seasons:

Snow Is Falling by Franklyn M. Branley. How snow enhances our lives and how it hinders us. (HarperCollins, ISBN 0-06-445058-9)

The Reasons for the Seasons by Gail Gibbons. How the sun warms the earth and affects seasons and weather. (Holiday House, ISBN 0-8234-1174-5)

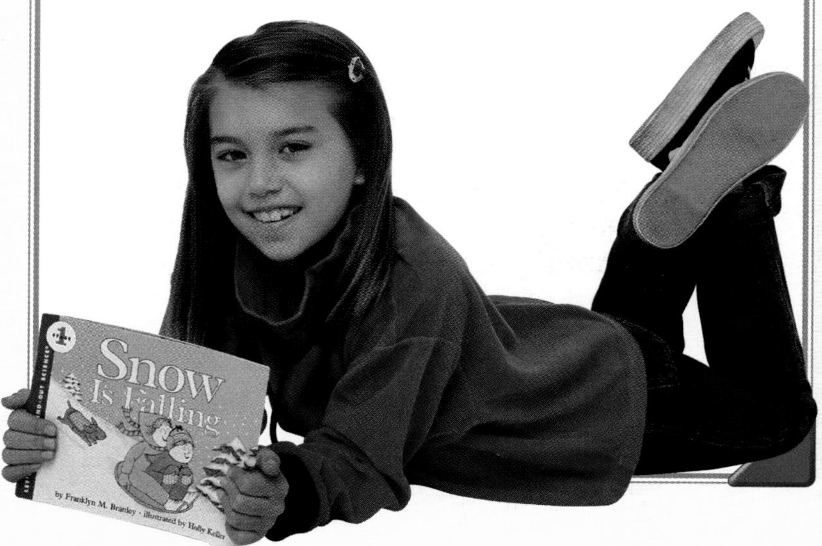

Cross-Curricular Options

LITERATURE

Questions and Answers About Weather

Use the book to learn about weather.

Materials *Questions and Answers About Weather* by M. Jean Craig. (Scholastic, ISBN 0-590-41142-X)

Procedure

- Display the book's cover and the table of contents. Point out that this is nonfiction about weather.
- Read some questions and answers.
- Encourage children to ask other questions about weather.
- They can seek out other media such as newspapers, CD-ROMs, the Internet, and maps for answers.

Multiple Intelligences linguistic

Gifted and Talented Provide a prism and invite children to explore how the colors of the rainbow are refracted through it.

MATH

Hot or Cold?

Record daily temperatures.

Materials drawing paper, red crayons, large outdoor thermometer

Procedure

- Hang a large thermometer outside a classroom window.
- Have children draw five thermometers on a large sheet of drawing paper.
- Children use a red crayon to show the temperature for five days, labeling each date.
- Encourage children to compare the temperatures.

Multiple Intelligences spatial

Special Needs Pair children with limited writing/drawing ability with partners who can draw and record the temperatures as children read the thermometers.

Today's Weather

Write a weather report.

Materials paper, pencil

Procedure

- Organize children into four groups. Assign each group a season.
- Have children write and present a short weather report for their assigned season.
- Encourage them not only to report the weather but also to include events that might be taking place during that time. For example, "It's a good day for a picnic with warm, sunny weather."

Multiple Intelligences linguistic

Fun with Clouds

Make cloud pictures.

Materials colored chalk, dark construction paper

Procedure

- Take children outdoors where they can observe and sketch cloud shapes.
- Back indoors, have them use chalk to draw pictures of clouds or pictures of scenes that include clouds.

- Display their artwork and invite children to share their pictures with classmates.

Multiple Intelligences spatial

Lesson Organizer

Objective
Describe the water cycle.

Vocabulary
evaporates, condenses, water cycle

Process Skills observing

Materials
Kit Items plastic wrap, 9-ounce plastic cup

School-Supplied Items warm water, tape, clock

Additional Resources
- Lab Manual
- Teacher Demonstration Kit
- Wall Chart

Introduce

Activate Prior Knowledge
Point out that water exists in different forms. Have children complete **Wall Chart** page 41 to name as many forms of water as they can.

Language Development *Scientific Language*
Explain that when *water vapor* condenses, it is often seen as haze, fog, or mist.

Flip Chart
Discuss the picture of the water cycle. Have children explain what the words *condenses* and *evaporates* mean.

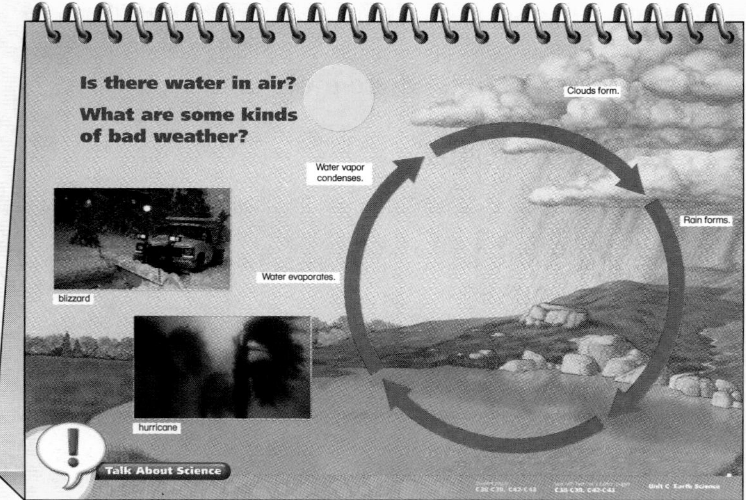

Is there water in air?

Drip, drop, drip, drop. Rain is falling. Puddles form on the ground. What happens to a puddle after the rain stops?

Over time, the water in the puddle evaporates. When water **evaporates** it changes into a gas called water vapor.

The water vapor rises into the air and condenses into tiny drops of water. When water vapor **condenses**, it changes from a gas to a liquid. The tiny drops of water form clouds. Some of the drops freeze. If the air is cold, the drops fall as snow. If the air is warm, they fall as rain.

The way water moves from the clouds to the earth and back to the clouds again is called the **water cycle**. The picture shows the water cycle.

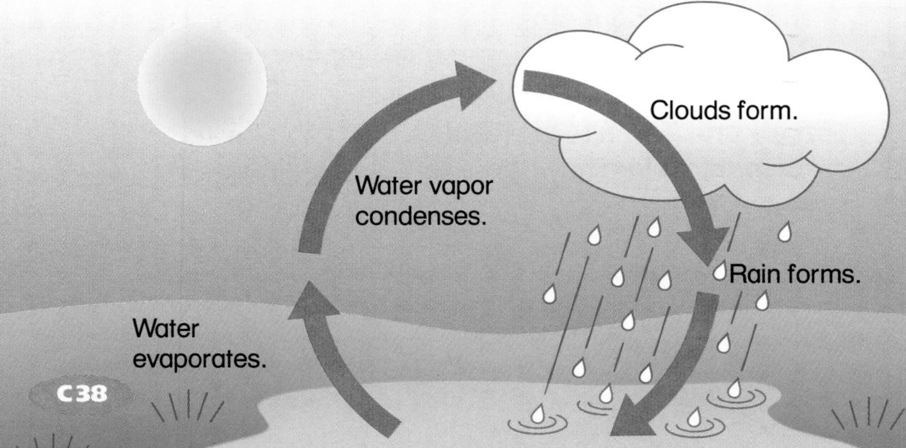

Science Background

- The water cycle includes evaporation, condensation, and precipitation.
- The light from the sun causes water from the oceans, lakes, and rivers to become warm and evaporate. Some of the water plants absorb through their roots evaporates through their leaves. Some of the water animals drink returns to the atmosphere in their exhalations.

Possible Misconceptions Some children may not understand that fog is a cloud that is close to the ground. Relate fog and clouds to a fine mist of tiny water droplets that hang in the air. You may want to spray a mister of water to demonstrate. Ask children who have flown through clouds in an airplane to share their experiences.

Room _____ Block _____ ID# ______________ Name ____________________________________

Teacher ___________________________________ Date: ___ / ___ / ___ Period _____

MSB193

MSB-Wet All Over

While watching, complete this video guide.

Three things I knew that were confirmed in the video:

A- ____

B- ____

C- ____

Three things I didn't know but I now know because I watched the video.

A- ____

B- ____

C- ____

___ Δ 1. An instrument used to measure rain fall is called a ___________________________.

___ Δ 2. _________________________ is water that has been evaporated by the sun.

___ Δ 3. When water vapor ________________________ it changes back to liquid water.

___ Δ 4. Clouds move across the sky by <u>wind / gravity</u>.

___ Δ 5. The lowest spot to which water flows is the ___________________________.

___ Δ 6. Water condenses into droplets to form <u>rain /clouds.</u>

___ Δ 7. The process of water evaporating, condensing, falling and collecting is the ____________________.

___ Δ 8. A ___________________ is where our drinking water is collected.

___ Δ 9. The first step to cleaning our water happens in the ___________________ basin.

___ Δ 10. <u>Alum / soap</u> is added to the dirty water to help clean the water.

___ Δ 11. In the settling basin, the dirty alum settles to the bottom and ____________ water is on top.

___ Δ 12. The clear water is ________________ through sand and gravel to catch small particles.

___ Δ 13. After the water is cleaned, it then travels through ______________ pipes to faucets.

___ Δ 14. Water in a _________________ can take almost 10,000 years to melt.

___ Δ 15. The Earth's surface is ______________ water but only a tiny amount of the water is drinkable.

Observe the water cycle.

Materials

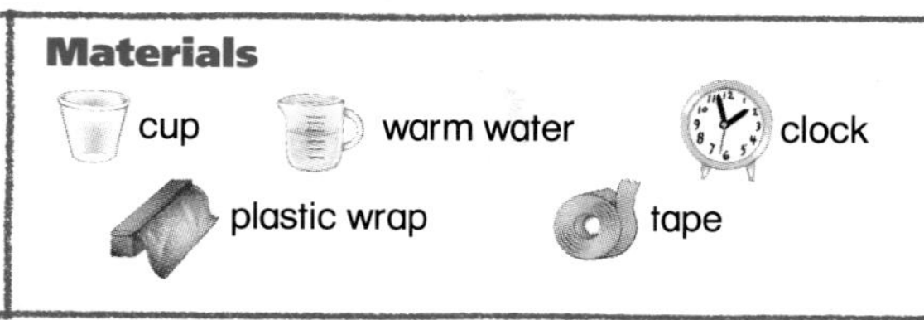

Process Skills

- observing

Steps

1. Fill your cup halfway with warm water.
2. Tape the plastic wrap over the top of the cup.
3. Put the cup in a sunny place for 30 minutes.
4. Observe.

Share. Tell how your cup shows the water cycle.

Lesson Review

1. What does evaporate mean?
2. What is the water cycle?
3. **Draw** how your cup and plastic wrap look after 30 minutes.

Lab Manual

Is there water in air?

Draw how your cup and plastic wrap look when you start and after 30 minutes.

Start

After 30 minutes

Lab Manual p. 78

Activity Rubric

Use the following activity scoring rubric to assess students' performance.

Scoring Criteria	1	2	3	4
Student followed directions to complete this activity.				
Student observed the formation of water condensation.				
Student observed the role of heat on the formation of condensation.				
Student recorded the appearance of water in the cup after 30 minutes.				
Student represented the water cycle in a drawing.				

Scoring Key
4 points correct, complete, detailed
3 points partially correct, complete, detailed
2 points partially correct, partially complete, lacks some detail
1 point incorrect or incomplete, needs assistance

Lab Manual p. T28

Teach and Apply

Student Page C38

Explain that the water that evaporates into the air condenses and then returns to the earth. Water falls to the earth as rain, sleet, hail, or snow. The rain soaks into the ground, or it runs off into streams, lakes, and oceans, and evaporates again.

Reading Assist *Vocabulary*

Remind children that the word *cycle* means circle. The *water cycle* repeats itself again and again in a circle.

Student Page C39

Explore Activity

Time about 35 minutes

Grouping individual

- Point out that children's models of the water cycle do not show a complete picture of the water cycle.
- Children can complete Lab Manual page 78.

Integrating the Sciences

Physical Science

In this lesson, children learn how water changes states in the water cycle. In Unit B, Chapter 1, children learn ways they can change states of water.

Assess and Extend

Answers to Lesson Review

1. Evaporate means to change water into water vapor.
2. The water cycle is the way water moves from the clouds to the earth and back to the clouds again.
3. **Draw** (*Portfolio Assessment or Journal*) Drawings should show that some of the water has evaporated and condensed on the underside of the plastic wrap, and some of that water has precipitated down.

Inquire Further

Ask the following questions to guide further inquiry: **How is what happened in the cup like what happens in the water cycle? How is it different?**

Higher Order Thinking *Evaluate*

Ask children to explain how the water cycle helps plant and animal life on the earth.

Call 1-888-537-4908 with your Activity questions or comments.

Activity Organizer

Objective
Learn that air contains water.

Process Skills observing

Materials
Kit Items food coloring

School-Supplied Items 2 cans, ice water, warm water, clock

Additional Resources
- Lab Manual
- Teacher Demonstration Kit

Introduce

The Lesson 6 Investigate Activity, *How does water vapor condense?,* is on the **Flip Chart.**

Activate Prior Knowledge
Ask children if they have ever taken a cold jar of food out of the refrigerator on a warm humid day. Ask: **After the jar was out for a while, did you notice any change on the outside of the jar? If so, what?**

Language Development *Vocabulary*
Discuss the meaning of the word *condense*—to change from a gas or vapor to a liquid.

Investigate  Activity

How does water vapor condense?

Process Skills
- observing

Materials

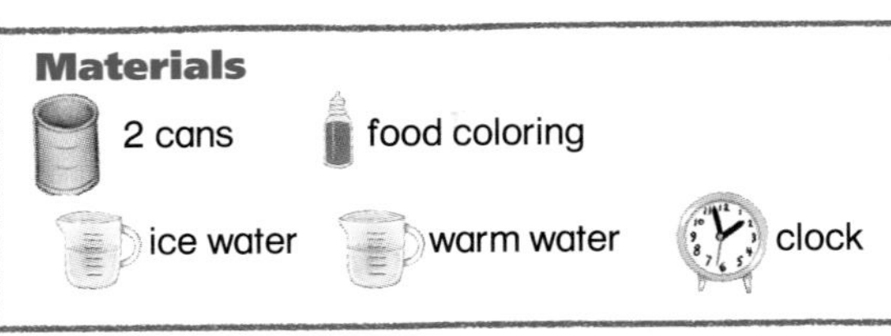

Steps
1. Fill one can halfway with warm water.
2. Fill one can halfway with ice water.
3. Add two or three drops of food coloring to each can.
4. Wait five minutes.
5. Look at the cans. What changes do you see on the outside of each can?

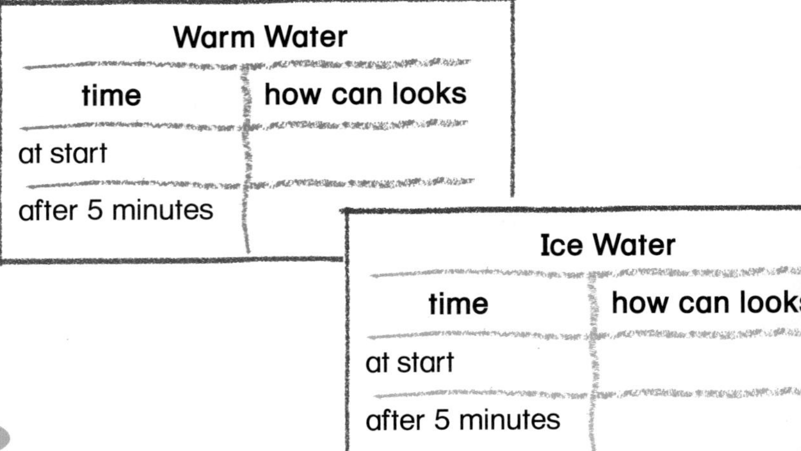

Warm Water

time	how can looks
at start	
after 5 minutes	

Ice Water

time	how can looks
at start	
after 5 minutes	

C40

Science Background
The temperature at which water vapor condenses is called the dew point. The more water vapor in the air, the higher the dew point. As the air temperature decreases on a humid night, it may reach the dew point. At this temperature, water vapor condenses, leaving a layer of dew on surfaces.

Science Across Cultures Some desert-dwelling cultures pile stones around the base of plants. Dew forms on the rocks overnight and drips off the rocks to plants' roots. In this way, plants can be grown for food even in a desert climate.

Technology

Review the demonstration of this Investigate's procedure on the *Earth Science* **Activity Video,** Segment 3.

Think About Your Results

1. How do the cans look different?
2. What caused the water vapor to condense?

Inquire Further

What are some other places that show water that condensed from water vapor in the air?

Teach and Apply

- In this activity, children learn how water vapor condenses. In advance, collect metal cans. You will need 2 cans per group. Tape over the rim of each can with masking tape before distributing them.
- Suggest that children tape a name for their group on their containers to keep them separate from the others.
- Children can complete Lab Manual page 79.

Reading Assist *Use Graphic Organizers*

Discuss the headings on the charts. Ask children to tell what they will write in each column.

What to Expect

Water from the air condenses on the outside of the can with the ice water.

Assess and Extend

Answers to Think About Your Results

1. There is water on the outside of the can containing ice water but no water on the outside of the can containing warm water.
2. The cold water in the can caused the water vapor to condense.

Inquire Further

Children may suggest windows, bathroom mirrors, or grass covered with dew.

Enrichment

Repeat the experiment on a day when the humidity is different. The higher the humidity, the more condensation there will be.

Higher Order Thinking *Hypothesize*

Ask: **How do you know that the water on the outside of the can wasn't caused by a leak in the can?** (*The water in the can had food coloring in it, but the water on the outside of the can did not.*)

Lab Manual

How does water vapor condense?

Draw the can with warm water.

At start	After 5 minutes

What changes do you see?

Draw the can with ice water.

At start	After 5 minutes

What changes do you see?

Lab Manual
p. 79

Activity Rubric

Use the following activity scoring rubric to assess students' performance.

Scoring Criteria	1	2	3	4
Student followed directions to complete this activity.				
Student observed a can with warm water at the start and after five minutes.				
Student observed a can with cold water at the start and after five minutes.				
Student recorded the changes he or she observed in both cans.				
Student explained how water vapor condenses.				

Scoring Key
4 points correct, complete, detailed
3 points partially correct, complete, detailed
2 points partially correct, partially complete, lacks some detail
1 point incorrect or incomplete, needs assistance

Lab Manual
p. T28

Call 1-888-537-4908 with your Activity questions or comments.

Lesson Organizer

Objective

Describe severe weather conditions and ways to stay safe in severe weather.

Vocabulary tornado, drought

Additional Resources

- Wall Chart

Introduce

Activate Prior Knowledge

Have children name different types of severe weather conditions and then list ways they can stay safe in those conditions. Record children's responses on **Wall Chart** page 42. Save the chart for use as a **baseline assessment.**

Language Development *Vocabulary*

Ask children to share their experiences with bad weather. Have them talk about their feelings and what they did to stay safe.

Flip Chart

Have children describe the bad weather they see in the pictures. Ask: **What are some other kinds of bad weather?**

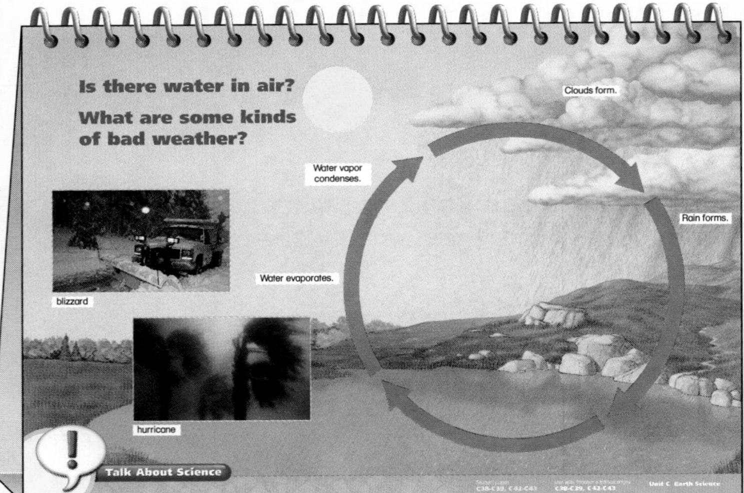

What are some kinds of bad weather?

Flash! Boom! You see lightning and hear thunder! A storm is coming.

A thunderstorm is a heavy rain with lightning and thunder. Never stand under a tree during a thunderstorm. Go indoors as soon as you can. If you are swimming, get out of the water quickly.

A **tornado** is a very strong wind storm. If there is a tornado warning, stay indoors and away from windows. Go to the basement or the lowest part of the building that you are in.

Lightning Storm
Stay indoors or low to the ground.
C42

Science Background

- Tornadoes are formed over land, mainly in the spring and early summer. If a storm shelter or basement is not available, take shelter in the lowest and most central part of a building, possibly a bathroom, closet, or hallway. Cover the body with a blanket or pillow and sit on the floor.
- A hurricane is a large tropical storm that forms over warm oceans. Warm, moist air spirals upward around a low-pressure area. Clouds form a circular pattern around the eye, or center, of the hurricane. Wind speeds in a hurricane can be more than 120 kilometers per hour.

If a lot of rain falls in a short time, there can be a flood. Flood water is not safe to play in. To stay safe, go to a place that is higher than the water.

If it has not rained in a long time, a **drought** can occur. During a drought, the land is very dry and there is very little water available.

What other kinds of bad weather do you know about?

Lesson Review

1. How can you stay safe in a thunderstorm?
2. If you hear a warning about a tornado, what should you do?
3. **Tell** how a flood and a drought are different.

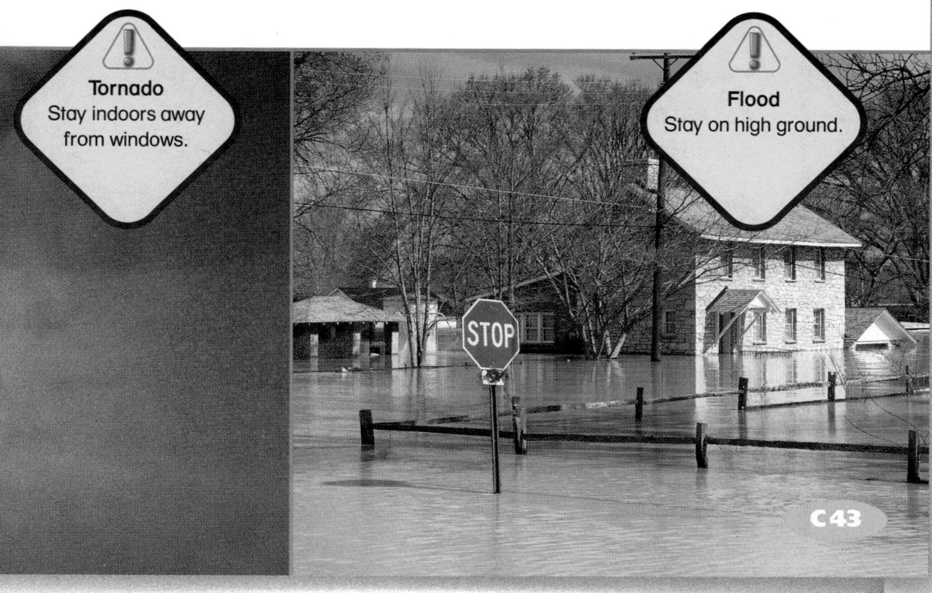

Tornado
Stay indoors away from windows.
Flood
Stay on high ground.
STOP
C43

ESL Strategy

Invite children to draw and label pictures of each type of bad weather discussed in the lesson. Then have them share and discuss their pictures with a friend.

Teach and Apply

Student Pages C42–C43

- Explain that children can learn about bad weather in their community by listening to the weather report on television or radio.
- Point out that the most important thing to know in bad weather is how to stay safe. Ask children to name the types of bad weather they have in their area. Then have them tell things they do to stay safe. Share other safety tips with them.

Reading Assist *Vocabulary*

Point out that although *droughts* are not caused by stormy weather, they still can be disastrous. Ask children to describe what might happen to an area with fields planted with corn and wheat if there were a drought.

Real-World Applications

To put together your own disaster supplies kit, contact your local American Red Cross chapter; your local or state Office of Emergency Management; or the Federal Emergency Management Agency (*FEMA*). You can write to FEMA at 500 C Street SW, Washington, DC 20472; Web site http://www.fema.gov.

Assess and Extend

Answers to Lesson Review

1. Go indoors, stay away from trees, and get out of water if swimming.
2. Stay indoors, stay away from windows, and go to the basement or lowest part of the building.
3. **Tell** (*Interview*) A flood is a lot of water, and a drought is very little water.

Check for Understanding

To follow up on the **baseline assessment,** have children add to their chart other types of weather disasters and/or things they can do to stay safe in bad weather.

Reteach

Organize children into groups. Have each group select a type of bad weather and make a poster telling about that type of weather and how to stay safe.

Enrichment

Invite children to write a short story about a time they were in a storm and what happened. Have them tell how they felt and what precautions they took. If children do not remember being in a storm, have them imagine being in one.

Science Center

Flip Chart

Explore evaporation.

Objective

Observe and describe the results of evaporation.

Process Skills observing

Materials

Kit Items eye dropper, cup

School-Supplied Items paper towel, water, cardboard

Procedure

- You may need to demonstrate how to use a dropper.
- Have each child place two paper towels far apart on a table.
- Encourage children to use droppers to put five drops of water on each paper towel.
- Children **observe** what happens to the water when they fan the paper towels.
- You can use **Lab Manual** page 80 with this activity.

What to Expect

Children discover that water evaporates more quickly when they fan the paper towels.

Lab Manual

Explore evaporation.

Draw a picture of another way you could get your paper towel to dry more quickly. Write about what you did.

Lab Manual, p. 80

Connections

School and Community

Ideas for bringing the school and community together:

Field Trips

- TV station
- Red Cross office
- National Weather Service office

Guest Speakers

- weather forecaster
- Red Cross representative
- tornado spotter

Themes

The activities on these pages can be used with classroom themes such as:

- storms
- weather
- disasters
- nature
- geography

Books for Children

Children might enjoy these books about weather:

Tornado Alert by Franklyn M. Branley. Thunder rumbles and lightning colors the sky! What to do on a tornado day. (HarperCollins, ISBN 0-06-445094-5)

Flash, Crash, Rumble, and Roll by Franklyn M. Branley. How air affects weather and what makes thunder and lightning. (HarperCollins, ISBN 0-06-445012-0)

The Playhouse by Pauline Cartwright. How floods affect the earth and the environment. (Learning Media, ISBN 0-478-20523-6)

Cross-Curricular Options

LITERATURE

Thunder Cake

Use the book to discuss weather conditions.

Materials *Thunder Cake* by Patricia Polacco. (Philomel, ISBN 0-399-22231-6)

Procedure

- A grandmother helps her granddaughter overcome a fear of thunderstorms.
- Help children evaluate the grandmother's loving feelings toward her granddaughter.
- Have children talk about their own experiences with storms.
- You may want to copy the recipe for Thunder Cake for children to take home.

Multiple Intelligences linguistic

Gifted and Talented Challenge children to write a weather report. Have them prepare text and make posters to show the weather.

SOCIAL STUDIES

Lotto Game

Play a game about weather.

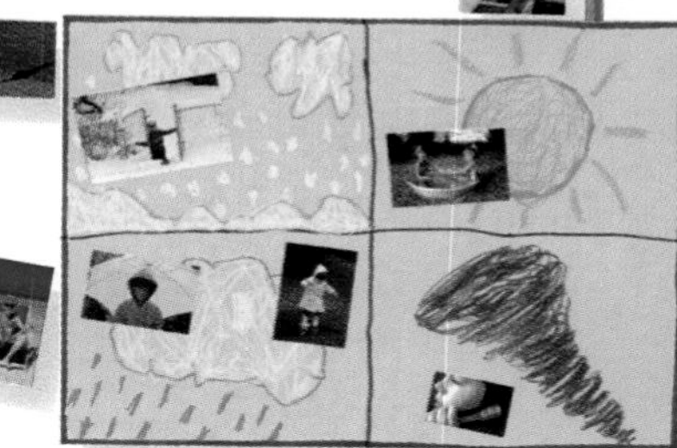

Materials poster board; magazine pictures showing clothing and activities in different weather, including people taking precautions/shelter in bad weather

Procedure

- Make game board grids with four sections. Have volunteers draw a picture in each section depicting rainy, sunny, snowy, and stormy weather.
- Have small groups play the game by matching pictures of clothing and activities to each type of weather.

Multiple Intelligences spatial, linguistic

WRITING

Weather Alert

Make minibooks on safety in severe weather.

Materials paper, pencil, crayons

Procedure

- Invite children to make minibooks about safety in severe weather. Have each child choose one type of weather, such as a thunderstorm, tornado, or flood.
- Children fold a sheet of paper in half to make a booklet. On the front they write the name of their weather condition and draw a picture of it.
- On the inside and back of the booklet, children write ways and draw pictures to show how people can stay safe in the bad weather, or how they can protect plants and animals.

Multiple Intelligences spatial, linguistic

ESL Provide sentence frames to help children compose their safety rules. For example: *Go to the _______ when a tornado is spotted. Hide under a _______. Protect your _______ from flying glass.*

PHYSICAL EDUCATION

Weather Expressions

Demonstrate weather conditions through dance.

Materials various kinds of music

Procedure

- Ask children to act out the calm before a storm, then the increase of the wind or snow and rain, and finally its aftermath.
- Organize children into small groups and invite them to make up a dance demonstrating a severe weather condition.
- Encourage children to listen to a variety of music and choose the music that best suits their chosen weather.

Multiple Intelligences kinesthetic, musical

Review Organizer

Materials

Kit Items none

School-Supplied Items paper, markers or crayons

Time about 20 minutes

Grouping individual

Additional Resources

- Chapter 2 Assessment: Teacher's Assessment Package

Chapter Main Ideas

Lesson 1 Scientists use thermometers and anemometers to measure the weather.

Lesson 2 Changes in temperature can be measured.

Lesson 3 Weather and seasonal changes in spring and summer affect plants and animals.

Lesson 4 In the fall and winter, weather and seasonal changes affect plants and animals.

Lesson 5 The movement of water from clouds to the earth and back to clouds again is the water cycle.

Lesson 6 Condensation on the outside of a can of ice water shows that there is water in the air.

Lesson 7 Thunderstorms and tornadoes can be dangerous. Safety precautions need to be followed.

Reviewing Science Words

1. A thermometer measures the temperature of the air.
2. An anemometer measures wind speed.
3. When water evaporates, it changes into a gas.
4. Water vapor changes from a gas into a liquid.
5. In the water cycle, water moves from the clouds to the earth and back to the clouds.
6. A tornado is a very severe wind storm.
7. A drought can occur when it has not rained.

Reviewing Science Ideas

1. Scientists can use thermometers and anemometers.
2. Spring: warm weather and rain. Summer: warm or hot weather and blooming. Fall: leaves falling and cooler weather. Winter: snow and cold weather.
3. Stay indoors, don't stand under a tree in a storm, go to a basement, get under a strong table.

Chapter 2 Review

Reviewing Science Words

1. What does a **thermometer** measure?
2. What does an **anemometer** measure?
3. Describe what happens when water **evaporates**.
4. What happens when water vapor **condenses**?
5. Describe the **water cycle**.
6. What is a **tornado**?
7. When can a **drought** occur?

Reviewing Science Ideas

1. How can scientists measure the weather?
2. Name some signs of spring, summer, fall, and winter.
3. Name some ways to stay safe in bad weather.

Technology

Children can review *Weather and Seasons* with the **Practice & Assessment CD-ROM.**

Children can use the **Production Studio** to show what they've learned about *Weather and Seasons.*

Children can use The KnowZone™ at **www.kz.com** to review and test their science knowledge.

You can use **TestWorks™** to customize assessment for your children.

Draw one place in two seasons.

Materials

 paper

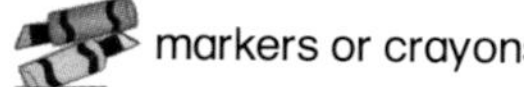 markers or crayons

1. Choose two seasons of the year.
2. Think about how these two seasons are different.
3. Draw a place, such as a park or a pond, in one season of the year.
4. Then draw the same place in the other season you have chosen.
5. Compare your drawings. How do they look different? How do they look the same?

Chapter Assessment

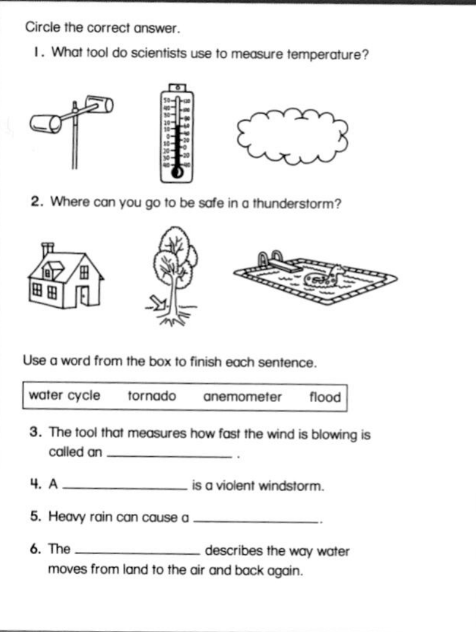

Circle the correct answer.

1. What tool do scientists use to measure temperature?

2. Where can you go to be safe in a thunderstorm?

Use a word from the box to finish each sentence.

water cycle	tornado	anemometer	flood

3. The tool that measures how fast the wind is blowing is called an ____________.
4. A ____________ is a violent windstorm.
5. Heavy rain can cause a ____________.
6. The ____________ describes the way water moves from land to the air and back again.

Teacher's Assessment Package pp. 47–48

Assessment Rubric

	Compare Seasons
4	Correctly compares the same place in two seasons and communicates ways they are alike and different.
3	Makes some errors comparing the same place in two seasons and communicating ways they are alike and different.
2	Has difficulty comparing the same place in two seasons and communicating ways they are alike and different.
1	Is unable to compare the same place in two seasons and communicate ways they are alike and different.

Performance Assessment Teaching Tips

- Before beginning the activity, list the four seasons on the chalkboard. Have children brainstorm words and phrases associated with each season.
- Picture books on weather and the seasons provide good resources for this activity.
- Have children draw their pictures on two separate sheets of paper. Be sure children understand that their drawings should show how the same place, such as a park, changes from one season to another.
- As children share their pictures, ask: **How does your picture show what season it is? How would you dress for the weather shown in your picture?**

Enrichment

Have children collect the completed pictures and gather them into a booklet titled "Signs of the Seasons." They can use colored paper to separate the pictures into four distinct groups, one group for each season.

Chapter 2 Skills Trace

Process Skills Development

	Estimating and Measuring	Experimenting	Observing
Skill Introduced	xiv	xv	xiv
Skill Applied	C29 C32–C33	C32–C33	C39 C40–C41
Skill Assessed	End Matter 12–13	End Matter 28–29	End Matter 6–7

 Chapter Review pages are also on the **Flip Chart.**

Lesson/Activity and Flip Chart	Objectives/Process Skills	Time Options/Activity Materials
Chapter Opener Student Edition pp. C46–C47 and **Flip Chart** ***Up in the Sky***		**Have less time?** Use the Graphic Organizer on Teacher's Assessment Package p. 51 for an overview of the lessons. Use the Flip Chart to teach lesson concepts and science activities. **Have more time?** Use the Flip Chart to reinforce and extend lesson concepts and activities. Use the Cross-Curricular Options in the Activity Idea Bank on Teacher's Edition pp. C53b and C59b.
Lesson 1 Student Edition pp. C48–C49 ***What causes day and night?*** **Explore Activity** ***Show how Earth rotates.*** **Flip Chart** ***Talk About Science***	**Objective** Describe how the rotation of the earth causes day and night. **Process Skills** observing	**Kit Items** flashlight, D battery **School-Supplied Items** globe, stickers
Lesson 2 Student Edition pp. C50–C51 ***What do we know about the moon?*** **Flip Chart** ***Talk About Science***	**Objective** Describe features and phases of the moon.	**Have more time?** Use the following teaching guide option: Interactive Transparency 9, Interactive Transparency Package
Lesson 3 Student Edition pp. C52–C53 and **Flip Chart** **Investigate Activity** ***How can you record the phases of the moon?***	**Objective** Observe and record the phases of the moon. **Process Skills** collecting and interpreting data, observing	**Kit Items** none **School-Supplied Items** calendar, crayons or markers
Activity Idea Bank Teacher's Edition pp. C53a–C53b **Flip Chart** **Science Center Explore Activity** ***Make a moon project.***	**Objective** Identify and sequence the phases of the moon. **Process Skills** observing	**Kit Items** none **School-Supplied Items** pictures of different phases of the moon; art supplies such as crayons, markers, paper, yarn, glue, craft sticks, paint, paintbrush, clay, scissors
Reading for Science Student Edition pp. C54–C55 ***Using Picture Clues***	**Objective** Use picture clues.	
Lesson 4 Student Edition pp. C56–C57 ***What is in our solar system?*** **Flip Chart** ***Talk About Science***	**Objective** Identify the sun and planets in our solar system.	
Lesson 5 Student Edition pp. C58–C59 ***How do we learn about the solar system?*** **Flip Chart** ***Talk About Science***	**Objective** Identify space exploration as a way we have learned about the solar system.	
Activity Idea Bank Teacher's Edition pp. C59a–C59b **Flip Chart** **Science Center Explore Activity** ***Make a model of a rocket.***	**Objective** Create a model of a rocket. **Process Skills** making and using models	**Kit Items** none **School-Supplied Items** pictures of spacecraft, foil, string, magazines, paper, yarn, cardboard paper rolls, craft sticks, cloth, empty containers, art supplies
Chapter Review Student Edition pp. C60–C61 and **Flip Chart**		**Kit Items** 2 paper plates **School-Supplied Items** safety goggles, scissors, markers, fastener

Lesson/Activity and Flip Chart	Additional Resources		Technology
Chapter Opener Student Edition pp. C46–C47 and **Flip Chart** ***Up in the Sky***	**Teacher's Assessment Package** • Graphic Organizer, p. 51 **Instructional Resources** • Family Activity, pp. 65–66 • Vocabulary Preview, p. 67	**Songs & Activities Package** • *Up in the Sky*, pp. 25–26 **Wall Chart,** p. 43	**Practice & Assessment CD-ROM** **AudioText** **Production Studio** **www.sfscience.com** **Songs & Activities Package** **Teacher's Resource Planner CD-ROM**
Lesson 1 Student Edition pp. C48–C49 ***What causes day and night?*** **Explore Activity** ***Show how Earth rotates.*** **Flip Chart** ***Talk About Science***	**Lab Manual** • Lab Manual, p. 81 • Activity Rubric, p. T29	**Teacher Demonstration Kit** **Wall Chart,** p. 44	
Lesson 2 Student Edition pp. C50–C51 ***What do we know about the moon?*** **Flip Chart** ***Talk About Science***	**Interactive Transparency Package** • Interactive Transparency 9	**Wall Chart,** p. 45	
Lesson 3 Student Edition pp. C52–C53 and **Flip Chart** **Investigate Activity** ***How can you record the phases of the moon?***	**Lab Manual** • Lab Manual, p. 83 • Activity Rubric, p. T30	**Teacher Demonstration Kit** **Wall Chart,** p. 46	*Earth Science* **Activity Video**
Activity Idea Bank Teacher's Edition pp. C53a–C53b **Flip Chart** **Science Center Explore Activity** ***Make a moon project.***	**Lab Manual** • Lab Manual, p. 85 • Activity Rubric, p. T30		
Reading for Science Student Edition pp. C54–C55 ***Using Picture Clues***	**Instructional Resources** • Reading for Science, p. 68		
Lesson 4 Student Edition pp. C56–C57 ***What is in our solar system?*** **Flip Chart** ***Talk About Science***		**Wall Chart,** p. 47	
Lesson 5 Student Edition pp. C58–C59 ***How do we learn about the solar system?*** **Flip Chart** ***Talk About Science***		**Wall Chart,** p. 48	
Activity Idea Bank Teacher's Edition pp. C59a–C59b **Flip Chart** **Science Center Explore Activity** ***Make a model of a rocket.***	**Lab Manual** • Lab Manual, p. 87 • Activity Rubric, p. T31		
Chapter Review Student Edition pp. C60–C61 and **Flip Chart**	**Teacher's Assessment Package** • Chapter 3 Assessment, pp. 53–54		**Practice & Assessment CD-ROM** **Production Studio** **The KnowZone™ at www.kz.com** **TestWorks™**

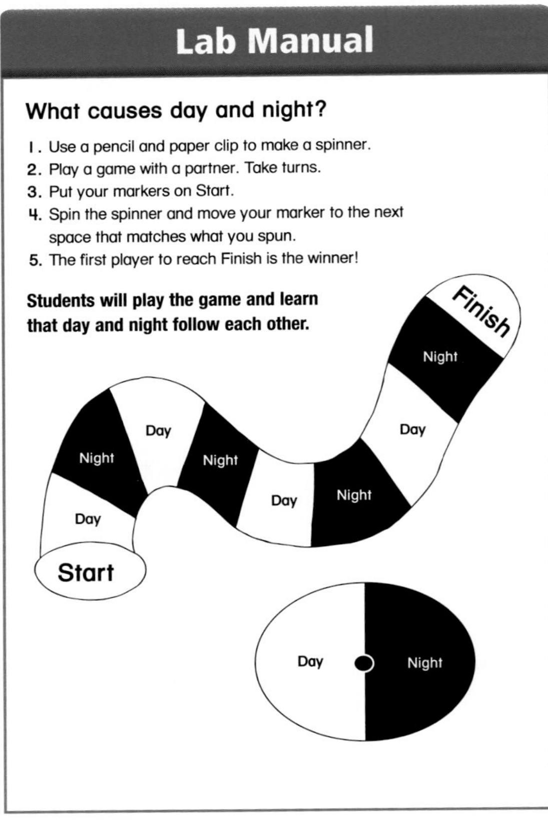

Lab Manual

What causes day and night?

1. Use a pencil and paper clip to make a spinner.
2. Play a game with a partner. Take turns.
3. Put your markers on Start.
4. Spin the spinner and move your marker to the next space that matches what you spun.
5. The first player to reach Finish is the winner!

Students will play the game and learn that day and night follow each other.

Lab Manual
p. 81

Lab Manual

How can you record the phases of the moon?

Fill in the month and the dates. Draw how the moon looks every night.

Students will complete a month of observations of the phases of the moon. Their drawings should approximate the variations in the appearance of the moon.

Sunday	Monday	Tuesday	Wednesday	Thursday	Friday	Saturday

Lab Manual
p. 83

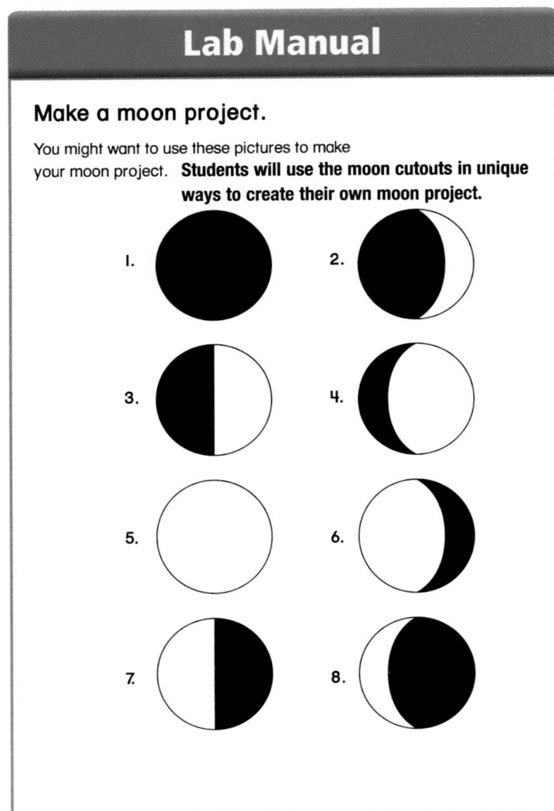

Lab Manual

Make a moon project.

You might want to use these pictures to make your moon project. **Students will use the moon cutouts in unique ways to create their own moon project.**

Lab Manual
p. 85

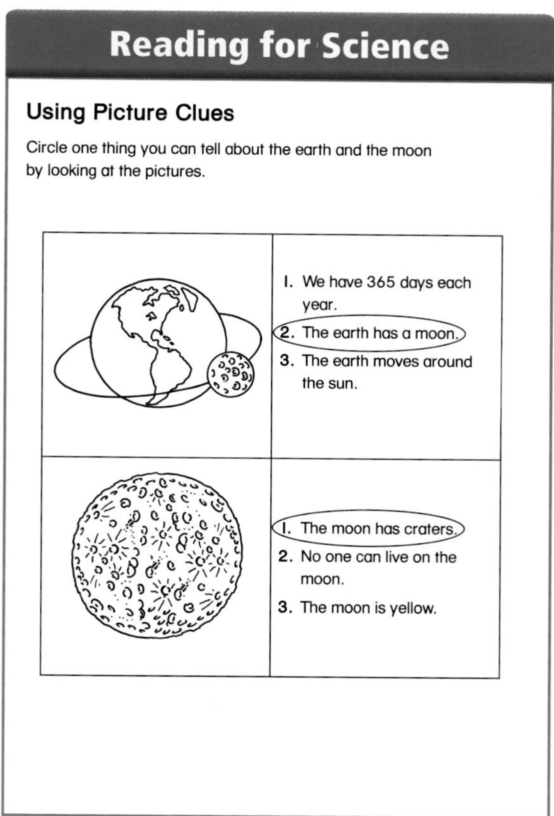

Reading for Science

Using Picture Clues

Circle one thing you can tell about the earth and the moon by looking at the pictures.

1. We have 365 days each year.
2. The earth has a moon. (circled)
3. The earth moves around the sun.

1. The moon has craters. (circled)
2. No one can live on the moon.
3. The moon is yellow.

Instructional Resources p. 68

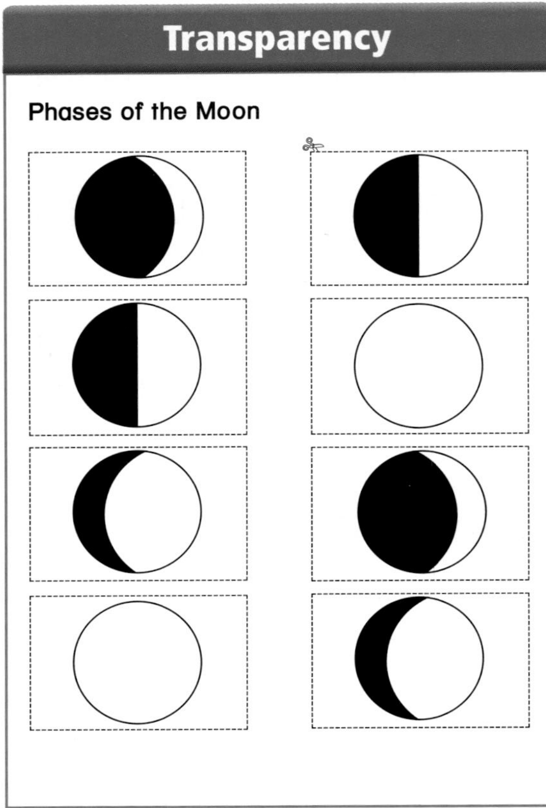

Interactive Transparency Package
Transparency 9

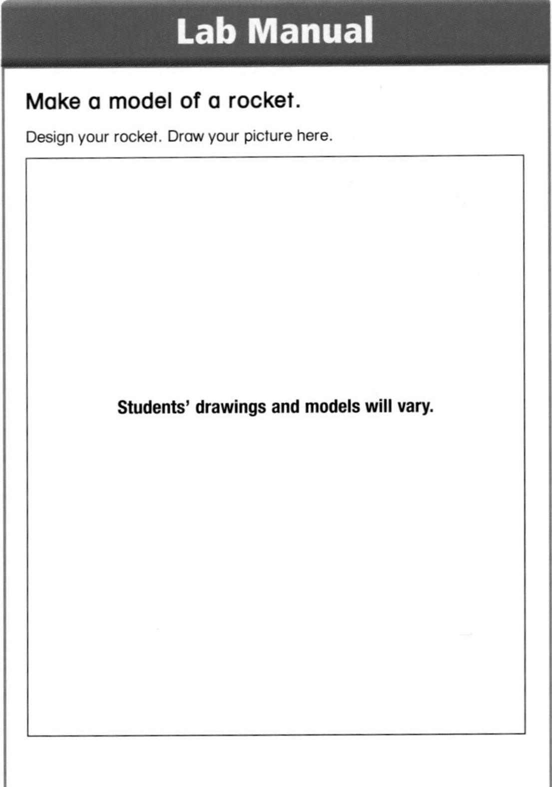

Lab Manual
p. 87

Chapter 3 Assessment

Use a word from the box to finish each sentence.

crater	solar system	telescope	phases	orbit

1. The sun and planets are parts of the **solar system**.
2. A **crater** is a hole on the moon's surface.
3. The planets **orbit** the sun.
4. The different shapes of the moon are called **phases**.
5. Scientists use a **telescope** to study planets that are far away.

Write **Yes** or **No**.

6. **No** You have nighttime on the side of Earth facing the sun.
7. **No** The sun is always moving across the sky.
8. **Yes** It takes about one month to see all the phases of the moon.
9. **No** A telescope makes close things look far away.
10. **Yes** The sun is the center of our solar system.

Teacher's Assessment Package p. 53

Chapter 3 Assessment

Draw a line from each word to the correct part of the picture.

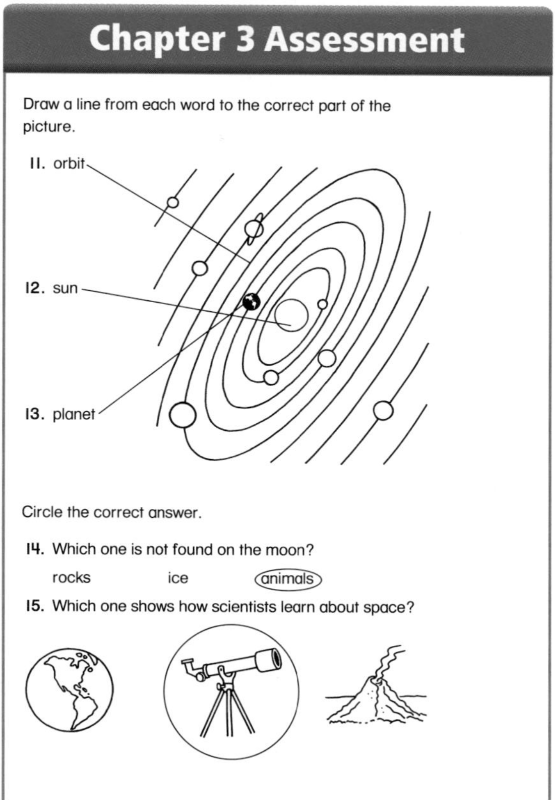

Circle the correct answer.

14. Which one is not found on the moon?

rocks ice (animals)

15. Which one shows how scientists learn about space?

Teacher's Assessment Package p. 54

Table of Contents

Introducing the Chapter

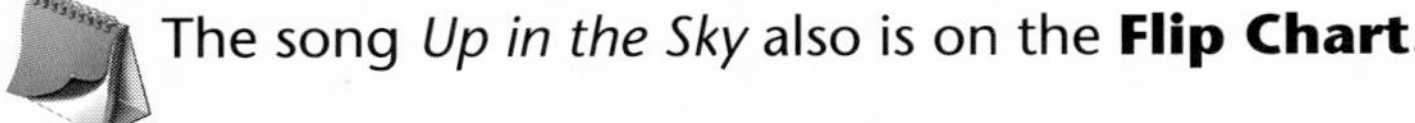

The song *Up in the Sky* also is on the **Flip Chart.**

- Ask children what they know about the planets. Tell children that in this chapter they will learn more about the planets and our solar system.
- Distribute the Family Activity blackline master page.

Singing the Song

Have children sing the song *Up in the Sky* on side 2 of the CTW cassette. Distribute pages 25–26 from the CTW Song Activity Book.

Reading Assist *Synonyms*

Have children find the word *spins* in the song. Mention that in this song, Earth *spins* or *orbits* the sun. Point out that the song uses *spins* as a synonym for *orbits.* Remind children that a synonym is a word that means the same or almost the same as another word.

Vocabulary Preview

Use the Vocabulary Preview blackline master to introduce the vocabulary words for this chapter.

Lesson 2 craters, phases
Lesson 4 orbit
Lesson 5 telescope

Chapter 3

The Solar System

Up in the Sky

Sing to the tune of *The Eensy Weensy Spider.*

The planets and their moons and the sun up in the sky
Make up our solar system stretching far and wide.
The Earth and other planets all spin around the sun.
What spins around the Earth and can be seen by everyone?

Round and round the Earth spins a moon that's all our own.
With mountains and craters that are hard as stone.
The moon seems to change from full to very thin.
Did you notice it last night? Did it look just like a grin?

C46

Technology

Practice & Assessment CD-ROM

AudioText

Production Studio

www.sfscience.com

Teacher's Resource Planner

Songs & Activities Package

CTW Song & Activity

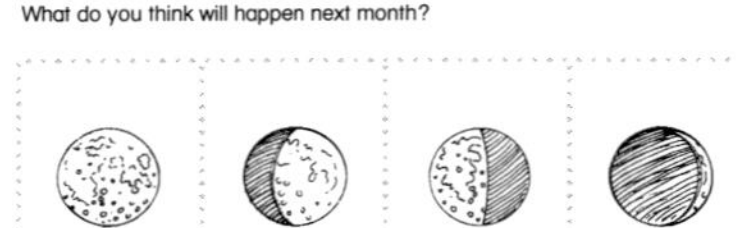

See how thw moon seems to change every night!
1. Keep this chart for one month.
2. Look at the moon two or three times each week.
3. When the moon looks like one of the pictures, write the date under that picture.
4. Keep going for one month until you have a date on every picture
What do you think will happen next month?

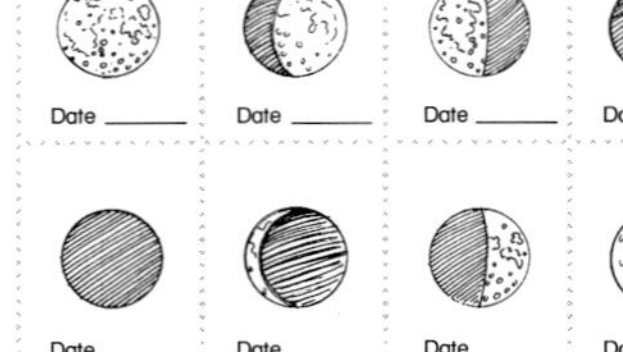

Songs & Activities Package pp. 25–26

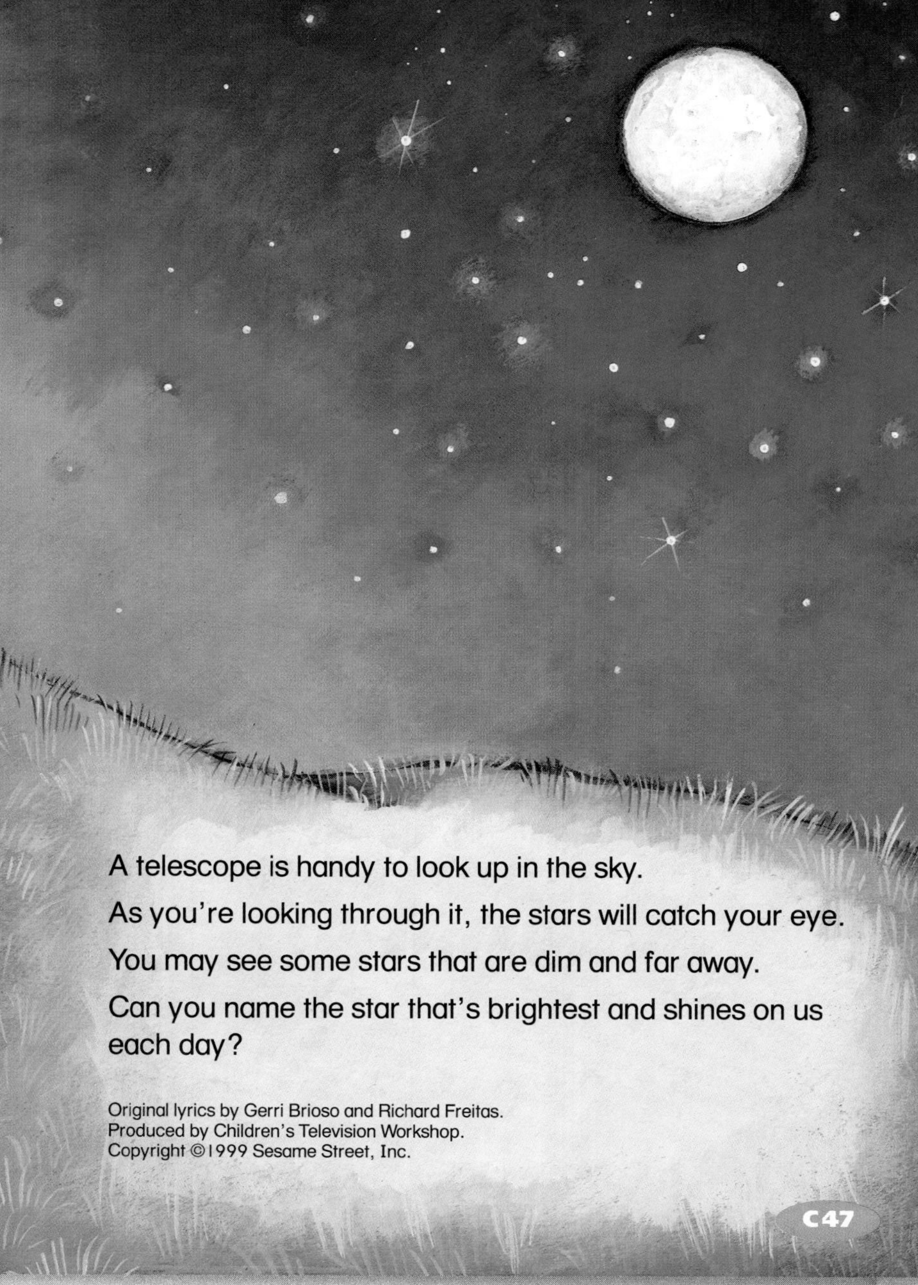

A telescope is handy to look up in the sky.

As you're looking through it, the stars will catch your eye.

You may see some stars that are dim and far away.

Can you name the star that's brightest and shines on us each day?

Original lyrics by Gerri Brioso and Richard Freitas.
Produced by Children's Television Workshop.

Family Activity — Science at Home

Dear Family:

Our class is starting Chapter 3. We will be learning about the solar system. These are the main ideas for Chapter 3.

- Day and night happen because the earth turns.
- The moon does not have air or living things. We see only the lighted part of the moon. The shapes we see are called phases of the moon.
- The sun is the center of our solar system, and planets orbit the sun.
- Astronauts and equipment in space teach us about the solar system.

We will also be learning science vocabulary words for Chapter 3. By the end of Chapter 3, we will be able to read the vocabulary words and tell what they mean.

Word Bank

craters
phases
orbit
telescope

Home Projects

Here are some activities that will help your child understand the main ideas in Chapter 3. The activities are easy, fast, and fun.

Activities

- With your child, observe the phases of the moon. Make a simple calendar by dividing a piece of paper into 7 columns and 5 rows to resemble a calendar. Then look at the moon each night for a week, starting with the full moon. Draw what the moon looks like each night.

Instructional Resources
pp. 65–66

Vocabulary Preview

craters	phases
orbit	telescope
solar system	planets
astronaut	scientist

Instructional Resources
p. 67

INQUIRY

Use a KWL chart at the beginning of each chapter. In the *K* column, record what children already *know* about the solar system. In the *W* column, list what they *want* to know. Throughout the chapter, ask children what they have *learned.* Record their responses in the *L* column. A KWL chart is on **Wall Chart** page 43.

Chapter 3 Skills Trace

Process Skills Development	Observing	Collecting and Interpreting Data
Skill Introduced	xiv	xv
Skill Applied	C49 C52–C53	C52–C53
Skill Assessed	End Matter 6–7	End Matter 24–25

Exploring Space
by Lesley Sims.
Pictures and color illustrations of spacecraft, astronauts and various instruments used in space exploration help describe the atmosphere and the science of astronomy. (Steck-Vaughn, ISBN 0-8114-4947-5)

Lesson Organizer

Objective

Describe how the rotation of the earth causes day and night.

Process Skills observing

Materials

Kit Items flashlight, D battery

School-Supplied Items globe, stickers

Additional Resources

- Lab Manual
- Teacher Demonstration Kit
- Wall Chart

Introduce

Activate Prior Knowledge

Ask: **What causes day and night?** Allow children to take turns offering suggestions.

Language Development *Scientific Language*

Ask children to identify a globe that is on display. Help children understand that the globe is a model representing Earth. Invite volunteers to locate first the United States and then the state in which they live.

Flip Chart

Have volunteers point to the part of Earth that has daytime and to the part that has nighttime.

What causes day and night?

Stand up and spin around! How do you feel? You may be dizzy.

Did you know Earth is spinning too? Even though you cannot feel it, Earth is always turning.

Day and night happen because Earth turns. When your side of Earth is facing the sun, you have daytime. When your side of Earth is not facing the sun, you have nighttime.

We say that the sun rises and sets, but really the sun does not. The sun only seems to move across the sky. It looks like it is moving because Earth is moving.

Look at the picture. Find the part of Earth that is facing the sun. It is daytime there. Which part of Earth would have nighttime?[1]

[1]the part not facing the s

Sun

Earth

C48

Science Background

Earth rotates its axis once a day. The day is divided into 24 hours. However, the length of daylight at any one location varies during the course of the year. This is because Earth's axis is tilted toward the sun in summer and tilted away from the sun in winter. Thus, there are more daylight hours in summer than in winter.

Math-Science Connection

Have children take turns using **Wall Chart** page 44 to show the approximate times of sunrise, noon, and sunset.

Show how Earth rotates.

Materials

globe stickers  flashlight

Process Skills

- observing

Steps

1. Put the globe on a desk or table.
2. Put your sticker where you live.
3. Shine the flashlight on the globe.
4. Spin the globe. Let it stop on its own.
5. Observe whether your sticker ends up in daytime or nighttime.

Share. Show a friend which side of the globe is in daytime and which is in nighttime.

Lesson Review

1. Why do day and night happen?
2. When do you have nighttime?
3. **Draw** a picture of Earth and the sun. Label the day and night sides of Earth.

Lab Manual

What causes day and night?

1. Use a pencil and paper clip to make a spinner.
2. Play a game with a partner. Take turns.
3. Put your markers on Start.
4. Spin the spinner and move your marker to the next space that matches what you spun.
5. The first player to reach Finish is the winner!

Start Day Night Day Night Day Night Day Night Finish

Day Night

Lab Manual p. 81

Activity Rubric

Use the following activity scoring rubric to assess students' performance.

Scoring Criteria	1	2	3	4
Student assembled the proper materials to perform this activity.				
Student observed that light is associated with day and darkness with night.				
Student made a game to represent the passage of day and night.				
Student interacted appropriately with a partner to play the game.				
Student explained that the rotation of the earth causes day and night.				

Scoring Key

4 points correct, complete, detailed
3 points partially correct, complete, detailed
2 points partially correct, partially complete, lacks some detail
1 point incorrect or incomplete, needs assistance

Lab Manual p. T29

Teach and Apply

Student Page C48

Explain that Earth rotating on its axis causes day and night. Help children realize that Earth's rotation makes it appear as if the sun is moving slowly across the sky, but it is actually Earth that is moving.

Reading Assist *Word Meanings*

Ask children for various meanings of the word *face.* Tell them that in this lesson, *face* means "to turn toward." For example, Earth is facing or turning toward the sun.

Student Page C49

Explore Activity

Time about 5 minutes

Grouping cooperative groups of 2

- If you do not have stickers, children can tape a small piece of paper to identify their state.
- Tell children to spin the globe slowly.
- Children can complete Lab Manual page 81.

Safety Note *Be sure children do not shine their flashlights into anyone's eyes.*

Assess and Extend

Answers to Lesson Review

1. Day and night happen because Earth turns.
2. You have nighttime when your side of Earth is not facing the sun.
3. **Draw** (*Portfolio Assessment or Journal*) Drawings should show the sun shining on the side of Earth that is labeled "Day." The side that is not facing the sun should be labeled "Night."

Inquire Further

Ask the following question to guide further inquiry: **Which parts of Earth do you think have the longest days?** (*Children should suggest that parts of Earth that face the sun longer have longer days.*)

Higher Order Thinking *Draw Conclusions*

Ask children to look at the picture on page C48 and tell if the top part or the bottom part of Earth is getting more sunlight. (*top*) Then ask which part they think is having summer. (*top*)

Call 1-888-537-4908 with your Activity questions or comments.

Lesson Organizer

Objective
Describe features and phases of the moon.

Vocabulary
craters, phases

Additional Resources
- Wall Chart
- Interactive Transparency

Introduce

Activate Prior Knowledge
Display **Wall Chart** page 45. As children speculate on the different characteristics that the moon might have, record their ideas on the word web. Save the web for use as a **baseline assessment.**

Language Development *Story Starter*
Have children create a story about a group of astronauts and their trip to the moon. Start the story and have each child add a sentence to continue it. Encourage them to mention what the astronauts see and do on the moon.

Flip Chart
Discuss the pictures of phases of the moon. Have children tell what else they know about the moon. Point out the features of the surface of the moon.

What do we know about the moon?

Think about what you see in the sky at night. You have probably seen the moon. Have you ever wondered what the moon is like?

The moon is not like Earth. The moon has rocks and soil, but it does not have air or living things. Ice has been found on the moon.

Look at the picture of the surface of the moon. You can see craters. A **crater** is a hole in the ground that is shaped like a bowl. These craters were made long ago when rocks from space crashed into the moon.

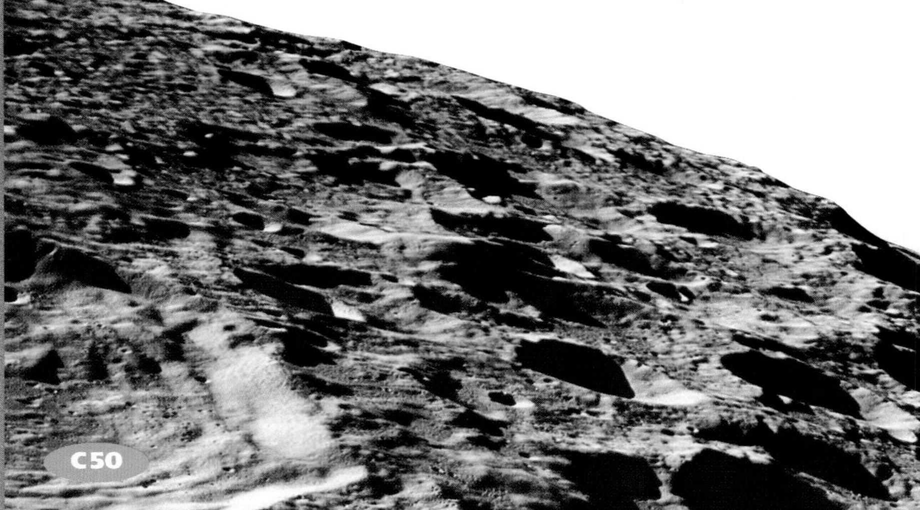

Science Background

- The moon's diameter is about one-fourth that of Earth's. It takes about 28 days for the moon to revolve around Earth.
- Phases of the moon happen when the moon moves around Earth. Because the moon changes positions relative to Earth and the sun, we sometimes see only portions of it reflected by the sun.

Science Across Cultures Dr. Mae Jemison was the first African American woman to travel in space. On September 12, 1992, she traveled in the space shuttle *Endeavor* to conduct experiments on how tadpoles mature in weightlessness.

What does the moon look like to you? It may look like it has a different shape every day.

The moon seems to change shape because you only see the part that has light shining on it. The rest of the moon looks dark to you.

The shapes that you see are called the **phases** of the moon. These pictures show some of the moon's phases. It takes about a month to see all the phases of the moon.

Lesson Review

1. What are craters?
2. Why does the moon seem to change shape?
3. **Draw** two phases of the moon.

ESL Strategy

Ask students if they have ever heard someone say, "He's going through a phase." Help them understand that this means the person's behavior will change sometime soon. Relate this to the fact that the phases of the moon change, going through all the changes, or phases, in about a month.

Transparency

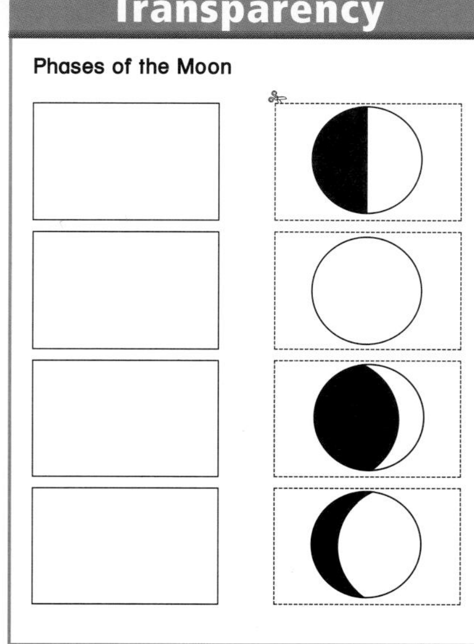

Interactive Transparency Package Transparency 9

Teach and Apply

Student Pages C50–C51

- Explain that the surface of the moon not only has craters, but it also has mountains and smooth lowlands that appear dark and resemble seas on Earth. Most rocks and dust on the moon's surface appear dark gray.
- Explain that the moon does not have any light of its own. Light from the sun shines on the moon; the light we see is sun light reflected off the moon.

Reading Assist *Vocabulary*

Ask children to tell what a crater looks like and to describe one phase of the moon.

Real-World Applications

For centuries, people believed that the sun, moon, and stars moved around a stationary Earth. Aristarchus, an early Greek astronomer, and later Nicolaus Copernicus thought otherwise. In the 1500s, Copernicus illustrated how he thought Earth, other planets, and stars moved around the sun. His work is the foundation of modern astronomy.

Assess and Extend

Answers to Lesson Review

1. Craters are holes that were made long ago when rocks from space crashed into the moon.
2. The moon seems to change shape because you see only the part that has sunlight shining on it.
3. **Draw** (*Portfolio Assessment or Journal*) Drawings will vary.

Check for Understanding

To follow up on the **baseline assessment,** have children review the word web they made about the moon. Encourage them to make any necessary changes.

Reteach

- Use the Interactive Transparency to reteach Lesson 2 concepts.
- Provide children with modeling clay and cardboard. Invite them to shape the clay to form the moon's surface. Be sure they include craters, mountains, and flat places. Encourage them to add small rocks and sand to complete their surface. When clay moons have dried, provide paint for children to paint them.

Activity Organizer

Objective
Observe and record the phases of the moon.

Process Skills collecting and interpreting data, observing

Materials

Kit Items none

School-Supplied Items calendar, crayons or markers

Time about 20 minutes initially; then about 5 minutes every night for one month

Grouping individual

Additional Resources
- Lab Manual
- Teacher Demonstration Kit
- Wall Chart

Introduce

The Lesson 3 Investigate Activity, *How can you record the phases of the moon?*, is on the **Flip Chart.**

Activate Prior Knowledge
Ask children to describe the moon's phases that they saw in the previous lesson.

Language Development *Vocabulary*
Display a calendar for the current month. Ask children to name ways people use calendars.

Reading Assist *Preview and Predict*
Ask children to predict what they will do in this lesson by looking at the lesson title and the pictures on the pages.

Investigate Activity

How can you record the phases of the moon?

Process Skills
- collecting and interpreting data
- observing

Materials

 calendar

 crayons or markers

Steps
1. Start with a blank calendar.
2. Fill in all the dates for this month.
3. Collect data by observing the moon every night for one month.
4. On your calendar, draw how the moon looks every night.

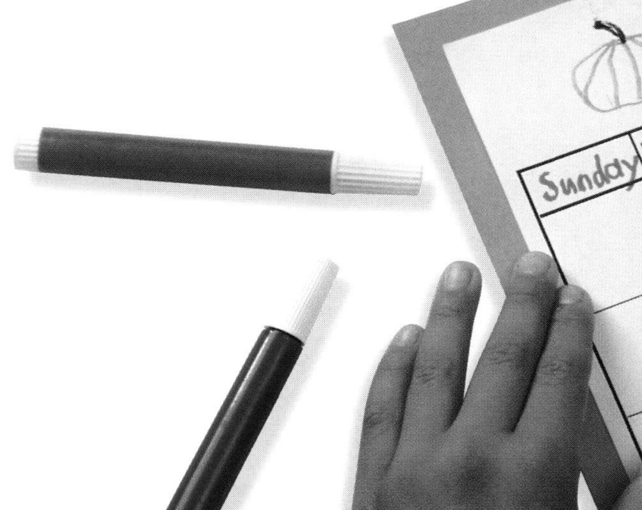

Science Background

- As the moon revolves around Earth, we see different parts of the moon that are lighted by the sun.
- All the moon's phases are visible as the moon makes one revolution around Earth.

Possible Misconceptions Make sure children understand that the dark part of the moon is the part on which the sun is not shining; the shadow is not caused by Earth's shadow.

Technology

Review the demonstration of this Investigate's procedure on the *Earth Science* **Activity Video,** Segment 4.

Think About Your Results

1. In what ways did the moon look different every night?
2. Do any of your pictures look the same? If so, which ones?

Inquire Further

Would your data be the same or different next month? How could you find out?

C53

Lab Manual

How can you record the phases of the moon?

Fill in the month and the dates. Draw how the moon looks every night.

Sunday	Monday	Tuesday	Wednesday	Thursday	Friday	Saturday

Lab Manual
p. 83

Activity Rubric

Use the following activity scoring rubric to assess students' performance.

Scoring Criteria	1	2	3	4
Student followed directions to fill in the calendar and complete this activity.				
Student observed the appearance of the moon each night for a month.				
Student collected and recorded data about the moon for a month.				
Student drew the appearance of the moon each night for a month.				
Student explained the cycle of the moon using a calendar chart.				

Scoring Key
4 points correct, complete, detailed
3 points partially correct, complete, detailed
2 points partially correct, partially complete, lacks some detail
1 point incorrect or incomplete, needs assistance

Lab Manual
p. T30

Teach and Apply

- Children can complete Lab Manual page 83 as they do the activity, or use any blank monthly calendar.
- Help children fill in the month's name and dates, making sure they start numbering in the correct box.
- As an alternative, assign two children each night to look at the moon and report back to the class. Then have children fill in their calendars.
- Tell children that the moon will not be visible every night. Sometimes it will rise too late for children to see. Other times it is visible only during the day.
- Children can leave their calendar at home each night, or draw on scratch paper and transfer the drawing to their calendar each day at school.
- Invite children to take turns recording their daily observations on a class chart. Use **Wall Chart** page 46.
- Allow time for children to discuss changes they **observe.**

What to Expect

Children should make a drawing of the moon each night for a month. You may want to monitor their progress every few days to check for understanding. Children may not be able to discern daily differences. Also, rain, snow, or clouds may make viewing difficult.

Assess and Extend

Answers to Think About Your Results

1. The shape of the moon looked different every night.
2. Some of their pictures may look the same since some phases are only slightly different. Also, some children may inadvertently reverse the image of the moon, making waxing and waning moons look the same.

Inquire Further

Children may say that their data would be the same, because the phases will repeat; or different, because the phases would happen on different days. The phases show a four-week pattern, and most months are longer than four weeks. They could find out by repeating the activity next month, or by reading some books about the moon.

Higher Order Thinking *Infer*

Ask: **Why do the phases of the moon occur in the same order each time?** (*The moon moves around Earth in the same path each month.*)

Call 1-888-537-4908 with your Activity questions or comments.

Science Center

Flip Chart

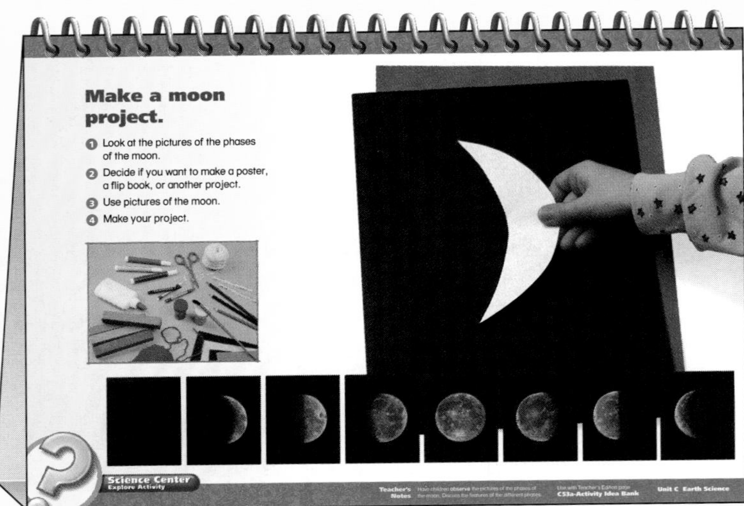

Make a moon project.

Objective

Identify and sequence the phases of the moon.

Process Skills observing

Materials

Kit Items none

School-Supplied Items pictures of different phases of the moon; art supplies, such as crayons, markers, paper, yarn, glue, craft sticks, paint, paintbrush, clay, scissors

Safety Note *Tell children about the proper use of scissors*

Procedure

- Invite children to look at pictures of the phases of the moon.
- Encourage children to create projects, such as a poster or flip book, that shows the sequence of the phases.
- Children **observe** the phases of the moon to tell about their projects.
- You can use **Lab Manual** page 85 with this activity.

What to Expect

Children should correctly sequence the pictures of the phases of the moon.

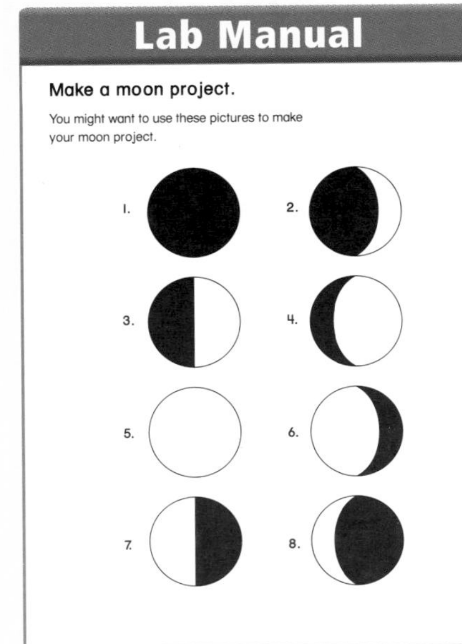

Lab Manual
Make a moon project.
You might want to use these pictures to make your moon project.
1.
2.
3.
4.
5.
6.
7.
8.

Lab Manual, p. 85

Connections

School and Community

Ideas for bringing the school and community together:

Field Trips

- planetarium
- natural history museum
- space museum

Guest Speakers

- astronomer
- astronaut

Themes

The activities on these pages can be used with classroom themes such as:

- day and night
- space exploration
- change

Books for Children

Children might enjoy these books about night/day and space:

Barn Dance
by Bill Martin Jr. and John Archambault. An enchanting rhyme about a night on the farm under the light of a full moon. (Henry Holt, ISBN 0–8050–0089–5)

Moon, Sun, and Stars
by John Lewellen. Beautiful photos of bodies in space. (Childrens Press, ISBN 0–516–41637–5)

The Earth and the Moon
by David Drew. A simple comparison between the earth and the moon. (Celebration Press ISBN 0–673–77636–0)

Cross-Curricular Options

LITERATURE

The Moon Book

Use the book to learn more about the moon.

Materials *The Moon Book* by Gail Gibbons. (Holiday House, ISBN 0-823401364-0)

Procedure

- This book offers a great deal of information about the moon: its orbits and phases, eclipses, tides, a history of moon exploration, and the legends the moon has inspired in various cultures.
- Read the book aloud once, focusing on the narrative text.
- Reread the book, paying attention to the pictures that are most suited to the interests of your class.

Multiple Intelligences linguistic

MATH

Tracking the Sun

Make and use a sundial.

Materials cardboard, toothpicks or straws, markers

Procedure

- Explain that the sun can be used to tell time.
- Children can make a simple sundial using a square of cardboard and a toothpick or piece of a drinking straw for the shadow indicator.
- Invite children to monitor the sundial throughout the day, marking where the shadow falls every hour on the hour.

Multiple Intelligences linguistic, logical-mathematical, spatial

ESL Review the numbers 1 through 12 with children.

WRITING

Our Address: The Moon

Write about living on the moon.

Materials paper, pencils

Procedure

- Ask children to imagine that your class could go live on the moon.
- Have partners work together to list good things about living on the moon—for example, children could jump very high—and bad things—there is no snow to play in.
- Let pairs share their lists and then have the class decide which is a better place to live—the earth or the moon.

Multiple Intelligences linguistic

Gifted and Talented Pairs can write a short story about living on the moon.

LANGUAGE ARTS

Fact or Fiction?

Differentiate facts from fiction about the moon.

Materials books, magazines, index cards, pencils

Procedure

- Have children look through books and magazines to find things written about the moon.
- Have children write statements on index cards describing what they read.
- Children share their index cards with the class. Talk about which statements are true and which are fictional.

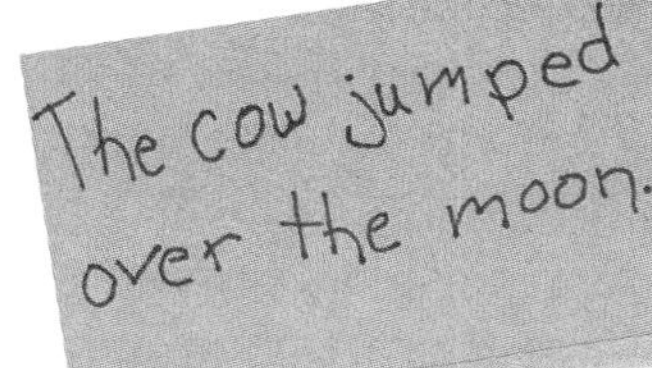
Craters are holes on the moon.

Multiple Intelligences linguistic

Reading Organizer

Objective
Use picture clues.

Additional Resources
- Reading for Science blackline master

Teaching Reading for Science

- Pictures often accompany science writings to support the written words. This is because pictures and illustrations can be used to clarify points, provide additional facts, show relationships among components, and help children visualize the written word. Knowing how to use picture clues to gather information is an important developmental skill.
- Using picture clues to gather information strengthens skills needed during the processes of inquiry, including **observing, inferring,** and **communicating.** Children use observation skills to focus on details presented in the picture. They use inference to draw conclusions based on their observations of information in the picture and their personal experiences. They use communication skills to share what they have learned from the picture clues.
- Have children read and complete the Reading for Science lesson and the Reading for Science blackline master.

Student Page C54

- Children might be familiar with using pictures to find information from reading picture books.
- Before asking specific questions about the picture on page C54, have children discuss what they noticed in the picture. Point out that children gathered information about astronauts landing on the moon from picture clues.
- As volunteers answer the questions on page C54, have them explain what clues in the picture they used to answer the questions.
- Invite volunteers to ask other questions about the picture. Have children use picture clues to answer the questions.

Using Picture Clues

You can use pictures to get information. Use the picture to answer these questions.

Astronauts have landed on the moon. What did the astronauts do when they got there? What did they bring with them? What else can you learn from looking at the picture?

ESL Strategy

Provide several pictures and have children tell about the pictures. Encourage them to notice the details in the pictures and to tell what they think the pictures are about. Then provide children with sentence frames that work as captions for the pictures. For example, if you have given children a picture of a moon, the frame might be: *I can see the _______ in the sky at night.*

Look at the picture on this page. Write one thing about the picture. Ask a friend to write one thing about the picture.

Share what you wrote. Did you both write the same thing?

How many other things can you write about the picture? Share your ideas.

Turn the page to find out how pictures can help you learn about the solar system.

Student Page C55

- Discuss why partners may or may not have written about the same thing.
- Have partners take turns asking questions about the picture. Remind children that they should use picture clues to answer the questions. Be sure children know that they must ask questions that can be answered by looking at the picture.
- After partners have had time to ask each other several questions, ask: **What information did you get from the picture?** After discussion, point out how much information was available using the picture clues.

Apply Reading for Science to Lesson 4

Children will use what they learned about using picture clues to get information to complete the next lesson.

Reading for Science

Using Picture Clues

Circle one thing you can tell about the earth and the moon by looking at the pictures.

	1. We have 365 days each year. 2. The earth has a moon. 3. The earth moves around the sun.
	1. The moon has craters. 2. No one can live on the moon. 3. The moon is yellow.

Instructional Resources p. 68

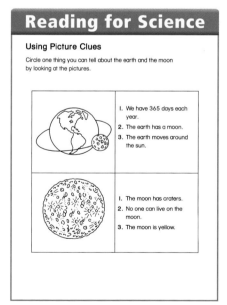

Lesson Organizer

Objective
Identify the sun and planets in our solar system.

Vocabulary orbit

Additional Resources
- Wall Chart

Introduce

Activate Prior Knowledge

Display **Wall Chart** page 47. Provide children with self-stick notes labeled with the names of the planets, the moon, and the sun. Invite children to identify the objects in our solar system and discuss where they think each is located on the diagram. Have volunteers stick labels where they think they should go on the chart. Save children's chart for use as a **baseline assessment.**

Language Development *Vocabulary*

Explain that a planet is a large body of matter that moves around the sun and reflects the sun's light. Our solar system is made up of the sun and the nine planets and other objects that orbit the sun.

Flip Chart

Discuss the drawing of the solar system. Ask: **What is in the center of the solar system? Which planet is closest to the sun? Which one is farthest away?**

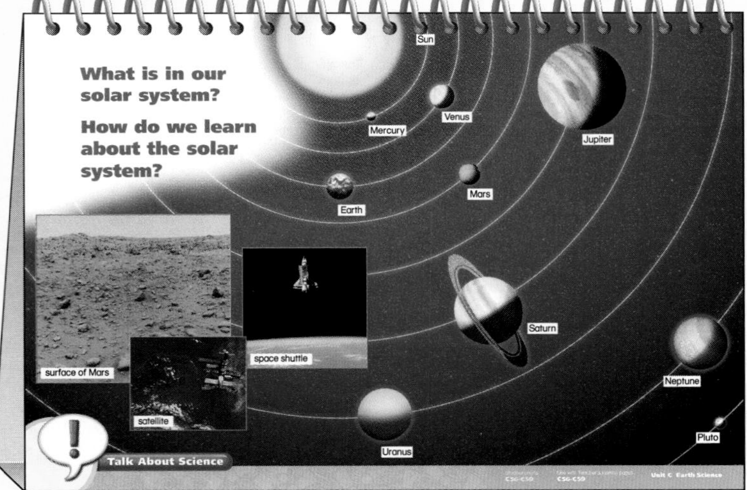

What is in our solar system?

Did you know that there is a star you can see during the day? Which star is it? It is the sun!

The sun is in the center of our solar system. All of the planets in our solar system orbit the sun. To **orbit** means to move around another object along a path. What else can you learn about the solar system from this picture?

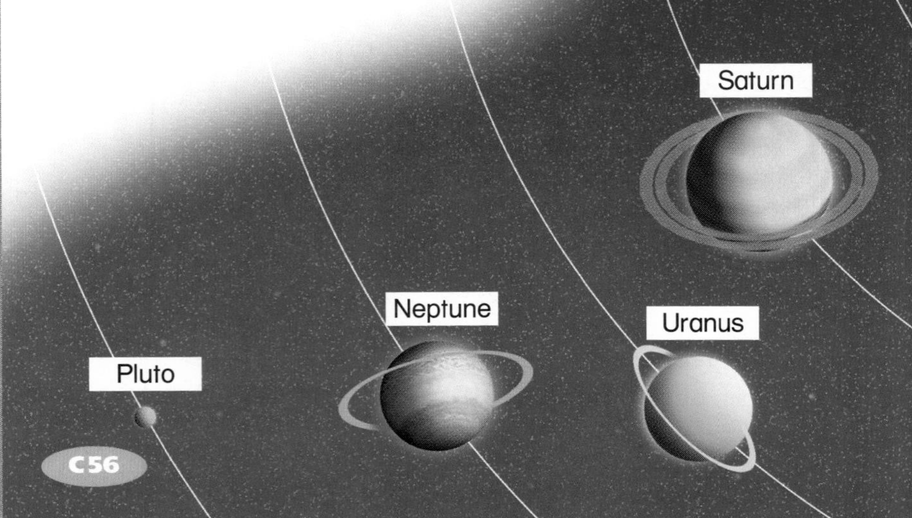

Science Background

The orbits of the planets are not circular. They are elliptical, or oval, paths. The paths of the nine planets are not concentric. The orbits of Neptune and Pluto cross. As a result, there are times when Pluto is closer to the sun than Neptune is. However, most of the time, Pluto is farther from the sun than Neptune.

Possible Misconceptions Children may have difficulty understanding that the sun is a star. Its nearness to Earth is the reason it appears so much bigger and brighter than other stars.

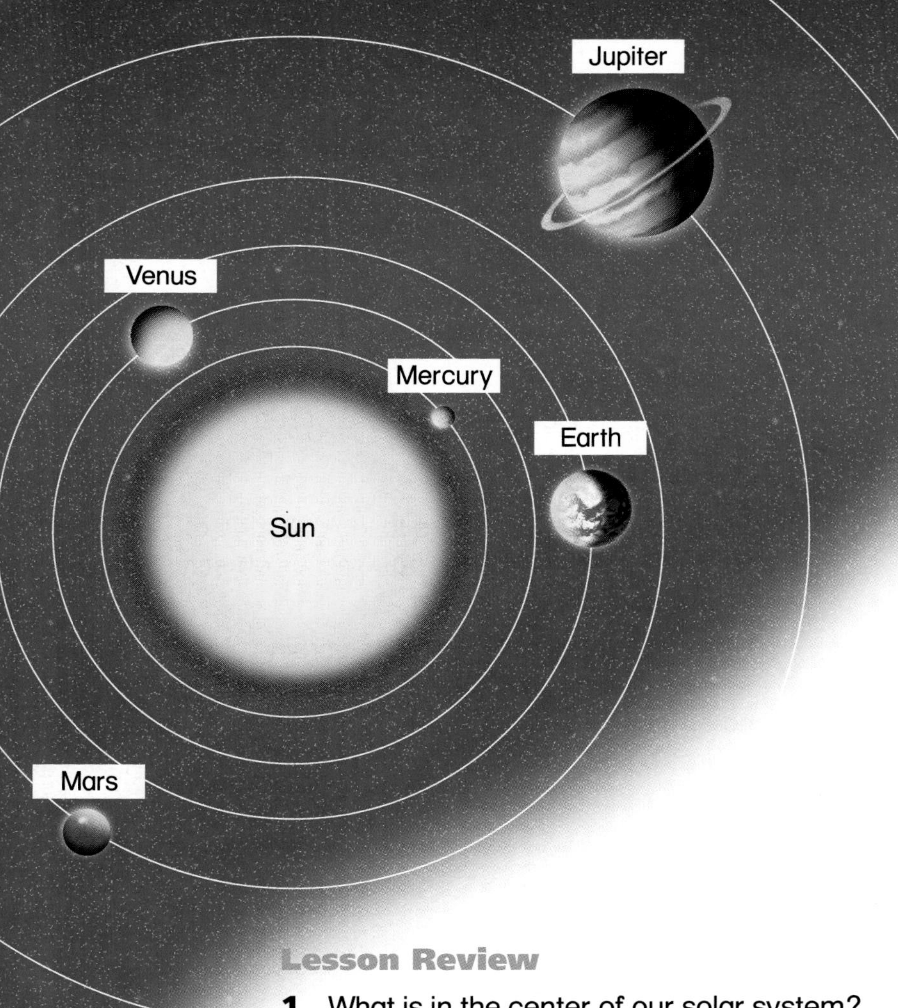

Lesson Review

1. What is in the center of our solar system?
2. What does orbit mean?
3. **Tell** what is in our solar system.

ESL Strategy

To reinforce the meaning of *orbit*, place a chair in the center of the floor. Draw an ellipse shape around the chair with chalk. Have a child walk around the shape. As the child is walking, have him or her say, "I am making an orbit around the chair."

Teach and Apply

Student Pages C56–C57

Explain that the solar system is named after the sun—*solar* is another word for *sun.* Have children name the nine known planets in our solar system in order from the sun. (*Mercury, Venus, Earth, Mars, Jupiter, Saturn, Uranus, Neptune, and Pluto*) Point out that these planets move around the sun in regular orbits, and most of them have one or more moons that orbit around them. Some of the planets have no moons at all, some have one moon, and some have several moons.

Reading Assist *Parts of Speech*

Discuss the meaning of the word *orbit* as a noun and a verb. As a verb, it means to travel in a path around something. As a noun, it is the path.

Assess and Extend

Answers to Lesson Review

1. The sun is in the center of our solar system.
2. Orbit means to move around something in a path.
3. Tell (*Interview*) Children will need to use the picture to answer this question. Answers may include the sun, planets, moons, and stars.

Check for Understanding

To follow up on the **baseline assessment,** have children readjust the labels on the **Wall Chart** to reflect what they have learned.

Reteach

Have children take turns pretending to be the sun and planets. Assign children roles and have them draw and label a picture of the planet, sun, or moon that they plan to be. Select one group to act out the planets orbiting the sun while others watch. Continue the activity until all children have a turn.

Lesson Organizer

Objective
Identify space exploration as a way we have learned about the solar system.

Vocabulary
telescope

Additional Resources
- Wall Chart

Introduce

Activate Prior Knowledge
Ask children to name all the ways they know that they find out about things in space today. Record their ideas on the word web on **Wall Chart** page 48. Save the web for use as a **baseline assessment.**

Language Development *Storytelling*
Point out that long ago, people made up stories about the sun, moon, and stars because they knew nothing about them. Have small groups of children make up their own stories about the sun, moon, and the stars. Then have groups share their stories with the class.

Real-World Applications
Some telescopes are so huge they fill up a whole building. Others, such as the Hubble Telescope, have been launched into space.

Flip Chart
Have children name things in the pictures that give scientists information about the solar system. Ask: **Why do you think scientists want to learn about the solar system?**

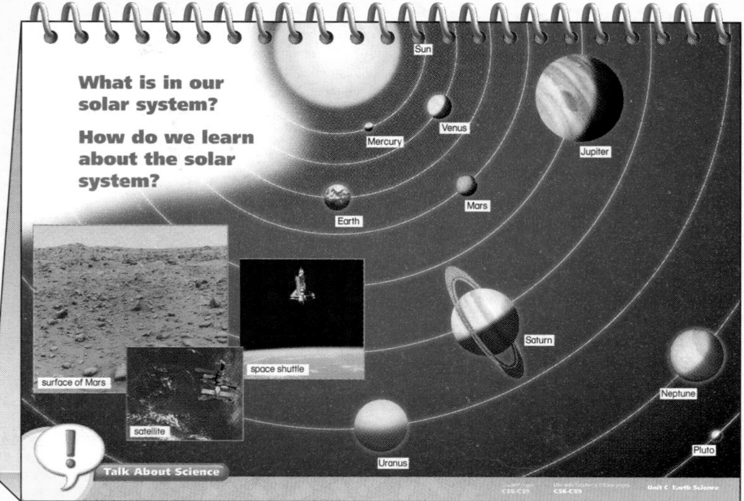

How do we learn about the solar system?

What do you see when you look at the sky? You may see the sun, moon, or stars. How could you get a better look at the sky?

Scientists use telescopes to look at parts of the solar system. A **telescope** makes objects that are far away look closer.

Scientists have other ways of learning about the solar system too. They can send cameras and other equipment into space to take pictures and collect information. They can also send astronauts into space.

What would you like to know about the solar system?

▲ A satellite that coll[ects] information in space

◀ Telescope

C58

Science Background
The first instrument used to study the solar system was a telescope invented by Galileo in 1609. Beginning in 1959, rockets have been used to send probes into space and send information about the solar system back to Earth.

Science Across Cultures Throughout history, different cultures have tried to explain natural phenomena that occur in the sky, such as eclipses, shooting stars, and phases of the moon. Share with children some folktales and legends relating to the sun, moon, and stars.

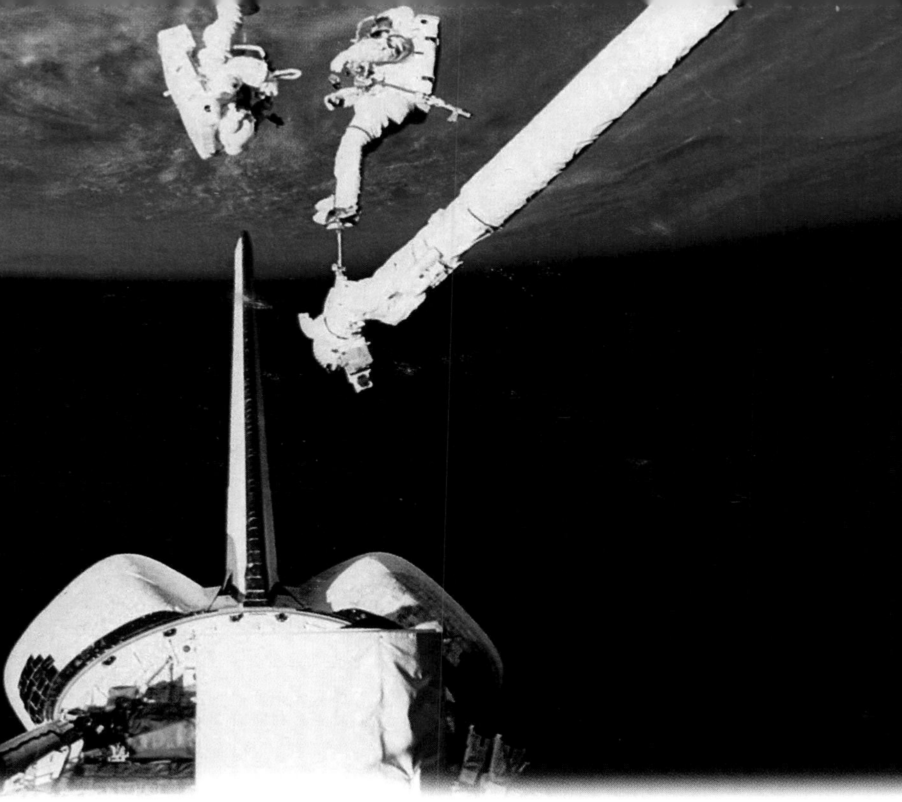

▲ Astronauts in space

Lesson Review

1. What does a telescope do?
2. What are some reasons scientists send astronauts into space?
3. **Tell** some ways scientists learn about the solar system.

C59

ESL Strategy

Provide sentence frames for children to complete. For example: *A _______ is used to help us see objects that are far away in space. _______ are people who travel in space. Our solar system has _______ planets. Special _______ are used to take pictures in space.*

Teach and Apply

Student Pages C58–C59

- Help children realize that people have always been curious about things they can see in the sky and things that are far away in space. Point out that this is why people look for better ways to observe things in space.
- Explain that Neil Armstrong and Edwin Aldrin became the first people to walk on the moon on July 20, 1969. They were the first U.S. astronauts to travel to the moon and back to Earth. Since then, many astronauts have traveled in space. Point out the astronauts in the picture and ask children to describe the special clothing they are wearing. Explain that scientists designed protective clothing because the air is different in space.

Reading Assist *Pronunciation*

Remind children that when they are learning to read a word like *telescope,* they should break the word into parts to help them figure out how to pronounce it.

Assess and Extend

Answers to Lesson Review

1. A telescope makes faraway objects look closer.
2. Scientists send astronauts into space to learn about the solar system.
3. **Tell** (***Interview***) Answers may include using telescopes, sending cameras and other equipment into space, and sending people into space.

Check for Understanding

To follow up on the **baseline assessment,** allow children to revise or add to the word web about how we explore space.

Reteach

Provide children with a variety of space and science magazines. Ask them to cut out or draw pictures of things that can be used to explore space. Then have them make a space exploration collage with the pictures.

Science Center

Flip Chart

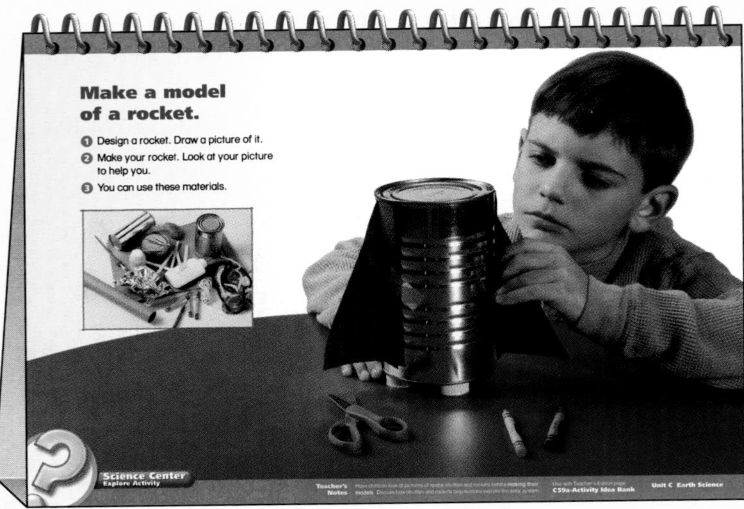

Make a model of a rocket.

Objective

Create a model of a rocket.

Process Skills making and using models

Materials

Kit Items none

School-Supplied Items pictures of spacecraft, foil, string, magazines, paper, yarn, cardboard paper rolls, craft sticks, cloth, empty containers, art supplies

Procedure

- Have children look at pictures of space shuttles and rockets. Discuss how humans explore the solar system.
- Have children design their rockets by drawing pictures, then gather materials and **make models** of their rockets.
- You can use **Lab Manual** page 87 with this activity.

What to Expect

Children should use information and details from the pictures of spacecraft to make their models.

Lab Manual

Make a model of a rocket.

Design your rocket. Draw your picture here.

Lab Manual, p. 87

Connections

School and Community

Ideas for bringing the school and community together:

Field Trips

- planetarium
- natural history museum
- space museum
- science museum

Guest Speakers

- science teacher
- astronomer
- NASA representative

Themes

The activities on these pages can be used with classroom themes such as:

- sun and stars
- planets
- solar system

Books for Children

Children might enjoy these books about the solar system:

Floating in Space by Franklyn M. Branley. What astronauts do and wear in space and how they sleep, eat, and move around. (HarperCollins, ISBN 0-06-445142-9)

The Magic School Bus, Lost in the Solar System by Joanna Cole. Ms. Frizzle and her class study the solar system. (Scholastic, ISBN 0-590-41429-1)

How Many Stars in the Sky? by Lenny Hort. Father and son explore the night sky and learn about each other. (Mulberry, ISBN 0-688-15218-X)

Cross-Curricular Options

LITERATURE

Insects from Outer Space

Read a humorous fantasy book.

Materials *Insects from Outer Space* by Vladimir Vagin and Frank Asch. (Scholastic, ISBN 0-590-45489-7)

Procedure

- Alien insects invade the earth. Two earthly insects save the day.
- Read the story aloud to children and display the vibrant illustrations.
- Ask children to visualize what mammals, fish, amphibians, and reptiles might look like if they really lived in space.
- Have children draw pictures of their images.

Multiple Intelligences linguistic, spatial

Gifted and Talented Challenge children to design an animal space vehicle.

MATH

The Planets

Make models of the planets.

Materials books about the solar system, different colors of clay, large sheets of cardboard

Procedure

- Have children work in groups of nine, each child responsible for researching and creating a model of one of the planets.
- Challenge the group to work together to figure out the size relationship of the planets.
- On cardboard, have children place the planets in order of their distance from the sun and label them.

Multiple Intelligences spatial, linguistic, logical-mathematical

ESL Explain that distance means how far away something is. Check children's understanding by having them find the distance in steps from their desk to the chalkboard.

ART

Launch into Space!

Create a board game about space.

Materials poster board, plastic tokens, markers and crayons, ruler, pencil

Procedure

- Invite partners to design and create a board game with a space theme.
- Have children discuss the purpose of the game, how it should be played, by how many people, and what kind of tokens or spinners are needed.
- Then they can sketch the design of their game and write or record rules on cassette tape before they actually draw the layout on the poster board.
- Place the finished games and rules in a central spot for children to play during independent time.

Multiple Intelligences spatial, linguistic

SOCIAL STUDIES

Historic Moments in Space

Make a time line chain.

Materials encyclopedia, 3" × 12" paper strips, markers, crayons, stapler

Procedure

- Help children research important events in U.S. space exploration. You might begin by telling children about some astronauts, such as Alan B. Shepard, Jr., the first American in space in 1961.
- Invite each child to choose an event to illustrate. Have them assemble the strips in order by date. Then staple the strips to make a chain.
- Suspend the chain across a the wall.

Multiple Intelligences spatial, logical-mathematical

Review Organizer

Materials

Kit Items 2 paper plates

School-Supplied Items scissors, markers, fastener, safety goggles

Time about 30 minutes

Grouping individual

Additional Resources

- Chapter 3 Assessment: Teacher's Assessment Package

Chapter Main Ideas

Lesson 1 Day and night happen because Earth rotates. The sun only appears to be moving across the sky because Earth moves.

Lesson 2 The moon is not like Earth because it does not have air or living things. The moon seems to change shape because we see only the part of the moon that has sunlight shining on it.

Lesson 3 The phases of the moon can be recorded by observing and drawing a picture of the moon each night to show its shape.

Lesson 4 The sun is a star at the center of our solar system. All planets in our solar system orbit the sun.

Lesson 5 Scientists gain information about our solar system through space exploration and the use of telescopes on Earth and cameras in space.

Reviewing Science Words

1. The phases of the moon are the shapes you see.
2. Craters formed long ago when rocks from space crashed into the moon.
3. All the planets in our solar system orbit the sun.
4. A telescope helps scientists learn about the solar system by making objects that are far away look closer.

Reviewing Science Ideas

1. Earth turning causes day and night.
2. The moon seems to change shape because you see only the part of the moon that has light shining on it.
3. Answers may include the sun and planets.
4. Answers may include using telescopes, sending cameras and other equipment into space, and sending people into space.

Chapter 3 Review

Reviewing Science Words

1. What are **phases** of the moon?
2. How did **craters** form on the moon?
3. What **orbits** the sun?
4. How does a **telescope** help scientists learn about the solar system?

Reviewing Science Ideas

1. What causes day and night?
2. Why does the moon seem to change shape?
3. What is in our solar system?
4. How do scientists learn about the solar system?

C60

Technology

Children can review *The Solar System* with the **Practice & Assessment CD-ROM.**

Children can use the **Production Studio** to show what they've learned about *The Solar System.*

Children can use The KnowZone™ at **www.kz.com** to review and test their science knowledge.

You can use **TestWorks™** to customize assessment for your children.

Show the phases of the moon.

Materials

- safety goggles
- two paper plates
- markers
- scissors
- fastener

1. Put on your safety goggles.
2. On one plate, draw some phases of the moon in order around the outer edge.
3. On the other plate, draw where you live. Cut a hole above your picture.
4. Put the plate with the hole on top of the other plate.
5. Use your scissors to make a small hole in the center of both plates. Hold them together with the fastener.
6. To see the phases of the moon, turn the bottom plate.

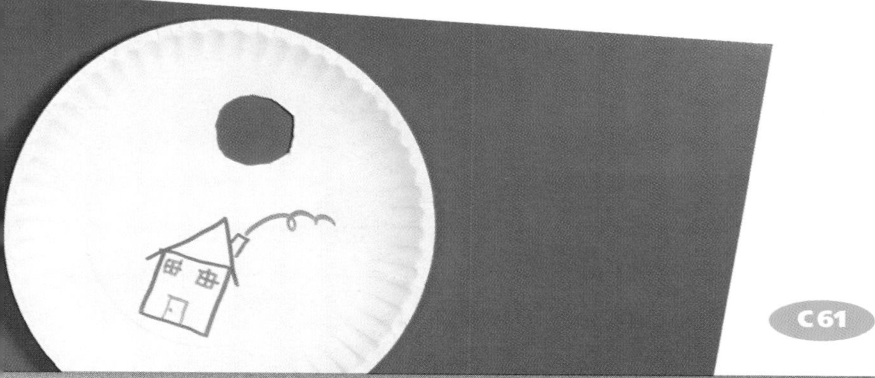

Performance Assessment Teaching Tips

- Before children begin this activity, have them recall the four phases of the moon.
- Encourage them to refer to pages C50–C51 in their books as needed.

Safety Note *Have children wear safety goggles during the activity to protect their eyes from accidents with scissors and fasteners.*

- Help children determine where to make the hole in the second plate so that they can view the phases of the moon drawn on the first plate. You may want to demonstrate this.
- Demonstrate how to attach the two plates in the center with a fastener.
- Invite partners to take turns moving their plates and telling about the phases of the moon that appear.
- Ask questions such as these: **Is there really only part of a moon in the sky? Why do you say that? How long does it take for the moon to go through all its phases?**

Enrichment

Have children make up a story that includes the phases of the moon. Invite them to tell their stories to a friend, using the plate to demonstrate the phases.

Chapter 3 Skills Trace

Process Skills Development

	Observing	Collecting and Interpreting Data
Skill Introduced	xiv	xv
Skill Applied	C49 C52–C53	C52–C53
Skill Assessed	End Matter 6–7	End Matter 24–25

Chapter Review pages are also on the **Flip Chart.**

Chapter Assessment

Use a word from the box to finish each sentence.

crater solar system telescope phases orbit

1. The sun and planets are parts of the ________.
2. A ________ is a hole on the moon's surface.
3. The planets ________ the sun.
4. The different shapes of the moon are called ________.
5. Scientists use a ________ to study planets that are far away.

Write **Yes** or **No**.

6. ________ You have nighttime on the side of Earth facing the sun.
7. ________ The sun is always moving across the sky.
8. ________ It takes about one month to see all the phases of the moon.
9. ________ A telescope makes close things look far away.
10. ________ The sun is the center of our solar system.

Teacher's Assessment Package pp. 53–54

Assessment Rubric

	Phases of the Moon
4	Shows a good understanding of how the shape of the moon appears to change.
3	Shows a partial understanding of how the shape of the moon appears to change.
2	Has difficulty showing understanding of how the shape of the moon appears to change.
1	Shows no understanding of how the shape of the moon appears to change.

Review Organizer

Using Multiple Intelligences

The following activities can be used to assess children's understanding of Unit C concepts. Assign the activities based on each child's strongest learning modality. The following chart shows which intelligences are developed in each assessment option.

Activity	Intelligence
Make a backpack.	spatial
Talk to a friend.	bodily-kinesthetic
Write a postcard.	linguistic

Plan your adventure.

Unit Performance Review pages are also on the **Flip Chart.**

Have individuals or groups of children choose one or more of the following activities in which to participate. You may want to set aside a portion of one or more days when children can work on their projects and then present them to classmates.

Make a backpack.

Before children begin making their backpacks, encourage them to ask themselves questions such as: What clothes will I need? Will I need food and water? How long will I be gone? Suggest that they make a list of items they might need to include. After they have finished making the backpacks, encourage children to explain to others how their backpacks will be useful on their adventure.

Talk to a friend.

Children should choose places they might want to visit, either real or imaginary. Have them visualize themselves making this trip and imagine what they could see, smell, and hear. Have them think about land and water features in the places they plan to visit. Provide a play telephone for children to use as a prop when they talk to a friend.

Write a postcard.

Suggest that children think about what kind of weather they might experience on their adventure. Ask them in what season they will be traveling.

Unit C Performance Review

If you could go anywhere on the earth, where would you go? What if you could visit the sun, moon, and stars too? Think about an adventure you would like to have. Where could you go? What would you see?

Plan your adventure.

1. Pick a project to show something you have learned.
2. What steps will you follow to complete your project?
3. How will your project look when you finish it?

Make a backpack.

What will you take on your adventure? What clothes or gear will you need? Will you bring food? Make a backpack for your adventure. Make things to put inside. Show your classmates what is in your backpack. Tell how you will use these things.

Talk to a friend.

Pretend that you just got back from your adventure. Telephone a friend to describe the places you visited. Tell about land, water, and other things you saw. What else will you tell your friend about your adventure? What questions might your friend ask you?

Write a postcard.

Think of a place you visited on your adventure. What did you see? What was the weather like? What did you do? Write a postcard. Draw a picture on your postcard to go with your message.

C63

Assessment Rubric

	Make a backpack.	Talk to a friend.	Write a postcard.
4	Shows a good understanding of the earth and/or the solar system.	Shows a good understanding of land, water, and other features of the earth.	Shows a good understanding of something learned in earth science.
3	Shows a fair understanding of the earth and/or the solar system.	Shows a fair understanding of land, water, and other features of the earth.	Show a fair understanding of something learned in earth science.
2	Has difficulty showing an understanding of the earth and/or the solar system.	Has difficulty showing an understanding of land, water, and other features of the earth.	Has difficulty showing an understanding of something learned in earth science.
1	Is unable to show an understanding of the earth and/or the solar system.	Is unable to show an understanding of land, water, and other features of the earth.	Is unable to show an understanding of something learned in earth science.

Portfolio Assessment

Suggested items from this unit to include in children's portfolios are listed on the following pages in the Teacher's Assessment Package:

- Chapter 1: page 37
- Chapter 2: page 43
- Chapter 3: page 49

Unit C Performance Assessment

- The formal Performance Assessment for this unit is on pages 88A–88B of the Lab Manual Teacher's Edition.
- The student recording sheet for the formal Performance Assessment for this unit is on pages 89–90 of the Lab Manual, both in the Teacher's Edition and the Student Edition.

Writing Organizer

Objective
Write a persuasive advertisement.

Teaching Writing for Science

The Writing for Science page is also on the **Flip Chart.**

Explain to children that their purpose is to write sentences that persuade people to recycle. Point out that they will share their writing with classmates.

Writing an Ad

Guide children through the steps of the writing process.

1. **Prewrite** Think of reasons to recycle. How can you persuade people to recycle?
   Remind children that prewriting is getting ready to write. Help children list reasons to recycle, such as to conserve our natural resources and to keep from over-filling our landfills. You may want to model this stage of the process. Let children hear how you might select a topic. Then give them some ideas about how you might draw pictures and write sentences to convince people to recycle.
2. **Draft** Write an ad that will persuade people to recycle.
   Explain that the most important thing in this step is to get their ideas on paper. Emphasize that children's sentences must persuade the reader to recycle.
3. **Revise** Read your ad. Will it persuade people to recycle?
   Remind children that in this step, they should try to make their writing more clear and interesting to readers. They should try to make the ideas in their writing better.
4. **Edit** Check your writing to make sure it is correct. Make a neat copy.
   Remind children that they can correct errors in capitalization, spelling, and so on during this step. Encourage them to read their writing carefully to make sure others will be able to read it.
5. **Publish** Share your ad with others. Did you persuade them to recycle?
   Suggest that children display their ads on the wall. Have them read their ads to classmates. Encourage listeners to tell how the ad persuades someone to recycle.

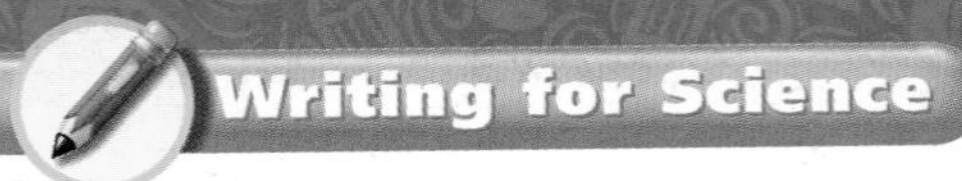

Writing an Ad

When you persuade people, you get them to do something. You can also persuade people that something is important. Write an ad to persuade people. Draw pictures and write sentences for your ad.

1. **Prewrite** Think of reasons to recycle. How can you persuade people to recycle?
2. **Draft** Write an ad that will persuade people to recycle.
3. **Revise** Read your ad. Will it persuade people to recycle?
4. **Edit** Check your writing to make sure it is correct. Make a neat copy.
5. **Publish** Share your ad with others. Did you persuade them to recycle?

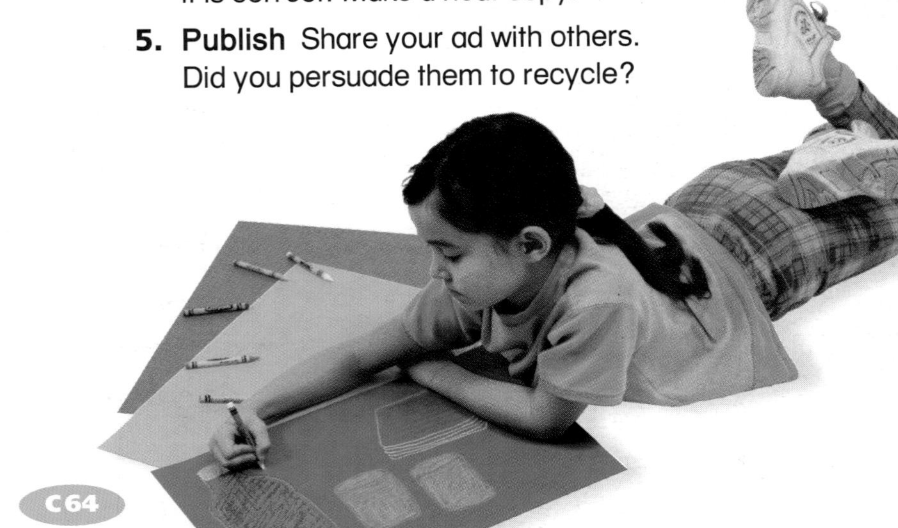

C64

Writing Rubric

	4	3	2	1
Follows steps of writing process in order				
Communicates specific details and information				
Includes ideas related to topic				
Writes clear sentences				
Uses correct capitalization				

Scoring Key **Total Score** ______
4 points correct, complete, detailed
3 points partially correct, complete, detailed
2 points partially correct, partially complete, lacks some detail
1 point incorrect or incomplete, needs assistance

Technology

Children can share their persuasive advertisements at **www.sfscience.com.**

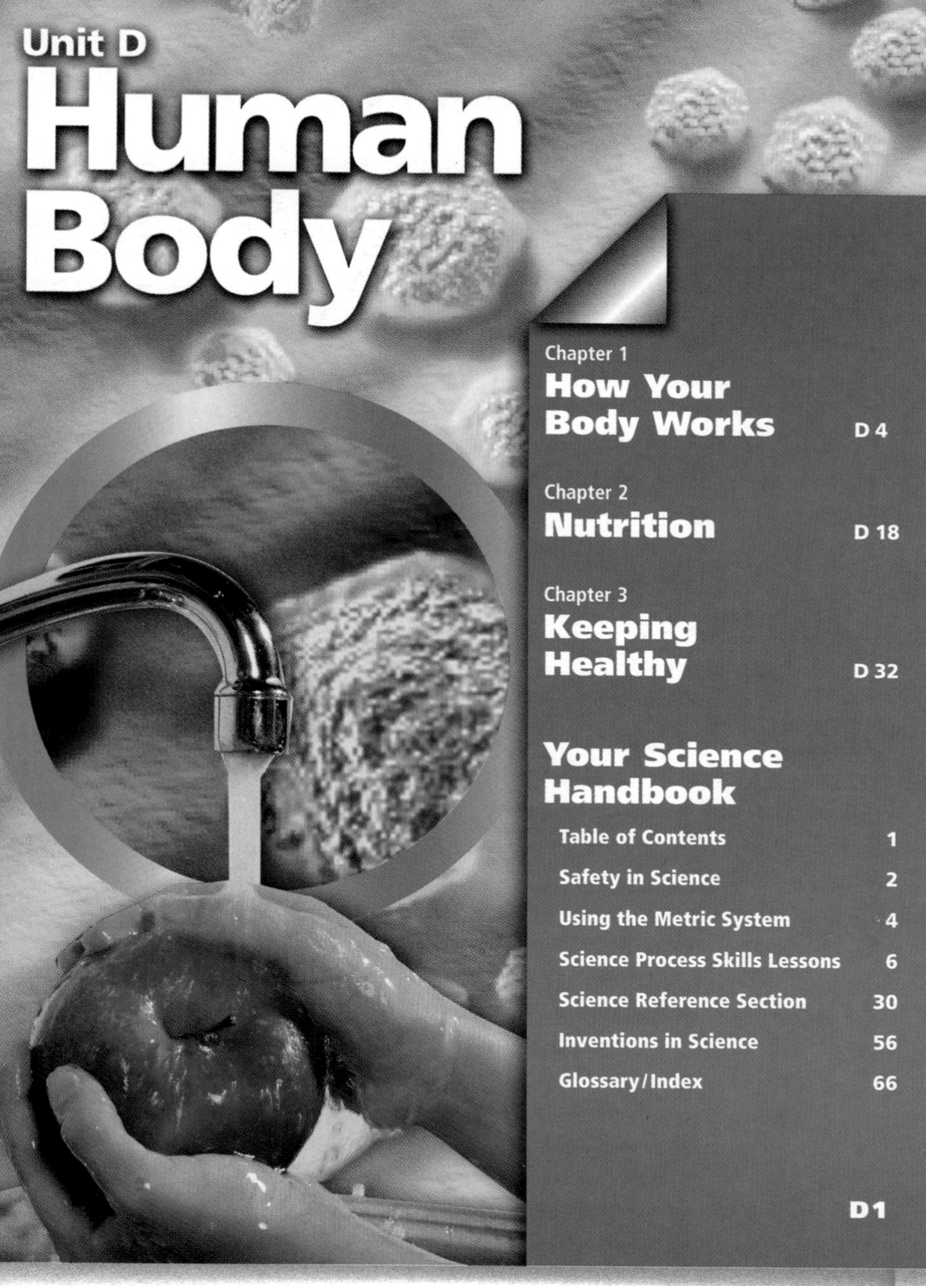
Unit D

Human Body

D1

Science Background

What Is Health and the Human Body? Health and the human body is the study of how are bodies work and how to take care of our bodies. For young children this means exploring some body organs and systems and ways to keep them healthy through rest, exercise, and food. Health and the human body can help answer such questions as these: Why do the heart and lungs work together? What happens to food when you eat it? How much exercise do you need?

About the Photograph The photograph on this page shows an apple. Point out that fruits such as apples, are an important part of a healthful diet. Ask children to tell about foods they like. Tell children they will learn more about foods that contribute to good health in Chapter 2, "Nutrition."

Technology

You can use the **Teacher's Resource Planner** to plan and organize your curriculum.

In This Unit

In this unit, children learn how their bodies work and how to keep them healthy. They experiment with lung capacity and exercise. They discover which foods are healthful and how food is digested. They learn how to take care of and keep their bodies clean.

Books for Teachers

Chapter 1

The Body Book by Sara Bonnett Stein. Photos, diagrams, and text detail many of the body's functions and processes. (Workman Publishing Company, ISBN 0-89480-805-2)

Blood and Guts: A Working Guide to Your Own Insides by Linda Allison. Interesting facts and simple experiments to investigate the human body. (Little, Brown, ISBN 0-316-03443-6)

Chapter 2

Bones, Bodies, and Bellies by Diane Vaszily and Peggy Perdue. Interactive hands-on activities to help children learn about anatomy, physiology, and nutrition. (Good Year Books, ISBN 0-673-36034-2)

The Incredible Human Body Primary Science Resource Guide by Ilene L. Follman. Activities to help children learn about the human body. Also included are overhead transparencies. (Milliken, ISBN 0-7877-0036-3)

Chapter 3

Primary Health and Safety Curriculum by Max Fischer. Background information, hands-on activities, and suggestions for curriculum integration on topics such as nutrition, safety, and personal hygiene. Reproducible worksheets are included. (Instructional Fair, ISBN 1-56822-289-0)

The Safe & Sound Child by Larry Stone, Leslie Stone, and Laurie Levy. A safety handbook to help adults keep children safe both inside and outside the home. (Good Year Books, ISBN 0-673-36243-4)

Chapter Concepts/ National Science Education Standards	Lessons/Vocabulary

Chapter 1

How Your Body Works p. D4

Concepts The brain sends messages to all parts of the body so they work together properly. Your lungs take air that contains oxygen into your body. Your heart pumps blood to every part of your body. The blood is pumped away from the heart in arteries and carried back to the heart in veins. You can measure lung power by timing how long you can blow bubbles. You can experiment to determine that exercise increases the heart rate.

National Science Education Standards

Content Standard F, p. 138

- **Personal health**

Lesson 1 *What does the brain do? p. D6*
Vocabulary brain, nerves

Reading for Science *Reading Labels p. D8*

Lesson 2 *What do the heart and lungs do? p. D10*
Vocabulary lungs, heart, arteries, veins

Lesson 3 *How long can you blow bubbles? p. D12*

Lesson 4 *Experiment with exercise. p. D14*

Chapter 2

Nutrition p. D18

Concepts Food gives you energy. You need to eat the proper foods to be healthy. Food samples can be tested for fat content. Digestion begins in the mouth. The teeth and tongue break down and mix the food, and the saliva makes the food wet. The digestive system includes the esophagus, stomach, small intestine, and large intestine. Food must be digested so that nutrients can be used by the body.

National Science Education Standards

Content Standard F, p. 138

- **Personal health**

Reading for Science *Using a Diagram p. D20*

Lesson 1 *What foods help you stay healthy? p. D22*
Vocabulary Food Guide Pyramid

Lesson 2 *Which foods will leave a greasy spot? p. D24*

Lesson 3 *What happens when you chew? p. D26*
Vocabulary digestion

Lesson 4 *How is food digested? p. D28*
Vocabulary esophagus, small intestine, nutrients, large intestine

Chapter 3

Keeping Healthy p. D32

Concepts To be healthy, the body needs exercise. Exercise keeps your muscles strong and heart and lungs healthy. Keeping a record of daily exercise reminds you of how much and what kind of exercise you do. Germs are tiny living things that can make you sick. A healthful diet, exercise, and good hygiene habits are important ways to take care of yourself.

National Science Education Standards

Content Standard F, p. 138

- **Personal health**

Lesson 1 *Why is exercise important? p. D34*
Vocabulary exercise

Math in Science *Using a Calendar p. D36*

Lesson 2 *How much exercise do you get? p. D38*

Lesson 3 *Why is it important to keep clean? p. D40*
Vocabulary germs

Lesson 4 *How can you take care of yourself? p. D42*

Unit D Assessment

Unit Performance Review pp. D46–D47

Writing for Science p. D48

Activity Opportunities		Assessment Opportunities	
Student Edition • **Explore Activity** ***Play a catching game.*** p. D7 • **Investigate Activity** ***How long can you blow bubbles?*** pp. D12–D13 • **Experiment Activity** ***Experiment with exercise.*** pp. D14–D15 **Flip Chart** • **Science Center Explore Activity** *Play a brain game.*	**Teacher's Edition** • Activity Idea Bank, pp. D15a–D15b **Additional Resources** • Family Activity, Instructional Resources Package, pp. 73–74 • Vocabulary Preview, Instructional Resources Package, p. 75 • Graphic Organizer, Teacher's Assessment Package, p. 57 • Lab Manual, pp. 91, 92, 93–94, 95 • Interactive Transparency 10, Interactive Transparency Package • Wall Chart, pp. 49, 50, 51, 52 **Technology** • *Human Body* National Lab **www.sfscience.com**	**Student Edition** • Lesson 1 Review, p. D7 • Lesson 2 Review, p. D11 • Chapter 1 Review, pp. D16–D17 **Teacher's Edition** • Process Skills Development, pp. D5 & D17 • Assessment Rubric, p. D17	**Teacher's Assessment Package** • Chapter 1 Review, p. 58 • Chapter 1 Assessment, pp. 59–60 • Portfolio Ideas, p. 55 **Lab Manual** • Activity Rubric, pp. T31, T32, T33 **Technology** • **Practice & Assessment CD-ROM** • **Production Studio** • **The KnowZone™ at www.kz.com** • **TestWorks™**
Student Edition • **Explore Activity** ***Make a Food Guide Pyramid.*** p. D23 • **Investigate Activity** ***Which foods will leave a greasy spot?*** pp. D24–D25 • **Explore Activity** ***Observe how food can be changed.*** p. D27 **Flip Chart** • **Science Center Explore Activity** *Play Healthful Foods Bingo.* • **Science Center Explore Activity** *Measure the small intestine.*	**Teacher's Edition** • Activity Idea Bank, pp. D25a–D25b, D29a–D29b **Additional Resources** • Family Activity, Instructional Resources Package, pp. 81–82 • Vocabulary Preview, Instructional Resources Package, p. 83 • Graphic Organizer, Teacher's Assessment Package, p. 63 • Lab Manual, pp. 97, 99, 100, 101, 103 • Interactive Transparency 11, Interactive Transparency Package • Wall Chart, pp. 53, 54, 55, 56, 57 **Technology** • *Human Body* National Lab **www.sfscience.com**	**Student Edition** • Lesson 1 Review, p. D23 • Lesson 3 Review, p. D27 • Lesson 4 Review, p. D29 • Chapter 2 Review, pp. D30–D31 **Teacher's Edition** • Process Skills Development, pp. D19 & D31 • Assessment Rubric, p. D31	**Teacher's Assessment Package** • Chapter 2 Review, p. 64 • Chapter 2 Assessment, pp. 65–66 • Portfolio Ideas, p. 61 **Lab Manual** • Activity Rubric, pp. T33, T34, T35 **Technology** • **Practice & Assessment CD-ROM** • **Production Studio** • **The KnowZone™ at www.kz.com** • **TestWorks™**
Student Edition • **Explore Activity** ***Do exercises.*** p. D35 • **Investigate Activity** ***How much exercise do you get?*** pp. D38–D39 **Flip Chart** • **Science Center Explore Activity** *Stay fit.* • **Science Center Explore Activity** *Make a diorama.*	**Teacher's Edition** • Activity Idea Bank, pp. D39a–D39b, D43a–D43b **Additional Resources** • Family Activity, Instructional Resources Package, pp. 89–90 • Vocabulary Preview, Instructional Resources Package, p. 91 • Graphic Organizer, Teacher's Assessment Package, p. 69 • Lab Manual, pp. 105, 106, 107, 108 • Interactive Transparency 12, Interactive Transparency Package • Wall Chart, pp. 58, 59, 60, 61, 62 **Technology** • *Human Body* National Lab **www.sfscience.com**	**Student Edition** • Lesson 1 Review, p. D35 • Lesson 3 Review, p. D41 • Lesson 4 Review, p. D43 • Chapter 3 Review, pp. D44–D45 **Teacher's Edition** • Process Skills Development, pp. D33 & D45 • Assessment Rubric, p. D45	**Teacher's Assessment Package** • Chapter 3 Review, p. 70 • Chapter 3 Assessment, pp. 71–72 • Portfolio Ideas, p. 67 **Lab Manual** • Activity Rubric, pp. T36, T37 **Technology** • **Practice & Assessment CD-ROM** • **Production Studio** • **The KnowZone™ at www.kz.com** • **TestWorks™**
		Student Edition • Unit D Performance Review, pp. D46–D47 **Teacher's Edition** • Assessment Rubric, p. D47	**Technology** • *Writing for Science* **www.sfscience.com**

Activity Organizer

Objective
Experiment to find out the best way to clean an object.

Process Skills predicting, observing

Parallel Student Book Lesson
Chapter 3, Lesson 3

Materials spoons, cheese spread, water, brush, rag, soap, baking soda

EXTENDED INQUIRY

What is the best way to clean something?

The following activity is a model of an inquiry-based science fair project for you to do with the class. A list suggesting individual science projects follows the activity. Use these steps of scientific inquiry.

Steps

1 Ask a question about objects, organisms, and events in the environment.

- Pose the following question to children: **Which materials work best to clean an object?**
- Have children choose several materials that can be used to clean an object. Then ask children to predict the best way to clean a spoon that has cheese spread caked on it.

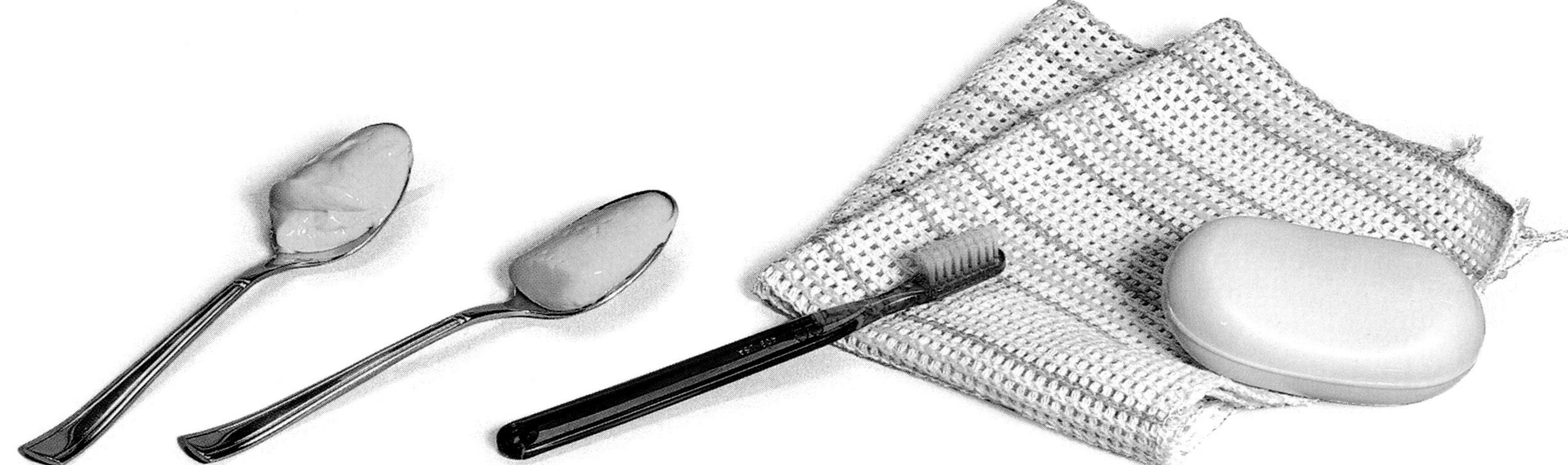

2 Plan and conduct a simple investigation.

- Have children coat several spoons with cheese spread. Children should compare the covered spoons to make sure they are as identical as possible.
- Let the spoons sit out overnight.
- The next day have children try various methods to clean the spoons, such as rinsing in water, scrubbing with a brush and water, scrubbing with soap and water, rubbing with a cloth, using baking soda, and so on.
- Have children compare the condition of the spoons.

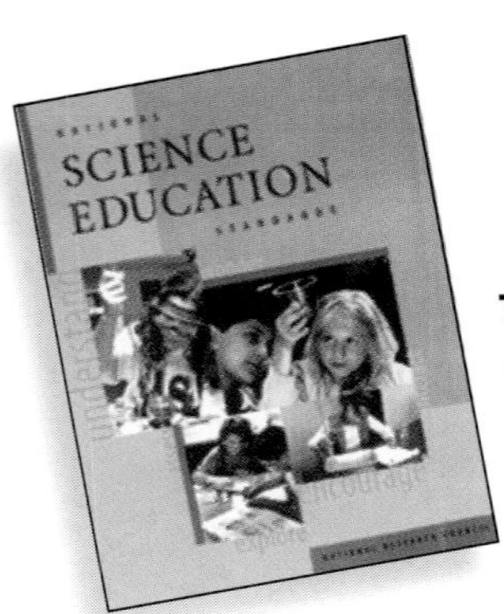

This activity follows methods of scientific inquiry suggested in the National Science Education Standards.

3 Employ simple equipment and tools to gather data and extend the senses.

To show what material works best to clean the spoons, children may want to:

- create an audiotape describing ways they cleaned the spoons and the results
- draw and label pictures showing before and after conditions of the spoons cleaned with various materials
- make a chart comparing the results of cleaning the spoons with different materials

How I cleaned the spoon	Is the spoon clean?
rinsed in water	no
with a rag and water	part clean
with a rag and soap and water	yes
with a brush and water	part clean
with a brush and soap and water	yes

4 Use data to construct a reasonable explanation.

- Ask: **Which method(s) cleaned the spoons? Which method(s) cleaned the spoons better than others?** (*Possible answers: Using water and a brush or cloth cleaned the spoons; using soap and water with a brush or cloth cleaned them better.*)

5 Communicate investigations and explanations.

- Have children discuss their observations. Children should conclude that although rinsing helps wash away some of the cheese spread, rubbing or brushing does a better job, and rubbing or brushing with soap does an even better job.

Inquire Further

Ask children if they think the results would be the same if they had a different substance on the spoons. Have them repeat the experiment using different substances.

Science Fair Projects

Chapter 1 Data Collection
Have children select a simple activity such as cutting, writing their name, or brushing their teeth. Have them record which hand they normally use to do the activity and then do it for a week using the other hand. Children can observe and record the ease or difficulty with which they accomplish the task over the course of the week. At the end of the week they can interpret their data and share their findings.

Chapter 2 Food Display Have children use the Food Guide Pyramid to plan a day's meals including breakfast, lunch, dinner, and snacks. Then have them create a display of the meals using clean, empty food packages, wrappers, or magazine cutouts.

Chapter 3 Good Health Game
Have children develop a game or obstacle course that will provide them with exercise, or a board game with a health-related theme.

Technology

Children can participate in the Human Body extended inquiry *National Lab* at **www.sfscience.com.**

Unit Overview

Teaching Science and Technology

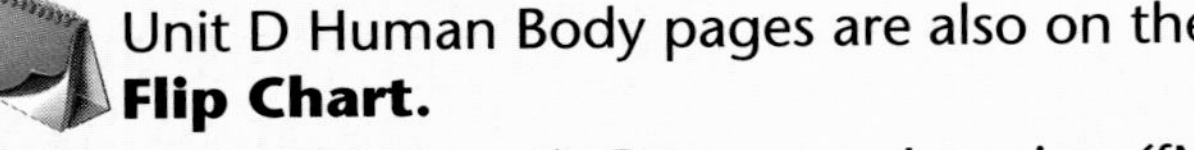

Unit D Human Body pages are also on the **Flip Chart.**

- Functional Magnetic Resonance Imaging (fMRI) uses a magnet to get impulses from a person's body. A computer analyzes the impulses and displays an image. The MRI allows doctors and scientists to study the brain and other parts of the body without surgery.
- The rind, pulp, and membranes of oranges and grapefruits used to make juice are used as cattle feed or thrown away. They are rich in dietary fiber and other nutrients. When used as a supplement to other flours, like wheat flour, citrus fiber can keep bread fresher longer and add important nutrients and fiber to the product.
- The name of this traveling exhibit is *Microbes: Invisible Invaders . . . Amazing Allies.* Visitors to the exhibit will be able to interact with 13 displays that use holograms, 3-D animation, and other high-tech toys.

Science and Technology In Your World!

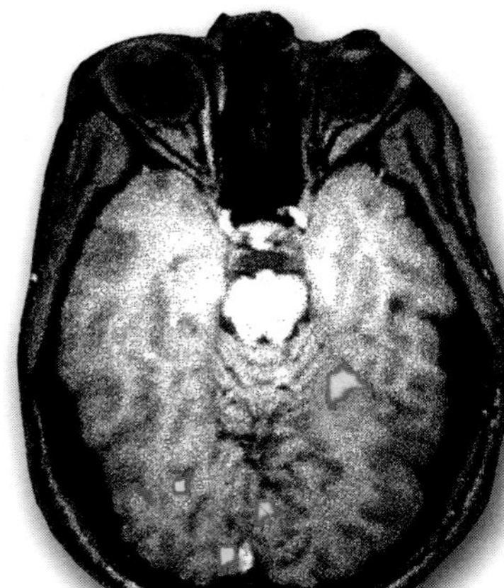

How can scientists see the brain at work?

A special machine takes pictures of the brain. The pictures show what happens in the brain as a person thinks, learns, and remembers.

Chapter 1
The Human Body

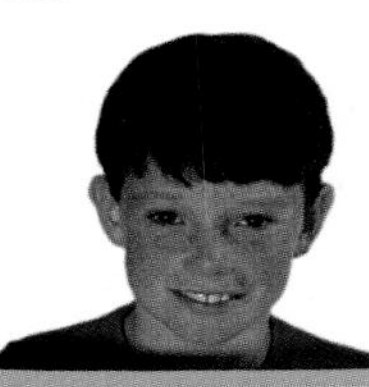

Scientists can make flour from fruits.

They use the pulp and rind. This flour has vitamins, minerals, and fiber that are important for a person's diet.

Chapter 2
Nutrition

D2

Writing for Science

Expository-Classificatory

Write a Paragraph

Invite children to write one or two paragraphs comparing how they feel and look when they are germ-free and well with how they feel and look when they have been exposed to germs and become ill. Remind children to follow the steps of the writing process: prewrite, draft, revise, edit, publish.

The Writing Process

The Writing Process

1. Prewrite
   - Talk with another person about things you can write about.
   - Choose one thing and draw a picture of it.
2. Draft
   Write sentences about your picture.
3. Revise
   Read what you wrote. Do you like it? Make changes if you want to.
4. Edit
   Check your writing to make sure it is correct. Make a neat copy.
5. Publish
   Share your picture and your writing with others.

Instructional Resources p. xi

A special exhibit is visiting science museums.

The exhibit has pictures made with light, models that move, and unusual kinds of toys. The exhibit helps people learn about germs.

Chapter 3
Keeping Healthy

D3

INQUIRY

One aspect of inquiry involves asking questions. Give each child three index cards, one for each chapter in this unit. After they read the Science and Technology pages, have children write one question about each chapter. Throughout each chapter, children should use their text and other resources to look for the answer to their question. At the conclusion of each chapter, children should share the answer to their question with the class.

Math-Science Connection

Charts and Graphs

Call children's attention to the fruit used as a flour supplement. Then ask children to name their favorite fruits. Create a list of the fruits they name, poll the class, and place a tally mark next to each fruit name to show how many children like that fruit. Have children count the tallies to determine which fruit is the class favorite. Help children create a graph with the information and interpret the graph. Ask questions such as these: **How many children like apples best? Do more children like apples or peaches? How many more?**

Lesson/Activity and Flip Chart	Objectives/Process Skills	Time Options/Activity Materials
Chapter Opener Student Edition pp. D4–D5 and **Flip Chart** ***Always Working***		**Have less time?** Use the Graphic Organizer on Teacher's Assessment Package p. 57 for an overview of the lessons. Use the Flip Chart to teach lesson concepts and science activities. **Have more time?** Use the Flip Chart to reinforce and extend lesson concepts and activities. Use the Cross-Curricular Options in the Activity Idea Bank on Teacher's Edition p. D15b.
Lesson 1 Student Edition pp. D6–D7 ***What does the brain do?*** **Explore Activity** ***Play a catching game.*** **Flip Chart** *Talk About Science*	**Objective** Describe the functions of the brain. **Process Skills** collecting and interpreting data	**Kit Items** none **School-Supplied Items** ruler
Reading for Science Student Edition pp. D8–D9 ***Reading Labels***	**Objective** Read labels.	
Lesson 2 Student Edition pp. D10–D11 ***What do the heart and lungs do?*** **Flip Chart** *Talk About Science*	**Objective** Describe the functions of the heart and lungs.	**Have more time?** Use the following teaching guide option: Interactive Transparency 10, Interactive Transparency Package
Lesson 3 Student Edition pp. D12–D13 and **Flip Chart** **Investigate Activity** ***How long can you blow bubbles?***	**Objective** Measure lung capacity by blowing bubbles. **Process Skills** predicting, collecting and interpreting data	**Kit Items** 9-ounce plastic cup, clear plastic straw **School-Supplied Items** water, clock with a second hand
Lesson 4 Student Edition pp. D14–D15 and **Flip Chart** **Experiment Activity** ***Experiment with exercise.***	**Objective** Experiment to determine pulse rate before and after exercising. **Process Skills** experimenting, estimating and measuring (*formulating hypotheses, identifying and controlling variables, collecting and interpreting data*)	
Activity Idea Bank Teacher's Edition pp. D15a–D15b **Flip Chart** **Science Center Explore Activity** ***Play a brain game.***	**Objective** Demonstrate how the body responds to messages from the brain. **Process Skills** communicating	**Kit Items** none **School-Supplied Items** none
Chapter Review Student Edition pp. D16–D17 and **Flip Chart**		**Kit Items** none **School-Supplied Items** paper, crayons

Lesson/Activity and Flip Chart	Additional Resources		Technology
Chapter Opener Student Edition pp. D4–D5 and **Flip Chart** ***Always Working***	**Teacher's Assessment Package** • Graphic Organizer, p. 57 **Instructional Resources** • Family Activity, pp. 73–74 • Vocabulary Preview, p. 75	**Songs & Activities Package** • *Always Working*, pp. 27–28 **Wall Chart,** p. 49	**Practice & Assessment CD-ROM** **AudioText** **Production Studio** **www.sfscience.com** **Songs & Activities Package** **Teacher's Resource Planner CD-ROM**
Lesson 1 Student Edition pp. D6–D7 ***What does the brain do?*** **Explore Activity** ***Play a catching game.*** **Flip Chart** ***Talk About Science***	**Lab Manual** • Lab Manual, p. 91 • Activity Rubric, p. T31	**Teacher Demonstration Kit** **Wall Chart,** p. 50	
Reading for Science Student Edition pp. D8–D9 ***Reading Labels***	**Instructional Resources** • Reading for Science, p. 76		
Lesson 2 Student Edition pp. D10–D11 ***What do the heart and lungs do?*** **Flip Chart** ***Talk About Science***	**Interactive Transparency Package** • Interactive Transparency 10	**Wall Chart,** p. 51	
Lesson 3 Student Edition pp. D12–D13 and **Flip Chart** **Investigate Activity** ***How long can you blow bubbles?***	**Lab Manual** • Lab Manual, p. 92 • Activity Rubric, p. T32	**Teacher Demonstration Kit** **Wall Chart,** p. 52	*Human Body* **Activity Video**
Lesson 4 Student Edition pp. D14–D15 and **Flip Chart** **Experiment Activity** ***Experiment with exercise.***	**Lab Manual** • Lab Manual, pp. 93–94 • Activity Rubric, p. T32	**Teacher Demonstration Kit**	*Human Body* **Activity Video**
Activity Idea Bank Teacher's Edition pp. D15a–D15b **Flip Chart** **Science Center Explore Activity** ***Play a brain game.***	**Lab Manual** • Lab Manual, p. 95 • Activity Rubric, p. T33		
Chapter Review Student Edition pp. D16–D17 and **Flip Chart**	**Teacher's Assessment Package** • Chapter 1 Assessment, pp. 59–60		**Practice & Assessment CD-ROM** **Production Studio** **The KnowZone™ at www.kz.com** **TestWorks™**

Lab Manual

What does the brain do?

Did you catch the ruler?
Write Yes or No each time.

The results of each student's trials will vary.

Trial #1	
Trial #2	
Trial #3	
Trial #4	
Trial #5	

How many times did you catch the ruler? ______

Lab Manual
p. 91

Reading for Science

Reading Labels

Look at this picture. Add labels for the brain and the nerves.

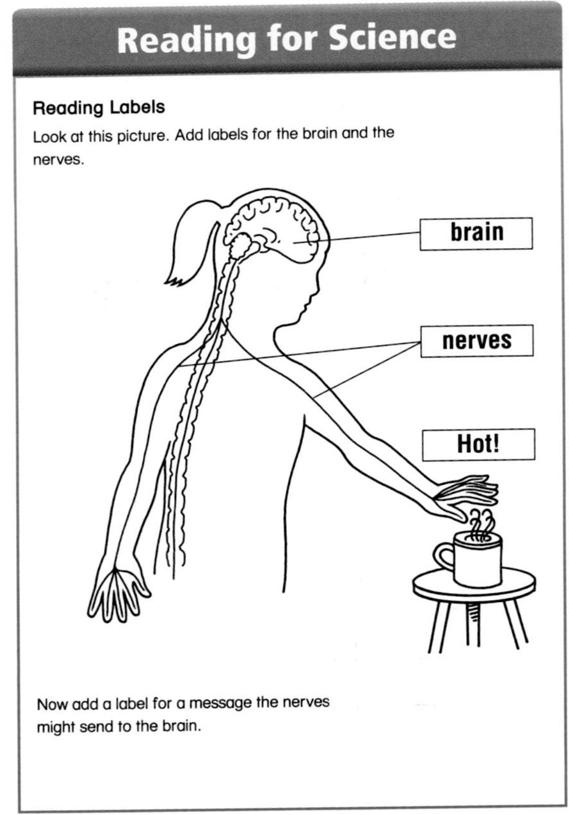

Now add a label for a message the nerves might send to the brain.

Instructional Resources
p. 76

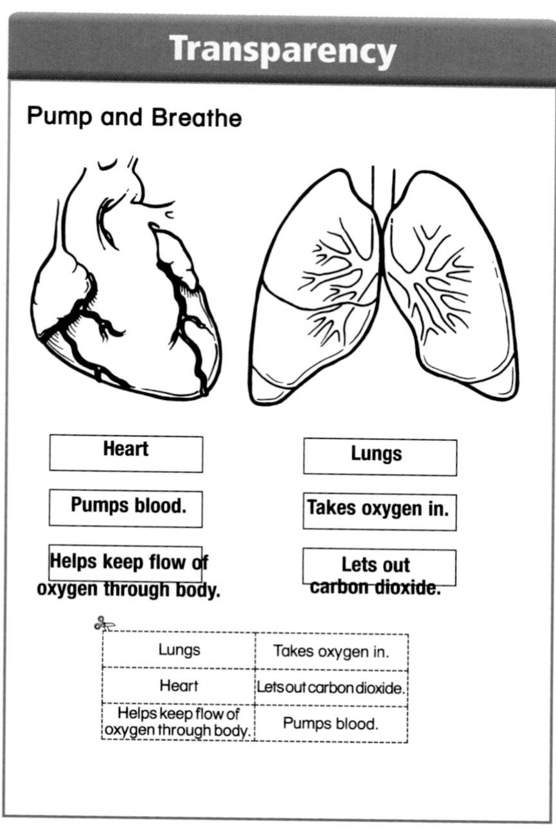
Transparency
Pump and Breathe
Heart
Lungs
Pumps blood.
Takes oxygen in.
Helps keep flow of oxygen through body.
Lets out carbon dioxide.
Lungs
Takes oxygen in.
Heart
Lets out carbon dioxide.
Helps keep flow of oxygen through body.
Pumps blood.

Interactive Transparency Package
Transparency 10

Lab Manual

How long can you blow bubbles?

Students' predictions about how long they can blow bubbles will vary. Students should record the number of seconds with the help of a partner.

I think I can blow bubbles for ____________ seconds.

Draw the hand that shows seconds for when you start and when you stop.

Start

Stop

I blew bubbles for ____________ seconds.

Lab Manual
p. 92

Lab Manual

Experiment with exercise.

Problem

How does exercise affect your heart rate?

Give Your Hypotheses

How will your heart rate change when you exercise?
Write what you think.

Control the Variables

Make sure you measure your heart rate for the same amount of time before and after running.

Test Your Hypothesis

Measure your heart rate.

Collect Your Data

Students' hypotheses will vary but most will probably indicate that the heart rate will increase after exercise. Their measurements will vary. Their conclusions should relate to their data.

Activity	Heart beats
Sitting	______ in 30 seconds
After running	______ in 30 seconds

Lab Manual
p. 93

Lab Manual

Tell Your Conclusion

How does exercise affect your heart rate?

Inquire Further

If you exercised for more than one minute, how would this affect your heart rate?

Lab Manual
p. 94

Lab Manual

Play a brain game.

Choose one command you followed.
Draw what you did.

Students' drawings will vary.

Lab Manual
p. 95

Chapter 1 Assessment

Choose a word from the box to finish each sentence.

brain	lungs	arteries	nerves

1. Your brain sends messages to your body through your **nerves**.
2. Your **lungs** take oxygen into your body when you breathe.
3. Your blood is pumped away from your heart in **arteries**.
4. Your **brain** controls what your body does.

Circle the correct answer.

5. How can you check your heart rate?
   (measure your pulse) breathe in and out
6. When does your body get oxygen?
   (when you breathe in) when you breathe out
7. When is your pulse rate higher?
   when you are sleeping (when you are jumping rope)

Teacher's Assessment Package
p. 59

Chapter 1 Assessment

Use this diagram to answer the questions below.

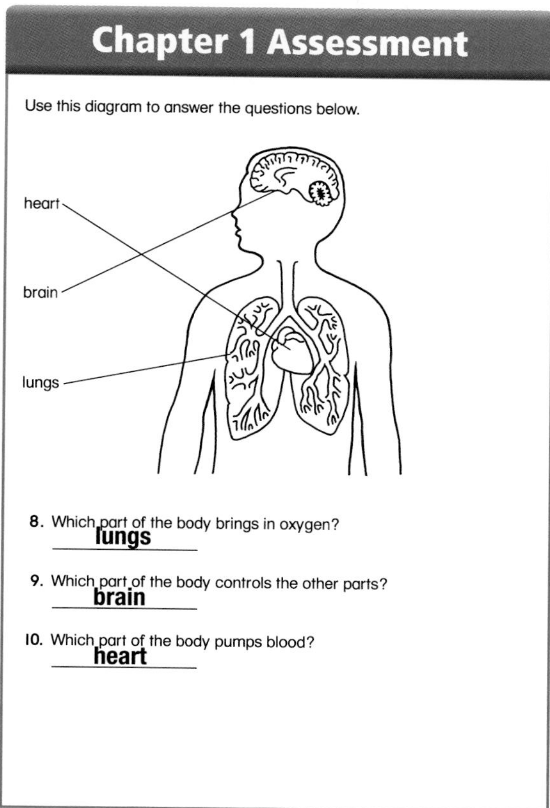

8. Which part of the body brings in oxygen? **lungs**
9. Which part of the body controls the other parts? **brain**
10. Which part of the body pumps blood? **heart**

Teacher's Assessment Package
p. 60

Table of Contents

Introducing the Chapter

The song *Always Working* also is on the **Flip Chart.**

- Have children walk quickly in place for one minute. Then ask: **What happened to your heart rate? To your breathing? Did you notice any changes to your body?**
- Distribute the Family Activity blackline master page.

Singing the Song

Have children sing the song *Always Working* on side 2 of the CTW cassette. Distribute pages 27–28 from the CTW Song Activity Book.

Reading Assist *Action Words*

Write the word *working* on the chalkboard. Have a volunteer use *working* in a sentence. Have children find other words in the song that have the *-ing* ending and that show action now. (*pumping, thinking, breathing*) Invite children to use these words in sentences.

Vocabulary Preview

Use the Vocabulary Preview blackline master to introduce the vocabulary words for this chapter.

Lesson 1 brain, nerves

Lesson 2 lungs, heart, arteries, veins

Chapter 1

How Your Body Works

Always Working

Sing to the tune of *Polly Wolly Doodle.*

Oh, your brain and nerves work together so hard.
They never stop, they're working all day.
Your nerves tell your brain what's going on.
And it makes decisions right away.

D4

Technology

Practice & Assessment CD-ROM

AudioText

Production Studio

www.sfscience.com

Teacher's Resource Planner

Songs & Activities Package

CTW Song & Activity

Body Trivia Game

1. Cut out the cards.
2. Pick a card. Ask another player the question.
3. If the answer is correct, he or she scores the points shown on the card.
4. Take turns. The first player to score 6 points wins.

Question: Name at least 3 things your brain does for you. *Answer:* The brain helps you move, feel, learn, remember, think. *3 points*	*Question:* How do messages travel to your brain? *Answer:* Nerves send messages to and from your brain. *2 points*	*Question:* What takes air into your body? *Answer:* your lungs *2 points*
Question: What gas is contained in air that your body needs? *Answer:* oxygen *1 point*	*Question:* What pumps blood to every part of your body? *Answer:* your heart *2 points*	*Question:* What does your blood pick up in your lungs? *Answer:* oxygen *1 point*
Question: What are the tubes called that carry blood away from your heart? *Answer:* arteries *2 points*	*Question:* What are the tubes called that carry blood to your heart? *Answer:* veins *2 points*	*Question:* How does exercise effect your heart rate? *Answer:* It makes your heart beat faster. *2 points*

Songs & Activities Package pp. 27–28

When you breathe your lungs go right to work.
Air comes in, then out it goes.
While your heart keeps working by pumping your blood
From your head down to your toes.

Never stops.
Always works.
It's amazing what your body can do.
Always working, always thinking,
Always breathing, always pumping,
All together, working hard for you!

Original lyrics by Gerri Brioso and Richard Freitas.
Produced by Children's Television Workshop.

D5

INQUIRY

Use a KWL chart at the beginning of each chapter to encourage inquiry. In the *K* column, record what children *know* about the human body. In the *W* column, list what they *want* to know. Throughout the chapter, ask children what they have *learned* and record their responses in the *L* column. A KWL chart is available on **Wall Chart** page 49.

Chapter 1 Skills Trace

Process Skills Development

	Collecting and Interpreting Data	Predicting	Experimenting	Estimating and Measuring
Skill Introduced	xv	xv	xv	xiv
Skill Applied	D7 D12–D13	D12–D13	D14–D15	D14–D15
Skill Assessed	End Matter 24–25	End Matter 16–17	End Matter 28–29	End Matter 12–13

Family Activity

Dear Family:
Our class is starting Chapter 1. We will be learning about the brain, heart, and lungs. These are the main ideas for Chapter 1.

- Nerves transmit messages to and from the brain to parts of the body.
- The lungs take air into the body.
- The heart pumps blood to every part of the body.
- Blood is pumped away from the heart in arteries. It travels back to the heart in veins.

We will also be learning science vocabulary words for Chapter 1. By the end of Chapter 1, we will be able to read the vocabulary words and tell what they mean.

Word Bank
brain
nerves
lungs
heart
arteries
veins

Home Projects
Here are some activities that will help your child understand the main ideas in Chapter 1. The activities are easy, fast, and fun.

Activities
- When you and your child do an active chore such as sweeping the floor or raking leaves, check your pulse rates before you start. To check your pulse, find a pulse point at your wrist and touch it gently with two fingers. Count the number of beats in a one-minute period. Compare the rates before and after exercising.

Instructional Resources pp. 73–74

Vocabulary Preview

brain	nerves
lungs	heart
arteries	veins
collect data	experiment

Instructional Resources p. 75

"Seeing" from ***You Can't Smell a Flower With Your Ear***
by Joanna Cole.
Easy-to-understand information and simple activities to help children understand how their eyes help them see.
(Grosset & Dunlap, ISBN 0-448-40469-9)

Lesson Organizer

Objective
Describe the functions of the brain.

Vocabulary brain, nerves

Process Skills collecting and interpreting data

Materials
Kit Items none

School-Supplied Items ruler

Additional Resources
- Lab Manual
- Teacher Demonstration Kit
- Wall Chart

Introduce

Activate Prior Knowledge
Invite children to sing and perform *The Hokey Pokey.* Ask: **What parts of your body did you use to sing and move? How did your body know what to do?**

Language Development *Make a Chart*
Invite children to brainstorm a list of things they tell their bodies to do, such as pick up a glass, as well as a list of things their bodies do without them really thinking about it, such as breathing. Use **Wall Chart** page 50 to record their responses.

Flip Chart
Discuss what the girl in the picture is doing. Ask: **What message is the brain sending?**

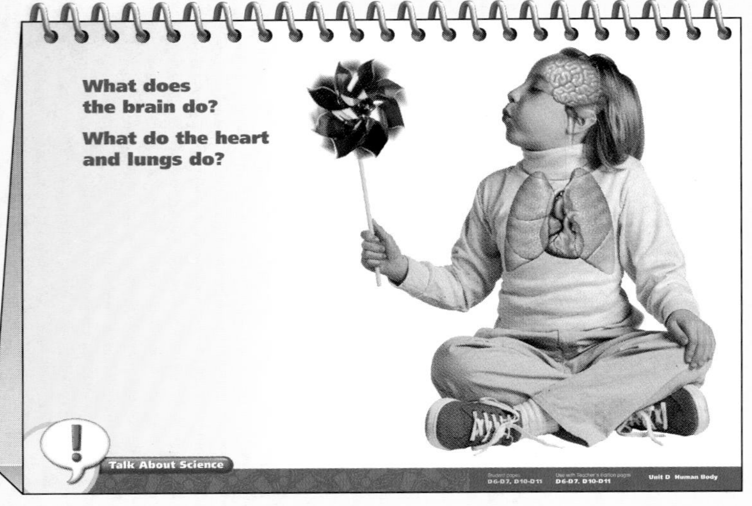

What does the brain do?
What do the heart and lungs do?
Talk About Science
Unit D Human Body

What does the brain do?

Imagine a ball coming your way. You run, reach out your arm, and try to catch it!

Your **brain** controls what your body does. You use your brain to move, think, feel, and remember.

Your brain sends and receives messages through your nerves. **Nerves** are the pathways that lead to and from your brain. They go through your whole body.

When you see, hear, feel, taste, or touch something, this information travels through your nerves to your brain. Your brain sends messages to the other parts of your body.

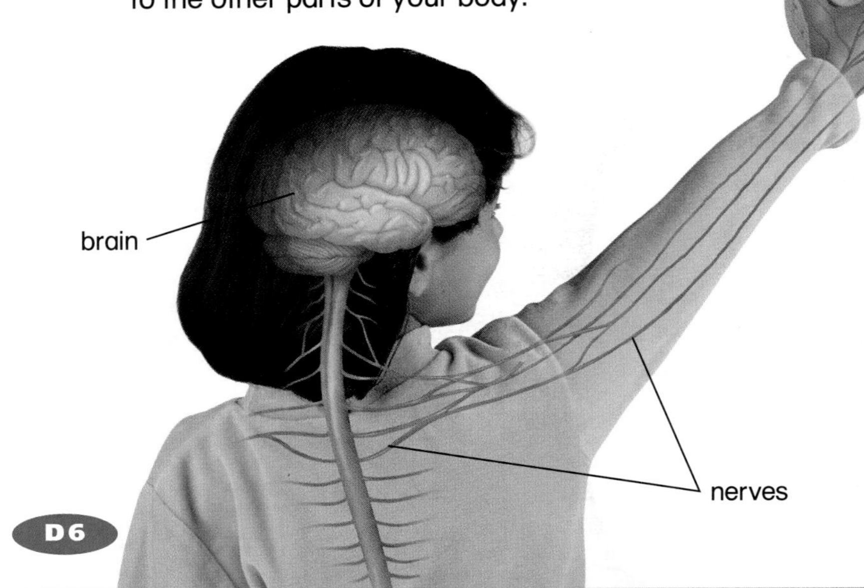

Science Background

- There are many parts to the brain. The medulla oblongata controls the rates of breathing and heartbeat, the cerebellum coordinates muscular activity, and the hypothalamus is the center of hunger and thirst.
- The largest part of the human brain is the cerebrum. All conscious activity, such as voluntary movement, feeling pain, dreaming, feelings, and thought, occurs here.

Science Across Cultures Among certain Southeast Asian groups, the head should not be patted or touched because it is considered the place of knowledge.

Play a catching game.

Materials

ruler

Process Skills

- collecting and interpreting data

Process Skills

Steps

1. Work with a partner. Take turns.
2. Have your partner hold the ruler above your fingers and then drop it.
3. Try to catch the ruler between your thumb and index finger.
4. Do this activity five times. How many times were you able to catch the ruler? Collect and record your data.

Share. Tell what happened.

Lesson Review

1. What does the brain do?
2. What are nerves?
3. **Tell** what your brain has to do to help you catch the ruler.

D7

Teach and Apply

Student Page D6

Give children the following directions: **Clap your hands; pull your ear; rub your tummy.** Ask: **How did you know what to do?** Help children realize that their brains control what their bodies do.

Reading Assist *Vocabulary*

Explain that *nerves* send messages from the brain to the body and back. Help children realize that the *nerves* and feeling "nervous" are two different things.

Student Page D7

Explore Activity

Time about 15 minutes

Grouping cooperative groups of 2

Demonstrate the activity with the help of a volunteer. Children can complete Lab Manual page 91.

Integrating the Sciences

Life Science

In this lesson, children learn about some important parts of their bodies. In Unit A, Chapter 1, children learn about the important parts of a plant.

Lab Manual

What does the brain do?

Did you catch the ruler? Write Yes or No each time.

Trial #1	
Trial #2	
Trial #3	
Trial #4	
Trial #5	

How many times did you catch the ruler? ____________

Lab Manual
p. 91

Activity Rubric

Use the following activity scoring rubric to assess students' performance.

Scoring Criteria	1	2	3	4
Student followed directions to complete this activity.				
Student collected data about the number of times he or she was able to catch a ruler when released by a partner.				
Student recorded data for 5 trials in chart form.				
Student worked with a partner to complete this activity.				
Student reported about the coordination of brain and nerves in the attempt to catch a falling ruler.				

Scoring Key

4 points correct, complete, detailed
3 points partially correct, complete, detailed
2 points partially correct, partially complete, lacks some detail
1 point incorrect or incomplete, needs assistance

Lab Manual
p. T31

Assess and Extend

Answers to Lesson Review

1. Answers may vary. The brain controls what the body does. The brain sends and receives messages. You use your brain to move, think, feel, and remember.
2. Nerves are pathways that lead to and from the brain.
3. **Tell** (*Interview*) The brain has to receive a message from the nerves and then send a message back telling the fingers to catch the ruler.

Inquire Further

Ask the following question to guide further inquiry: **What parts of your body did you use to catch the ruler?** (*Possible answers: hands, eyes, brain, nerves*)

Higher Order Thinking *Infer*

Have children close their eyes and not touch anything. Ask how their brain decides what is happening.

Call 1-888-537-4908 with your Activity questions or comments.

Reading Organizer

Objective

Read labels.

Additional Resources

- Reading for Science blackline master

Teaching Reading for Science

- Like other informational books, many science books use pictures with labels to help present information. Pictures provide concrete visualization of the topic being discussed, and labels add meaning to the pictures.
- Explain to children that looking at pictures and reading the labels is a good prereading strategy. This strategy helps readers visualize what will be in the text. A picture with labels helps familiarize readers with vocabulary they will encounter in the reading.
- Have children read and complete the Reading for Science lesson and the Reading for Science blackline master.

Student Page D8

- Before beginning the page, help children compare pictures in a story and in an informational book. Ask: **How might the pictures be the same? How might they be different?** Mention that pictures in informational books often have labels.
- Read aloud the explanatory information on page D8. Discuss why some labels have lines going from the label to a part of the picture. (*to be sure the correct part of the picture is associated with the label*)
- Have children who have seen labels in print tell about the labels. Ask: **What kind of pictures had labels? How did the labels help you understand the picture?**

Reading Labels

Some pictures and diagrams have labels. Labels give you information about the picture or diagram.

Labels can be next to a picture or underneath it. Sometimes a label has a line going from the label to the part of the picture it tells about.

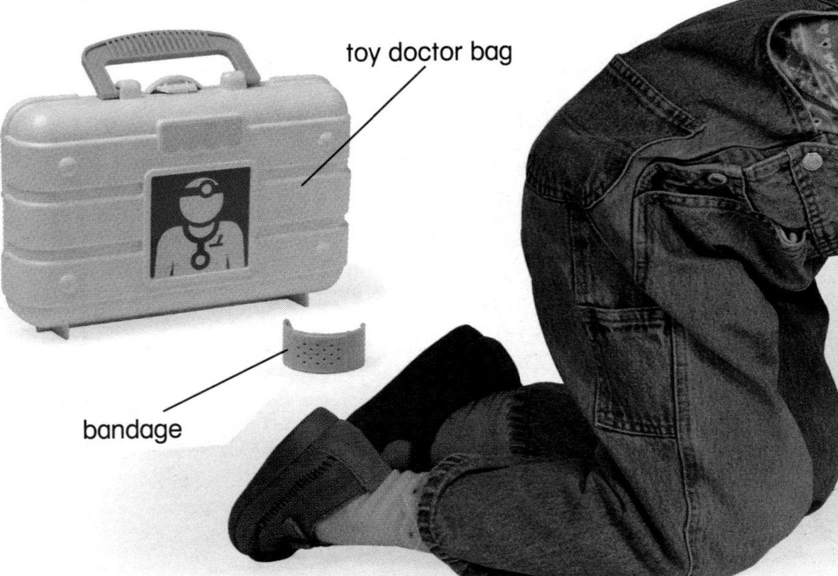

D8

ESL Strategy

To help children understand the use of label lines, give a child a card on which you have written the word *shoe* and ask him or her to point to a classmate's shoe. Help the child understand that he or she is doing the job of a label line.

This picture shows a girl playing. How do the labels help you understand what she is pretending to be?

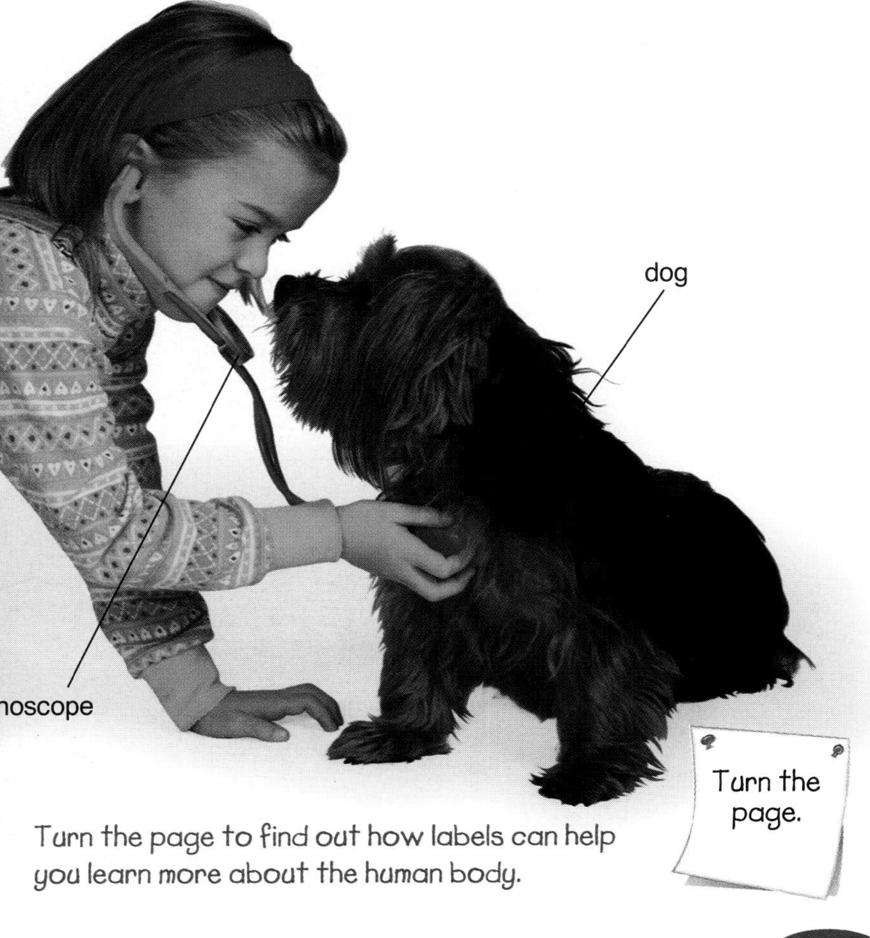

Turn the page to find out how labels can help you learn more about the human body.

D9

Student Page D9

- Have children point to each label as you read it and then use their fingers to trace the line from the label to its corresponding part.
- Discuss how the picture and labels in the previous lesson help children understand the information presented.
- After discussion, point out that some readers look at pictures and read labels before reading an informational article to help them preview the article.

Apply Reading for Science to Lesson 2

Children will use what they learned about reading labels to complete the next lesson.

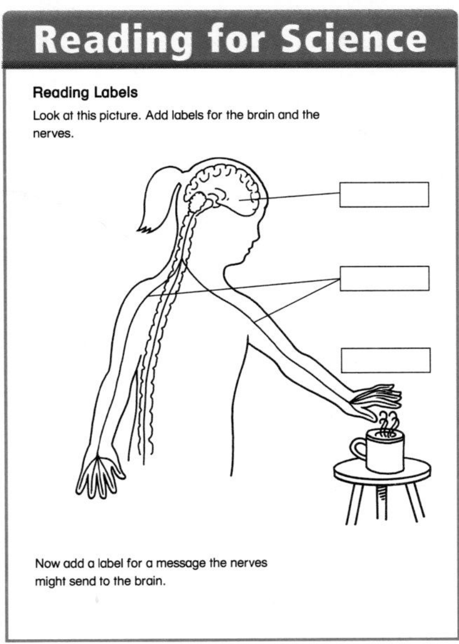
Reading for Science

Reading Labels

Look at this picture. Add labels for the brain and the nerves.

Now add a label for a message the nerves might send to the brain.

Instructional Resources p. 76

Lesson Organizer

Objective
Describe the functions of the heart and lungs.

Vocabulary
lungs, heart, arteries, veins

Additional Resources
- Wall Chart
- Interactive Transparency

Introduce

Activate Prior Knowledge
Have children draw pictures of what they think the heart and lungs look like. Have them write statements telling what they think both parts of the body do. Save their statements for use as a **baseline assessment.**

Language Development *Music*
Provide wind instruments, such as harmonicas, recorders, kazoos, and whistles. Invite children to blow on an instrument and place one hand on their upper abdomen while they do so. Ask children to describe what they feel and to guess what makes the instruments work.

Flip Chart
Ask children what the heart does. (*pumps the blood to every part of the body*) Discuss how the girl in the picture is using her lungs.

What does the brain do?
What do the heart and lungs do?
Talk About Science

What do the heart and lungs do?

Take a deep breath. Let it out. Your body does a lot of work with just one breath!

When you breathe, your **lungs** take in air. Air contains oxygen, a gas that your whole body needs. Oxygen enters your lungs first. The oxygen needs to reach the rest of your body too.

Your **heart** pumps blood to every part of your body. Blood contains materials that your body needs. When your heart pumps blood to your lungs, the blood picks up oxygen from the lungs. Then the blood carries the oxygen to all parts of your body.

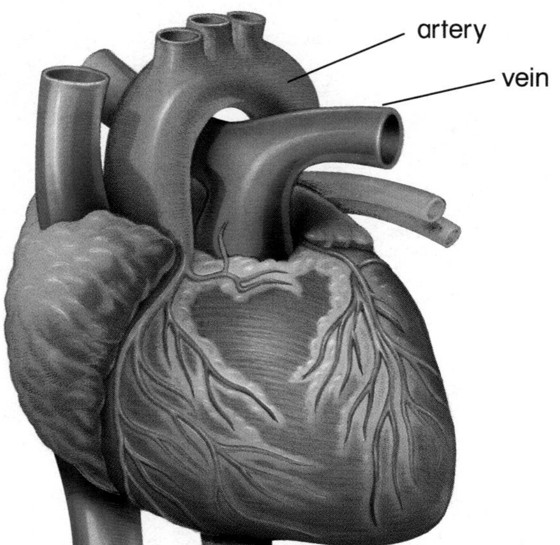

D10

Science Background
Each time the heart beats, some blood circulates from the heart to the lungs and back to the heart; some blood circulates from the heart to the body and back to the heart.

Possible Misconceptions When children think of a gas, they may think only of gasoline. Remind children that a gas is a state of matter. Explain that oxygen is a gas that we cannot see or smell. Another gas associated with breathing is carbon dioxide. We breathe in air containing oxygen and breathe out small amounts of carbon dioxide.

Blood is pumped away from your heart in tubes called **arteries**. Then it travels back to the heart in tubes called **veins**.

Your heart and lungs work together to keep you healthy.

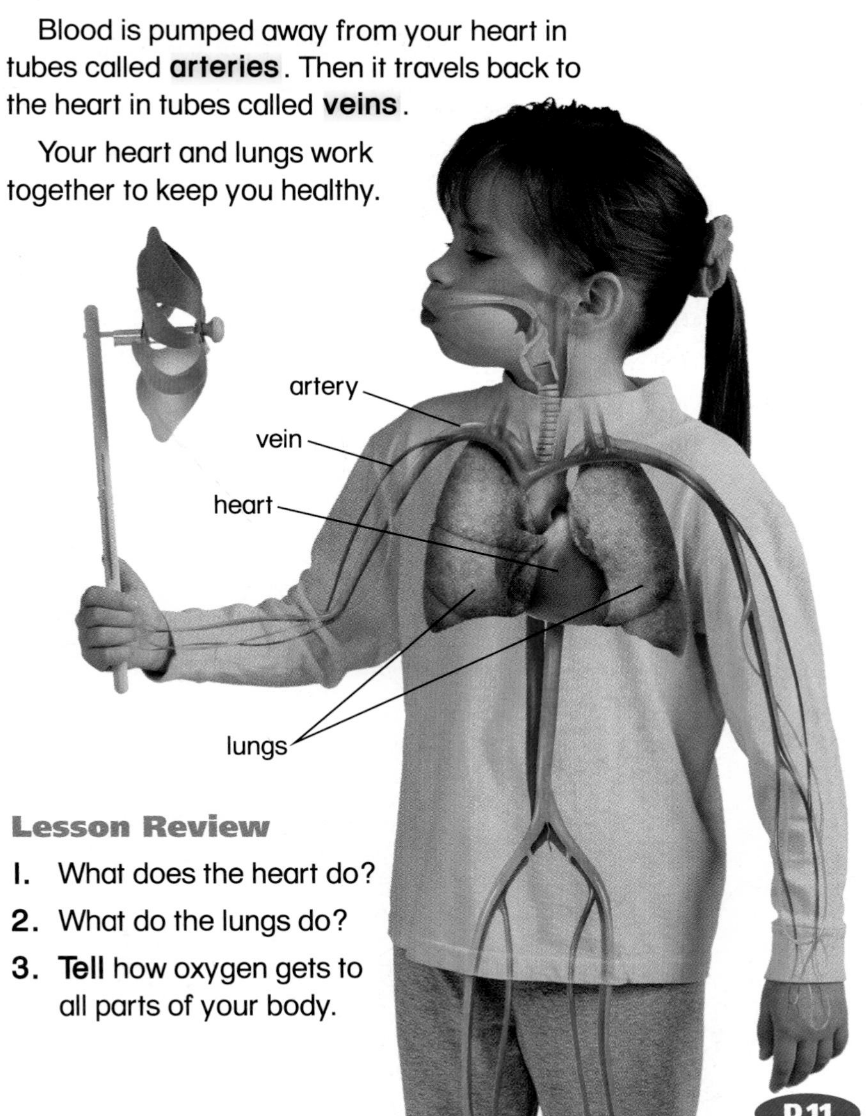

Lesson Review

1. What does the heart do?
2. What do the lungs do?
3. **Tell** how oxygen gets to all parts of your body.

ESL Strategy

Write these words on the chalkboard and say them aloud: *oxygen, lungs, heart.* Then invite children to use the words to complete the following sentences: ________ *is a gas that your whole body needs. You use your* ________ *to breathe. Your* ________ *pumps blood to every part of your body.*

Transparency

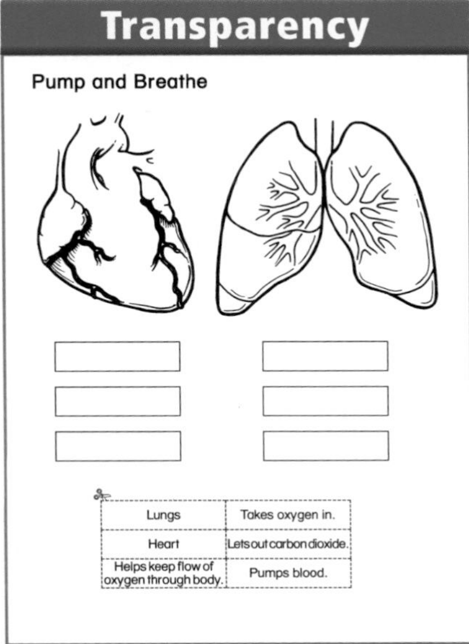

Pump and Breathe
Lungs
Takes oxygen in.
Heart
Lets out carbon dioxide.
Helps keep flow of oxygen through body.
Pumps blood.

Interactive Transparency Package
Transparency 10

Teach and Apply

Student Pages D 10–D 11

- Remind children that the brain does some things for us automatically—we do not have to tell it what to do. Two of these things are breathing and making our heart beat.
- Point out that we can do some things to keep our heart and lungs healthy. For example, we can eat healthful foods and exercise regularly. Also, we can avoid breathing polluted air such as smog and cigarette or cigar smoke.

Reading Assist *Decoding*

Point out the final consonant digraphs in *lung* and *breath.* Have children say each word with you, stressing the final sounds. Encourage them to think of other words ending in these sounds.

Assess and Extend

Answers to Lesson Review

1. The heart pumps blood to every part of the body.
2. The lungs take air into the body.
3. **Tell** (*Interview*) The lungs breathe in air containing oxygen. Blood picks up oxygen as it moves through the lungs. Then the blood takes the oxygen through the rest of the body.

Check for Understanding

To follow up on the **baseline assessment,** have children compare their pictures to ones in the lesson. Have them read the statements they made about the heart and the lungs and revise them as needed.

Reteach

- Use the Interactive Transparency to reteach Lesson 2 concepts.
- Have children talk about how the heart and lungs help us.

Enrichment

Have children use **Wall Chart** page 51, to label the heart, lungs, arteries, and veins. Then have them use the chart to describe how the blood gets to all parts of their bodies.

Activity Organizer

Objective

Measure lung capacity by blowing bubbles.

Process Skills predicting, collecting and interpreting data

Materials

Kit Items 9-ounce plastic cup, clear plastic straw

School-Supplied Items water, clock with a second hand

Time about 10 minutes

Grouping cooperative groups of 2

Additional Resources

- Lab Manual
- Teacher Demonstration Kit
- Wall Chart

Introduce

The Lesson 3 Investigate Activity, *How long can you blow bubbles?*, is on the **Flip Chart.**

Activate Prior Knowledge

Ask children to recall times when they have been "out of breath" from running or exercising. Ask them how they recover. (*by breathing hard*) Ask: **How is that different from the way you are breathing now?**

Language Development *Make a List*

Ask children what body parts they use when they breathe. (*Answers should include mouth, nose, lungs, throat.*)

Investigate Activity

How long can you blow bubbles?

Process Skills

- predicting
- collecting and interpreting data

Materials

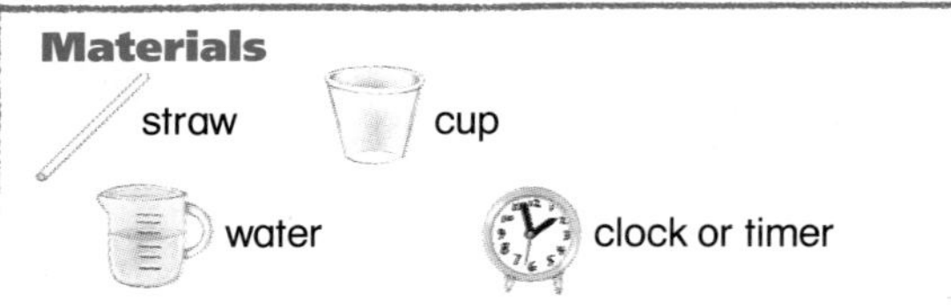

Steps

1. Fill a cup halfway with water.
2. How long can you blow bubbles without stopping? **Predict.**
3. Put your straw into your cup. Do not let the straw touch the bottom of the cup.
4. Blow bubbles for as long as you can. Have your partner time you.
5. How long did you blow bubbles? **Collect** and record your data.
6. Trade places with your partner. Do the activity again.

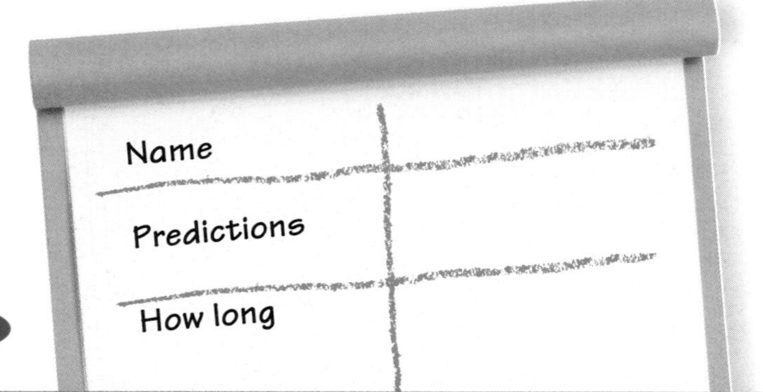

D12

Science Background

The lungs and the heart work closely together. When you breathe in, air containing oxygen is moved into the lungs. From there it enters the bloodstream. When you breathe out, carbon dioxide carried into the lungs by the bloodstream is exhaled.

Math-Science Connection After children complete the investigation, display **Wall Chart** page 52. Have children first tally how many children could blow bubbles for different lengths of time and then make a graph showing their results.

Technology

Review the demonstration of this Investigate's procedure on the *Human Body* **Activity Video,** Segment 1.

Think About Your Results

1. How long were you able to blow bubbles?
2. How close was your prediction to your results?

Inquire Further

How could you blow bubbles for a longer amount of time?

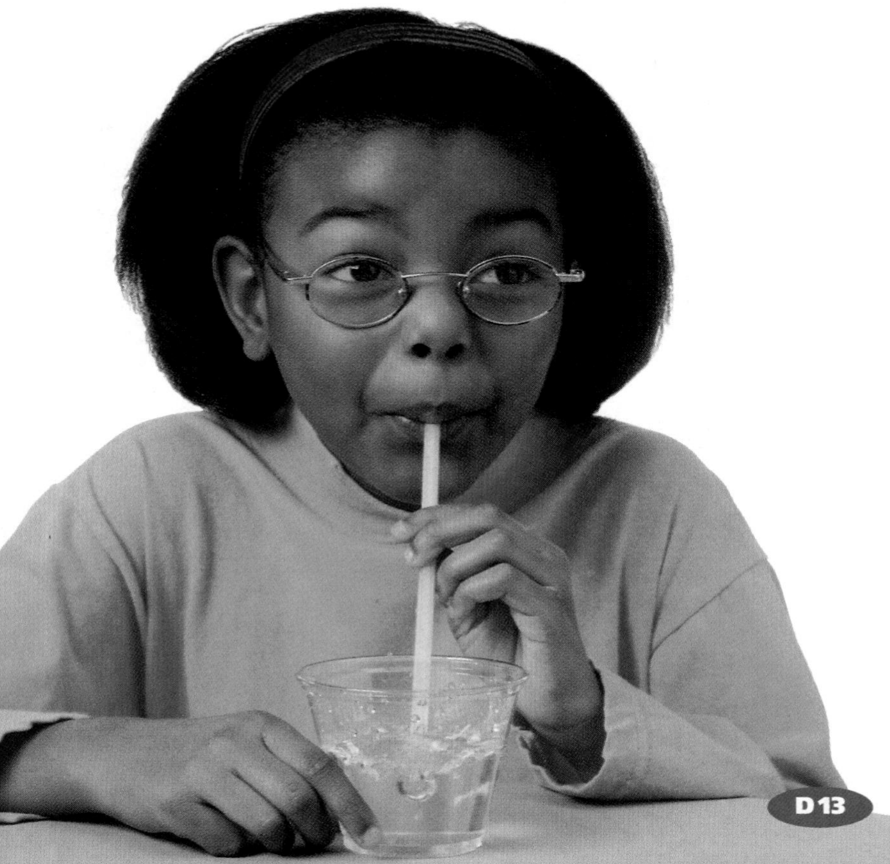

D13

Lab Manual

How long can you blow bubbles?

I think I can blow bubbles for ____________ seconds.

Draw the hand that shows seconds for when you start and when you stop.

Start Stop

I blew bubbles for ____________ seconds.

Lab Manual p. 92

Activity Rubric

Use the following activity scoring rubric to assess students' performance.

Scoring Criteria	1	2	3	4
Student assembled necessary materials to complete this activity.				
Student predicted how long he or she could blow bubbles in water.				
Student measured the time he or she was able to blow bubbles.				
Student visually represented the amount of time he or she could blow bubbles.				
Student compared his or her prediction with the actual time spent blowing bubbles.				

Scoring Key
4 points correct, complete, detailed
3 points partially correct, complete, detailed
2 points partially correct, partially complete, lacks some detail
1 point incorrect or incomplete, needs assistance

Lab Manual p. T32

Teach and Apply

- Advise children to fill their cups only halfway and blow only slowly and softly, so bubbles will not overflow.
- Be sure children do not put the straw all the way down to the bottom of the cup. There must be space for air to go into the water.
- If straws are individually wrapped, before beginning, you may want to draw a target on the chalkboard and give each child an attempt at hitting the target by blowing the straw wrapper off. This prevents wrappers from being blown all around the room.
- Children can use the Lab Manual page 92.

Safety Note *Make sure children do not share straws.*

Reading Assist *Use Picture Clues*

Remind children to look at the pictures as well as read the words to determine what to do in the activity.

What to Expect

It is not possible to inhale and blow bubbles at the same time, so children will be forced to stop blowing their bubbles when they run out of breath.

Real-World Applications

Scuba apparatus allows people to explore underwater while they breathe air from a tank. Besides pressurized air tanks, divers use masks, snorkels, fins, wet suits, and equipment that tells them their depth and how much time they can remain underwater.

Assess and Extend

Answers to Think About Your Results

1. Answers will vary but should give an approximate number of seconds.
2. Answers will vary, but children's results might show less time than they predicted.

Inquire Further

Children might say they can blow bubbles for a longer time by trying to breathe in more air before blowing the bubbles.

Higher Order Thinking *Infer*

Ask children why they think some people can blow bubbles longer than others.

Call 1-888-537-4908 with your Activity questions or comments.

Activity Organizer

Objective

Experiment to determine pulse rate before and after exercising.

Process Skills experimenting, estimating and measuring (formulating hypotheses, identifying and controlling variables, collecting and interpreting data)

Materials

Kit Items none

School-Supplied Items clock with a second hand

Time about 15 minutes

Grouping cooperative groups of 2

Additional Resources

- Lab Manual
- Teacher Demonstration Kit

Introduce

Activity Summary

The Experiment Activity is also on the **Flip Chart.** In this activity, children use scientific methods to determine how exercise affects their heart rate. The steps in this lesson follow a general procedure scientists use to solve problems. Traditionally labeled "scientific methods," these steps can be used in a variety of combinations. Children will find that their heart rate will increase after running.

Activate Prior Knowledge

Ask children if they have ever heard or felt their heartbeat. Have them share what it sounds like. Provide a stethoscope or empty paper rolls and allow children to take turns listening to each other's heartbeats.

Using Scientific Language

Review the vocabulary of scientific methods on pages xii–xiii.

Reading Assist *Word Meaning*

Explain that the word *affect* is an action word that signals a relationship. One action changes, or affects, another. In this experiment, children will find out if there is such a relationship between exercise and heart rate.

Experiment with exercise.

Process Skills
- experimenting
- estimating and measuring

Materials
clock or timer

Problem

How does exercise affect your heart rate?

Give Your Hypothesis

How will your heart rate change when you exercise? Tell what you think.

Control the Variables

Make sure you measure your heart rate for the same amount of time before and after running.

Test Your Hypothesis

Follow these steps to do the experiment.

1. Sit quietly. Measure your heart rate by taking your pulse for 30 seconds. Have your partner keep track of the time.
2. Now run in place for one minute. Have your partner keep track of the time.

D14

Science Background

Arteries, such as the one in the wrist or neck, carry blood through the body. Each time the heart beats, the blood vessels enlarge; in between beats, they contract. Each pulse beat represents one heartbeat.

Teaching Tips Before children begin the activity, make sure everyone is able to find his or her pulse. Demonstrate by placing your forefinger and middle finger lightly on the inside of your wrist or under your jaw. Make sure there is enough room to do the exercise safely.

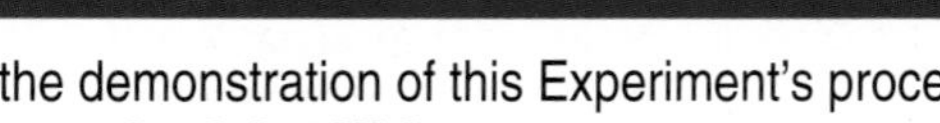

Technology

Review the demonstration of this Experiment's procedure on the *Human Body* **Activity Video,** Segment 2.

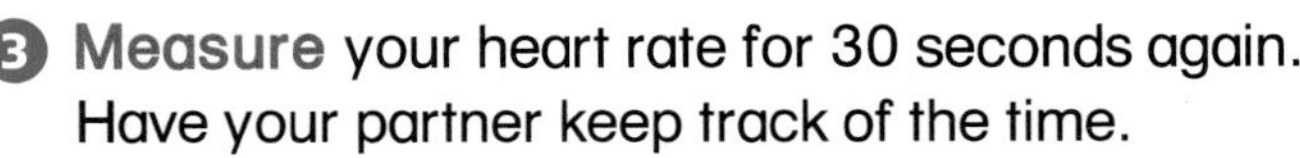

3. **Measure** your heart rate for 30 seconds again. Have your partner keep track of the time.
4. Trade places with your partner. Do the activity again.

Collect Your Data

Use a chart like this one. Record your heart rate while sitting and after running.

Tell Your Conclusion

Compare your results and hypothesis. How does exercise affect your heart rate?

Inquire Further

If you exercised for more than one minute, how would this affect your heart rate?

D15

Lab Manual

Experiment with exercise.

Problem

How does exercise affect your heart rate?

Give Your Hypotheses

How will your heart rate change when you exercise?
Write what you think.

Control the Variables

Make sure you measure your heart rate for the same amount of time before and after running.

Test Your Hypothesis

Measure your heart rate.

Collect Your Data

Activity	Heart beats
Sitting	______ in 30 seconds
After running	______ in 30 seconds

Lab Manual
pp. 93–94

Activity Rubric

Use the following activity scoring rubric to assess students' performance.

Scoring Criteria	1	2	3	4
Student followed directions to complete this activity.				
Student stated a hypothesis about the effect of exercise on heart rate.				
Student controlled the variable of heart rate measurement before and after exercise.				
Student measured his or her pulse before and after exercise.				
Student explained his or her conclusion about how exercise affected heart rate.				

Scoring Key
4 points correct, complete, detailed
3 points partially correct, complete, detailed
2 points partially correct, partially complete, lacks some detail
1 point incorrect or incomplete, needs assistance

Lab Manual
p. T32

Call 1-888-537-4908 with your Activity questions or comments.

Teach and Apply

Problem

Ask children to share their ideas about ways that exercise might affect their heart rates.

Give Your Hypothesis

Encourage children to hypothesize the relationship between their heart rates and exercise. Have children record their hypotheses.

Control the Variables

Be sure children time themselves exactly for 30 seconds both before and after running.

Safety Note *Children with heart conditions, asthma, or other health-related problems should check with a doctor before participating in this activity.*

Test Your Hypothesis

Have children take turns timing and measuring their heart rates.

Collect Your Data

Have children complete Lab Manual pages 93–94 as they do the activity. They record their pre-exercise pulse rate at the time they measure it. After exercising for one minute, they record their pulse rates again.

Assess and Extend

Tell Your Conclusion

Have children read their hypotheses and compare them with the results. Children should conclude that exercise causes the heart to beat faster.

Inquire Further

Children might say that if you exercised longer, your heart rate would increase more.

Enrichment

Children can exercise for two minutes instead of one.

Higher Order Thinking *Infer*

Ask: **Why do you think exercise is good for your heart?** (*Children might infer that exercise keeps your heart in shape as it does your muscles.*)

Science Center

Flip Chart

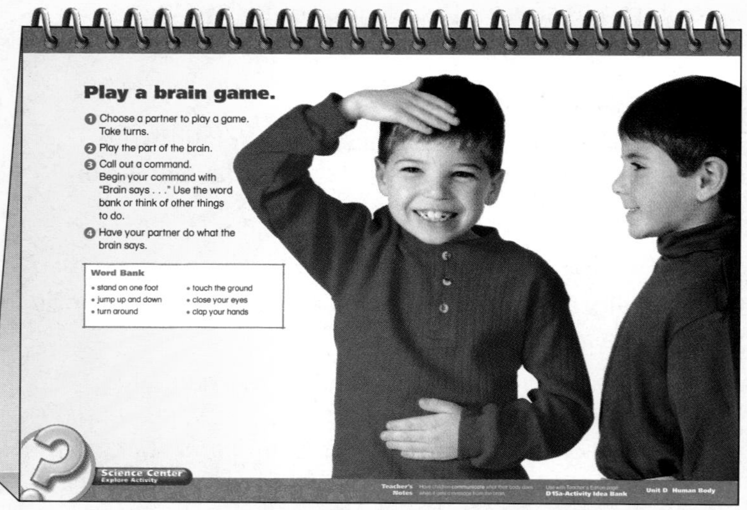

Play a brain game.

Objective

Demonstrate how the body responds to messages from the brain.

Process Skills communicating

Materials

Kit Items none

School-Supplied Items none

Procedure

- Invite children to take turns giving commands.
- Children move the appropriate body parts when commands are given.
- Have children **communicate** what their bodies are doing when they get messages from the brain.
- You can use **Lab Manual** page 95 with this activity.

Lab Manual

Play a brain game.

Choose one command you followed.
Draw what you did.

Lab Manual, p. 95

Connections

School and Community

Ideas for bringing the school and community together:

Field Trips

- science museum
- exercise facility

Guest Speakers

- sports-medicine doctor
- physical therapist
- gym instructor

Themes

The activities on these pages can be used with classroom themes such as:

- brain, heart, lungs
- exercise
- health
- physical education

Books for Children

Children might enjoy these books about the human body:

My Skin Looks After Me by Jane Buxton. A simple story telling about how our skin helps us. (Learning Media, ISBN 0-478-20512-0)

The Human Body At Your Fingertips by Judy Nayer. Illustrated descriptions of major body organs and processes. (McClanahan, ISBN 0-7681-0065-8)

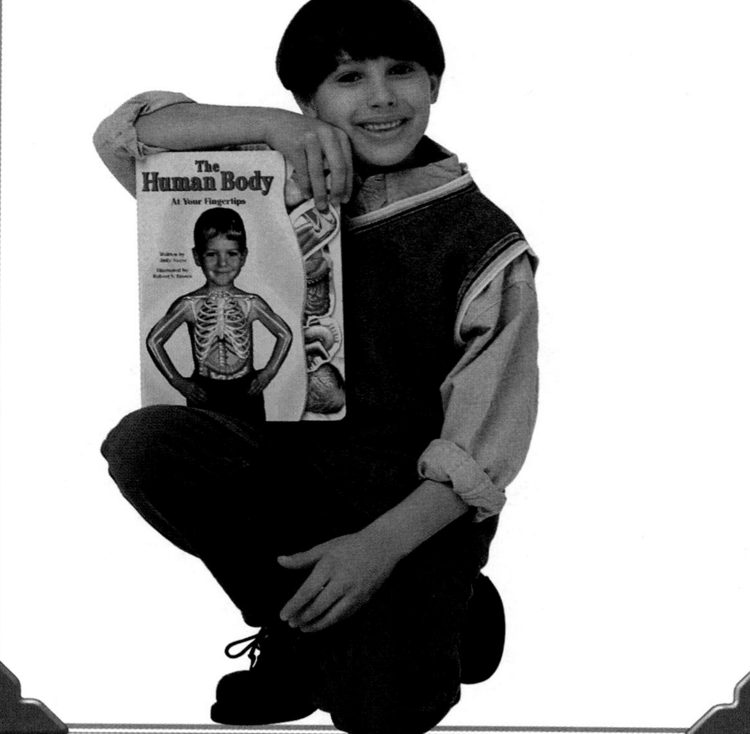

Cross-Curricular Options

LITERATURE

The Magic School Bus Inside the Human Body

Use the book to discuss the human body.

Materials *The Magic School Bus Inside the Human Body* by Joanna Cole. (Scholastic, ISBN 0-590-41427-5)

Procedure

- Ms. Frizzle's class takes a ride into the human body on the Magic School Bus.
- Have children use the pictures to retell how the lungs, heart, arteries, veins, and brain work.

Multiple Intelligences linguistic, spatial

Gifted and Talented Children can look at hair cells or skin cells through a microscope and draw pictures of what they see.

MATH

How Many?

Perform exercises and chart results.

Materials stopwatch or clock with a second hand

Name	How many?	How many?
Kathy	15	22
Juan	18	

Procedure

- Demonstrate jumping jacks or another exercise.
- Have one child count while doing the exercise for 30 seconds; the partner keeps track of the time. Then they switch roles.
- Have children use a two-column chart to record how many they do. Then have them repeat the activity to try to beat their first time.

Multiple Intelligences kinesthetic, spatial

Special Needs Children who cannot participate in physical activity can narrate one of the events, telling who is jumping, what is happening to the body, and how many jumps the child made.

WRITING

No Smoking Here!

Create no-smoking icons or posters.

Materials tagboard, drawing paper, crayons, paint, brushes, markers

Procedure

- Show children a no-smoking sign and talk about how the symbol conveys a message.
- Discuss why smoking is not good for the lungs.
- Have children create their own icons or posters on the theme of no smoking.

Multiple Intelligences linguistic, spatial

ART

Action!

Make a sculpture of the human body.

Materials pipe cleaners or craft wire

Procedure

- Discuss the numerous ways the body can move.
- Have children pantomime specific actions, such as throwing a ball, jumping over a puddle, scooting down a hill.
- Have children create sculptures of the human body in action.

Multiple Intelligences spatial, kinesthetic

Review Organizer

Materials

Kit Items none

School-Supplied Items paper, crayons

Time about 30 minutes

Grouping cooperative groups of 2

Additional Resources

- Chapter 1 Assessment: Teacher's Assessment Package

Chapter Main Ideas

Lesson 1 The brain sends messages to all parts of the body so that they work properly and work together.

Lesson 2 Your lungs take air containing oxygen into your body. Your heart pumps blood to every part of your body. The blood is pumped away from your heart through your arteries and carried back to your heart in your veins.

Lesson 3 You can measure lung power by blowing bubbles. First predict how long you can blow bubbles, blow the bubbles, and then record the length of time.

Lesson 4 You can experiment to determine that exercise increases the heart rate.

Reviewing Science Words

1. The brain controls what the body does. The brain sends and receives messages. You use your brain to move, think, feel, and remember.
2. Nerves carry messages to and from the brain.
3. The lungs take in oxygen.
4. The heart pumps blood to every part of the body.
5. Arteries are tubes that carry blood away from the heart.
6. Veins are tubes that carry blood back to the heart.

Reviewing Science Ideas

1. The lungs take in oxygen. When the heart pumps blood to the lungs, the blood picks up oxygen and carries it to the rest of the body.
2. Exercise increases the heart rate.

Chapter 1 Review

Reviewing Science Words

1. Name two things the **brain** does.
2. What do the **nerves** do?
3. What do the **lungs** take into the body?
4. What does the **heart** do?
5. What are **arteries** ?
6. What are **veins** ?

Reviewing Science Ideas

1. How do the heart and lungs work together?
2. How does exercise affect your heart rate?

D 16

Technology

Children can review *Human Body* with the **Practice & Assessment CD-ROM.**

Children can use the **Production Studio** to show what they've learned about *Human Body.*

Children can use The KnowZone™ at **www.kz.com** to review and test their science knowledge.

You can use **TestWorks™** to customize assessment for your children.

Draw a diagram of your body.

Materials

paper · crayons

1. Draw an outline of your body.
2. Draw your brain, lungs, and heart in the correct places. Label them.
3. You can use the pictures in this chapter to help you.
4. Tell a friend about your drawing.

Chapter Assessment

Choose a word from the box to finish each sentence.

brain · lungs · arteries · nerves

1. Your brain sends messages to your body through your ______.
2. Your ______ take oxygen into your body when you breathe.
3. Your blood is pumped away from your heart in ______.
4. Your ______ controls what your body does.

Circle the correct answer.

5. How can you check your heart rate?
   measure your pulse · breathe in and out
6. When does your body get oxygen?
   when you breathe in · when you breathe out
7. When is your pulse rate higher?
   when you are sleeping · when you are jumping rope

Teacher's Assessment Package pp. 59–60

Assessment Rubric

	How Your Body Works
4	Correctly identifies the brain, lungs, and heart and communicates information about their functions.
3	Makes few errors identifying the brain, lungs, and heart and communicating information about their functions.
2	Has difficulty identifying the brain, lungs, and heart and communicating information about their functions.
1	Is unable to identify the brain, lungs, and heart and communicate information about their functions.

Performance Assessment Teaching Tips

- Before beginning, review the key vocabulary words: *brain, lungs,* and *heart.* Write these words on the chalkboard.
- Mention to children that they can refer to the pictures in their books. Picture books on the human body are helpful too.
- Have children work with partners to trace their bodies.
- Remind children to check the spelling of their labels by using the words on the chalkboard.
- When children share their drawings, have partners ask: **What does the brain do? What do the lungs do? What does the heart do?**
- Have children save these pictures so that they can add the digestive system after they complete Chapter 2 of this unit.

Enrichment

Have children add veins and arteries to their drawings. Children can use blue crayons to show their veins and red crayons to show their arteries.

Chapter 1 Skills Trace

Process Skills Development

	Collecting and Interpreting Data	Predicting	Experimenting	Estimating and Measuring
Skill Introduced	xv	xv	xv	xiv
Skill Applied	D 7 D 12–D 13	D 12–D 13	D 14–D 15	D 14–D 15
Skill Assessed	End Matter 24–25	End Matter 16–17	End Matter 28–29	End Matter 12–13

Chapter Review pages are also on the **Flip Chart.**

Lesson/Activity and Flip Chart	Objectives/Process Skills	Time Options/Activity Materials
Chapter Opener Student Edition pp. D18–D19 and **Flip Chart** ***Good to Eat***		**Have less time?** Use the Graphic Organizer on Teacher's Assessment Package p. 63 for an overview of the lessons. Use the Flip Chart to teach lesson concepts and science activities. **Have more time?** Use the Flip Chart to reinforce and extend lesson concepts and activities. Use the Cross-Curricular Options in the Activity Idea Bank on Teacher's Edition pp. D25b and D29b.
Reading for Science Student Edition pp. D20–D21 ***Using a Diagram***	**Objective** Use a diagram.	
Lesson 1 Student Edition pp. D22–D23 ***What foods help you stay healthy?*** **Explore Activity** ***Make a Food Guide Pyramid.*** **Flip Chart** ***Talk About Science***	**Objective** Identify features of proper nutrition and how nutrition keeps us healthy. **Process Skills** classifying	**Kit Items** none **School-Supplied Items** large piece of paper, magazines or newspapers, scissors, glue **Advance Prep** Collect newspapers containing food advertisements.
Lesson 2 Student Edition pp. D24–D25 and **Flip Chart** **Investigate Activity** ***Which foods will leave a greasy spot?***	**Objective** Determine whether certain foods have a high or low fat content. **Process Skills** predicting, collecting and interpreting data	**Kit Items** none **School-Supplied Items** clean brown paper bag, marker, butter, carrot, snack foods
Activity Idea Bank Teacher's Edition pp. D25a–D25b **Flip Chart** **Science Center Explore Activity** ***Play Healthful Foods Bingo.***	**Objective** Classify foods. **Process Skills** classifying	**Kit Items** none **School-Supplied Items** paper, pencil, crayons, markers such as beans or paper squares
Lesson 3 Student Edition pp. D26–D27 ***What happens when you chew?*** **Explore Activity** ***Observe how food can be changed.*** **Flip Chart** ***Talk About Science***	**Objective** Describe how saliva begins the digestive process. **Process Skills** predicting, observing	**Kit Items** 2 resealable paper bags **School-Supplied Items** soda crackers, water
Lesson 4 Student Edition pp. D28–D29 ***How is food digested?*** **Flip Chart** ***Talk About Science***	**Objective** Describe the digestive system.	**Have more time?** Use the following teaching guide option: Interactive Transparency 11, Interactive Transparency Package
Activity Idea Bank Teacher's Edition pp. D29a–D29b **Flip Chart** **Science Center Explore Activity** ***Measure the small intestine.***	**Objective** Measure the length of the small intestine. **Process Skills** measuring	**Kit Items** red yarn **School-Supplied Items** meter stick
Chapter Review Student Edition pp. D30–D31 and **Flip Chart**		**Kit Items** none **School-Supplied Items** paper, pencil or marker

Lesson/Activity and Flip Chart	Additional Resources		Technology
Chapter Opener Student Edition pp. D18–D19 and **Flip Chart** ***Good to Eat***	**Teacher's Assessment Package** • Graphic Organizer, p. 63 **Instructional Resources** • Family Activity, pp. 81–82 • Vocabulary Preview, p. 83	**Songs & Activities Package** • *Good to Eat*, pp. 29–30 **Wall Chart,** p. 53	**Practice & Assessment CD-ROM** **AudioText** **Production Studio** **www.sfscience.com** **Songs & Activities Package** **Teacher's Resource Planner CD-ROM**
Reading for Science Student Edition pp. D20–D21 ***Using a Diagram***	**Instructional Resources** • Reading for Science, p. 84		
Lesson 1 Student Edition pp. D22–D23 ***What foods help you stay healthy?*** **Explore Activity** ***Make a Food Guide Pyramid.*** **Flip Chart** ***Talk About Science***	**Lab Manual** • Lab Manual, p. 97 • Activity Rubric, p. T33	**Teacher Demonstration Kit** **Wall Chart,** p. 54	
Lesson 2 Student Edition pp. D24–D25 and **Flip Chart** **Investigate Activity** ***Which foods will leave a greasy spot?***	**Lab Manual** • Lab Manual, p. 99 • Activity Rubric, p. T34	**Teacher Demonstration Kit** **Wall Chart,** p. 55	*Human Body* **Activity Video**
Activity Idea Bank Teacher's Edition pp. D25a–D25b **Flip Chart** **Science Center Explore Activity** ***Play Healthful Foods Bingo.***	**Lab Manual** • Lab Manual, p. 100 • Activity Rubric, p. T34		
Lesson 3 Student Edition pp.D26–D27 ***What happens when you chew?*** **Explore Activity** ***Observe how food can be changed.*** **Flip Chart** ***Talk About Science***	**Lab Manual** • Lab Manual, p. 101 • Activity Rubric, p. T35	**Teacher Demonstration Kit** **Wall Chart,** p. 56	
Lesson 4 Student Edition pp. D28–D29 ***How is food digested?*** **Flip Chart** ***Talk About Science***	**Interactive Transparency Package** • Interactive Transparency 11	**Wall Chart,** p. 57	
Activity Idea Bank Teacher's Edition pp. D29a–D29b **Flip Chart** **Science Center Explore Activity** ***Measure the small intestine.***	**Lab Manual** • Lab Manual, p. 103 • Activity Rubric, p. T35		
Chapter Review Student Edition pp. D30–D31 and **Flip Chart**	**Teacher's Assessment Package** • Chapter 2 Assessment, pp. 65–66		**Practice & Assessment CD-ROM** **Production Studio** **The KnowZone™ at www.kz.com** **TestWorks™**

Reading for Science

Using a Diagram

Which activities do you spend the most time doing each day? Write the activities from the box in order.
Write them from most time spent to least time spent.

sleep	play	school	eat	chores

Most time **sleep**
school
play
eat
Least time **chores**

Answers will vary. Page shows a sample of what a child might answer.

Write the activities on the Diagram.

Answers given below are based on sample answers given above.

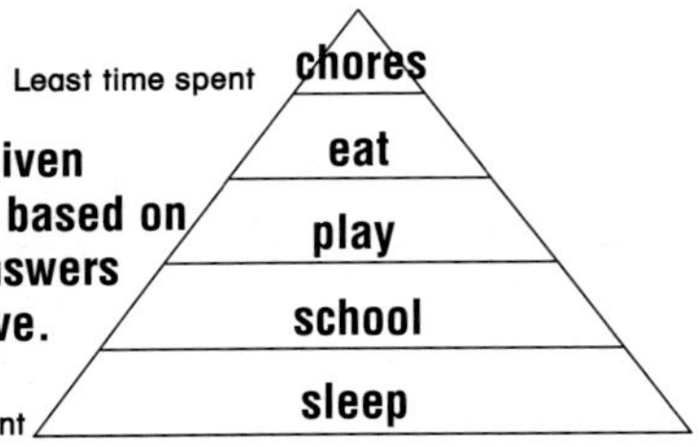

Least time spent
chores
eat
play
school
sleep
Most time spent

Instructional Resources p. 84

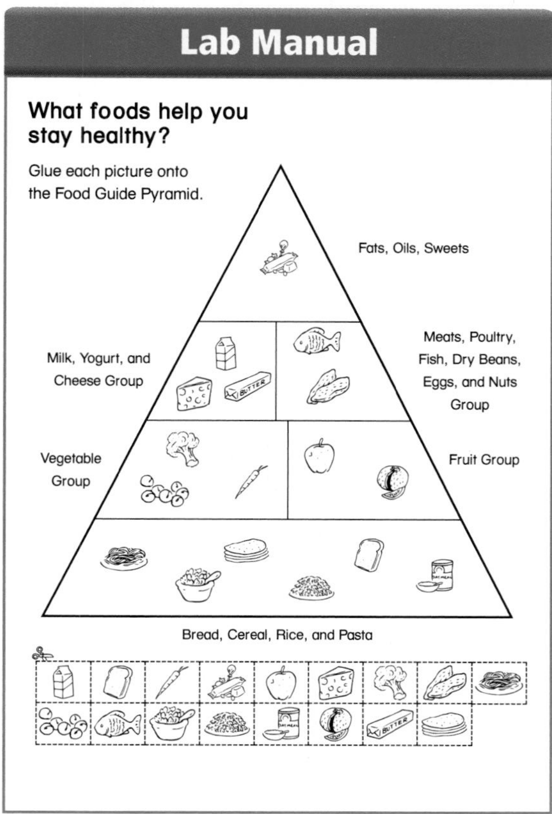

Lab Manual

What foods help you stay healthy?

Glue each picture onto the Food Guide Pyramid.

Lab Manual
p. 97

Lab Manual

Which foods will leave a greasy spot?

Use this chart to record your predictions and results for each food you test.

Food	Prediction	Results
Students should indicate that the butter left a greasy spot. Their choices of snack foods also probably left greasy spots. The carrot did not.		

Lab Manual
p. 99

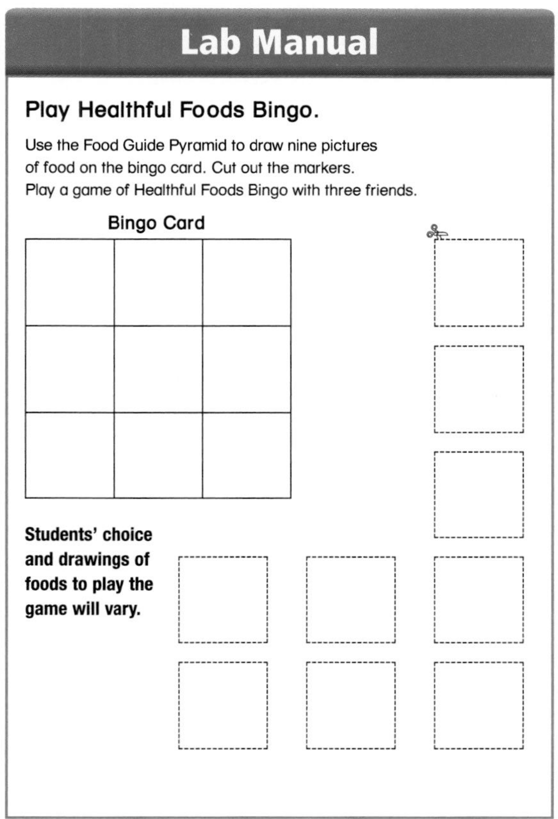

Lab Manual

Play Healthful Foods Bingo.

Use the Food Guide Pyramid to draw nine pictures of food on the bingo card. Cut out the markers.
Play a game of Healthful Foods Bingo with three friends.

Bingo Card

Students' choice and drawings of foods to play the game will vary.

Lab Manual
p. 100

Lab Manual

What happens when you chew?

What will happen if you shake the bags? Predict.

Draw how both crackers look after you shake the bags.

Students' predictions about what will happen to the crackers in the baggies will vary. They should observe that the broken cracker will be mushier after being shaken than the whole cracker.

Lab Manual
p. 101

Transparency

How Food is Digested

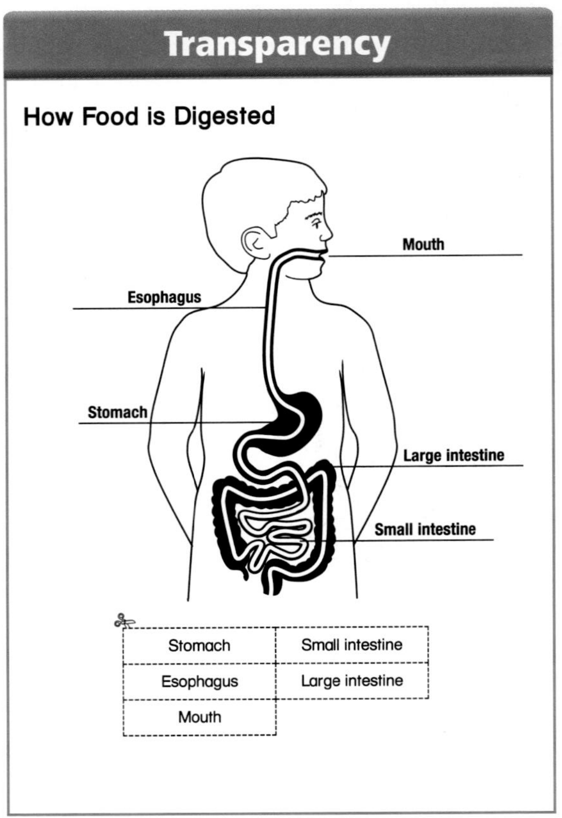

Interactive Transparency Package
Transparency 11

Lab Manual

Measure the small intestine.

What objects are about the same length as your small intestine?

Name of object	Picture of object
	Students will find various objects that are about as long as their small intestine (5 meters) and their drawings will vary.

Lab Manual
p. 103

Chapter 2 Assessment

Use the words in the box to finish each sentence.

nutrients	Food Guide Pyramid	small intestine
mouth	digestion	esophagus	stomach

1. Digestion begins in your ________________.
2. The ________________ squeezes food down to your stomach.
3. The ________________ shows how many servings of different foods you should eat each day.
4. Most food is digested in the ________________.
5. Our bodies get ________________ from foods.
6. Our bodies break down food in the process of ________________.

Circle your answer.

7. From which food group should you eat the most?

   fats, oils, sweets (bread, cereal, rice, pasta)

8. Which food will leave a greasy spot?

   (butter) carrot

9. Which food has the least fat?

   butter (carrot) pretzel

Teacher's Assessment Package p. 65

Chapter 2 Assessment

10. Draw food for each group in the Food Guide Pyramid.

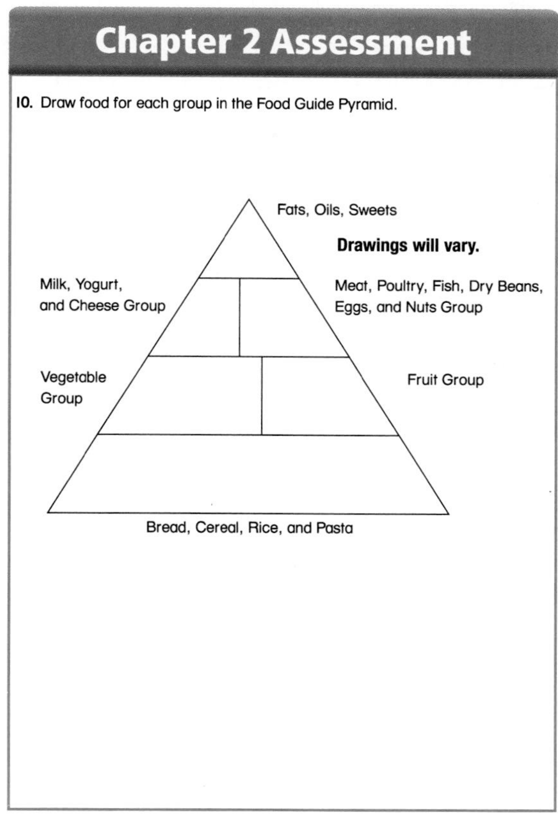

Teacher's Assessment Package p. 66

Table of Contents

Introducing the Chapter

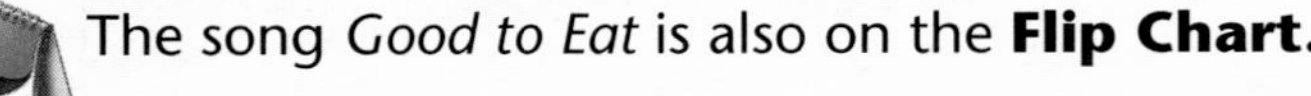

The song *Good to Eat* is also on the **Flip Chart.**

- Discuss nutrition and foods people need to eat to be healthy.
- Distribute the Family Activity blackline master page.

Singing the Song

Have children sing the song *Good to Eat* on side 2 of the CTW cassette. Distribute pages 29–30 from the CTW Song Activity Book.

Reading Assist *Decode Words*

Write the word *rice* on the chalkboard. Say the word and underline *ice.* Point out that the *ice* spelling pattern is pronounced with the long *i* sound and the *s* sound. Ask children to find other words in the song that have the same ending sound as *rice.* (*nice, spice, twice*)

Vocabulary Preview

Use the Vocabulary Preview blackline master to introduce the vocabulary words for this chapter.

Lesson 1 Food Guide Pyramid
Lesson 3 digestion
Lesson 4 esophagus, small intestine, nutrients, large intestine

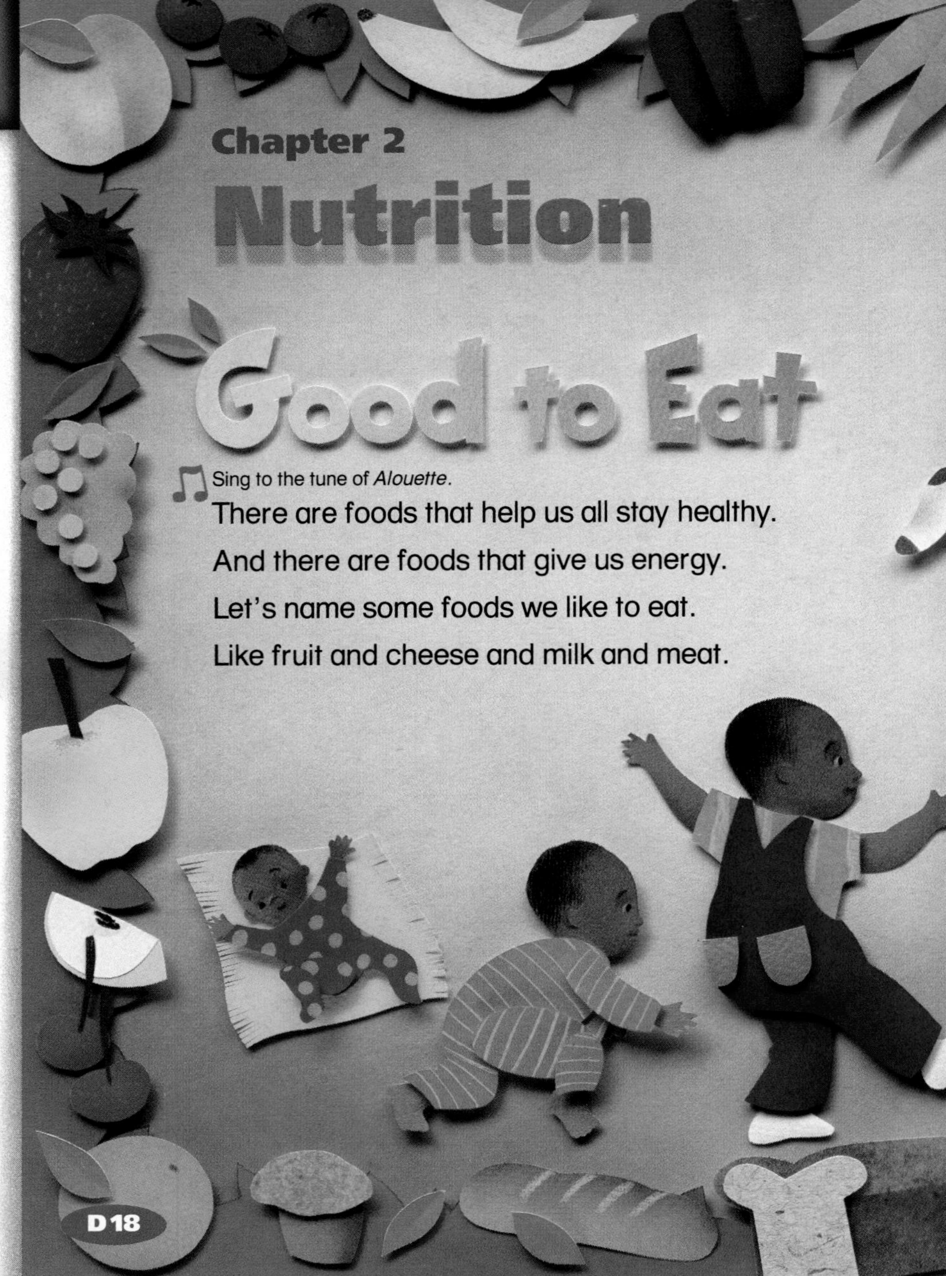

Chapter 2
Nutrition
Good to Eat
Sing to the tune of *Alouette*.
There are foods that help us all stay healthy.
And there are foods that give us energy.
Let's name some foods we like to eat.
Like fruit and cheese and milk and meat.
D18

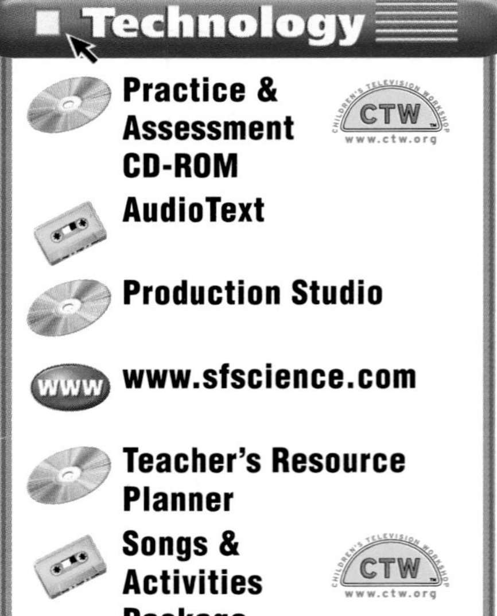

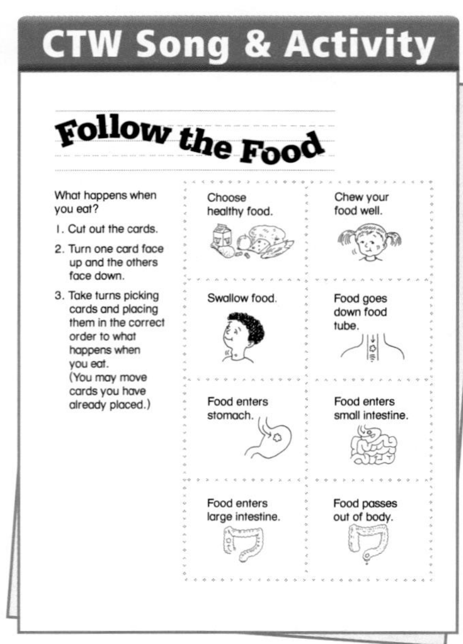

CTW Song & Activity
Follow the Food
What happens when you eat?
1. Cut out the cards.
2. Turn one card face up and the others face down.
3. Take turns picking cards and placing them in the correct order to what happens when you eat. (You may move cards you have already placed.)
Choose healthy food.
Chew your food well.
Swallow food.
Food goes down food tube.
Food enters stomach.
Food enters small intestine.
Food enters large intestine.
Food passes out of body.

Songs & Activities Package pp. 29–30

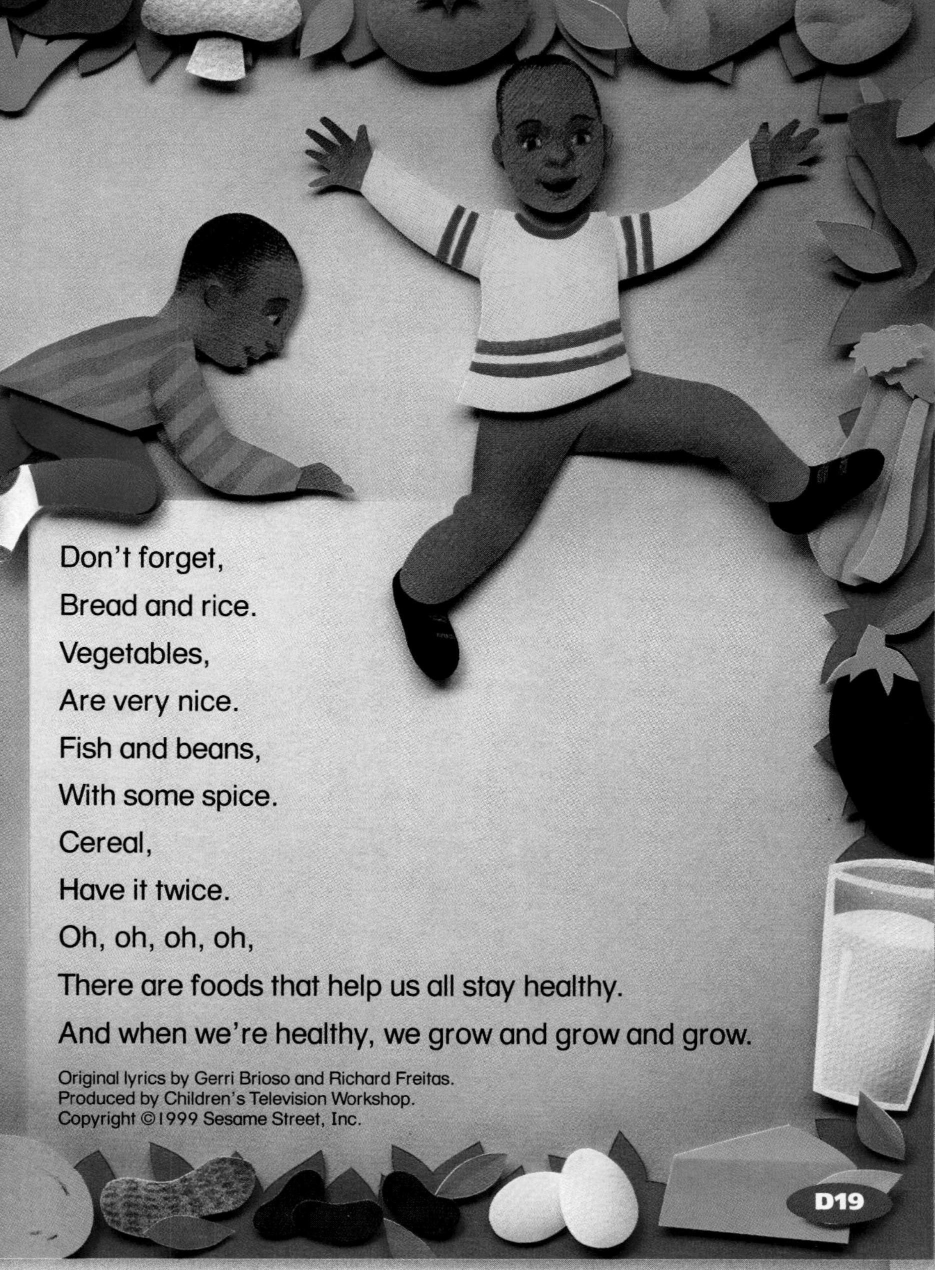
Don't forget,
Bread and rice.
Vegetables,
Are very nice.
Fish and beans,
With some spice.
Cereal,
Have it twice.
Oh, oh, oh, oh,
There are foods that help us all stay healthy.
And when we're healthy, we grow and grow and grow.

Original lyrics by Gerri Brioso and Richard Freitas.
Produced by Children's Television Workshop.

D19

INQUIRY

Use a KWL chart at the beginning of each new chapter to encourage inquiry. In the *K* column, record what children *know* about nutrition and being healthy. In the *W* column, list what they *want* to know. Throughout the chapter, ask children what they have *learned* and record their responses in the *L* column. A KWL chart is available on **Wall Chart** page 53.

Family Activity

Science at Home

Dear Family:
Our class is starting Chapter 2. We will be learning about nutrition. These are the main ideas for Chapter 2.

- Food gives us the energy we need to work, play, grow, and stay healthy.
- Digestion begins in the mouth. The teeth, tongue, and saliva help to break down food.
- The digestive system includes the mouth, esophagus, stomach, small intestine, and large intestine.
- Nutrients from digested food help our bodies grow and repair.

We will also be learning science vocabulary words for Chapter 2. By the end of Chapter 2, we will be able to read the vocabulary words and tell what they mean.

Word Bank
Food Guide Pyramid
digestion
esophagus
small intestine
nutrients
large intestine

Home Projects
Here are some activities that will help your child understand the main ideas in Chapter 2. The activities are easy, fast, and fun.

Activities
- With your child, spend some time looking at food labels, especially at charts and diagrams that show what nutrients are contained in the different foods you eat. Talk about whether your diet is missing any important nutrients.
- Plan a week of breakfast and dinner menus. Then take your child grocery shopping to buy the items needed for the menus.

Instructional Resources pp. 81–82

Vocabulary Preview

Food Guide Pyramid	digestion
esophagus	small intestine
nutrients	large intestine
diagram	energy

Instructional Resources p. 83

Chapter 2 Skills Trace

Process Skills Development	Classifying	Predicting	Collecting and Interpreting Data	Observing
Skill Introduced	xiv	xv	xv	xiv
Skill Applied	D 23	D 24–D 25 D 27	D 24–D 25	D 27
Skill Assessed	End Matter 10–11	End Matter 16–17	End Matter 24–25	End Matter 6–7

Science Literature Library

The Edible Pyramid: Good Eating Every Day
by Loreen Leedy.

The Food Guide Pyramid as a basis for healthful nutrition is presented in the form of a "menu" offered at the Edible Pyramid restaurant. Numerous examples from each food group are clearly and colorfully illustrated.
(Holiday House,
ISBN 0-8234-1126-5)

Reading Organizer

Objective

Use a diagram.

Additional Resources

- Reading for Science blackline master

Teaching Reading for Science

- Diagrams organize data or information. They are effective tools for communicating information because they provide visual representations of the data. In order to properly interpret the data associated with a diagram, the diagram should have a title and a proper label and should represent the data accurately.
- Reading a diagram includes being able to explain the information that is presented and to answer questions about it. Reading a diagram requires looking at and understanding the main idea of the diagram as well as the supporting details in order to draw conclusions about the data.
- Have children read and complete the Reading for Science lesson and the Reading for Science blackline master.

Student Page D20

- Before beginning ask: **What is a diagram? Where have you seen a diagram? Why do we use diagrams?**
- Children might be familiar with diagrams, especially the Food Guide Pyramid, from reading the nutritional information on food packages such as cereal boxes and bread wrappers. Have children look for empty boxes and wrappers with the diagram printed on them at home. Encourage them to bring the samples in to share.

Using a Diagram

A diagram gives information in a chart or picture instead of sentences.

The diagram on page D21 tells what this child likes to do in her free time. The bottom section is the biggest. This tells you that she spends most of her free time riding her bike.

She spends the least amount of her free time coloring. You can tell because that section is the smallest.

Does she spend more time watching TV or reading? How do you know?[1]

[1] reading, because that section is bigger

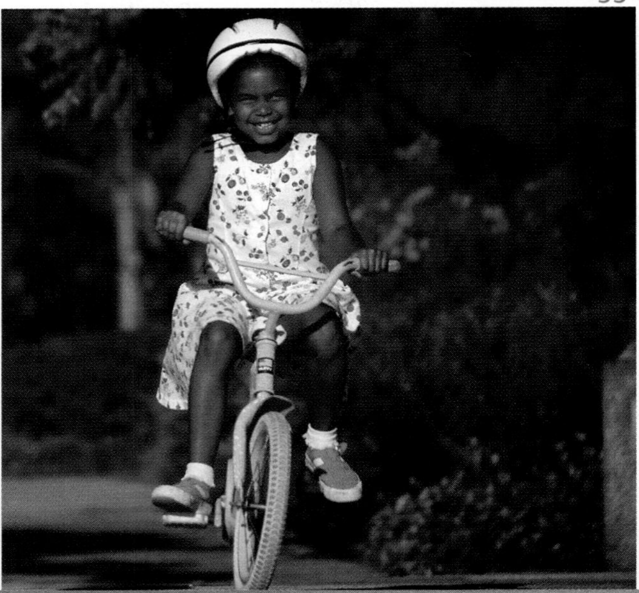

ESL Strategy

Have children point to sections of the diagram on page D21 as you read about them. Tell children that the title and picture for each section help them know what information is being presented in each section.

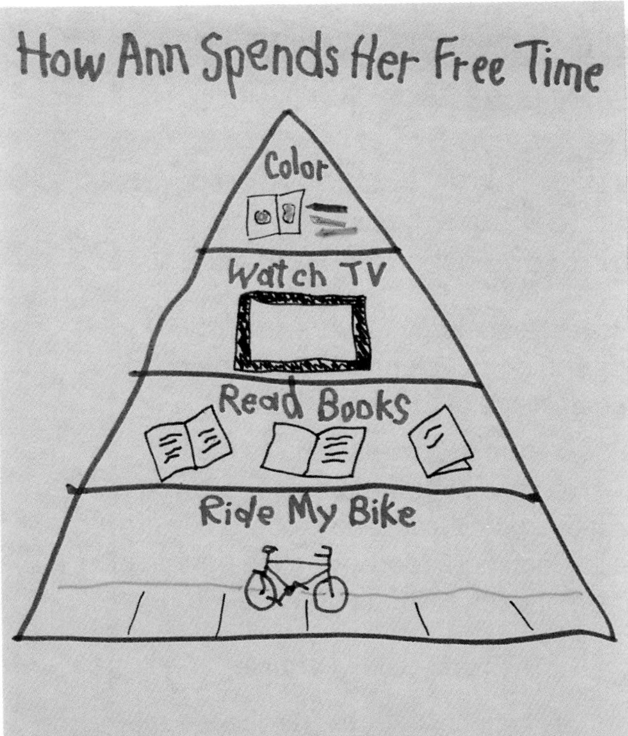

Turn the page to find out how a diagram can help you learn about food.

D21

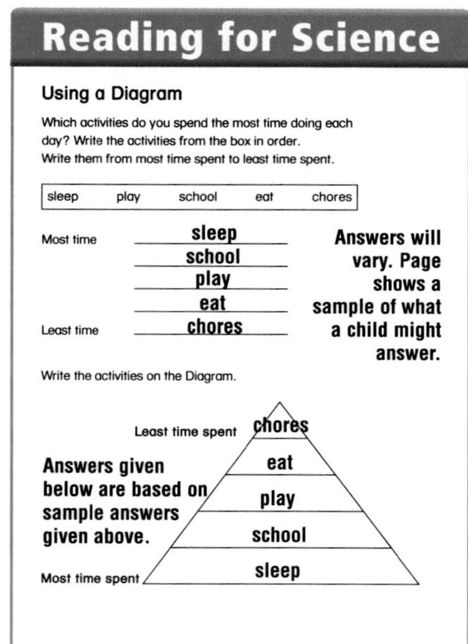

Reading for Science

Using a Diagram

Which activities do you spend the most time doing each day? Write the activities from the box in order. Write them from most time spent to least time spent.

sleep	play	school	eat	chores

Most time
sleep
school
play
eat
chores
Least time

Answers will vary. Page shows a sample of what a child might answer.

Write the activities on the Diagram.

Least time spent
chores
eat
play
school
sleep
Most time spent

Answers given below are based on sample answers given above.

Instructional Resources p. 84

Student Page D 21

- Ask: **What information does the diagram on page D 21 give us?** (*information about how Ann spends her free time*) **Why are the sections different sizes?** (*because Ann spends different amounts of time on the different activities*) **How do you know which activity Ann spends the most amount of time doing?** (*The biggest section equals the most amount of time. The title and the picture tell what that section represents.*)
- Have children ask questions that can be answered using the diagram.
- After discussion, point out that a diagram is read differently from a paragraph. When reading a diagram for information, you can start at the top and read down, or you can start at the bottom and read up. You do not always read a diagram in a certain order. The way you read a diagram depends on what information you are trying to gather.

Apply Reading for Science to Lesson 1

Children will use what they learned about diagrams to complete the next lesson.

Lesson Organizer

Objective

Identify features of proper nutrition and how nutrition keeps us healthy.

Vocabulary Food Guide Pyramid

Process Skills classifying

Materials

Kit Items none

School-Supplied Items large piece of paper, magazines or newspapers, scissors, glue

Additional Resources

- Lab Manual
- Teacher Demonstration Kit
- Wall Chart

Introduce

Activate Prior Knowledge

Invite children to cut out pictures of foods they like. Ask whether they think these foods are good for them. Have children save their pictures for the activity.

Language Development *Make a List*

Write the words *breakfast, lunch,* and *dinner* on the chalkboard. Invite children to name foods that would be good to eat at each meal. Record them under the proper heading.

Flip Chart

Discuss the Food Guide Pyramid in the picture. Have children name their favorite food in each group.

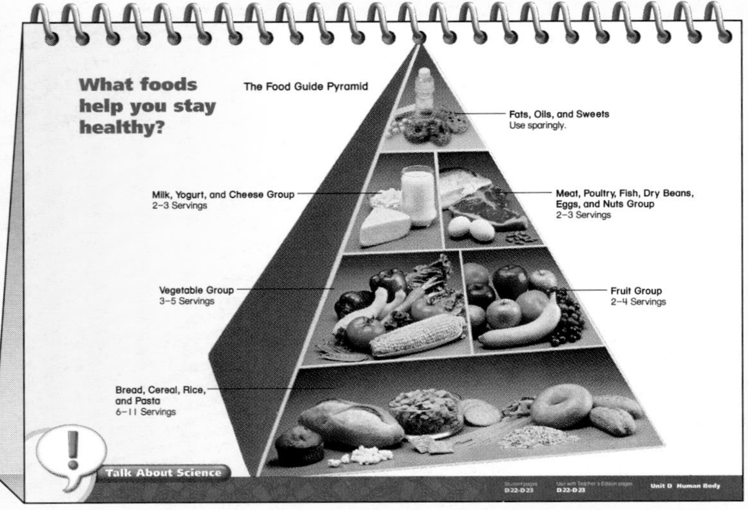

What foods help you stay healthy?

What is your favorite food? You may like that food because it tastes good. Did you know that food helps keep you healthy?

Food gives you energy to work and play. It also helps you grow. To stay healthy, you need to eat certain kinds of foods every day.

The **Food Guide Pyramid** shows the food groups. It also shows how many servings you should eat every day from each food group. To stay healthy, eat more foods from the bottom of the pyramid and fewer foods from the top.

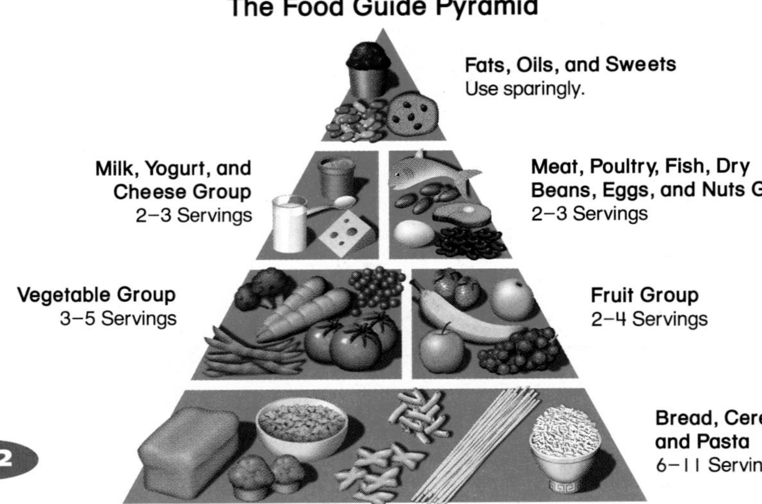

D22

Science Background

According to the USDA, the following are some typical serving sizes: 1 cup milk; 2 ounces cheese; 2–3 ounces meat, poultry, or fish; 1 egg; 2 tablespoons peanut butter; 1 cup raw leafy vegetables; 1/2 cup other vegetables; 1 apple, banana, or orange; 3/4 cup fruit juice; 1 slice bread; 1 ounce ready-to-eat cereal; 1/2 cup cooked cereal, rice, or pasta.

Math-Science Connection

Invite children to keep a record of all the foods they eat for one day. Ask volunteers to use self-stick notes to list their names at the top of **Wall Chart** page 54 and tally the number of servings from each food group. Discuss children's findings.

Explore Activity

Make a Food Guide Pyramid.

Materials
- large piece of paper
- scissors
- glue
- magazines or newspapers

Process Skills
- classifying

Steps

1. Draw a Food Guide Pyramid. Label each section.
2. Cut out pictures of food from magazines or newspapers.
3. Classify each picture into one of the food groups.
4. Glue the pictures onto the Food Guide Pyramid.

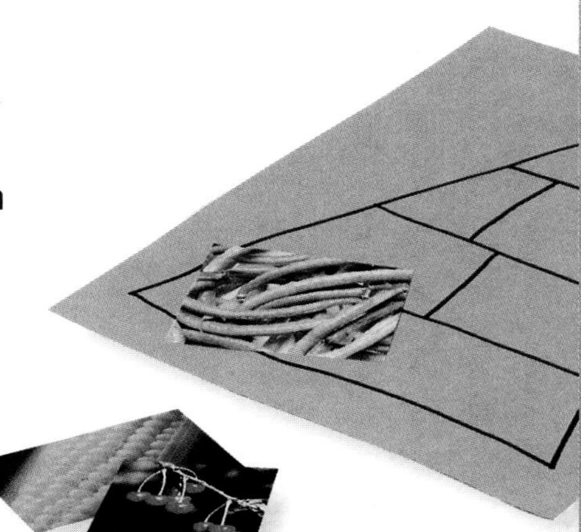

Share. Explain your Food Guide Pyramid to a friend.

Lesson Review

1. Why is food important?
2. What does the Food Guide Pyramid show?
3. **Tell** what food group your favorite food is in.

D23

Lab Manual

What foods help you stay healthy?

Glue each picture onto the Food Guide Pyramid.

Fats, Oils, Sweets
Milk, Yogurt, and Cheese Group
Meats, Poultry, Fish, Dry Beans, Eggs, and Nuts Group
Vegetable Group
Fruit Group
Bread, Cereal, Rice, and Pasta

Lab Manual
p. 97

Activity Rubric

Use the following activity scoring rubric to assess students' performance.

Scoring Criteria	1	2	3	4
Student followed directions to complete this activity.				
Student classified foods into categories on the Food Guide Pyramid.				
Student used the concept of the Food Guide Pyramid to identify kinds of food.				
Student represented the Food Guide Pyramid in a graphic representation.				
Student explained how the Food Guide Pyramid influences the choices of food he or she selects to eat.				

Scoring Key
4 points correct, complete, detailed
3 points partially correct, complete, detailed
2 points partially correct, partially complete, lacks some detail
1 point incorrect or incomplete, needs assistance

Lab Manual
p. T33

Teach and Apply

Student Page D22

To stay healthy, our bodies need the right foods. Help children understand that the number of servings listed for each food group on the Food Guide Pyramid is a guide to help them decide what foods they should eat each day.

Reading Assist *Vowel Combinations*
Write *food* and *good* on the board. Call attention to the different sounds the letters *oo* make in each word. Ask children to name other words that have the vowel sound in *food* (*pool, stool*) and in *good.* (*wood, hood*)

Student Page D23

Explore Activity

Time about 30 minutes

Grouping cooperative groups of 2

Provide children with newspapers containing market advertisements. As children work, point out that many foods cover several food groups. For example, a tuna sandwich covers bread, fish, and oil. Children can complete Lab Manual page 97 as they do the activity.

Assess and Extend

Answers to Lesson Review

1. Food is important because it gives people energy to work and play and helps them grow.
2. The Food Guide Pyramid shows the food groups and how many servings people should eat every day from each food group.
3. **Tell** (*Interview*) Answers will vary and may include any of the food groups.

Inquire Further

Ask the following question to guide further inquiry:
What are some other foods you could put on your Food Guide Pyramid?

Higher Order Thinking *Infer*
Ask children to tell how the Food Guide Pyramid can help them decide what to eat at each meal.

Call 1-888-537-4908 with your Activity questions or comments.

Activity Organizer

Objective

Determine whether certain foods have a high or low fat content.

Process Skills predicting, collecting and interpreting data

Materials

Kit Items none

School-Supplied Items clean brown paper bag, marker, butter, carrot, snack foods

Time about 30 minutes

Grouping cooperative groups of 4

Additional Resources

- Lab Manual
- Teacher Demonstration Kit
- Wall Chart

Introduce

The Lesson 2 Investigate Activity, *Which foods will leave a greasy spot?,* is on the **Flip Chart.**

Activate Prior Knowledge

Provide various food labels. Discuss ways children can tell which foods would be better for them to eat. Point out that the foods that are lower in fat are more healthful to eat.

Language Development *Write Sentences*

Ask children what they think the word *greasy* means. Then have them write sentences using the word.

Investigate  Activity

Which foods will leave a greasy spot?

Process Skills

- predicting
- collecting and interpreting data

Materials

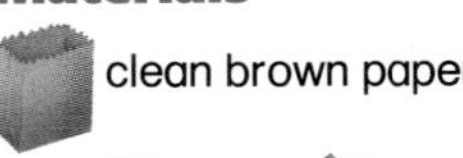

clean brown paper bag, butter, carrot

marker, snack foods

Steps

1. Draw four large circles on your bag.
2. Label one circle Butter. Label another circle Carrot. Label the last two circles with the snack foods you will test.
3. Use a chart like this one.

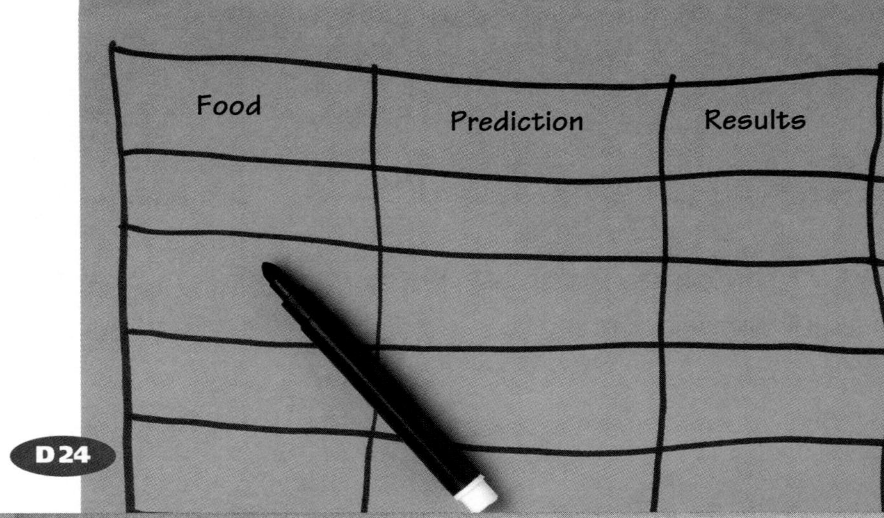

D24

Science Background

- Our bodies need a limited amount of fats.
- Fats give us energy and store energy from food for our bodies to use later. They help our skin and hair.

Science Across Cultures People have different ideas about what makes a good, healthful breakfast. The Japanese may eat *misoshiru,* a soup made of tofu, seaweed, and scallions or radishes. East Indians may eat *idli,* a steamed-rice pancake with coconut sauce, or *uppama,* hot porridge cooked with onions and curry. Invite children to share their own ideas about what makes a good breakfast.

Technology

Review the demonstration of this Investigate's procedure on the *Human Body* **Activity Video,** Segment 3.

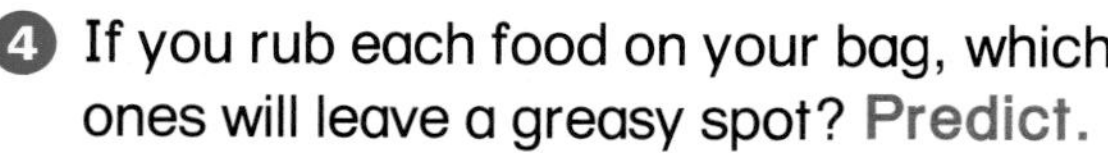

4. If you rub each food on your bag, which ones will leave a greasy spot? **Predict.**
5. **Collect data** by rubbing each food on your bag.
6. Hold your bag up to the light. Which foods left a greasy spot?
7. Record your results.

Think About Your Results

1. Which foods left a greasy spot?
2. Which foods did not leave a greasy spot?

Inquire Further

What other foods do you think would leave a greasy spot?

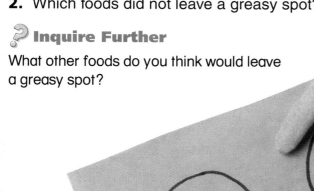

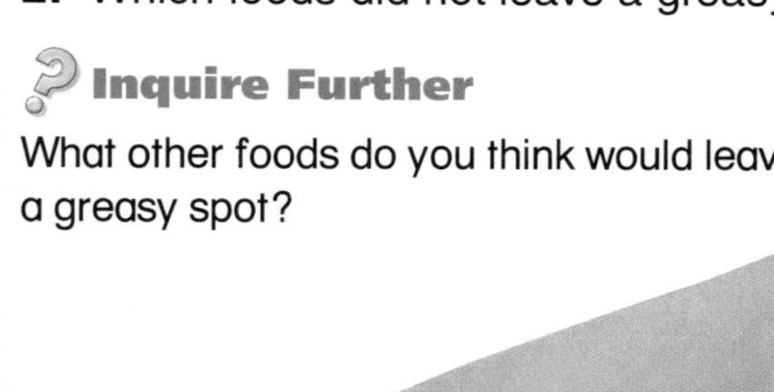

Lab Manual

Which foods will leave a greasy spot?

Use this chart to record your predictions and results for each food you test.

Food	Prediction	Results

Lab Manual
p. 99

Activity Rubric

Use the following activity scoring rubric to assess students' performance.

Scoring Criteria	1	2	3	4
Student followed directions to complete this activity.				
Student predicted which foods would leave a greasy spot.				
Student collected data and recorded results of his or her investigation.				
Student verified results using light to identify greasy spots.				
Student used a chart to present the results of his or her investigation.				

Scoring Key
4 points correct, complete, detailed
3 points partially correct, complete, detailed
2 points partially correct, partially complete, lacks some detail
1 point incorrect or incomplete, needs assistance

Lab Manual
p. T34

Teach and Apply

- In advance, cut the paper bags so that each child receives a large rectangular piece that is only one layer thick.
- You may want to provide two snack foods so all children will test the same foods, or provide a wide variety so children can choose which ones to test. Children may want to do the activity several times with different foods.

 **Safety Note** *Do not allow children to eat the food they are testing.*

- Children should predict by writing "yes" if they think a food will leave a greasy spot and "no" if they think it will not.
- Children can complete Lab Manual page 99.

Reading Assist *Decode Words*

Point out the double consonants in the words *butter* and *carrot.* Discuss the pronunciation of each word. Ask children to find other words on the pages that have double consonants. (*collect, rubbing*)

What to Expect

Foods that contain a lot of fat will leave a greasy spot.

Assess and Extend

Answers to Think About Your Results

1. Answers will vary for the snack foods. The butter should leave a greasy spot.
2. Answers will vary for the snack foods. The carrot should not leave a greasy spot.

Inquire Further

Answers should reflect an understanding that foods high in fat will leave a greasy spot.

Enrichment

Have children use **Wall Chart** page 55 to show which foods they tested were high in fat and which were low in fat. Suggest that children write the names of the foods in the proper columns.

Higher Order Thinking *Draw Conclusions*

Ask: **How often do you think you should eat a high-fat snack food?** (*Children should conclude that fatty foods shouldn't be eaten often.*)

Call 1-888-537-4908 with your Activity questions or comments.

Science Center

Flip Chart

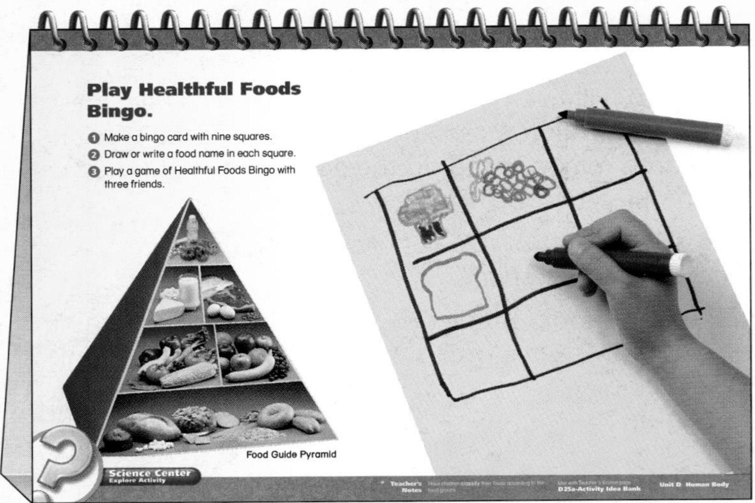

Play Healthful Foods Bingo.
1 Make a bingo card with nine squares.
2 Draw or write a food name in each square.
3 Play a game of Healthful Foods Bingo with three friends.
Food Guide Pyramid
Science Center

Play Healthful Foods Bingo.

Objective

Classify foods.

Process Skills classifying

Materials

Kit Items none

School-Supplied Items paper, pencil, crayons, markers such as beans or paper squares

Procedure

- Invite children to refer to the Food Guide Pyramid on the **Flip Chart** as they play the game.
- Have children work in groups of four. One child names food groups. The three others **classify** foods as they place markers to cover the foods on their cards that come from the called-out groups.
- The player who covers a row or the four corners of the card leads the next game.
- You can use **Lab Manual** page 100 with this activity.

What to Expect

Children classify different foods from the six groups of the Food Guide Pyramid.

Lab Manual

Play Healthful Foods Bingo.

Use the Food Guide Pyramid to draw nine pictures of food on the bingo card. Cut out the markers. Play a game of Healthful Foods Bingo with three friends.

Bingo Card

Lab Manual, p. 100

Connections

School and Community

Ideas for bringing the school and community together:

Field Trips

- science museum
- bakery
- grocery store
- restaurant

Guest Speakers

- school nurse
- dietitian or nutritionist
- dental hygienist
- cafeteria manager

Themes

The activities on these pages can be used with classroom themes such as:

- food and nutrition
- healthful snacks
- cooking
- human body

Books for Children

Children might enjoy these books about food:

Like Butter on Pancakes by Jonathan London. A young boy wakes up to pancakes and his day's adventures. (Viking, ISBN 0-670-85130-2)

Anansi and the Talking Melon retold by Eric A. Kimmel. A spider climbs inside a melon and causes all kinds of humorous confusion. (Holiday House, ISBN 0-8234-1104-4)

Cross-Curricular Options

LITERATURE

Jalapeño Bagels

Use the book to discuss cultural foods.

Materials *Jalapeño Bagels* by Natasha Wing. (Atheneum, ISBN 0-689-80530-6)

Procedure

- It is International Day at School, and Pablo brings Jalapeño bagels to reflect his culture.
- Discuss all the foods that are featured and have children share names of foods from their cultures.
- Duplicate copies of the recipes included and invite children to try them at home.

Multiple Intelligences linguistic

Gifted and Talented Invite children to put together an illustrated class cookbook with favorite family recipes.

MATH

Feeding Friends

Increase a recipe for different numbers of guests.

Materials red, orange, and yellow Snap Cubes; bowls; paper; pencil

Procedure

- Children use the Snap Cubes to make one serving of "fruit salad"—3 pieces of apple, 4 of banana, and 5 of orange.
- They make enough fruit salad for one friend to join them, then two friends.
- Children can make a chart to show how many pieces of fruit they need for one, two, and three people.

Multiple Intelligences logical-mathematical

ESL Help children practice counting from 1 to 15.

WRITING

Colorful Language

Write similes.

Materials paper, pencil

Procedure

- Explain that a simile compares two things using the word *like* or *as.*
- Generate a list of food-related similes, such as *jiggly as jelly, soft as a marshmallow, crunchy as a carrot.*
- Have children use the similes in descriptive sentences or stories.

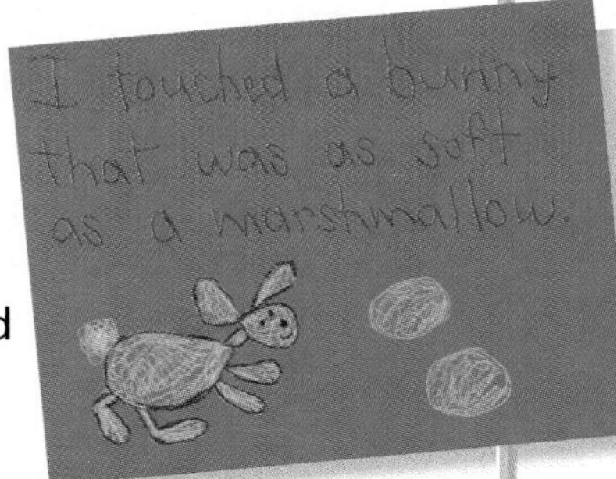

Multiple Intelligences linguistic

LANGUAGE ARTS

carrot

Food Fun

Make a food concentration game.

Materials index cards, magazines, paste, scissors, marker

Procedure

- Have children cut out or draw pictures of foods and paste them on index cards. Have children write the name of each food on separate cards.
- Combine pairs of cards for children to play "Concentration," matching pictures with their corresponding names.

Multiple Intelligences spatial, linguistic

Lesson Organizer

Objective
Describe how saliva begins the digestive process.

Vocabulary digestion

Process Skills predicting, observing

Materials
Kit Items 2 resealable plastic bags

School-Supplied Items soda crackers, water

Additional Resources
- Lab Manual
- Teacher Demonstration Kit
- Wall Chart

Introduce

Activate Prior Knowledge
Ask children to think about eating a crisp apple or carrot stick. Have volunteers describe what happens to an apple when they eat it.

Language Development *Word Web*
Have children use **Wall Chart** page 56 to brainstorm foods that do and do not have to be chewed. (*Apples have to be chewed; some ice creams and soups do not.*)

Flip Chart
Point out that the girl in the picture is about to bite the apple. Discuss what will happen to the apple when it is chewed. Ask: **Why is it important to chew food?**

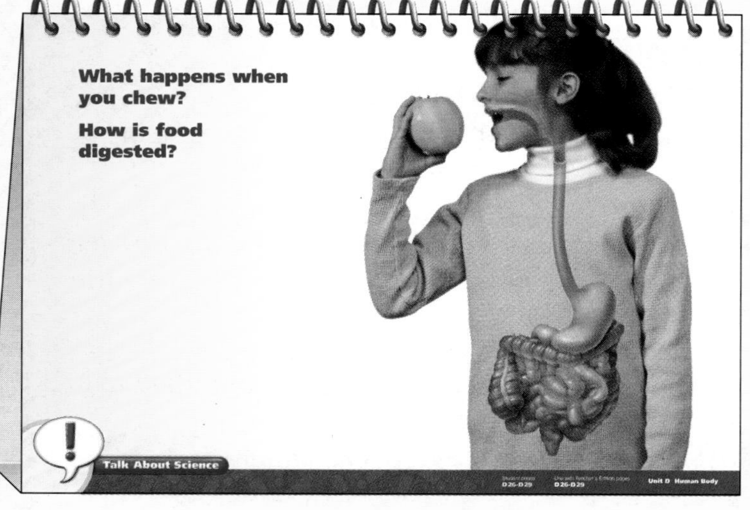

What happens when you chew?
How is food digested?
Talk About Science
Unit D Human Body

What happens when you chew?

Think about biting into a crisp apple. It might taste cool and sweet. It might feel crunchy in your mouth.

You know that food gives your body energy. Food needs to be broken down and changed so your body can use it. The process of breaking down food is called **digestion**.

Digestion begins in your mouth. When you chew, your teeth grind the food into small pieces. Your saliva makes the food wet, and your tongue mixes it. The food has started to change.

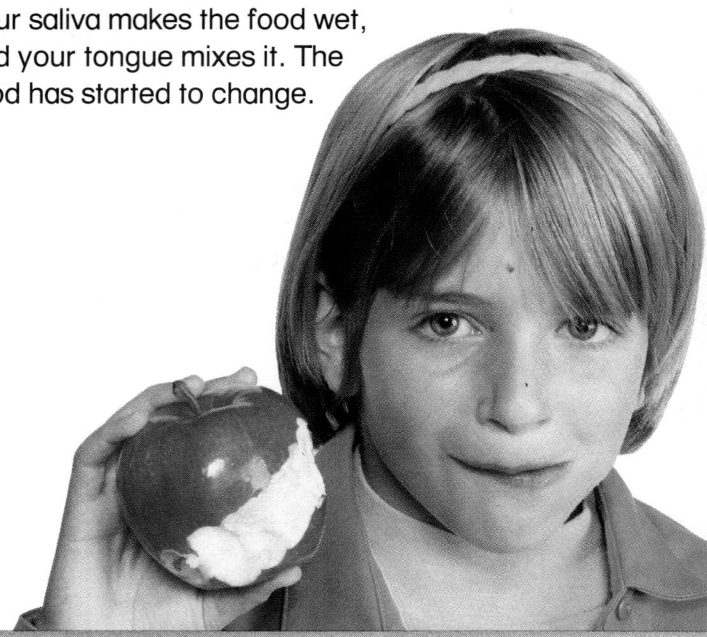

Science Background

Teeth, tongue, and saliva work together to moisten and soften food into a form that is easy to swallow.

Teaching Tips Children should add about two spoons of water. Advise children to add the same amount of water to each bag. You may want to provide spoons and have children count out how many spoonfuls of water they put in each bag. Or suggest that they draw a line on a paper cup and fill it to that line each time. Have children put the crackers into the bags before they break one of them into pieces.

Observe how food can be changed.

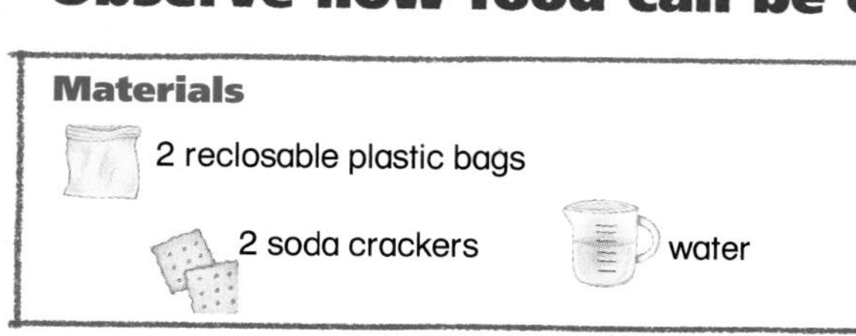

Materials

- 2 reclosable plastic bags
- 2 soda crackers
- water

Process Skills

- predicting
- observing

Process Skills

Steps

1. Put one cracker in each bag.
2. Break one of the crackers into small pieces. Leave the other cracker whole.
3. Add water to both bags. Seal the bags.
4. What will happen to the crackers if you shake the bags? **Predict.**
5. Shake each bag ten times. **Observe.**

Share. Compare the crackers.

Lesson Review

1. What is digestion?
2. What happens to food when you chew it?
3. **Tell** how chewing and saliva help digestion.

Lab Manual

What happens when you chew?

What will happen if you shake the bags? Predict.

Draw how both crackers look after you shake the bags.

Lab Manual
p. 101

Activity Rubric

Use the following activity scoring rubric to assess students' performance.

Scoring Criteria	1	2	3	4
Student followed directions to complete this activity.				
Student predicted what might happen to each of two bags of crackers (one with a whole cracker, one with cracker broken) when water is added.				
Student facilitated a change in the bags of crackers by shaking each.				
Student observed the effect of shaking on each of the bags.				
Student compared his or her observation about each of the bags of crackers with the process of digestion.				

Scoring Key

4 points correct, complete, detailed
3 points partially correct, complete, detailed
2 points partially correct, partially complete, lacks some detail
1 point incorrect or incomplete, needs assistance

Lab Manual
p. T35

Teach and Apply

Student Page D26

Remind children of how an apple changes as it is chewed. Point out that chewing and swallowing food is the first step in digestion.

Reading Assist *Decode Words*

Have children say the word *crisp* and listen for the *r* blend at the beginning of the word. Then encourage children to find other words in the text that begin with an *r* blend. (*crunchy, broken, breaking, grind*)

Student Page D27

Explore Activity

Time about 15 minutes

Grouping individual

Help children understand that this activity simulates chewing—breaking the cracker—and saliva—adding water. Ask them to note which cracker breaks down faster. Children can complete Lab Manual page 101 as they do the activity.

What to Expect

The cracker that is in small pieces should break down more quickly than the whole cracker.

Assess and Extend

Answers to Lesson Review

1. Digestion is the process of breaking down food.
2. When you chew, your teeth grind the food into small pieces.
3. **Tell** (*Interview*) Chewing helps digestion by grinding food into small pieces. Saliva helps digestion by getting the food wet and making it softer.

Inquire Further

Ask the following question to guide further inquiry: **How are the crackers different now?** (*The broken cracker is mushy. The unbroken cracker has solid lumps.*)

Higher Order Thinking *Draw Conclusions*

Ask children to tell why they think saliva and chewing are so important to digestion.

Call 1-888-537-4908 with your Activity questions or comments.

Lesson Organizer

Objective

Describe the digestive system.

Vocabulary

esophagus, small intestine, nutrients, large intestine

Additional Resources

- Interactive Transparency
- Wall Chart

Introduce

Activate Prior Knowledge

In advance, prepare self-stick notes with the following words on them: *mouth, esophagus, small intestine, large intestine,* and *stomach.* Then display **Wall Chart** page 57. Ask children to name parts of the body that are used to digest food and label the diagram with the notes. Save the chart for use as a **baseline assessment.**

Language Development *Scientific Language*

Explain that the body parts used to break down food are called the body's digestive system. In a system, each part is needed for the whole to function properly.

Flip Chart

Say the words *esophagus, stomach, large intestine,* and *small intestine* one at a time in random order. Have volunteers point to the corresponding body part on the **Flip Chart.**

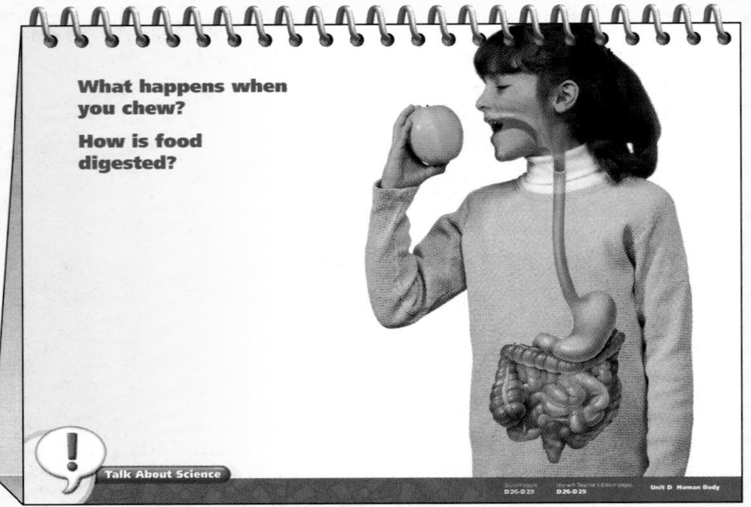

What happens when you chew?
How is food digested?
Talk About Science

How is food digested?

What did you have for dinner last night? After you chewed and swallowed your food, where did it go?

After you swallow, the food goes into a tube called the **esophagus**. The esophagus squeezes the food down to your stomach. Inside your stomach, the food is mixed until it is a liquid.

Next, the liquid goes into the small intestine. The **small intestine** is a long, thin tube that is curled up. Most of the digestion takes place in the small intestine. You need nutrients from the digested food. **Nutrients** are materials in food that you need to grow and stay healthy.

The leftover liquid goes into the large intestine. The **large intestine** squeezes out the rest of the liquid and then passes solid wastes out of the body.

D28

Science Background

- Food stays in the stomach for two to five hours before it passes into the small intestine.
- Although properly chewed food is more easily digested, chewing has no effect on the delivery of nutrients to the body.

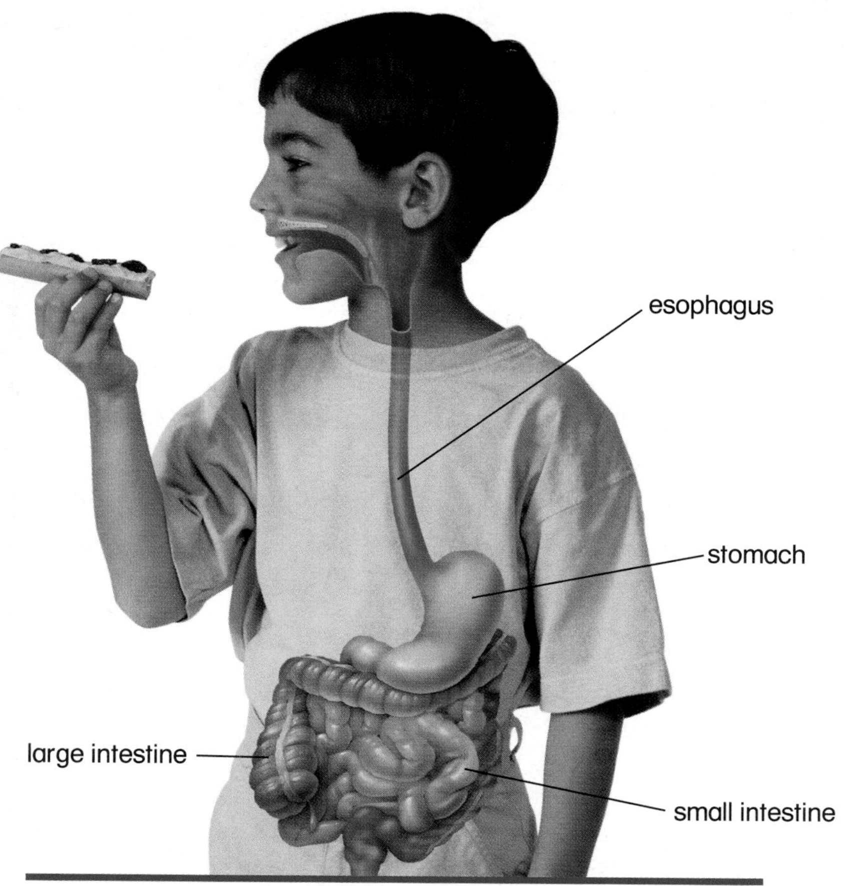

Lesson Review

1. What happens inside the stomach?
2. Where does most of the digestion take place?
3. **Draw** the path food takes through the body.

ESL Strategy

As you name each part of the body in the digestive process, have children point to it on page D29. Encourage children to say the names aloud as they point.

Transparency

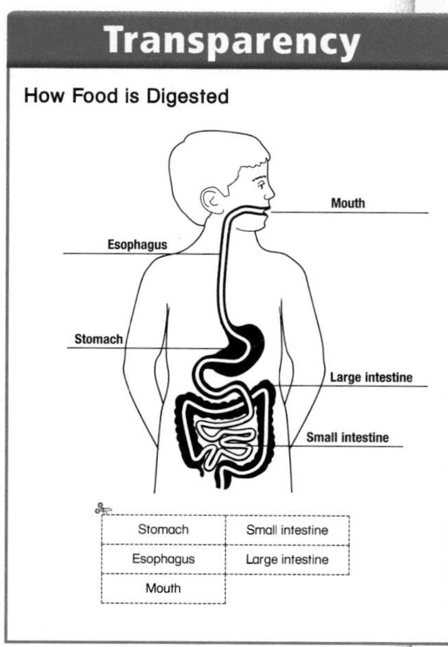

Interactive Transparency Package
Transparency 11

Teach and Apply

Student Pages D28–D29

- Refer children to the picture of the digestive system and ask them to name some important parts. Have children use their fingers to trace the path food takes through the body.
- Mix up note cards listing the parts of the body used in the digestive system. Have children take turns selecting a card and telling what that body part does.

Reading Assist *Decode Words*

Point out that the letters *ph* in the word *esophagus* make the /f/ sound. Ask children if they can think of any other words that contain the letters *ph.*

Assess and Extend

Answers to Lesson Review

1. Inside the stomach, food is mixed until it is a liquid.
2. Most of the digestion takes place in the small intestine.
3. **Draw** (*Portfolio Assessment or Journal*) Children should draw a basic human form and include the mouth, esophagus, stomach, small intestine, and large intestine.

Check for Understanding

To follow up on the **baseline assessment,** have children review the **Wall Chart.** Then have them revise their labels as needed.

Reteach

- Use the Interactive Transparency to reteach Lesson 4 concepts.
- On separate cards, list each step in the process of digestion. Mix the cards and have children take turns placing them in the proper order. Then ask them to describe the process using the cards.

Science Center

Flip Chart

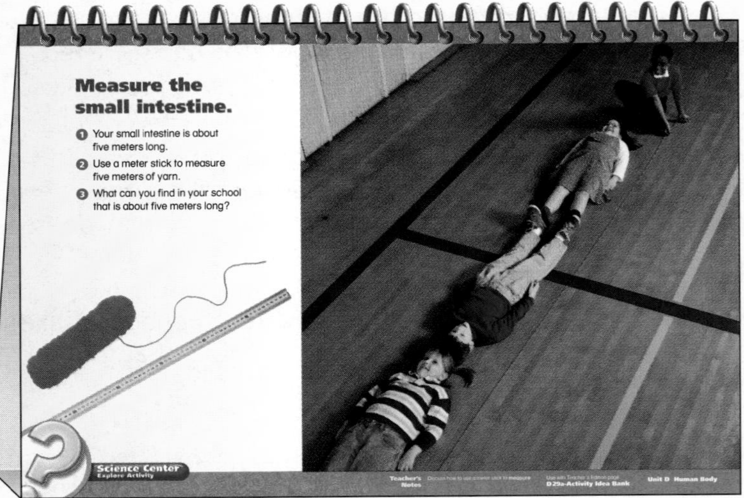

Measure the small intestine.
1 Your small intestine is about five meters long.
2 Use a meter stick to measure five meters of yarn.
3 What can you find in your school that is about five meters long?
Science Center
Explore Activity

Measure the small intestine.

Objective

Measure the length of the small intestine.

Process Skills measuring

Materials

Kit Items red yarn

School-Supplied Items meterstick

Procedure

- You may want to demonstrate how to use a meterstick.
- Children **measure** and cut 5 meters of yarn to match the length of the small intestine.
- Suggest that children use the yarn to measure themselves and infer how much longer than themselves the small intestine is.
- You can use **Lab Manual** page 103 with this activity.

What to Expect

Children use yarn to measure 5 meters, which is the length of their small intestines.

Lab Manual

Measure the small intestine.

What objects are about the same length as your small intestine?

Name of object	Picture of object

Lab Manual, p. 103

Connections

School and Community

Ideas for bringing the school and community together:

Field Trips

- science museum
- doctor's office
- cafeteria kitchen
- pizzeria

Guest Speakers

- school nurse
- dietitian or nutritionist
- dental hygienist
- doctor

Themes

The activities on these pages can be used with classroom themes such as:

- nutrition
- senses
- human body

Books for Children

Children might enjoy these books about food:

The Lunchbox by Diana Noonan. A humorous account of what happens to food in a lunch box if left uncovered. (Learning Media, ISBN 0-478-20510-4)

Hold the Anchovies! A Book about Pizza by Shelly Rotner and Julia Pemberton Hellums. How pizza is made, from growing the ingredients to happy eaters. (Orchard Books, ISBN 0-531-09507-X)

Gregory, the Terrible Eater by Mitchell Sharmat. Gregory the goat, a picky eater, refuses the usual goat diet of shoes and tin cans in favor of fruits, vegetables, eggs, and orange juice. (Scholastic, ISBN 0-590-43350-4)

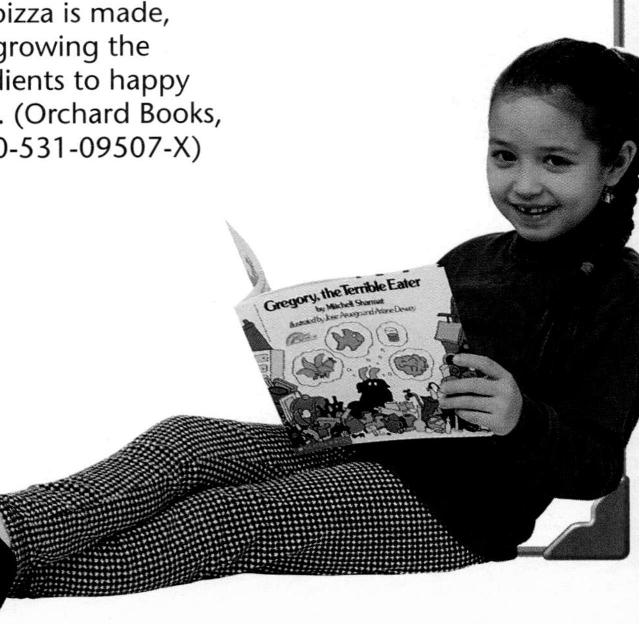

Cross-Curricular Options

LITERATURE

How Pizza Came to Queens

Use the book to talk about a favorite food.

Materials *How Pizza Came to Queens* by Dayal Kaur Khalsa. (Clarkson Potter, ISBN 0-517-88538-7)

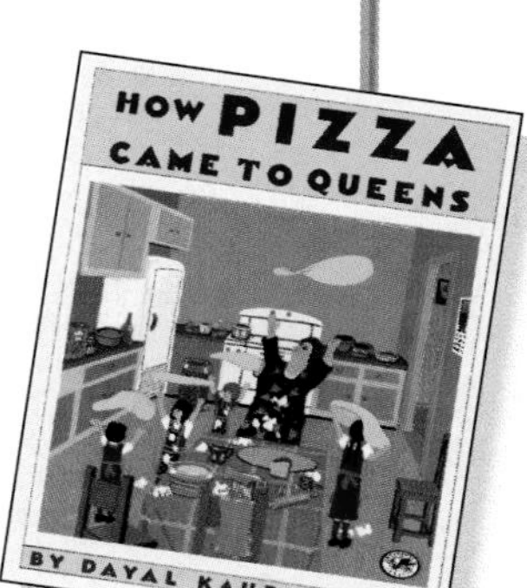

Procedure

- Mrs. Pelligrino comes from Italy to visit cousins in Queens, New York, before anyone in the neighborhood knows about pizza.
- As you read aloud the beginning of the story, ask children to predict what Mrs. Pelligrino has in her green package.
- The book includes a recipe for pizza which you might duplicate and give to children to prepare at home.

Multiple Intelligences linguistic

MATH

Nutrition Math

Write and solve problems.

Materials paper, pencil, Snap Cubes or other manipulatives

Procedure

- Have children refer to the Food Guide Pyramid on page D 22.
- Ask children to use the suggested servings to make up math problems for a partner to solve. For example: 2 servings of milk + 5 servings of vegetables + 3 servings of fruit = how many servings in all?
- Children can use manipulatives to help them solve the problems.

Multiple Intelligences logical-mathematical

WRITING

Happy Tummy

Make posters about good digestion.

Materials poster board, markers or crayons

Procedure

- Help children generate a list of practices for maintaining good digestion, such as not overeating, eating slowly, chewing food, drinking a lot of water, and resting after eating.
- Have partners make posters using pictures and slogans to illustrate good practices for digestion.

For Good Digestion
Eat slowly,
chew your food,
drink plenty of water.

Multiple Intelligences linguistic, spatial

Gifted and Talented Have children ask the school nurse what causes stomachaches and report their findings to the class.

ART

Nutritious Vegetables

Make clay models of nutritious foods.

Materials clay in a variety of colors, newspaper, paper, pencil

Procedure

- Write a list of fruits and vegetables on the chalkboard as children suggest them.
- Invite children to choose a fruit or vegetable and create a model of it out of clay.
- Have children research their foods in the library, on the computer, or in the grocery store to find which vitamins and minerals the food provides.
- Encourage children to prepare an oral report about the nutrients in their foods.

Multiple Intelligences spatial, linguistic

ESL To check children's understanding, ask children to name one nutritious food and one food that is not very nutritious.

Review Organizer

Materials

Kit Items none

School-Supplied Items paper, pencil or marker

Time about 30 minutes

Grouping cooperative groups of 6

Additional Resources

- Chapter 2 Assessment: Teacher's Assessment Package

Chapter Main Ideas

Lesson 1 Food gives you energy to work, play, and grow. You need to eat the proper foods to be healthy.

Lesson 2 Food samples can be tested for fat content. Predictions can be proved or not proved based on observation and collection of data.

Lesson 3 The process of digestion begins in the mouth. The teeth and tongue break down and mix the food, and the saliva makes the food wet.

Lesson 4 The digestive system includes the mouth, esophagus, stomach, small intestine, and large intestine. Food must be digested so that nutrients can be used by the body for growth and repair.

Reviewing Science Words

1. The Food Guide Pyramid shows you how many servings to eat every day from each food group.
2. Digestion begins in your mouth.
3. The esophagus squeezes food down to the stomach.
4. Most of digestion takes place in the small intestine.
5. You need nutrients to grow and stay healthy.
6. The large intestine squeezes out the rest of the liquid and passes solid waste out of the body.

Reviewing Science Ideas

1. Bread, cereal, rice, and pasta group; vegetable group; fruit group; milk, yogurt, and cheese group; meat, poultry, fish, dry beans, eggs, and nuts group; fats, oils, and sweets group
2. Children should mention chewing and saliva in the mouth; the small intestine; and the large intestine.

Chapter 2 Review

Reviewing Science Words

1. How does the **Food Guide Pyramid** help you stay healthy?
2. Where does **digestion** begin?
3. What does the **esophagus** do?
4. What happens in the **small intestine**?
5. How do **nutrients** help you?
6. What does the **large intestine** do?

Reviewing Science Ideas

1. Name three of the food groups.
2. Explain how food is digested.

D30

Technology

 Children can review *Nutrition* with the **Practice & Assessment CD-ROM.**

 Children can use the **Production Studio** to show what they've learned about *Nutrition.*

 Children can use The KnowZone™ at **www.kz.com** to review and test their science knowledge.

 You can use **TestWorks™** to customize assessment for your children.

Make a daily menu.

Materials

paper

pencil or markers

1. Work with a group.
2. Talk about what you like to eat for breakfast, lunch, and dinner.
3. Use the Food Guide Pyramid to plan meals that have all the servings you need from each food group.
4. Make your menu and share it with the class.

Chapter Assessment

Use the words in the box to finish each sentence.

nutrients	Food Guide Pyramid	small intestine
mouth	digestion	esophagus	stomach

1. Digestion begins in your ________.
2. The ________ squeezes food down to your stomach.
3. The ________ shows how many servings of different foods you should eat each day.
4. Most food is digested in the ________.
5. Our bodies get ________ from foods.
6. Our bodies break down food in the process of ________.

Circle your answer.

7. Which food will be digested faster?

Teacher's Assessment Package pp. 65–66

Assessment Rubric

	Food Groups
4	Correctly uses the Food Guide Pyramid to plan meals that have all the servings needed from each food group.
3	Uses the Food Guide Pyramid and makes few errors planning meals that have all the servings needed from each food group.
2	Has difficulty using the Food Guide Pyramid to plan meals that have all the servings needed from each food group.
1	Is unable to use the Food Guide Pyramid to plan meals that have all the servings needed from each food group.

Performance Assessment Teaching Tips

- Before beginning the activity, review the Food Guide Pyramid and the recommended number of servings from each food group on page D 22.
- Food magazines or grocery store advertisement flyers are good sources of pictures for this activity. Children can draw or paste pictures of food on their menus to enhance them.
- Assign cooperative roles or have each child in the group be responsible for making sure a particular food group is represented in the menu.
- Have each group make a nutrition chart to show how their menus for breakfast, lunch, and dinner provide nutritious meals. You might provide the following nutrition chart for groups to complete:

Food Group	Breakfast	Lunch	Dinner	Total Daily Servings

Enrichment

Gather the completed menus into a class book. Have children select a menu from the booklet and write about why they would or would not eat the foods on the menu. Have them suggest other foods in the same food group to replace ones they would not like to eat.

Chapter 2 Skills Trace

Process Skills Development	Classifying	Predicting	Collecting and Interpreting Data	Observing
Skill Introduced	xiv	xv	xv	xiv
Skill Applied	D 23	D 24–D 25 D 27	D 24–D 25	D 27
Skill Assessed	End Matter 10–11	End Matter 16–17	End Matter 24–25	End Matter 6–7

Chapter Review pages are also on the **Flip Chart.**

Lesson/Activity and Flip Chart	Objectives/Process Skills	Time Options/Activity Materials
Chapter Opener Student Edition pp. D32–D33 and **Flip Chart** ***Exercise Today***		**Have less time?** Use the Graphic Organizer on Teacher's Assessment Package p. 69 for an overview of the lessons. Use the Flip Chart to teach lesson concepts and science activities. **Have more time?** Use the Flip Chart to reinforce and extend lesson concepts and activities. Use the Cross-Curricular Options in the Activity Idea Bank on Teacher's Edition pp. D39b and D43b.
Lesson 1 Student Edition pp. D34–D35 ***Why is exercise important?*** **Explore Activity** ***Do exercises.*** **Flip Chart** ***Talk About Science***	**Objective** Determine that exercise is important for health. **Process Skills** predicting, collecting and interpreting data	**Kit Items** none **School-Supplied Items** clock with a second hand or stopwatch
Math in Science Student Edition pp. D36–D37 ***Using a Calendar***	**Objective** Use a calendar.	
Lesson 2 Student Edition pp. D38–D39 and **Flip Chart** **Investigate Activity** ***How much exercise do you get?***	**Objective** Keep track of daily exercise. **Process Skills** collecting and interpreting data	**Kit Items** none **School-Supplied Items** blank calendar, pencil or crayons
Activity Idea Bank Teacher's Edition pp. D39a–D39b **Flip Chart** **Science Center Explore Activity** ***Stay fit.***	**Objective** Demonstrate a stretch and an exercise. **Process Skills** classifying	**Kit Items** none **School-Supplied Items** paper, pencil, crayons, tape, markers
Lesson 3 Student Edition pp. D40–D41 ***Why is it important to keep clean?*** **Flip Chart** ***Talk About Science***	**Objective** Determine that cleanliness contributes to good health.	
Lesson 4 Student Edition pp. D42–D43 ***How can you take care of yourself?*** **Flip Chart** ***Talk About Science***	**Objective** Identify ways to stay healthy.	**Have more time?** Use the following teaching guide option: Interactive Transparency 12, Interactive Transparency Package
Activity Idea Bank Teacher's Edition pp. D43a–D43b **Flip Chart** **Science Center Explore Activity** ***Make a diorama.***	**Objective** Demonstrate an understanding of the importance of cleanliness and ways to stay healthy. **Process Skills** communicating	**Kit Items** none **School-Supplied Items** shoe box, construction paper, glue, scissors, magazines, art supplies
Chapter Review Student Edition pp. D44–D45 and **Flip Chart**		**Kit Items** none **School-Supplied Items** big piece of paper, pencils or markers

Lesson/Activity and Flip Chart	Additional Resources		Technology
Chapter Opener Student Edition pp. D32–D33 and **Flip Chart** ***Exercise Today***	**Teacher's Assessment Package** • Graphic Organizer, p. 69 **Instructional Resources** • Family Activity, pp. 89–90 • Vocabulary Preview, p. 91	**Songs & Activities Package** • *Exercise Today*, pp. 31–32 **Wall Chart,** p. 58	**Practice & Assessment CD-ROM** **AudioText** **Production Studio** **www.sfscience.com** **Songs & Activities Package** **Teacher's Resource Planner CD-ROM**
Lesson 1 Student Edition pp. D34–D35 ***Why is exercise important?*** **Explore Activity** ***Do exercises.*** **Flip Chart** ***Talk About Science***	**Lab Manual** • Lab Manual, p. 105 • Activity Rubric, p. T36	**Teacher Demonstration Kit** **Wall Chart,** p. 59	
Math in Science Student Edition pp. D36–D37 ***Using a Calendar***	**Instructional Resources** • Math in Science, p. 92		
Lesson 2 Student Edition pp. D38–D39 and **Flip Chart** **Investigate Activity** ***How much exercise do you get?***	**Lab Manual** • Lab Manual, p. 106 • Activity Rubric, p. T36	**Teacher Demonstration Kit** **Wall Chart,** p. 60	*Human Body* **Activity Video**
Activity Idea Bank Teacher's Edition pp. D39a–D39b **Flip Chart** **Science Center Explore Activity** ***Stay fit.***	**Lab Manual** • Lab Manual, p. 107 • Activity Rubric, p. T37		
Lesson 3 Student Edition pp. D40–D41 ***Why is it important to keep clean?*** **Flip Chart** ***Talk About Science***		**Wall Chart,** p. 61	
Lesson 4 Student Edition pp. D42–D43 ***How can you take care of yourself?*** **Flip Chart** ***Talk About Science***	**Interactive Transparency Package** • Interactive Transparency 12	**Wall Chart,** p. 62	
Activity Idea Bank Teacher's Edition pp. D43a–D43b **Flip Chart** **Science Center Explore Activity** ***Make a diorama.***	**Lab Manual** • Lab Manual, p. 108 • Activity Rubric, p. T37		
Chapter Review Student Edition pp. D44–D45 and **Flip Chart**	**Teacher's Assessment Package** • Chapter 3 Assessment, pp. 71–72		**Practice & Assessment CD-ROM** **Production Studio** **The KnowZone™ at www.kz.com** **TestWorks™**

Math in Science

Using a Calendar

May						
Sunday	Monday	Tuesday	Wednesday	Thursday	Friday	Saturday
1	2	3	4	5	6	7
8	9	10	11	12	13	14
15	16	17	18	19	20	21
22	23	24	25	26	27	28
29	30	31				

1. Draw a circle on the first day in May.
   What day of the week is it? **Sunday**
2. Put an X on the last day in May.
   How many days are in May? **31**
   What day of the week is the last day in May? **Tuesday**
3. How many Mondays are in the month shown? **5**
4. How many Fridays are in the month shown? **4**

Instructional Resources
p. 92

Lab Manual

Why is exercise important?

Write the names of other exercises you can do.
Predict how many times you can do each exercise in one minute.
Record your results.

Exercise	Prediction	Results
Students' identification of the exercise they do will vary as will their predictions about the number of times they can perform an exercise in one minute. The results they record will also vary.		

Lab Manual
p. 105

Lab Manual

How much exercise do you get?

Draw how you get exercise each day.
Write about it.

Students' drawings and descriptions of their exercise will vary.

Lab Manual
p. 106

Lab Manual

Stay fit.

Draw a picture of your stretch and your exercise.
Write about your pictures.

Students' drawings of their stretch and exercise will vary.

Stretch

Exercise

Lab Manual
p. 107

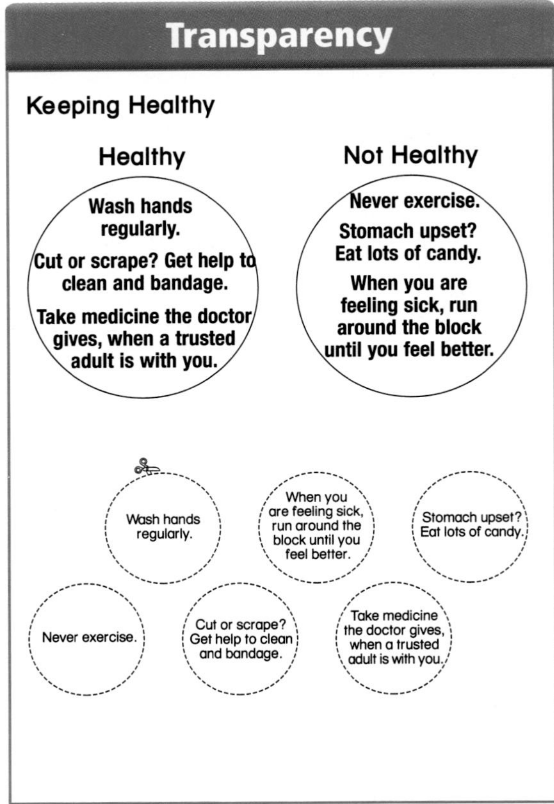

Transparency

Keeping Healthy

Healthy	Not Healthy
Wash hands regularly. Cut or scrape? Get help to clean and bandage. Take medicine the doctor gives, when a trusted adult is with you.	Never exercise. Stomach upset? Eat lots of candy. When you are feeling sick, run around the block until you feel better.

Wash hands regularly.

When you are feeling sick, run around the block until you feel better.

Stomach upset? Eat lots of candy.

Never exercise.

Cut or scrape? Get help to clean and bandage.

Take medicine the doctor gives, when a trusted adult is with you.

Interactive Transparency Package
Transparency 12

Lab Manual

Make a diorama.

Draw another way to keep clean or take care of yourself.
Write a sentence about it.

Students' dioramas will vary.

Lab Manual
p. 108

Chapter 3 Assessment

Circle all the correct answers.

1. What are ways to get exercise?
   (run a race) read a book (climb a hill)
2. What are ways germs can get inside your body?
   (nose) (mouth) (cuts)
3. What should you do if you are sick?
   play soccer (get rest) (stay home from school)

Mark an X in the box next to the best answer.

4. What is the best way to clean your teeth?
   - ☐ bar of soap
   - ☒ toothpaste and toothbrush
   - ☐ glass of water
5. Who should give you medicine when you are sick?
   - ☐ a younger brother or sister
   - ☐ a classmate
   - ☒ a trusted adult
6. Why is exercise important?
   - ☒ keeps your muscles strong
   - ☐ makes you sweat
   - ☐ helps you find friends

Teacher's Assessment Package
p. 71

Chapter 3 Assessment

Write **Yes** or **No**.

yes 7. It is important to go to your doctor for checkups.

yes 8. Washing with soap and water removes germs.

no 9. You should go to school even when you have a fever.

yes 10. When you get a small cut, wash it and cover it with a bandage.

Teacher's Assessment Package
p. 72

Table of Contents

Introducing the Chapter

The song *Exercise Today* is also on the **Flip Chart.**

- Ask children to share experiences with exercise. Discuss how and why people exercise.
- Distribute the Family Activity blackline master page.

Singing the Song

Have children sing the song *Exercise Today* on side 2 of the CTW cassette. Distribute pages 31–32 from the CTW Song Activity Book.

Reading Assist *Word Meaning*

Explain that exercise is actively using your body such as by doing jumping jacks or playing soccer. Have children find all the examples of exercise in the song. *(running, jumping, climbing, play ball, take a walk, swim, ride a bike)*

Vocabulary Preview

Use the Vocabulary Preview blackline master to introduce the vocabulary words for this chapter.

Lesson 1 exercise

Lesson 3 germs

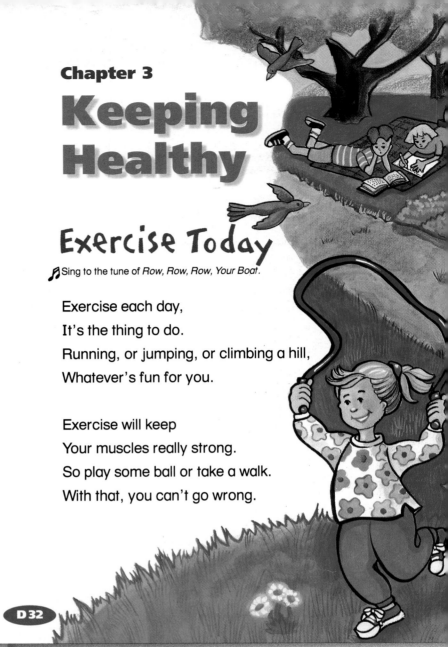

Chapter 3

Keeping Healthy

Exercise Today

Sing to the tune of *Row, Row, Row, Your Boat.*

Exercise each day,
It's the thing to do.
Running, or jumping, or climbing a hill,
Whatever's fun for you.

Exercise will keep
Your muscles really strong.
So play some ball or take a walk.
With that, you can't go wrong.

D32

Technology

Practice & Assessment CD-ROM

AudioText

Production Studio

www.sfscience.com

Teacher's Resource Planner

Songs & Activities Package

CTW Song & Activity

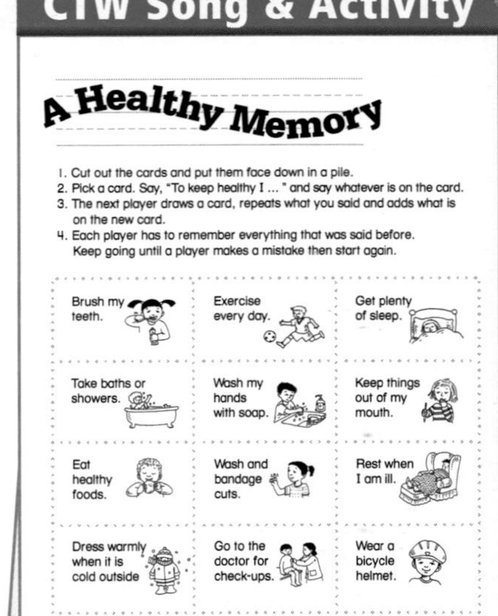

A Healthy Memory
1. Cut out the cards and put them face down in a pile.
2. Pick a card. Say, "To keep healthy I ..." and say whatever is on the card.
3. The next player draws a card, repeats what you said and adds what is on the new card.
4. Each player has to remember everything that was said before. Keep going until a player makes a mistake then start again.
Brush my teeth.
Exercise every day.
Get plenty of sleep.
Take baths or showers.
Wash my hands with soap.
Keep things out of my mouth.
Eat healthy foods.
Wash and bandage cuts.
Rest when I am ill.
Dress warmly when it is cold outside.
Go to the doctor for check-ups.
Wear a bicycle helmet.

Songs & Activities Package pp. 31–32

Keep your lungs and heart
Healthy, don't delay.
Swim in a pool or ride a bike.
Exercise today!
Original lyrics by Gerri Brioso and Richard Freitas.
Produced by Children's Television Workshop.
Copyright ©1999 Sesame Street, Inc.
D33

INQUIRY

Use a KWL chart at the beginning of each new chapter to encourage inquiry. In the *K* column, record what children *know* about being healthy. In the *W* column, list what they *want* to know. Throughout the chapter, ask children what they have *learned* and record their responses in the *L* column. A KWL chart is available on **Wall Chart** page 58.

Chapter 3 Skills Trace

Process Skills Development		
	Predicting	Collecting and Interpreting Data
Skill Introduced	xv	xv
Skill Applied	D 35	D 35 D 38–D 39
Skill Assessed	End Matter 16–17	End Matter 24–25

Science Literature Library

Carlos and the Squash Plant
by Jan Romero Stevens.
Carlos, a Mexican-American boy living in New Mexico ignores his mother's warnings about what will happen if he does not bathe. A squash plant grows out of his ear as a result. A simple story that suggests the importance of cleanliness. (Northland, ISBN 0-87358-559-3)

Family Activity

Science at Home

Dear Family:
Our class is starting Chapter 3. We will be learning about ways to stay healthy. These are the main ideas for Chapter 3.
- Exercise and rest help our bodies stay healthy.
- Keeping an exercise record is a good reminder.
- Germs are tiny living things that can make us sick. Staying clean helps protect us from germs.
- A good diet, exercise, and cleanliness are good ways to take care of ourselves.

We will also be learning science vocabulary words for Chapter 3. By the end of Chapter 3, we will be able to read the vocabulary words and tell what they mean.

Word Bank
exercise
germs

Home Projects
Here are some activities that will help your child understand the main ideas in Chapter 3. The activities are easy, fast, and fun.

Activities
- Plan a regular family activity such as walking or bike riding one or more days a week. Write it on a calendar so that you keep the time free.
- With your child, talk about important things that should go in a household first-aid kit. Make a list and put together a kit. Choose a place to store it.

Instructional Resources pp. 89–90

Vocabulary Preview

exercise	germs
muscles	calendar
healthy	bandage
medicine	checkup

Instructional Resources p. 91

Lesson Organizer

Objective
Determine that exercise is important for health.

Vocabulary exercise

Process Skills predicting, collecting and interpreting data

Materials

Kit Items none

School-Supplied Items clock with a second hand or stopwatch

Additional Resources
- Lab Manual
- Teacher Demonstration Kit
- Wall Chart

Introduce

Activate Prior Knowledge
Ask children to name some things that they can do every day to stay healthy.

Language Development *Word Web*
Ask children to name ways to exercise. Record their responses on **Wall Chart** page 59.

Flip Chart
Discuss the different activities shown. Ask: **Which of these activities are good exercise?** (*all of them*)

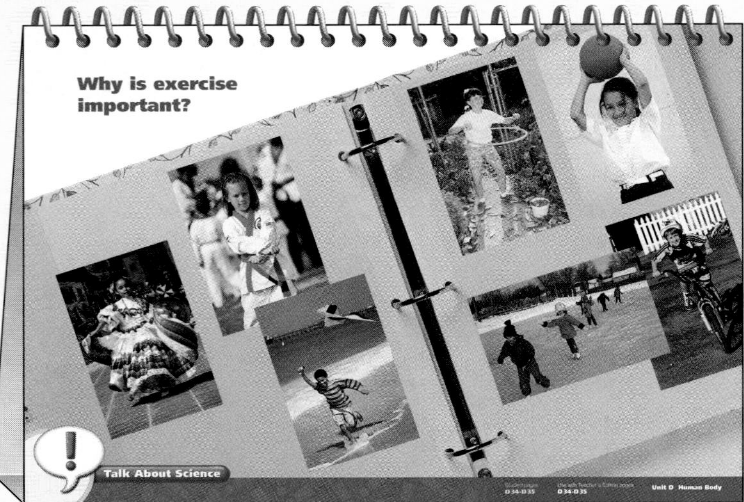

Why is exercise important?

At recess, you may play a game, throw a ball, or take a walk. What do you like to do at recess?

When you are active, your body is getting exercise. You can get **exercise** by walking, running, swimming, playing, and doing many other activities. What kinds of exercise do you get every day?

Exercise helps your body stay healthy. It keeps your muscles strong and your heart and lungs healthy. How is the girl in the picture keeping herself healthy?[1] [1]by walking

Science Background

- The heart is mainly muscle. Like all muscles, the heart muscle becomes stronger with exercise.
- Aerobic exercises strengthen the heart muscle. Aerobic exercise is any exercise that can be sustained for at least 25 minutes. During that time, the rate of breathing and the heartbeat are higher than normal.

Possible Misconceptions Children may think that as long as they are not sick, they are healthy. Some may also think that if you are very thin then you are healthy. Help children realize that to maintain good health, a person must eat healthful foods, exercise regularly, and get plenty of rest.

Do exercises.

Materials

 clock or stopwatch

Process Skills

- predicting
- collecting and interpreting data

Steps

1. How many jumping jacks can you do in one minute? Predict.
2. Take turns with your partner.
3. Do jumping jacks for one minute. Be sure to count each one.
4. Have your partner time you.
5. How many jumping jacks did you do? Collect and record your data.

Share. Compare your prediction with your results.

Lesson Review

1. Why is exercise important?
2. How can you get exercise?
3. **Show** a friend some exercises you can do in one minute.

D35

Lab Manual

Why is exercise important?

Write the names of other exercises you can do.
Predict how many times you can do each exercise in one minute.
Record your results.

Exercise	Prediction	Results

Lab Manual
p. 105

Activity Rubric

Use the following activity scoring rubric to assess students' performance.

Scoring Criteria	1	2	3	4
Student followed directions to complete this activity.				
Student predicted the number of times he or she could do an exercise in one minute.				
Student worked with a partner to collect data.				
Student recorded data about the exercise he or she did.				
Student explained the importance of exercise for living a healthy life.				

Scoring Key
4 points correct, complete, detailed
3 points partially correct, complete, detailed
2 points partially correct, partially complete, lacks some detail
1 point incorrect or incomplete, needs assistance

Lab Manual
p. T36

 **Call 1-888-537-4908 with your Activity questions or comments.**

Teach and Apply

Student Page D34

Emphasize that any form of activity can be exercise. Exercise can be fun and enjoyable, such as riding a bike, playing ball, or dancing. Also, many things we do as a natural part of our day are types of exercise, such as walking the dog, walking to school, or raking the leaves.

Reading Assist *Vocabulary*

Exercise is a series of movements used to strengthen some part of the body. Point out that the letter *c* in the word *exercise* has the /s/ sound because the *c* is followed by the letter *i.*

Student Page D35

Explore Activity

Time about 10 minutes

Grouping cooperative groups of 2

- Before children begin the activity, lead them in some gentle stretches, such as reaching high into the air.
- Have children use Lab Manual page 105.

Safety Note *Children with heart conditions, asthma, and other serious health considerations should not participate in this activity.*

Assess and Extend

Answers to Lesson Review

1. Exercise is important because it helps your body stay healthy.
2. Children might say that walking, running, swimming, and playing are ways to get exercise.
3. **Show** (*Performance Assessment*) Children may run in place, hop on one foot, and so on.

Inquire Further

Ask the following question to guide further inquiry:
What are some exercises you could do for a long period of time? (*Answers will vary.*)

Higher Order Thinking *Infer*

Ask: **How does exercise help you stay healthy?** (*Children may infer that it builds up their muscles including their heart. It makes them feel better.*)

Math Organizer

Objective

Use a calendar.

Additional Resources

- Math in Science blackline master

Teaching Math in Science

- **Collecting and interpreting data** is an important science process skill. Data must be collected and recorded accurately and clearly. Using a calendar provides an established system for recording data daily.
- Grids, such as calendars, are frequently used to record data. Reading a calendar builds background for interpreting data displayed on other types of grids. As children learn to read the days of the week, they become familiar with reading column heads. As they learn to read dates and answer questions about a calendar, they become familiar with the rows and columns.
- Have children read and complete the Math in Science lesson and the Math in Science blackline master.

Student Page D36

- Before beginning the page, display and discuss the class calendar. Ask: **What information can you get from a calendar? Why do people use calendars?**
- Invite children who have a birthday this month to point to their birthdays, then tell the class the date and the day.
- As you name parts of the calendar, have children point to them with their fingers.
- Before children answer the questions, model how to read the calendar. Point out how to use the column heads to figure out what day of the week each date is.

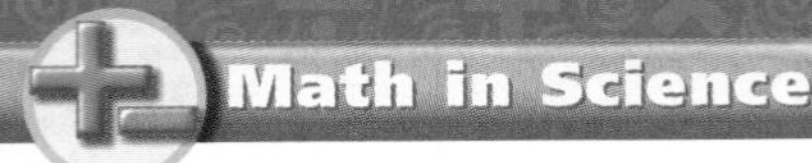

Using a Calendar

A calendar tells you the name of the month, the days of the week, and the dates.

There are seven days in a week. The days of the week are always in order on a calendar. What is the first day of the week?[1] What is the last day of the week?[2]

[1] Sunday
[2] Saturday

The dates are always in order too. Sometimes the first day of the month is a Sunday and sometimes it is not.

Find March 8 on the calendar on page D37. What day of the week is it on?[3]

[3] Wednes

Find the second Tuesday of the month. What is the date?[4] [4] 14th

How many days are there in March?[5]

[5] 31

D36

ESL Strategy

Help children practice saying the days of the week and counting to 31. First, point to and model how to say the name of a day of the week. Then have children point to that name and say it aloud. Practice counting to 31 by pointing to each number as you say it aloud and having children do the same.

March

Sunday	Monday	Tuesday	Wednesday	Thursday	Friday	Saturday
			1	2	3	4
5	6	7	8	9	10	11
12	13	14	15	16	17	18
19	20	21	22	23	24	25
26	27	28	29	30	31	

Turn the page to learn how a calendar can help you keep track of exercise.

Student Page D37

- Be sure children understand that the first day of the month can be any day of the week. If possible, show each month of a twelve-month calendar and have children raise their hands when the first day of a month is a Sunday.
- Have volunteers ask additional questions about the calendar on the page.

Apply Math in Science to Lesson 2

Children will use what they learned about using calendars to complete the next lesson.

Math in Science

Using a Calendar

May						
Sunday	Monday	Tuesday	Wednesday	Thursday	Friday	Saturday
1	2	3	4	5	6	7
8	9	10	11	12	13	14
15	16	17	18	19	20	21
22	23	24	25	26	27	28
29	30	31				

1. Draw a circle on the first day in May.
   What day of the week is it? ____________
2. Put an X on the last day in May.
   How many days are in May? ____________
   What day of the week is the last day in May? ____________
3. How many Mondays are in the month shown? ____________
4. How many Fridays are in the month shown? ____________

Instructional Resources p. 92

Activity Organizer

Objective
Keep track of daily exercise.

Process Skills collecting and interpreting data

Materials
Kit Items none

School-Supplied Items blank calendar, pencil or crayons

Time about 20 minutes the first day; 10 minutes per day for a week or more

Grouping cooperative groups of 4

Additional Resources
- Lab Manual
- Teacher Demonstration Kit
- Wall Chart

Introduce

The Lesson 2 Investigate Activity, *How much exercise do you get?*, is on the **Flip Chart.**

Activate Prior Knowledge
Invite volunteers to take turns demonstrating exercises they like to do while others follow along.

Language Development *Vocabulary*
Remind children that a *calendar* is a grid that shows the month and each day of the month. Display a calendar for the current month and ask children to find the current date. Have children name the days of the week.

How much exercise do you get?

Process Skills
- collecting and interpreting data

Materials

 calendar  pencil or crayons

Steps
1. Label the month, days, and dates on your calendar.
2. Collect data. Draw or write how you got exercise each day.

Think About Your Results
1. What are some ways you got exercise?
2. How many different activities are on your calendar?

D38

Science Background
- Aerobic exercise results in more efficient muscle metabolism and in greater endurance, strength, and resistance to fatigue.
- Aerobic exercise also makes overall body metabolism and neuromuscular coordination more efficient and improves elimination.

Math-Science Connection Use **Wall Chart** page 60 to explore exercise on a graph. Ask children to color in a box above their favorite exercise on the graph. After children finish, discuss which is the class' favorite exercise.

Technology

Review the demonstration of this Investigate's procedure on the *Human Body* **Activity Video,** Segment 4.

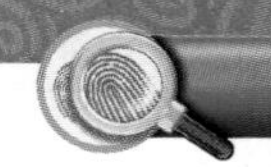

Inquire Further

If you kept track of your daily exercise during a different month, would your activities be the same or different? Why?

D39

Teach and Apply

- Have children use Lab Manual page 106.
- Remind them that any form of activity can be considered exercise. For example, raking leaves, riding a bike, playing outdoors, and doing sports or activities in physical education are all forms of exercise.
- Suggest that groups discuss ways they can exercise more often.

Real-World Applications

Invite children who are interested in getting more activity to check out their local community center to see what programs they offer.

Safety Note *Children with health conditions, such as heart problems or asthma, should ask their doctor to recommend exercises they can do.*

Reading Assist *Word Meaning*

Help children understand that the word *daily* means every day, from Sunday through Saturday.

What to Expect

Some children will do many different activities a day while others will have fewer activities to report.

Assess and Extend

Answers to Think About Your Results

1. Answers may include walking, biking, or sports.

2. Answers will vary according to child's activity.

Inquire Further

Children may say that their activities would be the same, because they would still enjoy the same types of activity. Or they may say that their activities would be different, because the weather influences what they can do.

Enrichment

Suggest that children create an exercise plan to follow every day. Have them record their daily plan and then attempt to follow it each day for a month.

Higher Order Thinking *Make Decisions*

Ask: **Why might you want to do a different exercise every day?** (*Children might decide that doing different exercises would be better because it would be more fun or it would exercise different muscles.*)

Lab Manual

How much exercise do you get?

Draw how you get exercise each day.
Write about it.

Lab Manual
p. 106

Activity Rubric

Use the following activity scoring rubric to assess students' performance.

Scoring Criteria	1	2	3	4
Student followed directions to complete this activity.				
Student identified an exercise he or she got each day.				
Student recorded his or her exercise data as a drawing.				
Student wrote about his or her daily exercise.				
Student explained the importance of regular exercise for healthy living.				

Scoring Key
4 points correct, complete, detailed
3 points partially correct, complete, detailed
2 points partially correct, partially complete, lacks some detail
1 point incorrect or incomplete, needs assistance

Lab Manual
p. T36

Call 1-888-537-4908 with your Activity questions or comments.

Science Center

Flip Chart

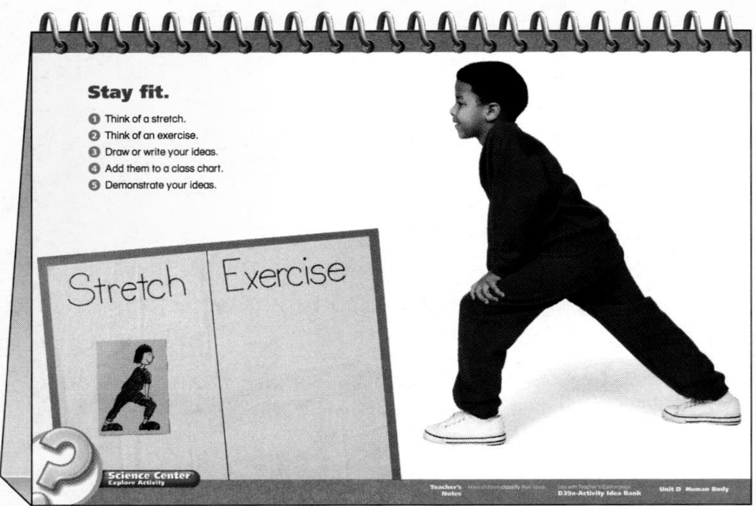

Stay fit.

Objective

Demonstrate a stretch and an exercise.

Process Skills classifying

Materials

Kit Items none

School-Supplied Items paper, pencil, crayons, tape, markers

 ***Safety Note*** *Make sure children stretch properly before they start exercising.*

Procedure

- In advance, prepare a class chart. Help children develop working definitions of *stretch* and *exercise.* For example, a stretch may be a slower and less vigorous activity than an exercise.
- Children **classify** their drawings and written ideas on the class chart.
- You can use **Lab Manual** page 107 with this activity.

What to Expect

Children understand the importance of stretching and exercising.

Lab Manual

Stay fit.

Draw a picture of your stretch and your exercise. Write about your pictures.

Stretch

Exercise

Lab Manual, p. 107

Connections

School and Community

Ideas for bringing the school and community together:

Field Trips

- school gym
- sports center
- local Y

Guest Speakers

- gym teacher
- sports/exercise counselor
- aerobics instructor

Themes

The activities on these pages can be used with classroom themes such as:

- human body
- health
- nutrition

Books for Children

Children might enjoy these books about the human body and health:

Swish! by Bill Martin Jr. and Michael Sampson. Written in verse, this book describes two girls' teams that play a close and intense game of basketball. (Henry Holt, ISBN 0-8050-4498-1)

The Berenstain Bears Go to the Doctor by Stan and Jan Berenstain. True to form, Papa gets his comeuppance when he takes the cubs for yearly checkups. (Random House, ISBN 0-394-84835-7)

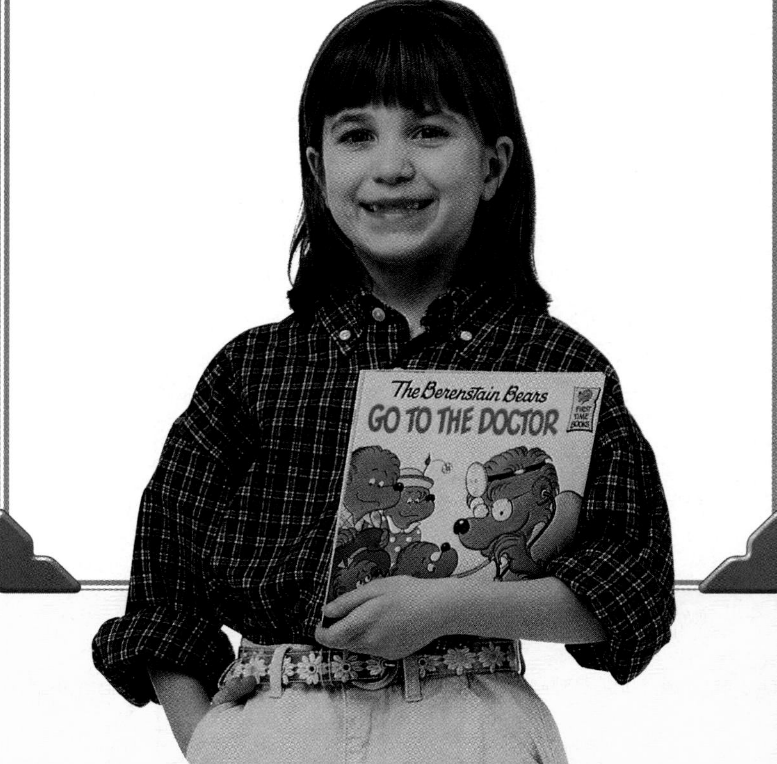

Cross-Curricular Options

LITERATURE

Red Dancing Shoes

Use the book to discuss dancing as exercise.

Materials *Red Dancing Shoes* by Denise Lewis Patrick. (Mulberry Books, ISBN 0-688-15850-1)

Procedure

- In this story, a young girl is given red dancing shoes by her grandmama.
- Discuss the dances mentioned in the story and how dance is a form of exercise. Encourage children to demonstrate dances they know.
- Have children explain how they think the girl felt after her red dancing shoes got full of mud.

Multiple Intelligences linguistic, kinesthetic

Gifted and Talented Children might prepare a skit to retell *Red Dancing Shoes.* Encourage them to include some dance steps that they perform.

MATH

Bedtime!

Make a chart.

Materials chart paper, lined paper, pencil, crayons

Chart

Name	Bedtime P.M.	Get Up A.M.	Hours of Sleep
Andy	8	6	10
Darma	10	7	9
Jose	9	5	8
Jeff	9	6	9
April	9	7	10
Jeni	9	6	9
Eric	10	6	8

Hours of Sleep

Number of Children	Hours of Sleep
0	7
2	8
3	9
2	10
0	11
0	12

Procedure

- Discuss the importance of getting a good night's sleep.
- Have children suggest how many hours of sleep they need each night. (*at least 9 hours*)
- Have children take a survey to see what times classmates go to bed and what times they get up. Then help them make charts to show how many hours of sleep they get.
- Ask: **What is the most frequent bedtime for children in this class? How many hours of sleep do most children in this class get?**

Multiple Intelligences spatial, linguistic

WRITING

Jumping Jack

Write a story.

Materials paper, pencil

Once upon a time there was a boy called Jumping Jack.

Procedure

- Invite small groups to write stories about a character named Jumping Jack. Have them write their stories to tell how Jack gets his daily exercise.
- Have children present their stories to the class, complete with body movements.

Multiple Intelligences linguistic, bodily-kinesthetic

ESL Provide sentence frames such as the following to help children compose their story: *Jumping Jack got into town by _______. He _______ the stairs into the store.*

PHYSICAL EDUCATION

Field Day!

Plan a class field day.

Materials sports equipment, measuring tools

Activities for Field Day
Relay races
Sack races
Throwing
Jumping

Procedure

- Generate a list of activities that children might do on a class field day, such as relay races, sack races, throwing and jumping contests. Organize small groups and assign each group one of the activities to plan.
- Schedule a day and time for the field day, either in the school gym or on the playground. Write the date on the classroom calendar.

Multiple Intelligences bodily-kinesthetic

Special Needs Some children may need the help of an adult to participate in the races. Others with more limited physical abilities might enjoy giving the start signals and determining winners.

Lesson Organizer

Objective
Determine that cleanliness contributes to good health.

Vocabulary
germs

Additional Resources
- Wall Chart

Introduce

Activate Prior Knowledge
Invite children to sing *Here We Go Round the Mulberry Bush,* acting out washing their faces and brushing their teeth. Then have them fold a sheet of paper into fourths. Ask them to draw a different way to keep clean in each section. Save their drawings for use as a **baseline assessment.**

Language Development *Label a Diagram*
Ask children to list things they use to keep their bodies clean on **Wall Chart** page 61.

Flip Chart
Discuss the pictures with children. Ask: **How are the children in the pictures taking care of themselves? Why do you think it is important to keep your body clean?**

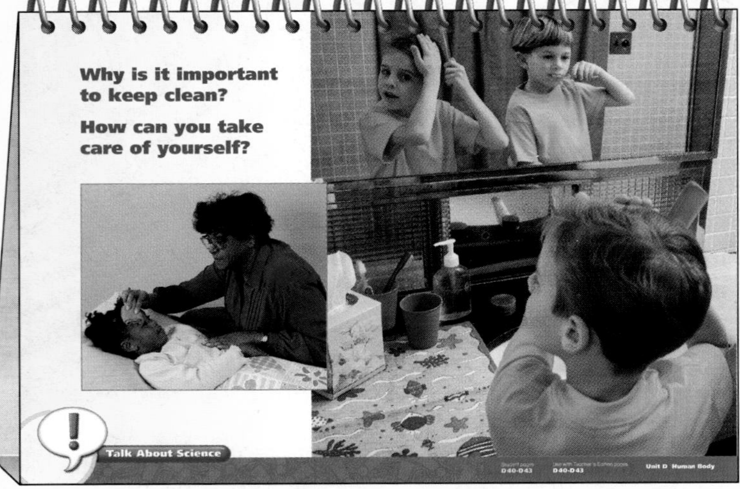
Why is it important to keep clean?
How can you take care of yourself?
Talk About Science

Why is it important to keep clean?

It's bath time! You will need soap and water. Why do you need to take a bath?

A bath gets your body clean. You need to be clean to stay healthy.

Germs are tiny living things. Some germs can make you sick. Germs can be in the air and on things you touch.

Some germs can get into your body through your nose, mouth, or cuts in your skin. Washing with soap and water removes dirt and many germs.

It is important to wash your hands and scrub under your fingernails before you eat. This will help keep germs from getting into your body.

Science Background

- Some viruses that cause the common cold and flu are thought to be picked up by the hands and then transferred to the mouth. Washing hands frequently can reduce the risk of getting these illnesses.
- Viruses, bacteria, fungi, and protozoans cause many kinds of diseases. They feed on body cells or fluids; some produce poisons or destroy tissue. The body's main defense is the immune system, which includes the white blood cells.

Possible Misconceptions Children may think that germs are found only in places that look dirty. Explain that germs often cannot be seen and are found everywhere, such as doorknobs and phone handles.

Brushing your teeth helps keep your mouth clean. If you brush every day, your teeth and gums will stay healthy.

What are some things you do to keep clean and stay healthy?

Lesson Review

1. What are germs?
2. Why is it important to brush your teeth?
3. **Tell** why it is important to keep your body clean.

ESL Strategy

Ask children to pantomime different ways to keep their bodies clean, such as brushing teeth, taking a bath, and washing hands, while others guess what they are doing.

Teach and Apply

Student Pages D40–D41

- Explain that washing with soap and water is one way people can protect themselves from getting sick. Point out that some illnesses, such as colds and flu, are caused by germs, and staying clean is one preventative measure.
- Point out that people should floss their teeth every day as well as brush. Flossing removes material from between the teeth.

Reading Assist *Decode Words*

Point out and review the sound of the consonant digraph *th* at the end of *bath*. Encourage children to find other words in the text with the consonant digraph *th* at the beginning or end.

Assess and Extend

Answers to Lesson Review

1. Germs are tiny living things that can make you sick.
2. Brushing you teeth every day keeps your teeth and gums healthy.
3. **Tell** (*Interview*) It is important to keep your body clean in order to remove dirt and germs from your skin.

Check for Understanding

To follow up on the **baseline assessment,** have children review their drawings of ways to keep clean. Allow them to draw additional ways on the back of their original drawing.

Reteach

Have children cut out magazine pictures showing people keeping their bodies clean in different ways. Suggest that they use the pictures to make a collage.

Lesson Organizer

Objective
Identify ways to stay healthy.

Additional Resources
- Wall Chart
- Interactive Transparency

Introduce

Activate Prior Knowledge
Ask children to name things they should do when they are hurt or sick. Record their responses and save them for use as a **baseline assessment.**

Language Development *Picture Clues*
Remind children to look at the pictures as they read to help them better understand the meanings of the words.

Flip Chart
Point out how the adult is taking care of the sick child. Ask children to tell about a time they were sick or hurt.

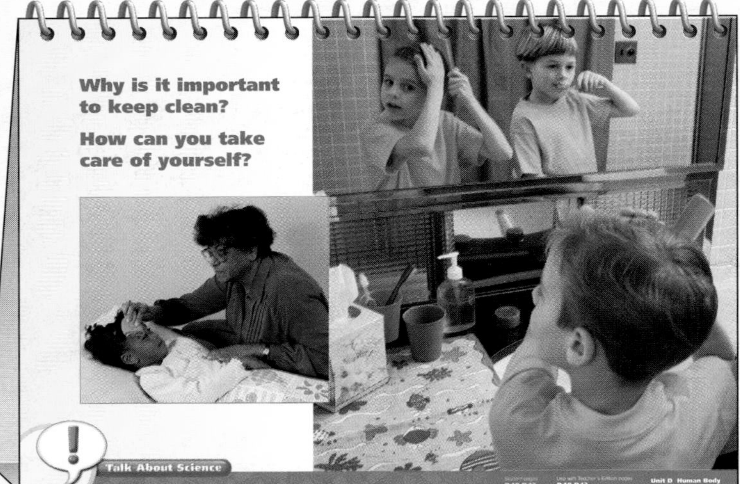
Why is it important to keep clean?
How can you take care of yourself?
Talk About Science

How can you take care of yourself?

You eat healthful foods. You get exercise every day. You wash your hands and take a bath. These are good ways to take care of yourself.

Even though you take care of yourself, sometimes you still get hurt or sick.

If you get a cut or a scrape, show it to your parent or teacher. They can help you wash the area and cover it with a bandage.

Some days you might not feel well. You may have a fever. Your stomach may be upset. Let your parent or teacher know you do not feel well. You may need to stay home and rest until you feel better.

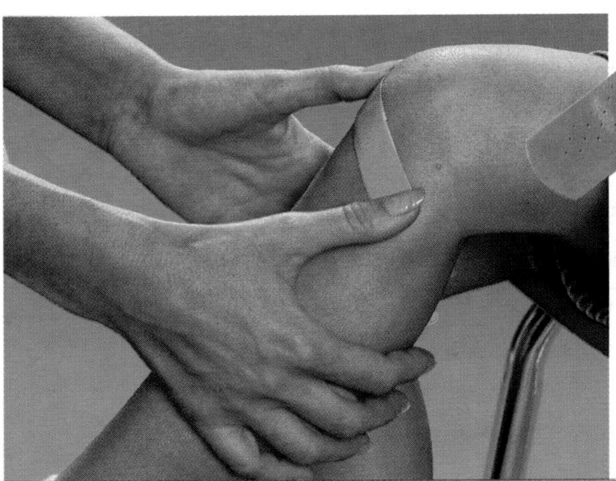

D42

Science Background

- A number of diseases can be prevented by vaccinations.
- A vaccine contains a disease-causing organism such as a bacterium or virus that has been so weakened that it will not cause the disease but will stimulate the development of memory white blood cells to fight it. A sufficient number of memory white blood cells can destroy the pathogen.

Science Across Cultures People in some countries, such as Japan, wear masks that cover their noses and mouths when they have colds.

Sometimes you may need medicine to help your body fight an illness. Never take medicine by yourself. Only a trusted adult should give you medicine.

Visit your doctor for regular checkups. This will help you stay healthy.

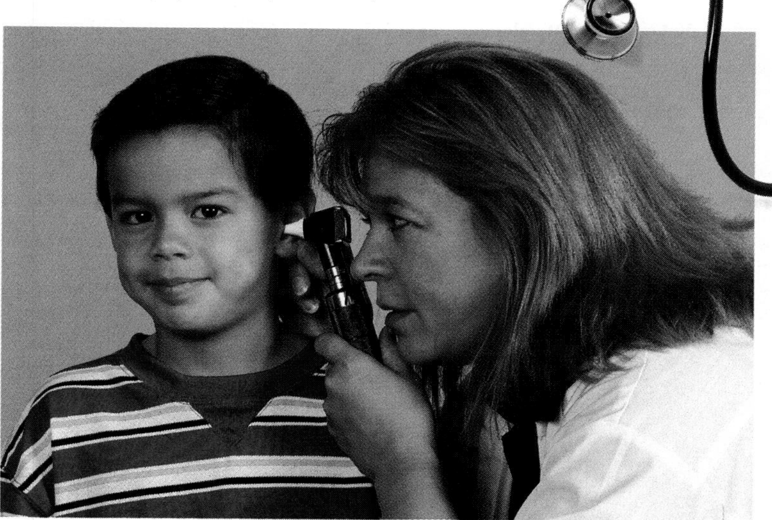

Lesson Review

1. What can you do if you get a cut or a scrape?
2. What can you do if you do not feel well?
3. **Write** a list of some ways you can take care of yourself.

Teach and Apply

Student Pages D42–D43

Remind children that to be and stay healthy the body needs proper nutrition, exercise, rest, and good hygiene. Point out that sometimes even though we practice healthful habits we still get sick or hurt. In that case, we need to know what to do.

Reading Assist *Compound Words*

As children read, remind them to look for compound words. Explain that these words may be long, but they are easy to read because they are really two short words put together to form one word. Ask children to point out the compound words in the text. (*sometimes, yourself, upset, checkups*)

Assess and Extend

Answers to Lesson Review

1. If you get a cut or a scrape, show it to a parent or teacher, wash the area, and cover it with a bandage.
2. Answers may include letting a parent or teacher know, staying home and resting, going to the doctor, getting medicine from a trusted adult.
3. **Write** (*Portfolio Assessment or Journal*) Answers may include eating healthful foods, getting exercise, keeping clean, and visiting the doctor for regular checkups.

Check for Understanding

To follow up on the **baseline assessment,** ask children to review the things they should do when they are hurt or sick. Suggest that they add to or change the list as necessary.

Reteach

- Use the Interactive Transparency to reteach Lesson 4 concepts.
- Have children draw a picture of one way they can take care of themselves when they are hurt or sick. Suggest that they write captions for their pictures.

Enrichment

Invite children to research how to make an emergency call to a doctor or fire department in your area. Point out that in many communities, 911 is the number to call. Have children use **Wall Chart** page 62 to practice calling the emergency number. Then invite them to demonstrate to the class how to call the emergency number, give their name and address, and tell what is wrong.

ESL Strategy

Read the following sentence starters aloud and ask children to finish them. *Show cuts and scrapes to _______. When you have a fever, stay home and _______. The only people who should give you medicine are _______. Visit your doctor for regular _______.*

Transparency

Keeping Healthy

Healthy

Not Healthy

Wash hands regularly.

When you are feeling sick, run around the block until you feel better.

Stomach upset? Eat lots of candy.

Never exercise.

Cut or scrape? Get help to clean and bandage.

Take medicine the doctor gives, when a trusted adult is with you.

Interactive Transparency Package Transparency 12

Science Center

Flip Chart

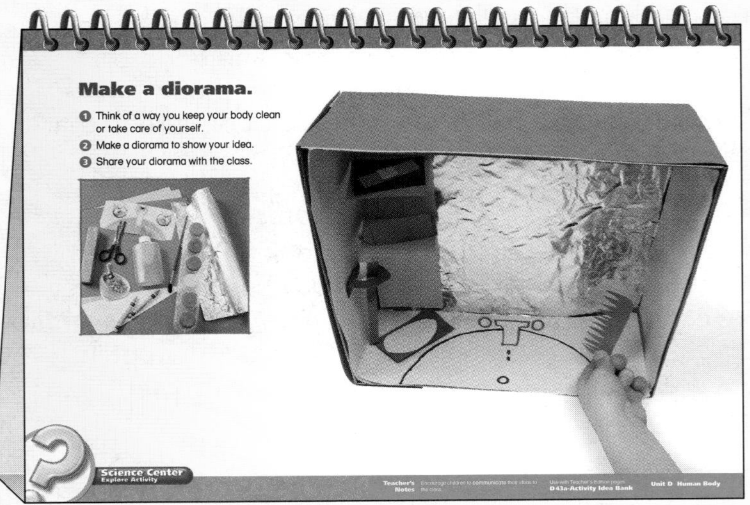

Make a diorama.
1 Think of a way you keep your body clean or take care of yourself.
2 Make a diorama to show your idea.
3 Share your diorama with the class.
Science Center

Make a diorama.

Objective

Demonstrate an understanding of the importance of cleanliness and ways to stay healthy.

Process Skills communicating

Materials

Kit Items none

School-Supplied Items shoe box, construction paper, glue, scissors, magazines, art supplies

Safety Note *Tell children about the proper use of scissors.*

Procedure

- Have children brainstorm ways to keep their bodies clean and what they can do when they are hurt or sick.
- Invite children to use various materials, such as magazine pictures of bathroom fixtures or toiletries.
- Children **communicate** their ideas as they talk about their dioramas.
- You can use **Lab Manual** page 108 with this activity.

What to Expect

Children will expand on their ideas about how to stay clean and healthy.

Lab Manual

Make a diorama.

Draw another way to keep clean or take care of yourself.
Write a sentence about it.

Lab Manual, p. 108

Connections

School and Community

Ideas for bringing the school and community together:

Field Trips

- dental office
- school nurse's office
- doctor's office

Guest Speakers

- optometrist
- dental hygienist
- school nurse

Themes

The activities on these pages can be used with classroom themes such as:

- dental care
- hygiene

Books for Children

Children might enjoy these books about the human body and health:

The Magic School Bus Inside Ralphie: A Book About Germs by Beth Nadler. Ms. Frizzle's class travels through the bloodstream to learn about germs. (Scholastic, ISBN 0-590-40025-8)

Dinosaurs Alive and Well! A Guide to Good Health by Laurie Krasny Brown. Tips for good health, including nutrition and exercise. (Little, Brown, ISBN 0-316-11009-4)

Hygiene and Your Health by Jillian Powell. Colorful photographs and concise text describe the basic rules of hygiene. (Raintree Steck-Vaughn, ISBN 0-8172-4926-5)

Cross-Curricular Options

LITERATURE

Germs Make Me Sick!

Use the book to discuss germs, bacteria, and viruses.

Materials *Germs Make Me Sick!* by Melvin Berger. (HarperCollins, ISBN 0-06-445154-2)

Procedure

- Cartoon illustrations show how the body fights germ invasion.
- Discuss the book's colorful illustrations and explanations of how germs spread infection. Help children find examples of how the body fights back.
- Invite children to draw cartoons to show ways they can avoid getting sick, such as by washing their hands, eating good foods, exercising, or getting enough rest.

Multiple Intelligences linguistic, spatial

MATH

How Many Teeth?

Count teeth and make up number problems.

Materials paper, pencils, hand mirrors, calculators

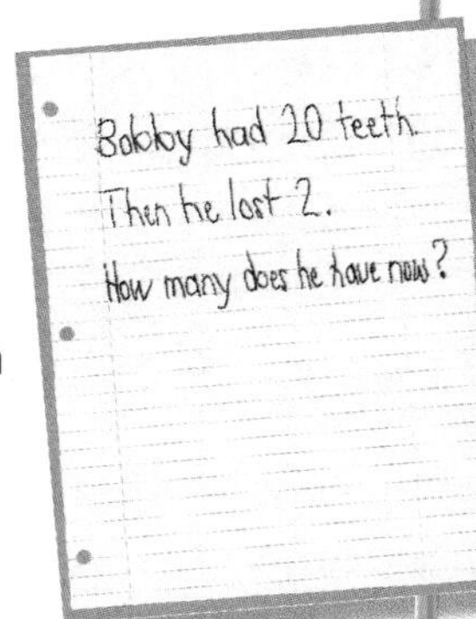

Bobby had 20 teeth.
Then he lost 2.
How many does he have now?

Procedure

- Discuss good dental health.
- Provide hand mirrors and have children count the number of teeth they have.
- Then have partners make up word problems about their teeth. For example: If Mike has 26 teeth and Jill has 23, how many in all?

Multiple Intelligences logical-mathematical, kinesthetic

Special Needs Some children might benefit by working with a diagram of teeth or a physical model of a set of teeth.

DRAMA

Smile Pretty!

Create a toothpaste commercial.

Materials cardboard tubes, markers

Procedure

- Discuss the importance of brushing teeth regularly, seeing a dentist, and eating healthful foods to maintain good dental health.
- Have children work in groups to create a TV commercial for a make-believe brand of toothpaste.
- Have children reenact the commercial for classmates.

ESL Children who are not comfortable performing in front of a group might prefer to draw a print advertisement for a newspaper or billboard.

ART

Bathtub Fun

Draw or design a bath toy.

Materials drawing paper, crayons, paint, balsa wood, glue

Procedure

- Discuss the importance of regular bathing.
- Ask children to tell about their favorite bath toys, ones that they enjoy now or when they were younger.
- Have children draw a picture of their favorite bath toy or make one they would like to have.

Multiple Intelligences spatial

Review Organizer

Materials

Kit Items none

School-Supplied Items big piece of paper, pencils or markers

Time about 20 minutes

Grouping cooperative groups of 4

Additional Resources

- Chapter 3 Assessment: Teacher's Assessment Package

Chapter Main Ideas

Lesson 1 To be healthy, the body needs exercise. Exercise keeps your muscles strong and your heart and lungs healthy.

Lesson 2 Keeping a record of your daily exercise reminds you how much and what kind of exercise you do.

Lesson 3 Germs are tiny living things that can make you sick. Staying clean is an important part of being healthy.

Lesson 4 A healthful diet, exercise, and good hygiene habits are important ways to take care of yourself.

Reviewing Science Words

1. Answers may include running, walking, swimming, playing, and other activities.
2. Germs get into your body through your nose, mouth, or cuts.

Reviewing Science Ideas

1. Exercise helps your body stay healthy. It keeps your muscles strong and your heart and lungs healthy.
2. Answers may include washing hands, brushing teeth, taking a bath, and so on.
3. Answers may include eating healthful foods, getting exercise, keeping clean, getting help from a parent or teacher when not feeling well, and visiting the doctor for regular checkups.

Chapter 3 Review

Reviewing Science Words

1. Name some ways you can get **exercise**.
2. How can **germs** get into your body?

Reviewing Science Ideas

1. How does exercise help your body?
2. What are some ways to keep your body clean?
3. Name some ways you can take care of yourself.

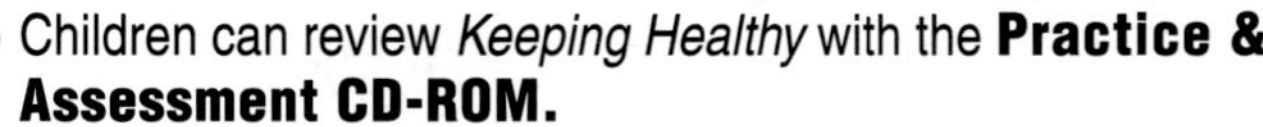

Technology

Children can review *Keeping Healthy* with the **Practice & Assessment CD-ROM.**

Children can use the **Production Studio** to show what they've learned about *Keeping Healthy.*

Children can use The KnowZone™ at **www.kz.com** to review and test their science knowledge.

You can use **TestWorks™** to customize assessment for your children.

Put on a skit.

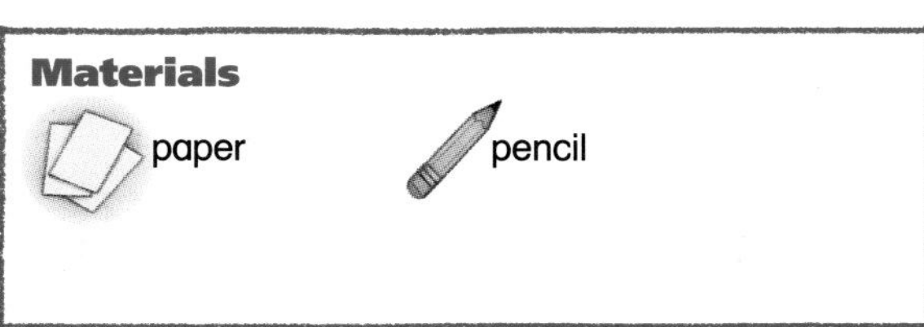

1. Work with a group.
2. Make a list of ways to keep healthy.
3. Choose one thing to act out.
4. Plan a way to show your idea to the class.
5. Be sure each person in your group has a part.
6. Put on your skit for the class.

D45

Chapter Assessment

Circle all the correct answers.

1. What are ways to get exercise?
   run a race read a book climb a hill
2. What are ways germs can get inside your body?
   nose mouth cuts
3. What should you do if you are sick?
   play soccer get rest stay home from school

Mark an X in the box next to the best answer.

4. What is the best way to clean your teeth?
   - ❑ bar of soap
   - ❑ toothpaste and toothbrush
   - ❑ glass of water
5. Who should give you medicine when you are sick?
   - ❑ a younger brother or sister
   - ❑ a classmate
   - ❑ a trusted adult
6. Why is exercise important?
   - ❑ keeps your muscles strong
   - ❑ makes you sweat
   - ❑ helps you find friends

Teacher's Assessment Package
pp. 71–72

Assessment Rubric

	Good Health Habits
4	Shows a good understanding of good health habits.
3	Shows a partial understanding of good health habits.
2	Has difficulty showing an understanding of good health habits.
1	Does not show an understanding of good health habits.

Performance Assessment Teaching Tips

- Before beginning, have children brainstorm ways they can stay healthy. Then discuss specific examples for each: healthful foods to eat, ways to exercise, and how to keep clean.
- Some groups may have trouble deciding which idea to act out. Help children come to a consensus.
- Emphasize that everyone should have a part in the skit.

Enrichment

Encourage children to create "Healthful Habit Tip of the Day!" posters. Invite children to draw and write about a healthful habit. Display and discuss a new poster each day.

Chapter 3 Skills Trace

Process Skills Development

	Predicting	Collecting and Interpreting Data
Skill Introduced	xv	xv
Skill Applied	D 35	D 35 D 38–D 39
Skill Assessed	End Matter 16–17	End Matter 24–25

Chapter Review pages are also on the **Flip Chart.**

Review Organizer

Using Multiple Intelligences

The following activities can be used to assess children's understanding of Unit D concepts. Assign the activities based on each child's strongest learning modality. The following chart shows which intelligences are developed in each assessment option.

Activity	Intelligence
Pack a lunch.	spatial
Play a guessing game.	linguistic
Make a poster.	linguistic, spatial

Plan your health expo.

Unit Performance Review pages are also on the **Flip Chart.**

Have individuals or groups of children choose one or more of the following activities in which to participate. You may want to set aside a portion of one or more days when children can work on their projects and then present them to classmates.

Pack a lunch.

Before they begin making their lunch packs, encourage children to ask themselves questions such as: What are some of my favorite snacks? How do these snacks help me? Provide a large selection of magazines and a brown paper lunch bag for each child. After children complete the project, encourage them to explain to others what they put in their bags and why.

Play a guessing game.

Have children work with partners. Invite one child silently to choose a part of the body, such as the heart, lungs, or brain, and the partner to guess the body part by asking questions. Remind children that they can only ask questions that can be answered *yes* or *no.* Have children continue to ask questions until they guess the mystery body part. Then have children switch roles and play the game again.

Make a poster.

Before children begin their posters, have them brainstorm different ways to get exercise, such as working outdoors, playing sports, walking to school. Remind them to write a title that tells about their poster. Display the posters and encourage children to share their work with classmates.

Unit D Performance Review

How does your body work? What do you do to stay well? Have a health expo to show others what you know about health and the human body.

Plan your health expo.

1. Choose a project you would like to do.
2. Get materials you will need for your project.
3. Decide how you will show your project to your class.

Pack a lunch.

Plan a healthful lunch you would like. Draw a picture of each food or cut out pictures from magazines. Put the pictures in an empty lunch bag. Explain to others what you put in your lunch bag and why.

D46

Play a guessing game.

Think of a part of the body you learned about in this unit. Have your partner ask questions that can be answered with a yes or no. Have your partner guess the part of the body.

Make a poster.

Make a poster about ways to get exercise. Draw pictures and write words on your poster. Remember to include a title.

D47

Assessment Rubric

	Pack a lunch.	Play a guessing game.	Make a poster.
4	Shows a good understanding of healthful foods and how they help us.	Shows a good understanding of parts of the body.	Shows a good understanding of ways to exercise.
3	Shows a fair understanding of healthful foods and how they help us.	Shows a fair understanding of parts of the body.	Shows a fair understanding of ways to exercise.
2	Has difficulty showing an understanding of healthful foods and how they help us.	Has difficulty showing an understanding of parts of the body.	Has difficulty showing an understanding of the ways to exercise.
1	Is unable to show an understanding of healthful foods and how they help us.	Is unable to show an understanding of parts of the body.	Is unable to show an understanding of ways to exercise.

Portfolio Assessment

Suggested items from this unit to include in children's portfolios are listed on the following pages in the Teacher's Assessment Package:

- Chapter 1: page 55
- Chapter 2: page 61
- Chapter 3: page 67

Unit D Performance Assessment

- The formal Performance Assessment for this unit is on pages 108 A–108 B of the Lab Manual Teacher's Edition.
- The student recording sheet for the formal Performance Assessment for this unit is on pages 109–110 of the Lab Manual, both in the Teacher's Edition and the Student Edition.

Writing Organizer

Objective
Write narrative sentences to tell a story in time order.

Teaching Writing for Science

The Writing for Science page is also on the **Flip Chart.**

Explain to children that their purpose is to write sentences that tell a story in order. Point out that they will share their writing with classmates.

Writing a Story

Guide children through the steps of the writing process.

1. **Prewrite** Think of things you did yesterday to stay healthy. Make a list to help plan your story. List things in the order that you did them.
   Before children begin writing, suggest that they name things people do to stay healthy, such as eat good foods, get exercise, and get plenty of sleep. Then have them list things they did yesterday to stay healthy in the order that they did them.
2. **Draft** Write a story about yesterday. What healthful foods did you eat? How did you get exercise? Write your story in order. What happened first? Then what happened? What happened last?
   Explain that a story is usually told in the order in which events take place. This helps the story make sense. Have children use their prewriting list to write their story.
3. **Revise** Read what you wrote. Do you want to change anything?
   Encourage children to look for ways to make their writing more interesting. Suggest that they ask themselves questions such as: Did I tell my story in the right order? Are my sentences clear?
4. **Edit** Check your writing to make sure it is correct. Make a neat copy.
   Have children read through their stories again and correct mistakes. Have them ask themselves: Did I use capital letters at the beginning of each sentence? Did I use the correct punctuation at the end of each sentence? Did I spell each word correctly? Have children write a title for their story.
5. **Publish** Share your story with others. You can draw pictures too.
   Suggest that children share their stories orally in small groups. Some children may want to draw pictures of each event and staple the pages together to make a book.

Writing a Story

When you write a story, you tell about something that happened. If you write what happened in order, others will be able to understand your story.

1. **Prewrite** Think of things you did yesterday to stay healthy. Make a list to help plan your story. List things in the order that you did them.
2. **Draft** Write a story about yesterday. What healthful foods did you eat? How did you get exercise? Write your story in order. What happened first? Then what happened? What happened last?
3. **Revise** Read what you wrote. Do you want to change anything?
4. **Edit** Check your writing to make sure it is correct. Make a neat copy.
5. **Publish** Share your story with others. You can draw pictures too.

D48

Writing Rubric

	4	3	2	1
Follows steps of writing process in order				
Communicates specific details and information				
Includes ideas related to topic				
Writes clear sentences				
Uses correct capitalization				

Scoring Key **Total Score** ______

4 points correct, complete, detailed
3 points partially correct, complete, detailed
2 points partially correct, partially complete, lacks some detail
1 point incorrect or incomplete, needs assistance

Technology

Children can share their narrative sentences at **www.sfscience.com.**

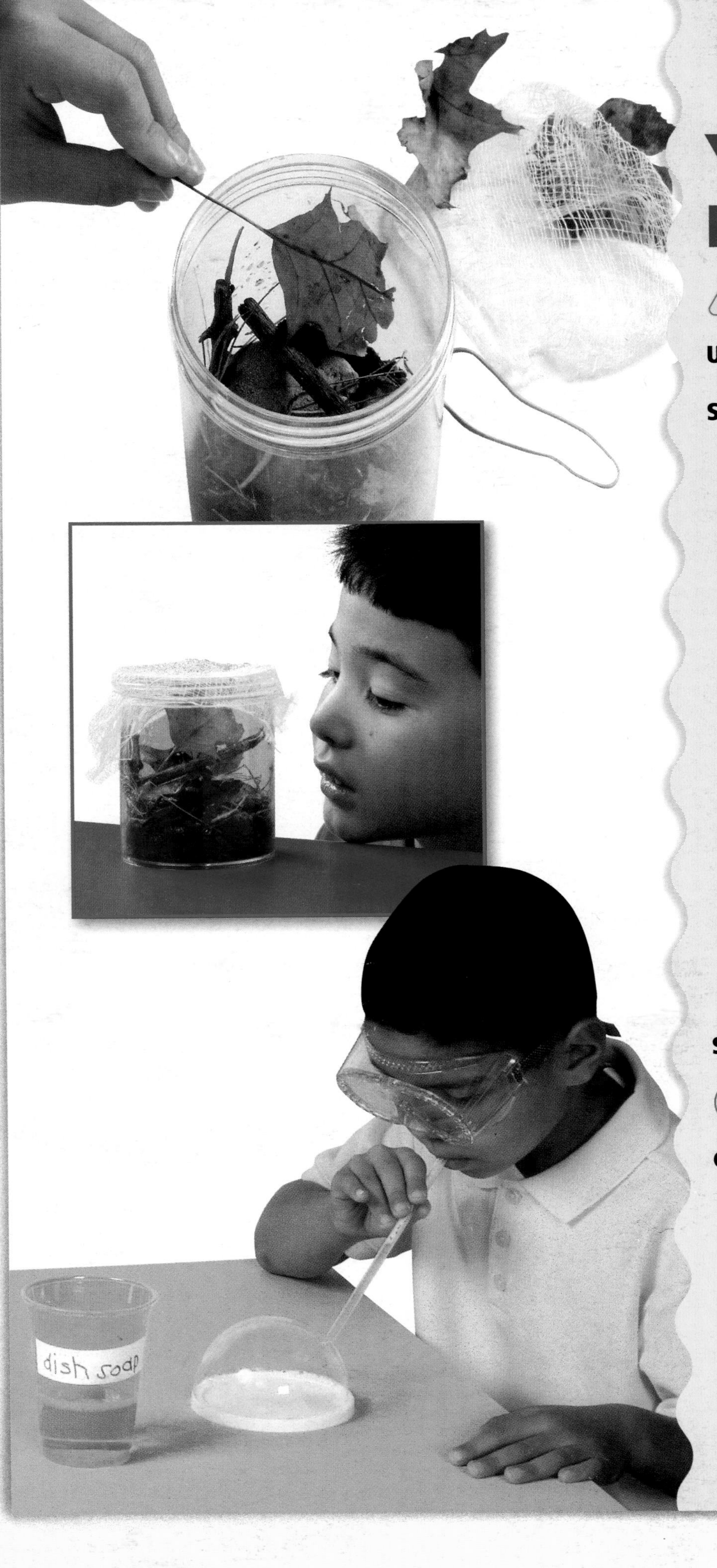

Your Science Handbook

1

Teaching Safety in Science

Activities throughout *Scott Foresman Science* use materials that are inherently safe. Students who use this program learn that safe procedure is part of sound scientific inquiry.

Safety Note *Safety notes at point of use throughout the program let you know and let students know when to exercise caution during activities.*

Helpful Hints

- Ask a group of students to make a safety poster listing safety tips for experiments or cardboard banners for each safety tip. Display the poster or banners in appropriate places throughout the room, such as over a sink or at workstations.

Safety in Science

Scientists do their experiments safely. You need to be careful when doing experiments too. The next page includes some safety tips to remember.

- Read each experiment carefully.
- Wear safety goggles when needed.
- Clean up spills right away.
- Never taste or smell materials unless your teacher tells you to.
- Tape sharp edges of materials.
- Put things away when you finish an experiment.
- Wash your hands after each experiment.

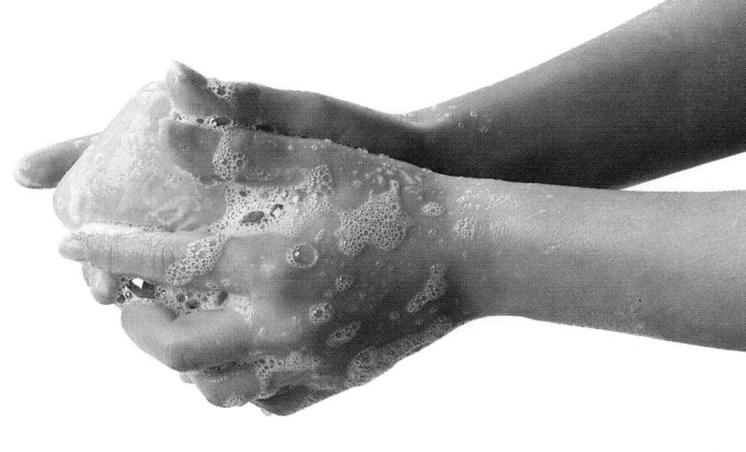

Helpful Hints *(continued)*

- Underscore the importance of each safety tip by asking students what could happen if each tip is not followed.
- Invite a scientist or high-school science teacher to your class. Ask him or her to discuss the importance of safety procedures in the classroom, in the laboratory, and in the field.

Using the Metric System

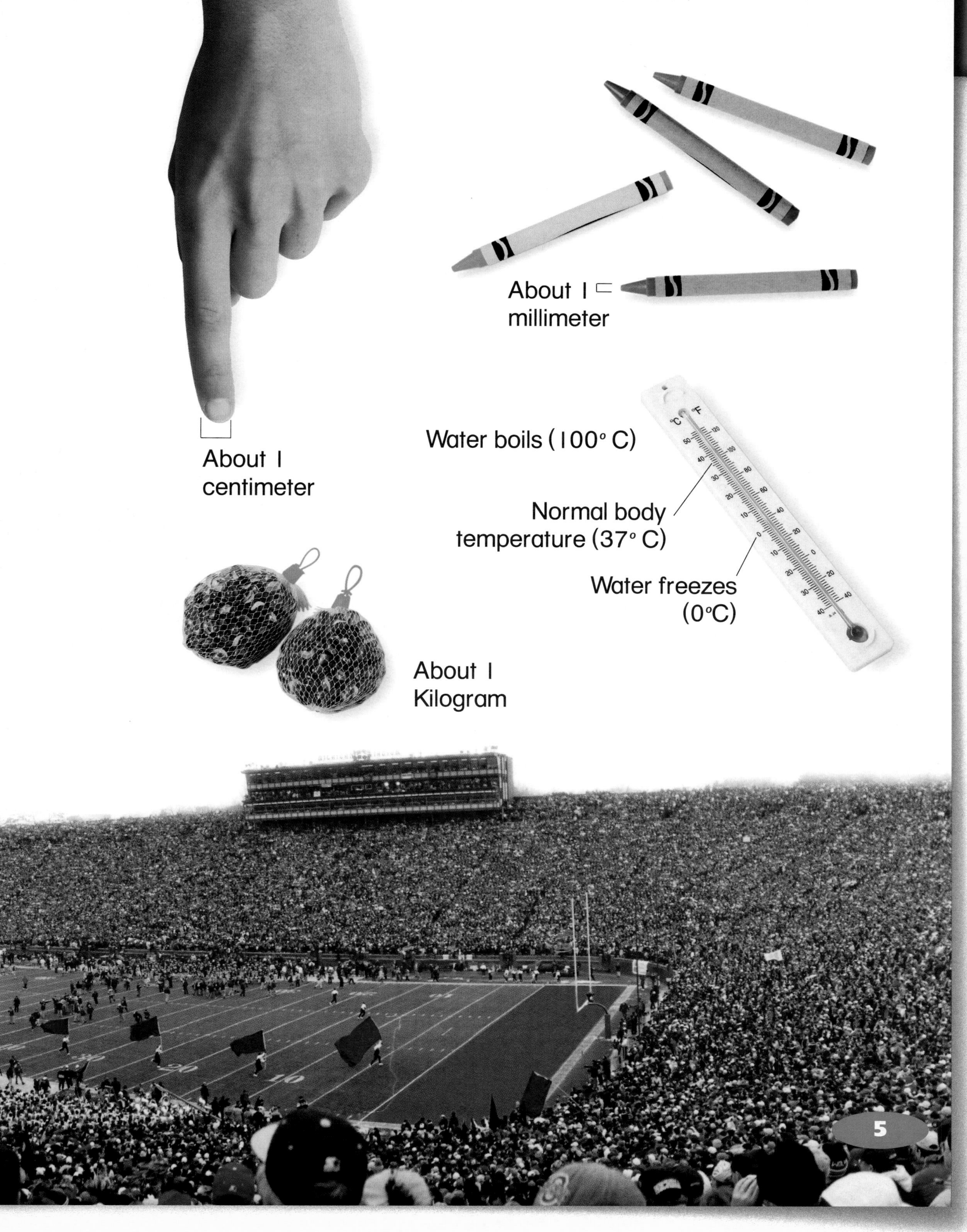
About 1
millimeter
About 1
centimeter
Water boils (100° C)
Normal body
temperature (37° C)
Water freezes
(0°C)
About 1
Kilogram
5

Activity Organizer

Objective
Use the process skill of observing.

Materials
classroom objects

Time about 15 minutes

Grouping individual

Additional Resources
- Process Skills blackline master

Introduce

Activity Summary

- An overview of all the process skills covered in Scott Foresman *Science* can be found in the front of the book on pages xiv–xv.
- Children will use their senses of seeing, hearing, and touching to **observe** several objects. Children pick an object to observe, then record their observations by writing and drawing about it. Children will complete the Process Skills blackline master on Lab Manual page 111 as they do the activity.

Activate Prior Knowledge

To activate and assess prior knowledge, invite children to name the five senses. Ask them what body parts they use for each sense and what each sense allows them to do. Then ask volunteers to describe experiences they have had using their senses. (*Children may say they touched an ice cube and it felt cold, or they heard a sound and recognized it was a dog barking.*)

Science Process Skill

Observing

How do you observe?

You use your senses when you observe. Your senses are seeing, hearing, touching, smelling and tasting.

You can use your eyes to look at an apple. You can pick it up and feel it with your hands. You can listen to the sounds it makes when you bite into it. You can smell it and taste it when you eat it.

6

ESL Strategy

Help children learn English sensory adjectives before doing the activity. Have them touch, hear, and look at a bell or shaker. Help them pronounce words, such as hard, loud, and shiny. Children may make word cards to refer to throughout the activity.

Practice Observing

Materials

    classroom objects

Follow these steps

1. Choose an object. Look at its color, shape, and size. Observe as many things as you can with your eyes.
2. Use your object to make sounds. Listen carefully.
3. Touch your object. Observe how it feels.
4. Draw a picture and write words to tell what you observe about your object.

Thinking About Your Thinking

Draw a picture of something you can observe by smelling or tasting.

7

Technology

The **Activity Videos** highlight where students use this process skill in Investigate and Experiment activities.

Lab Manual

Practice Observing

Follow these steps

Step 1 Look at your object's color, shape, and size. Observe as many things as you can with your eyes.

Step 2 Make sounds with your object.

Step 3 Touch your object. Observe how it feels.

Step 4 Name two things you want to observe by smelling or tasting. Draw a picture and write words to tell what you observe about your object.

Thinking About Your Thinking

Draw a picture of something you can observe by smelling or tasting.

Lab Manual p. 111

Teach and Apply

Follow these steps

Step 2 Children can use their objects to make sounds by shaking them or dropping them, or by other means.

Safety Note *Caution children about touching objects with sharp points so they will not hurt themselves.*

Assess and Extend

Answers to Thinking About Your Thinking

Children's drawings should show an object they can smell, such as a flower or perfume, or one they can taste, such as an apple or a lemon.

Activity Organizer

Objective
Use the process skill of communicating.

Materials
paper, crayons

Time about 45 minutes

Grouping individuals or cooperative groups of 3

Additional Resources
- Process Skills blackline master

Introduce

Activity Summary

- An overview of all the process skills covered in Scott Foresman *Science* can be found in the front of the book on pages xiv–xv.
- Children will draw pictures of animals that move in different ways. They will use drawings and words to **communicate** about how these animals are alike and different. Children will complete the Process Skills blackline master on Lab Manual page 112 as they do the activity.

Activate Prior Knowledge

To activate and assess prior knowledge, ask children to communicate what they have learned about different kinds of animals. (*Children may describe birds, fish, and mammals.*) Ask volunteers to dramatize different animals that walk, fly, and swim and have the class guess what they are. Point out to children that when they are acting, they are also communicating.

Communicating

How can you communicate?

There are many ways to communicate. You communicate when you talk. You also communicate when you draw, write, act something out, or make a chart or graph.

Writing for Science

Narrative
Have children pick an animal and ask them to write about it. They can describe the animal, and tell how the animal meets its needs.

Practice Communicating

Materials

 paper  crayons

Follow these steps

1. Draw a picture of an animal that walks.
2. Draw a picture of an animal that swims.
3. Draw a picture of an animal that flies.
4. Tell how these animals are alike and different.

Thinking About Your Thinking

Are your drawings the same as your classmates? How did they describe their animals?

Teach and Apply

Follow these steps

Step 1 You may want to have children brainstorm a list of animals before they start drawing.

Assess and Extend

Answers to Thinking About Your Thinking

Answers should reflect children's understanding that animals have specific body parts that allow them to move in a certain way, such as legs to walk, wings to fly, and fins to swim.

Possible answers include describing movements, body parts, and body coverings.

Technology

The **Activity Videos** highlight where students use this process skill in Investigate and Experiment activities.

Lab Manual

Practice Communicating

Follow these steps

Step 1 Draw a picture of an animal that walks.

Step 2 Draw a picture of an animal that swims.

Step 3 Draw a picture of an animal that flies.

Step 4 Tell how these animals are alike and different.

Thinking About Your Thinking

Are your drawings the same as your classmates' drawings? How did they describe their animals?

Lab Manual
p. 112

Activity Organizer

Objective
Use the process skill of classifying.

Materials
magazine pictures, yarn

Time about 30 minutes

Grouping individuals or cooperative groups of 2

Additional Resources
- Process Skills blackline master

Introduce

Activity Summary

- An overview of all the process skills covered in Scott Foresman *Science* can be found in the front of the book on pages xiv–xv.
- Children will cut out pictures of living things and nonliving things from magazines. They will **classify** the pictures into two groups: living and nonliving. They will tell about how they classified the pictures and compare the groups. Children will complete the Process Skills blackline master on Lab Manual page 113 as they do the activity.

Activate Prior Knowledge

To activate and assess prior knowledge, invite children to name one living and one nonliving thing, and then ask them to compare their properties. Have children use this information to formulate their own working definition of living and nonliving things. (*Children may say that living things grow and change, they need air and water, and they can be parents; nonliving things cannot grow or move on their own, they do not need air or water.*)

Science Process Skill

Classifying

How can you classify?

Classifying means sorting or grouping things by their properties. You can classify things by physical properties. Shape, color, and texture are some physical properties. You can classify things by whether they are living or nonliving.

10

Math-Science Connection

Comparing Totals

Have children count how many pictures they placed in each group. Write down the numbers on the chalkboard under two columns, living and nonliving things. Then invite children to total how many pictures of living and nonliving things the class classified. Ask, **Which group has more pictures? What is the difference?**

Practice Classifying

Materials

 magazine pictures  yarn

Follow these steps

1. Cut out pictures of living things and nonliving things.
2. Make 2 yarn circles.
3. Classify the pictures. Put pictures of living things in one circle.
4. Put pictures of nonliving things in the other circle.
5. Tell about each picture.

Thinking About Your Thinking

How are all the pictures in each group alike? How are pictures in the two groups different?

11

Technology

The **Activity Videos** highlight where students use this process skill in Investigate and Experiment activities.

Lab Manual

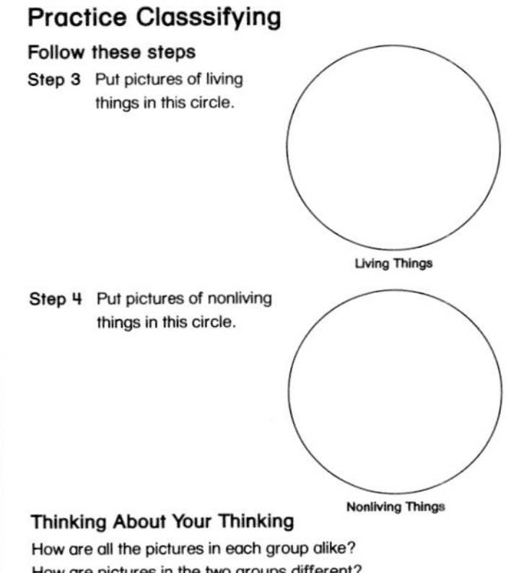

Practice Classsifying

Follow these steps

Step 3 Put pictures of living things in this circle.

Living Things

Step 4 Put pictures of nonliving things in this circle.

Nonliving Things

Thinking About Your Thinking

How are all the pictures in each group alike?

How are pictures in the two groups different?

Lab Manual
p. 113

Teach and Apply

Follow these steps

Step 1 Have children decide which pictures they will cut out. Encourage them to collect several pictures each of living and nonliving things.

Step 2 Tell children to make yarn circles large enough to accommodate the size of the pictures.

 ***Safety Note*** *Tell children to exercise caution when handling scissors.*

Assess and Extend

Answers to Thinking About Your Thinking

Answers should reflect what children know about living and nonliving things.

Children should recognize the properties of living things and of nonliving things.

Children may say that the pictures in the group of living things show things that need air and water to grow and change while the pictures in the other group show things that do not grow or change.

Activity Organizer

Objective
Use the process skill of estimating and measuring.

Materials
paper clips, classroom objects

Time about 30 minutes

Grouping cooperative groups of 2

Additional Resources
- Process Skills blackline master

Introduce

Activity Summary

- An overview of all the process skills covered in Scott Foresman *Science* can be found in the front of the book on pages xiv–xv.
- Children will **estimate** the length of a book by estimating how many paper clips match its length. They will then use paper clips to **measure** the book. They will compare the estimate to the actual measurement, and then repeat the process with different objects. Children will complete the Process Skills blackline master on Lab Manual page 114 as they do the activity.

Activate Prior Knowledge

To activate and assess prior knowledge, ask children to develop a working definition for the word estimate. (*Children may suggest that an estimate is a guess based on what you already know.*) Ask, **How many index fingers long is your desk?** Have children estimate the answer, and then measure their desk.

Science Process Skill

Estimating and Measuring

How can you estimate and measure length?

When you measure length, you find out how long something is. You can estimate before you measure. When you estimate, you tell about how long you think something is.

You can use different units to measure length. You can use a centimeter or inch ruler. You can use paper clips, math cubes, or other objects that are all the same size.

12

Math-Science Connection

Using Units of Measure

Have children select a different unit, other than a paper clip, to use for measuring the same objects. Ask questions such as: **Is your new unit longer or shorter than a paper clip? Did it take more or fewer units to measure the length of your object?** Help children observe that it requires fewer long units and more short units to measure an object

Practice Estimating and Measuring

Materials

 paper clips classroom objects

Follow these steps

1. Work with a partner.
2. Estimate the length of a book. Record on a chart like this one.
3. Measure the length of a book. Record.
4. Estimate and then measure the length of a pencil, school box, or other objects. Record.

Thinking About Your Thinking

Would you use paper clips or a ruler to measure how tall you are? Why?

Book
Estimate. _____ paper clips
Measure. _____ paper clips

Pencil
Estimate. _____ paper clips
Measure. _____ centimeters

13

Teach and Apply

Follow these steps

Step 3 Children may use linked paper clips to measure the length of the book and then count the paper clips they used.

Assess and Extend

Answers to Thinking About Your Thinking

Possible answers include using a ruler.

Children might think that it would be easier to use a ruler or a meter stick because it would take too many paper clips to measure how tall they are.

Technology

The **Activity Videos** highlight where students use this process skill in Investigate and Experiment activities.

Lab Manual

Practice Estimating and Measuring

Follow these steps

Step 2 Estimate the length of a book. Record your estimate on the chart.

Step 3 Measure the length of a book. Record.

Step 4 Estimate, measure, and record the length of a pencil or other object. Record.

Book

Estimate. ____________ paper clips

Measure. ____________ paper clips

Pencil

Estimate. ____________ paper clips

Measure. ____________ paper clips

Thinking About Your Thinking

Would you use paper clips or a ruler to measure how tall you are? Why?

Lab Manual
p. 114

Activity Organizer

Objective
Use the process skill of inferring.

Materials
flashlight, classroom objects

Time about 20 minutes

Grouping cooperative groups of 2

Additional Resources
- Process Skills blackline master

Introduce

Activity Summary

- An overview of all the process skills covered in Scott Foresman *Science* can be found in the front of the book on pages xiv–xv.
- Children work in pairs. One child will use a flashlight to make a shadow, the other child will **infer** what object his or her partner used. Children will complete the Process Skills blackline master on Lab Manual page 115 as they do the activity.

Activate Prior Knowledge

To activate and assess prior knowledge, ask children to tell when they have observed their shadow, and to describe it. (*Children may say it is shaped like a person.*) Have them use this information to **infer** when their shadows generally appear (*when their body blocks light*).

Inferring

What does it mean to infer?

You infer when you make a conclusion or a guess from what you observe or from what you already know.

You can infer from what you observe with your sense of hearing, seeing, touching, smelling, or tasting.

14

ESL Strategy

Make sure children understand the meaning of the verb **infer** by writing it on a word card and helping children formulate their own definition. Correct any misconceptions and add the definition on the word card. Display the card during the activity.

Practice Inferring

Materials

 flashlight

   classroom objects

Follow these steps

1. Work with a partner.
2. Choose an object. Do not let your partner see it.
3. Shine a flashlight on the object. Make a shadow on the wall.
4. Have your partner infer what made the shadow.
5. Take turns.

Thinking About Your Thinking

How were you able to infer what made the shadow? How did what you already know help you infer what the object was?

15

Teach and Apply

Follow these steps

Step 2 Have children prop up books or file folders to hide the objects from their partners.

Step 5 Encourage children to pick objects of different sizes and shapes.

Safety Note *Caution children not to shine the flashlights directly into the eyes of other children.*

Assess and Extend

Answers to Thinking About Your Thinking

Children's inferences should be based on the steps children followed.

Children should explain that they use what they know about the size and shape of objects to make good guesses about the shadows.

Technology

The **Activity Videos** highlight where students use this process skill in Investigate and Experiment activities.

Lab Manual

Practice Inferring

Follow these steps

Step 1 Work with a partner.

Step 2 Choose an object. Do not let your partner see it.

Step 3 Shine a flashlight on the object. Make a shadow on the wall.

Step 4 Have your partner infer what made the shadow.

Step 5 Take turns.

Thinking About Your Thinking

How were you able to infer what made the shadow?

How did what you already know help you infer what the object was?

Lab Manual p. 115

Activity Organizer

Objective
Use the process skill of predicting.

Materials
3 magnets, paper clips

Time about 20 minutes

Grouping cooperative groups of 2 or more

Additional Resources
- Process Skills blackline master

Introduce

Activity Summary

- An overview of all the process skills covered in Scott Foresman *Science* can be found in the front of the book on pages xiv–xv.
- Children will **predict** how many paper clips several magnets will pick up. Children record and test their predictions, and then compare the results with their predictions. Children will complete the Process Skills blackline master on Lab Manual page 116 as they do the activity.

Activate Prior Knowledge

To activate and assess prior knowledge, ask children what will happen if they try to pick up an eraser or a plastic ruler with a magnet. (*Children should answer that the magnet will not pick it up.*) Point out that this is a prediction and that they can test it.

Predicting

How do you predict?

When you predict, you tell what you think will happen. If you observe something carefully, you may be able to make better predictions.

Practice Predicting

Materials

 3 magnets  paper clips

Follow these steps

1. Use a chart like the one below.

	I predict.	I observe.
1 magnet		
2 magnets		
3 magnets		

Math-Science Connection

Making a Bar Graph

After children have completed the activity, have them report the results in a bar graph. Bars in the graph should how many paper clips one, two, and three magnets picked up. Ask: **What does the bar graph show?** (*It shows that the number of paper clips picked up increases with the number of magnets used.*)

2. Push one magnet into a pile of paper clips.
3. Count how many paper clips stick to the magnet. Record.
4. Stick three magnets together. Push them into a pile of paper clips.
5. Count how many paper clips stick to the magnets. Record.
6. Predict how many paper clips will stick to two magnets.
7. Record how many paper clips stick to two magnets.

Thinking About Your Thinking

What would happen if you used more magnets?

Teach and Apply

Follow these steps

Step 2 Spill a box of paper clips in front of each group.

Step 6 Children should make their predictions based on what they observed in the previous steps.

Assess and Extend

Answers to Thinking About Your Thinking

Children should recognize that if they use more magnets, they will pick up more paper clips.

Technology

The **Activity Videos** highlight where students use this process skill in Investigate and Experiment activities.

Lab Manual

Practice Predicting

Follow these steps

Step 3 Predict the number of paper clips that will stick to one magnet. Record your prediction and observation.

Step 4 Predict the number of paper clips two magnets will hold. Record your prediction and observation.

Step 6 Repeat the process for three magnets.

	I predict.	I observe.
1 magnet		
2 magnets		
3 magnets		

Thinking About Your Thinking

What would happen if you used more magnets?

Lab Manual p. 116

Activity Organizer

Objective
Use the process skill of making definitions.

Materials
pan balance

Time about 30 minutes

Grouping individuals or cooperative groups of 2

Additional Resources
- Process Skills blackline master

Introduce

Activity Summary
- An overview of all the process skills covered in Scott Foresman *Science* can be found in the front of the book on pages xiv–xv.
- Children will use what they already know to **make a definition** of a pan balance. They will write their definition and compare it with the one they read in their science glossary. Children will complete the Process Skills blackline master on Lab Manual page 117 as they do the activity.

Activate Prior Knowledge
To activate and assess prior knowledge, ask children what they think definitions are used for. Ask, **When do you need a definition? Where can you read definitions?** (*Children are likely to answer that they need a definition when they don't know the meaning of a word. They can read definitions in a dictionary or glossary.*) Have children pick a science word they know, such as magnet, and make a definition for it.

Making Definitions

How do you make a definition?

To make an definition, you use what you already know to describe something or tell what something means.

A good definition can help someone understand or guess the object you are describing.

Writing for Science

Glossary Entries
Have children write their definition of a pan balance on a sheet of paper, then brainstorm a word web of related words. Have them make a definition for each word and put the definition together to make a small glossary. (*The children's glossaries are likely to include words such as weight, measure, heavy, mass.*)

Practice Making Definitions

Materials

 pan balance

Follow these steps

1. Think of what you know about a pan balance. Write a definition of a pan balance.
2. Use the glossary in your science book. Look up **pan balance**. Write the definition.
3. Compare the two definitions. How are the definitions alike? How are they different?

Thinking About Your Thinking

Write a new definition of a pan balance. Use your own words.

19

Teach and Apply

Follow these steps

Step 1 Guide children by asking them questions such as: **What do you use a pan balance for? What does this pan balance look like?**

Step 2 Help children recognize that the entries in the glossary are alphabetized.

Assess and Extend

Answers to Thinking About Your Thinking

Children's answers should reflect their understanding of what a pan balance is, what it looks like, what it is used for, and how it works.

Technology

The **Activity Videos** highlight where students use this process skill in Investigate and Experiment activities.

Lab Manual

Practice Making Definitions

Follow these steps

Step 1 Write a definition of a pan balance.

Step 2 Write the glossary definition of **pan balance**.

Step 3 How are the definitions alike? How are they different?

Lab Manual p. 117

Activity Organizer

Objective
Use the process skill of making and using models.

Materials
safety goggles, clay, crayons, construction paper, pipe cleaners

Time about one hour

Grouping individuals or cooperative groups of 2

Additional Resources
- Process Skills blackline master

Introduce

Activity Summary
- An overview of all the process skills covered in Scott Foresman *Science* can be found in the front of the book on pages xiv–xv.
- Children will **make models** of different animals. They will **use their models** to share what they know about the animals. Children will complete the Process Skills blackline master on Lab Manual page 118 as they do the activity.

Activate Prior Knowledge
To activate and assess prior knowledge, show students an assortment of toy cars, airplanes, and telephones. Ask them to compare the models to the actual objects. (*Children are likely to answer that the models are smaller but that they are shaped like the actual objects.*)

Science Process Skill

Making and Using Models

What can you do with a model?

You can use a model to show what you know about something. A model can also help others learn about the thing that the model represents.

20

ESL Strategy

Use this activity to review the names of animals with children. Have children name the animals as you display different models. Correct the pronunciation if necessary and ask children to repeat the names. Have children make word cards for the animals and illustrate them with a picture of their models.

Practice Making and Using Models

Materials

 safety goggles  clay  crayons

 construction paper 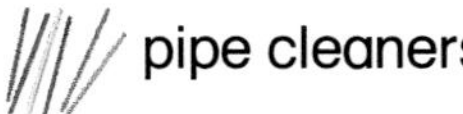 pipe cleaners

Follow these steps

1. Put on your safety goggles.
2. Make a model of an animal.
3. Use the model to show ways the animal can protect itself.
4. You can make a habitat for your animal.

Thinking About Your Thinking

How is your model like a real animal? How is it different? How does the model show how your animal protects itself?

21

Teach and Apply

Follow these steps

Step 2 Before they **make their models**, have children describe the characteristics of their animals, and then have them decide which materials they will use.

Assess and Extend

Answers to Thinking About Your Thinking

Possible answers include that the models have the same number and shape of body parts as the animals represented, but that the models are smaller.

Answers should reflect what children know about how the animals protect themselves using examples such as claws, teeth, camouflage, eyes, and ears.

Technology

The **Activity Videos** highlight where students use this process skill in Investigate and Experiment activities.

Lab Manual

Practice Making and Using Models

Follow these steps

Step 1 Put on your safety goggles.

Step 2 Make a model of an animal.

Step 3 Use the model to show ways the animal can protect itself.

Step 4 Draw the habitat the animal lives in.

Thinking About Your Thinking

How is your model like a real animal? How is it different?

How does the model show how your animal protects itself?

Lab Manual p. 118

Activity Organizer

Objective

Use the process skill of giving hypotheses.

Materials

masking tape

Time about 30 minutes

Grouping cooperative groups of 2

Additional Resources

- Process Skills blackline master

Introduce

Activity Summary

- An overview of all the process skills covered in Scott Foresman *Science* can be found in the front of the book on pages xiv–xv.
- Children will **give hypotheses** to answer whether they will jump farther from a standing position or with a running start. They will test their hypotheses. Children will complete the Process Skills blackline master on Lab Manual page 119 as they do the activity.

Activate Prior Knowledge

To activate and assess prior knowledge, ask children, **Can you balance longer standing on one foot, or on the tip-toes of both feet? Who will jump farther: a short or a tall person?** (*Children may say that the tall child will jump farther.*) Write down the answers. Point out that these are hypotheses, since they are statements that can be tested. Explain that a hypothesis is a possible answer to a question. Ask, **How can these hypotheses be tested?**

Science Process Skill

Giving Hypotheses

Why do you ask questions and give hypotheses?

You can ask questions to try to understand something. When you give a hypothesis, you make a statement. Then you can test it to see if it is correct.

Practice Giving Hypotheses

Materials

 masking tape

Follow these steps

1. Can you jump farther from a standing position or with a running start? Tell what you think. This is your hypothesis.
2. Test the hypothesis. Work with a partner. Make a starting line with masking tape.
3. Stand behind the line. Jump as far as you can. Your partner can use masking tape to mark the landing spot.
4. Stand far behind the line. Make a running start and jump when you reach the line. Have your partner mark the landing spot.

22

ESL Strategy

Model the pronunciation of the word *hypothesis* for children who are not native English speakers. Help children give a hypothesis. Ask, **Where will an ice cube melt faster: in the sun or in the shade?**

5 Make each jump 4 times. Take turns with your partner.

6 Did you jump farther from a standing position or with a running start?

Thinking About Your Thinking

Was your hypothesis correct? Why or why not? If your hypothesis was not correct, change it to make it correct.

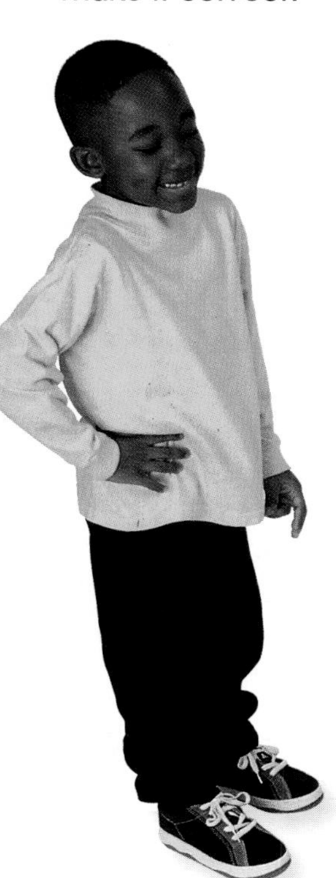

Teach and Apply

Follow these steps

Step 1 Hypotheses should be written as statements. Children may write "You can jump farther if you have a running start."

Step 5 You may wish to have children do these steps in the gym or another open area.

Safety Note *Make sure children wear the proper footwear so they are less likely to slip and fall while running.*

Assess and Extend

Answers to Thinking About Your Thinking

Answers will vary depending on children's hypotheses. Children should recognize that the jumping tests will allow them to say if their hypotheses are correct.

Technology

The **Activity Videos** highlight where students use this process skill in Investigate and Experiment activities.

Lab Manual

Practice Giving Hypotheses

Follow these steps

Step 1 Give your hypothesis. Do you think you can jump farther from a standing position or from a running start?

Step 2 Test your hypothesis.

Step 5 Make each jump 4 times. Take turns with your partner.

Step 6 Did you jump farther from a standing position or with a running start? Compare your results with your partner.

	Standing jump	Running jump
Trial #1		
Trial #2		
Trial #3		
Trial #4		

Thinking About Your Thinking

Was your hypothesis correct? Why or why not?

Lab Manual p. 119

Activity Organizer

Objective
Use the process skill of collecting data.

Materials
Snap Cubes

Time about 20 minutes

Grouping cooperative groups of 2

Additional Resources
- Process Skills blackline master

Introduce

Activity Summary
- An overview of all the process skills covered in Scott Foresman *Science* can be found in the front of the book on pages xiv–xv.
- Children **collect data** about patterns they make with Snap Cubes. They record and display the data they collected. Children will complete the Process Skills blackline master on Lab Manual page 120 as they do the activity.

Activate Prior Knowledge
To activate and assess prior knowledge have children give different kinds of data about themselves and write them on the chalkboard. (*Children may say their age, size, eye and hair color, date of birth.*) Tell children that these data are useful facts and numbers. Ask, **What can you use these data for?**

Science Process Skill

Collecting Data

How do you collect and interpret data?

You collect data when you record what you observe. You can use pictures, words, graphs or charts to display data.

You interpret data when you use what you have learned to explain something or answer a question.

24

Math-Science Connection

Patterns
Ask children to figure out how many Snap Cubes they would have in a given pattern. For instance, **If your pattern is red, yellow and it repeats four times, how many Snap Cubes would you have in all?**

Practice Collecting Data

Materials

 Snap Cubes

Follow these steps

1. Work with a partner.
2. Have your partner use Snap Cubes to make a pattern.
3. Tell about your partner's pattern. Predict what colors will come next. Continue the pattern.
4. Draw a picture of the pattern. Display it for others to copy.
5. Collect data. Record how many different patterns your classmates made.

Thinking About Your Thinking

Do the activity again. Make a pattern with numbers instead of colors.

25

Teach and Apply

Follow these steps

Step 2 Remind children that a pattern must repeat or be predictable.

Step 4 Point out to children that before they can draw the patterns, they first need to **collect data** by observing them. Ask, **What data are you collecting?** (*colors, patterns, number of cubes*) They record the data by drawing the patterns.

Assess and Extend

Answers to Thinking About Your Thinking

Children's numerical patterns should reflect what they learned about patterns. The pattern should repeat, as in 1, 3, 5, 1, 3, 5, or be predictable as in 1, 2, 2, 3, 3, 3, and so on.

Technology

The **Activity Videos** highlight where students use this process skill in Investigate and Experiment activities.

Lab Manual

Practice Collecting Data

Follow these steps

Step 1 Work with a partner.

Step 2 Have your partner make a pattern with Snap Cubes.

Step 3 Tell about your partner's pattern. Predict what colors will come next. Continue the pattern.

Step 4 Draw a picture of the pattern.

Thinking About Your Thinking

Do the activity again. Make a pattern with numbers instead of colors.

Lab Manual p. 120

Activity Organizer

Objective
Use the process skill of controlling variables.

Materials
1 block, Snap Cubes, pan balance

Time about 20 minutes

Grouping individuals or cooperative groups of 2

Additional Resources
- Process Skills blackline master

Introduce

Activity Summary

- An overview of all the process skills covered in Scott Foresman *Science* can be found in the front of the book on pages xiv–xv.
- Children will identify and **control variables** by testing how many Snap Cubes it will take to balance a block in a pan balance. Children will complete the Process Skills blackline master on Lab Manual page 121 as they do the activity.

Activate Prior Knowledge

To activate and assess prior knowledge, ask children what would happen if they put a toy in one of the pans of a balance. Then ask, **What would happen if you put a block that has the same weight in the other pan?** (*Children may say the pans will balance.*) Ask, **What would happen if you added a second block in the pan?** (*Children are likely to answer that the pan with the blocks will go down.*) **What variable have you changed?** (*the number of blocks*)

Controlling Variables

What does it mean to control variables?

You identify and control variables when you do an activity and change just one thing. The thing you change is called the variable. A variable can be almost anything. Only one variable changes at a time.

26

ESL Strategy

Explain to children that a variable is something that changes. A variable is something you can change. Each time the number of blocks is changed, emphasize the language by repeating something like: "We changed the number of blocks. The number of blocks is the variable."

Practice Controlling Variables

Materials

 1 block  Snap Cubes

 pan balance

Follow these steps

1. Predict how many Snap Cubes it takes to balance a block.
2. Put a block on one side of the pan balance.
3. Put one snap cube on the other side of the pan balance.
4. Add one snap cube at a time until the pan balance is level.
5. Record. How many Snap Cubes does it take to balance one block?
6. Draw a picture to show what happened. Tell about your picture.

Thinking About Your Thinking

What is the variable in this activity?
How did you change the variable?

Teach and Apply

Follow these steps

Step 1 You may wish to have children refer to the definition of pan balance they made in the activity on making definitions pages 18 and 19.

Step 4 Tell children to wait until the pans of the balance stop moving and observe the levels of the pans.

Assess and Extend

Answers to Thinking About Your Thinking

Children should recognize that the number of Snap Cubes is a variable. They changed the variable by adding cubes to the pans of the balance.

Technology

The **Activity Videos** highlight where students use this process skill in Investigate and Experiment activities.

Lab Manual

Practice Controlling Variables

Follow these steps

Step 1 Predict how many Snap Cubes it takes to balance a block.

Step 2 Put a block on one side of the pan balance.

Step 3 Put one snap cube on the other side of the pan balance.

Step 4 Add one snap cube at a time until the pan balance is level.

Step 5 Record the number of snap cubes it took to balance one block. ______

Step 6 Draw a picture to show what happened.

Thinking About Your Thinking

What is the variable in this activity? How did you change the variable?

Lab Manual
p. 121

Activity Organizer

Objective
Use the process skill of experimenting.

Materials
cup of water, yellow food color, blue food color, plastic spoon

Time about 15 minutes

Grouping cooperative groups of 2 or more

Additional Resources
- Process Skills blackline master

Introduce

Activity Summary
- An overview of all the process skills covered in Scott Foresman *Science* can be found in the front of the book on pages xiv–xv.
- Children test a hypothesis by **experimenting**. They will perform an experiment to test what happens when two different food colors are added to a cup of water. Children will complete the Process Skills blackline master on Lab Manual page 122 as they do the activity.

Activate Prior Knowledge
To activate and assess prior knowledge, ask students to think about paints. Ask, **What happens when you mix paints?** (*Children may say that the color changes.*) Ask them what they think would happen if they mixed a dark color with white. Ask them to plan an experiment to test their hypotheses.

Science Process Skill

Experimenting

How do you experiment?

When you do an experiment, you plan an investigation to answer a problem. This is also called testing a hypothesis. After an experiment, you make conclusions based on what you learn.

Practice Experimenting

Materials

 cup of water yellow food coloring

 blue food coloring  plastic spoon

Follow these steps

Problem

Does yellow food coloring change blue colored water?

Give Your Hypothesis

If you add yellow food coloring to blue colored water, will the color of the water change? Tell what you think.

28

Writing for Science

Persuasive
After children have performed their experiment about mixing food coloring, have them write a paragraph to convince others that their conclusions are correct. Children should give their hypotheses, describe the steps of the experiment, and explain the results they observed in order to support this hypothesis.

Control the Variables

Add the same number of drops of food coloring both times.

Test Your Hypothesis

Follow these steps to do the experiment.

1. Add water until your cup is half full.
2. Add 6 drops of blue food coloring to the water. Stir.
3. Predict what will happen when you add yellow food coloring to the water.
4. Add 6 drops of yellow food coloring to the water. Stir. Observe.

Collect Your Data

Make two drawings. Draw the cup with blue water. Draw another picture to show what happened after you added yellow food coloring.

Tell Your Conclusion

Compare your results and hypothesis. What happened when you added yellow food coloring to the blue water?

Thinking About Your Thinking

What do you think would happen if you added 6 more drops of yellow food coloring to the water?

29

Teach and Apply

Follow these steps

Steps 2 and 4 Tell children to use caution when tilting the bottles of food color so they will not add too much to the water.

Step 3 To help children make their predictions, have them think about what happens when they mix blue and yellow paint.

Safety Note *Do not allow children to taste the liquids. Have them clean up all spills immediately.*

Assess and Extend

Answers to Thinking About Your Thinking

Children should observe that adding yellow food color to blue-colored water changes its color to green.

Answers should include that the water will remain green, but the tint will change.

Technology

The **Activity Videos** highlight where students use this process skill in Investigate and Experiment activities.

Lab Manual

Practice Experimenting

Follow these steps

Give your hypothesis about adding yellow food color to blue colored water.

Step 4 Add 6 drops of yellow food color to the blue colored water. Stir. Observe.

Tell Your Conclusion

Show what happened to the water before and after adding the yellow food coloring.

Before After

Thinking About Your Thinking

What do you think would happen if you added 6 more drops of yellow food color to the water?

Lab Manual p. 122

Endangered Plants and Animals

Some plants and animals are endangered. That means that very few of them are living. People all over the world are working to protect many endangered plants and animals.

Endangered Plants

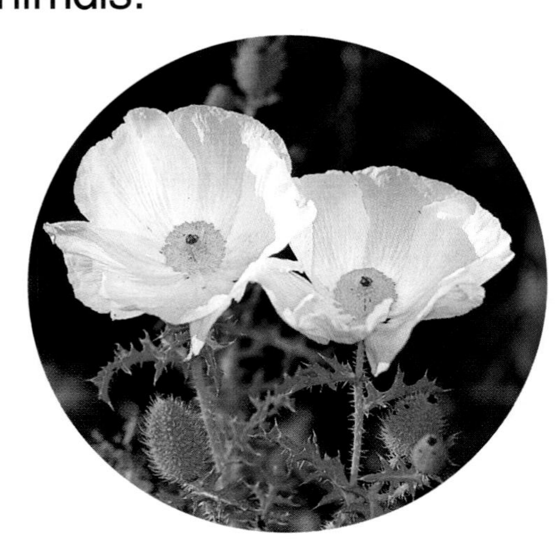

▶ Prickly Poppy
New Mexico, U.S.A.

▲ Thistle
California, U.S.A.

▼ Black Lace Cactus
Texas, U.S.A

Endangered Animals

▲ Indian Elephant
Indonesia

Tiger
India ▼

Silverback Gorilla
Africa ▼

Terrariums

A terrarium is a container with soil in it. It has plants in it. It can also have animals, such as lizards, toads, salamanders, and snakes. A lid on top keeps enough water inside. A terrarium is a habitat that has everything the plants and animals need.

Aquariums

Aquariums have water in them. Fish can live in an aquarium. People take care of the fish by feeding them and keeping the water clean. Snails and plants can live in an aquarium too. An aquarium is a habitat that has everything they need.

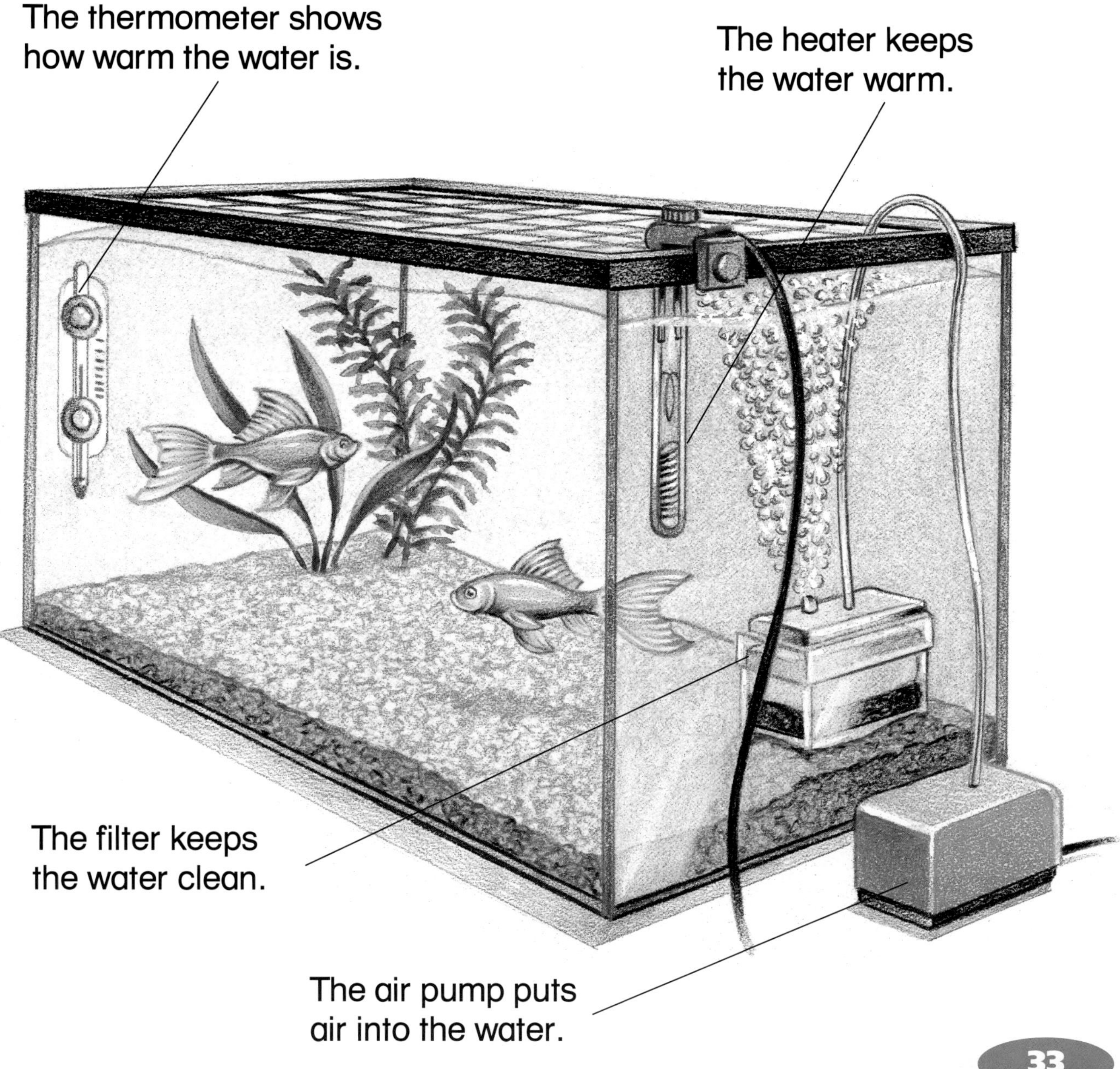

The thermometer shows how warm the water is.
The heater keeps the water warm.
The filter keeps the water clean.
The air pump puts air into the water.

33

Adaptations

Adaptations are parts or behaviors of a plant or animal that help it stay alive.

The pitcher plant has leaves that trap the insects it uses for food. ▶

◀ The spines of the cactus prevent it from being eaten by animals. The cactus also has a thick stem that holds water for a long time. This helps it live in the desert.

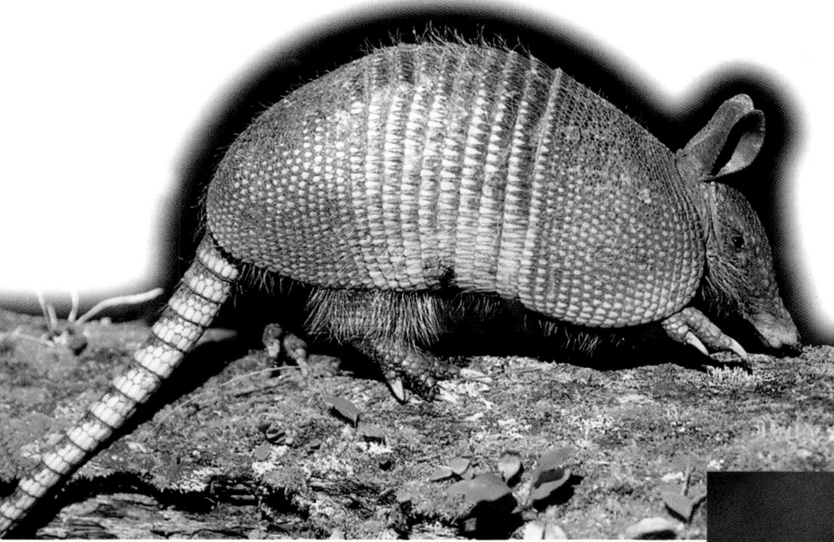

◀ Sharp claws help the armadillo dig burrows and tunnels in the ground. The armadillo also has a special shell that protects its body.

The porcupine has sharp quills that protect it from enemies. ▶

◀ Very good eyesight helps the hawk see things from high in the air. The hawk also has a sharp beak that helps it catch and eat food.

Dinosaur Time Line

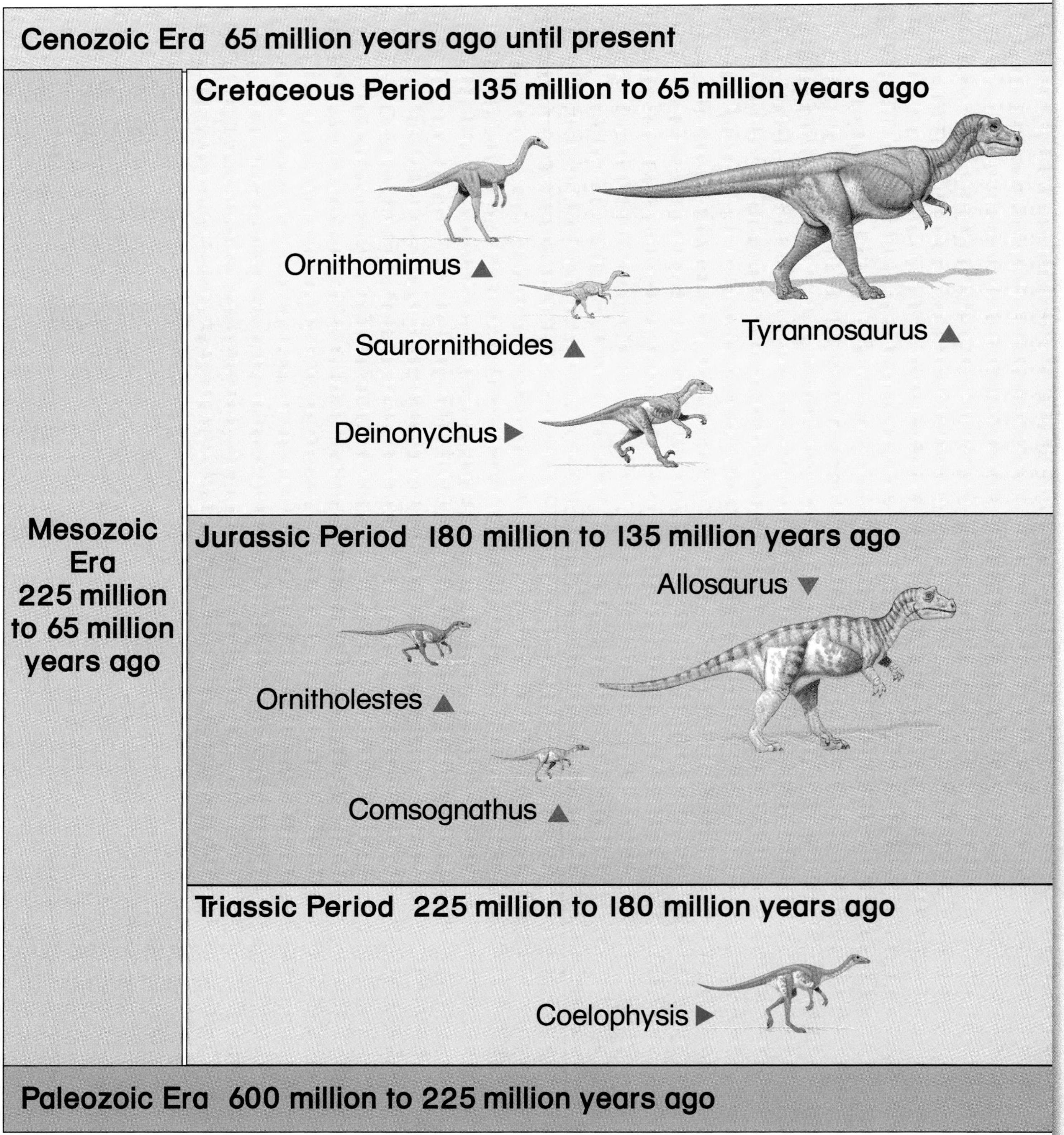

Cenozoic Era 65 million years ago until present	
Mesozoic Era 225 million to 65 million years ago	**Cretaceous Period** 135 million to 65 million years ago Ornithomimus ▲ Saurornithoides ▲ Tyrannosaurus ▲ Deinonychus ▶
	Jurassic Period 180 million to 135 million years ago Allosaurus ▼ Ornitholestes ▲ Comsognathus ▲
	Triassic Period 225 million to 180 million years ago Coelophysis ▶
Paleozoic Era 600 million to 225 million years ago	

36

Dinosaurs lived on the earth for millions of years. This time line shows some kinds of dinosaurs and when they lived.

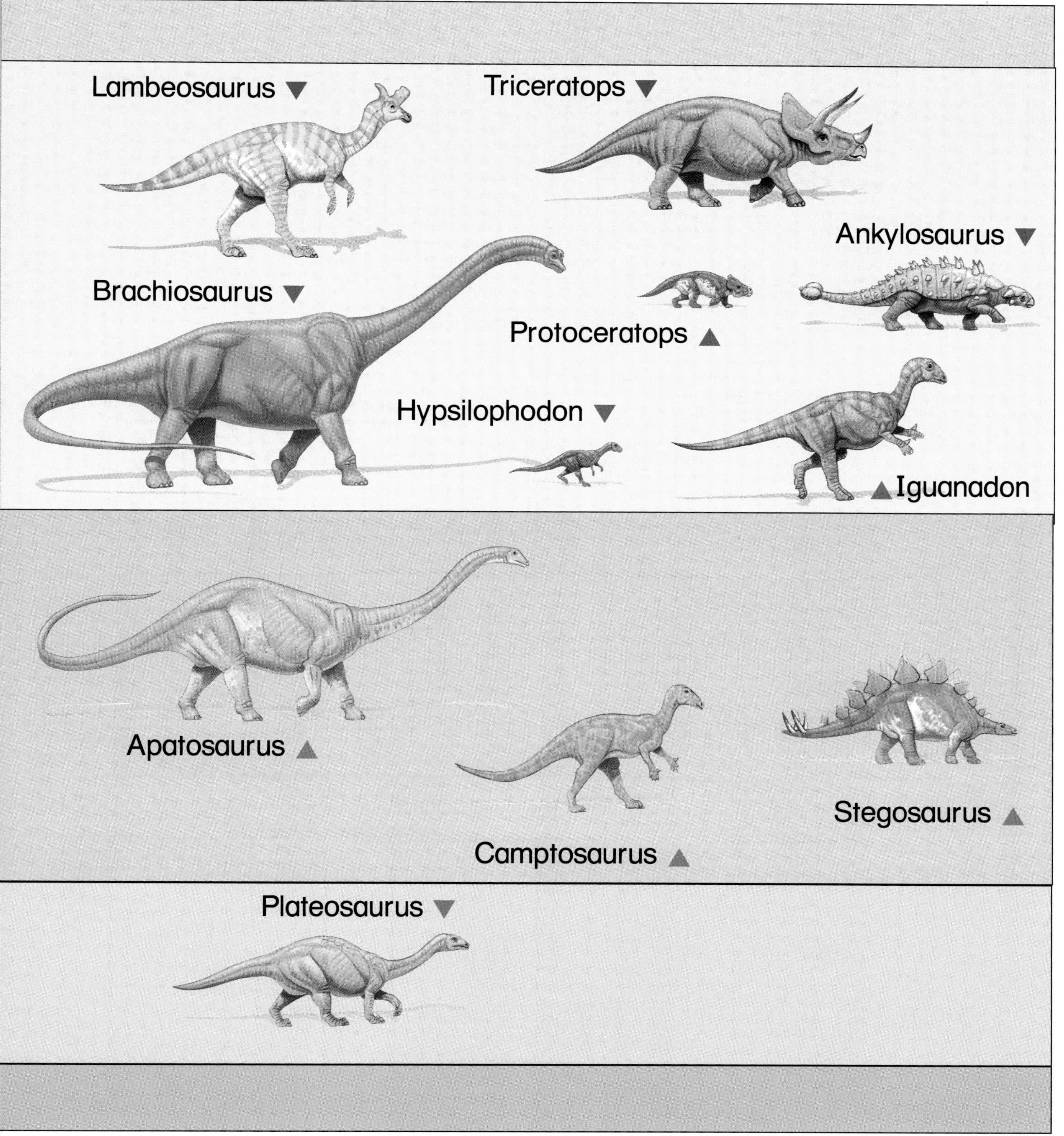

Using Graphs

The children in room 7 chose which dinosaur they liked best. The graphs show how many children chose each dinosaur.

Picture Graph

In this picture graph, each  means one child.

Favorite Dinosaur								
Tyrannosaurus								
Lambeosaurus								
Brachiosaurus								

Bar Graph

In this bar graph, one box is filled for each child.

Favorite Dinosaur								
Tyrannosaurus								
Lambeosaurus								
Brachiosaurus								

Circle Graph

This circle graph shows that two children like the Tyrannosaurus best and six children like the Brachiosaurus best. How many children like the Lambeosaurus best?

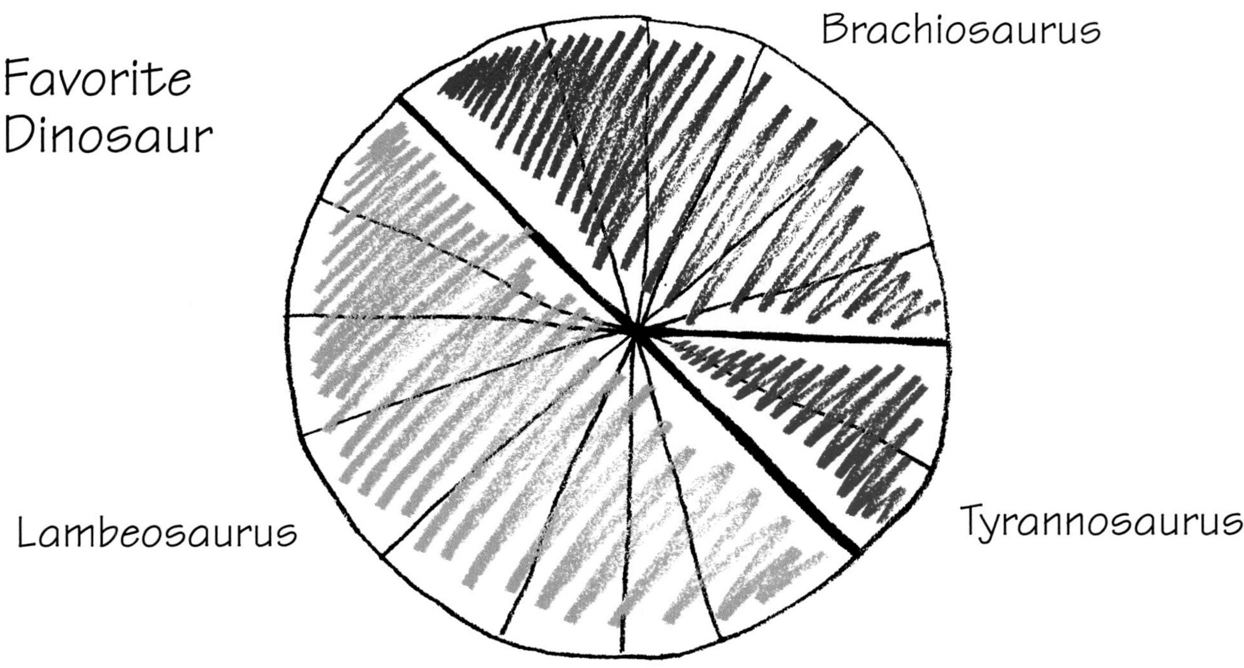

Look at these pictures. Which of these dinosaurs does your class like best? Make a graph to find out.

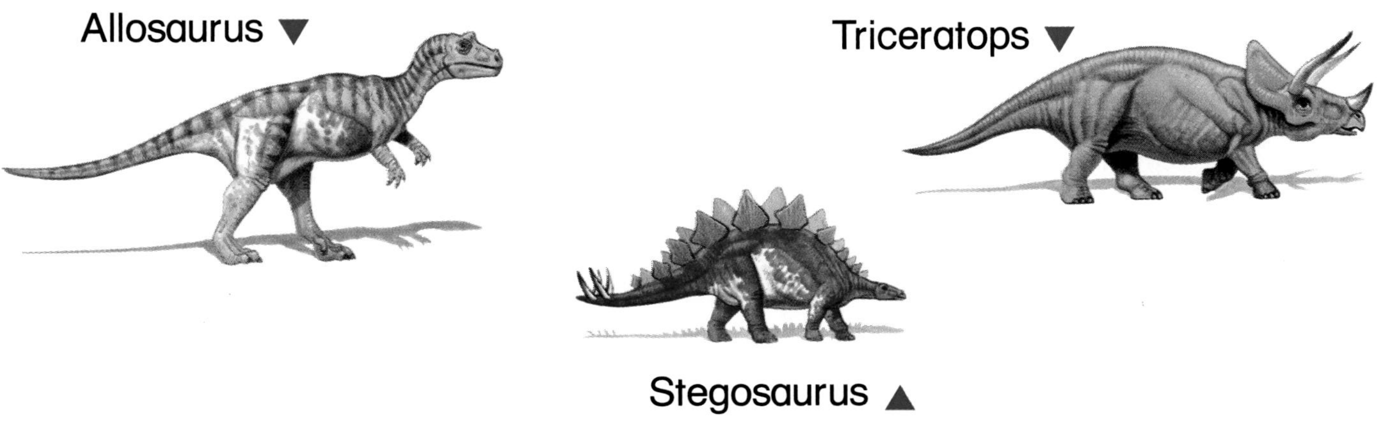

39

Map of Plant Products

This map of the United States shows where different plant products grow. Look at the key. It shows what the products are.

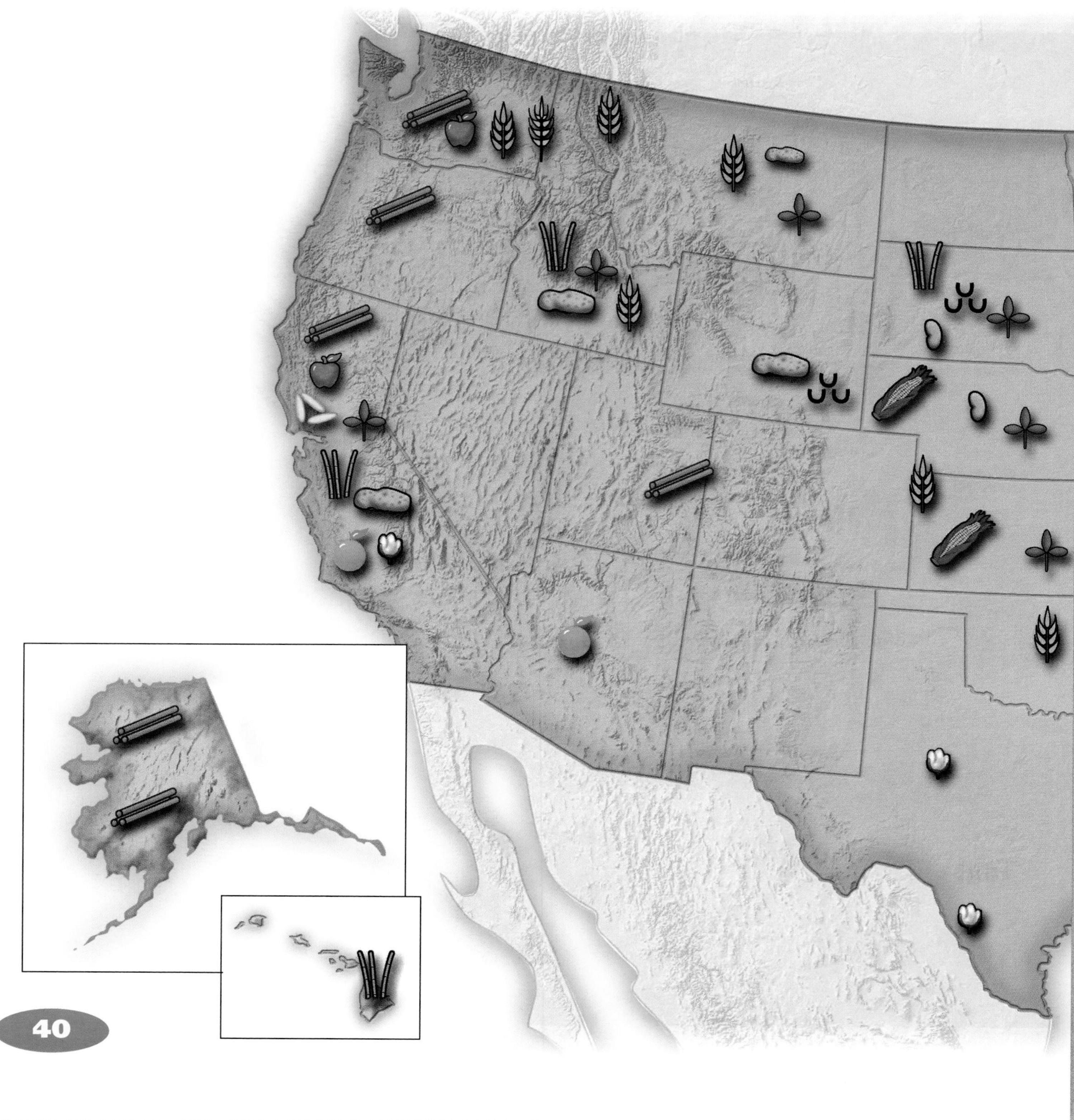

Find your state on the map. What products grow there or nearby?

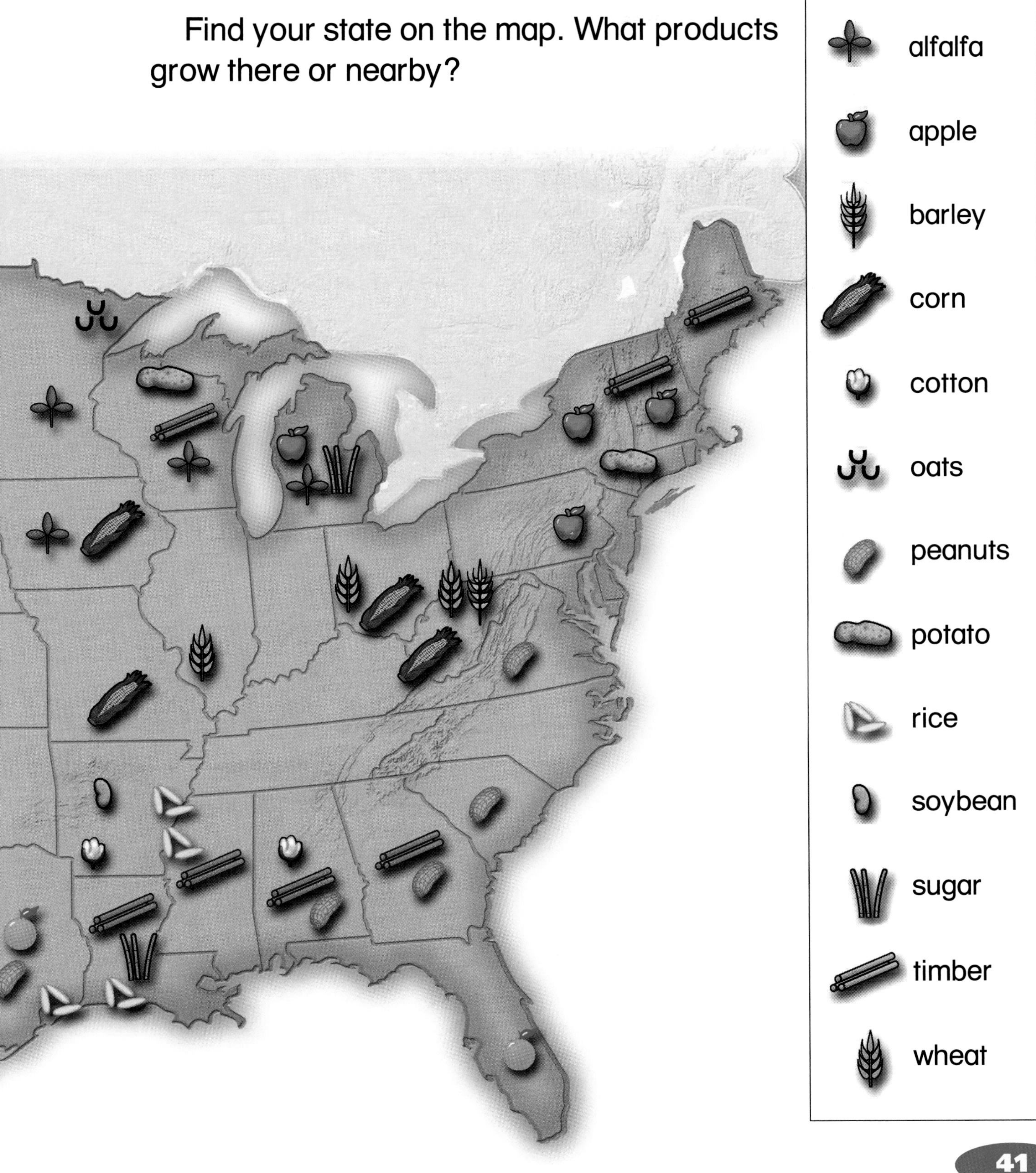

Physical Changes

A physical change is a change in how something looks. It can be a change in the size, shape, or state of matter. A physical change does not change what something is made of.

◀ When you fold paper, you change its shape. This is a physical change.

When you paint an object, you make a physical change. ▼

Chemical Changes

A chemical change takes place when one kind of matter changes to a completely different kind of matter.

When nails rust, a chemical change takes place. ▼

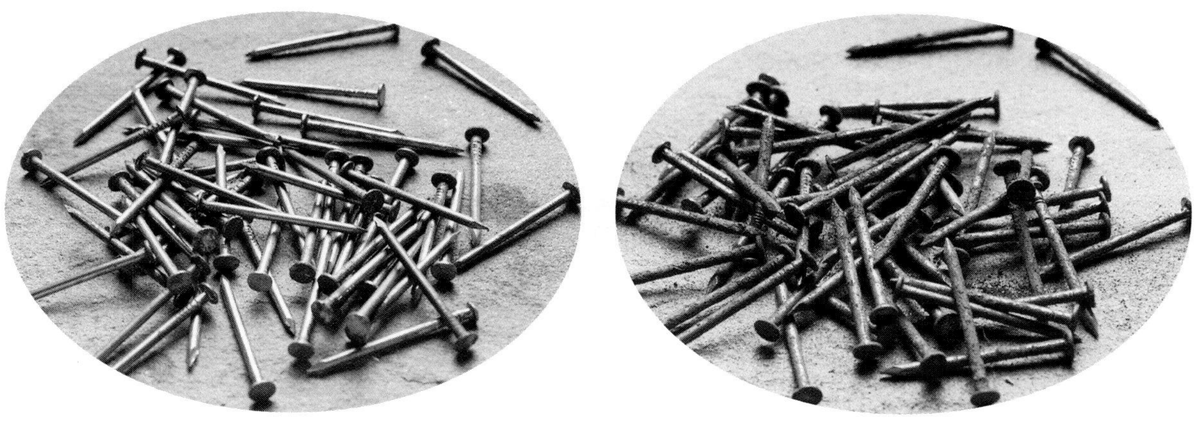

◀ Air causes silver to tarnish. This is a chemical change.

Simple Machines

A tractor and a car are both machines. Did you know that a hammer and a can opener are machines, too?

These workers use some kinds of **simple machines** to build a house. Simple machines make work easier.

Wheel and Axle
A wheel and axle is a simple machine made of a wheel attached to an axle, or rod. As the wheel turns, the axle moves.

Inclined Plane
A ramp is an inclined plane. It has a flat surface and one end is higher than the other. An inclined plane makes it easier to move things up or down.

44

Pulley
A pulley is a simple machine with a wheel and a rope. A pulley can move a heavy object up or down.
Lever
A lever can be used to take a lid off a box. Pushing down on one end of a lever lifts the object on the other end.
45

What is a Globe?

A globe is a sphere with a map on it. The blue places on the globe show water. The rest is land. Do you see more water or land on the globe?

Layers of Earth

If you could cut Earth in half, you would see that it is made of layers. The crust is the outside layer. It is the thinnest layer. It is made of rocks and soil. The mantle is the middle layer. It is a hot layer of rocks. The core is the inside of the earth. The outside part of the core is liquid. The inside part is solid. The core is the hottest part of Earth.

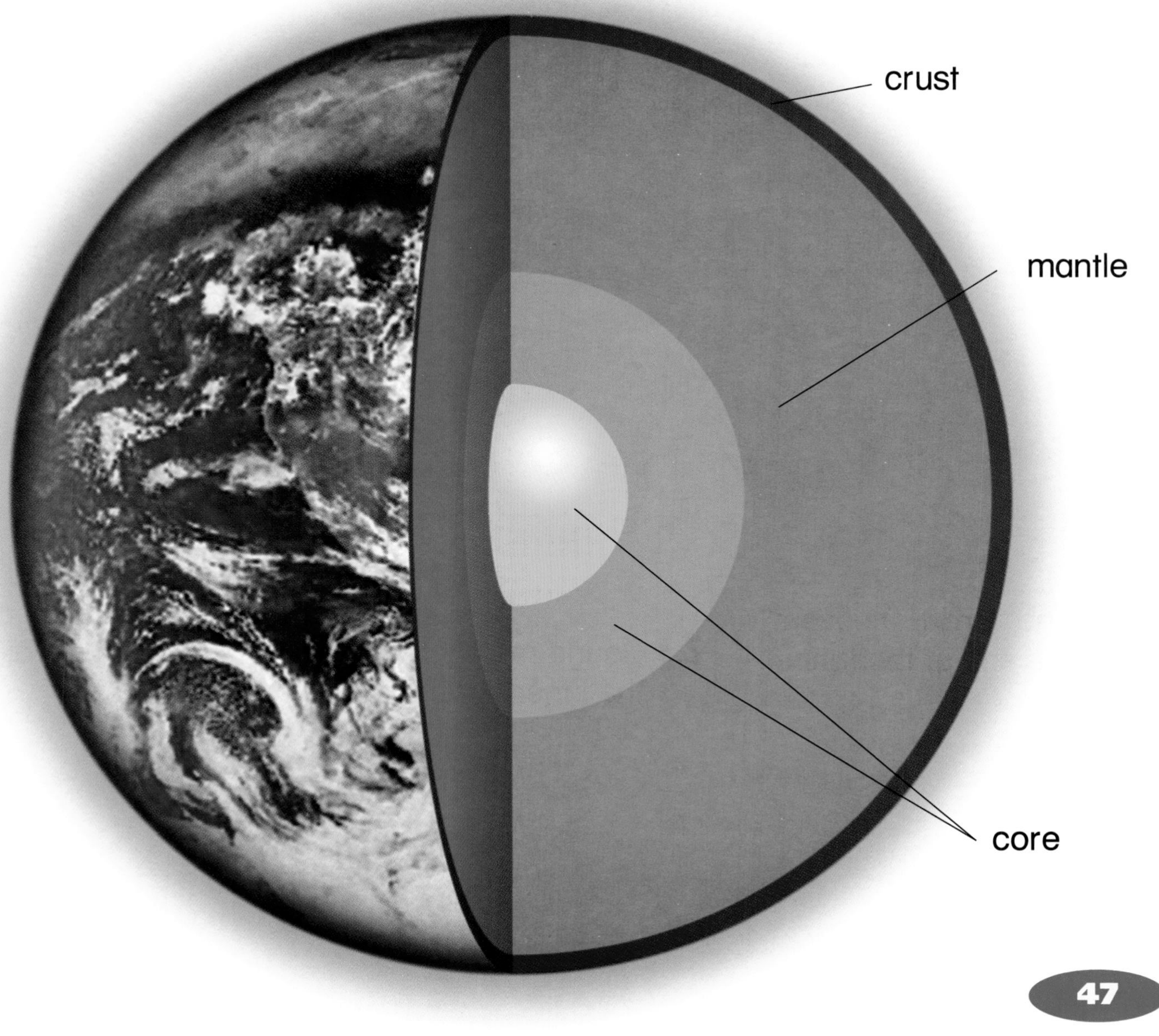

The Ear

You hear sound because sound travels through your ears.

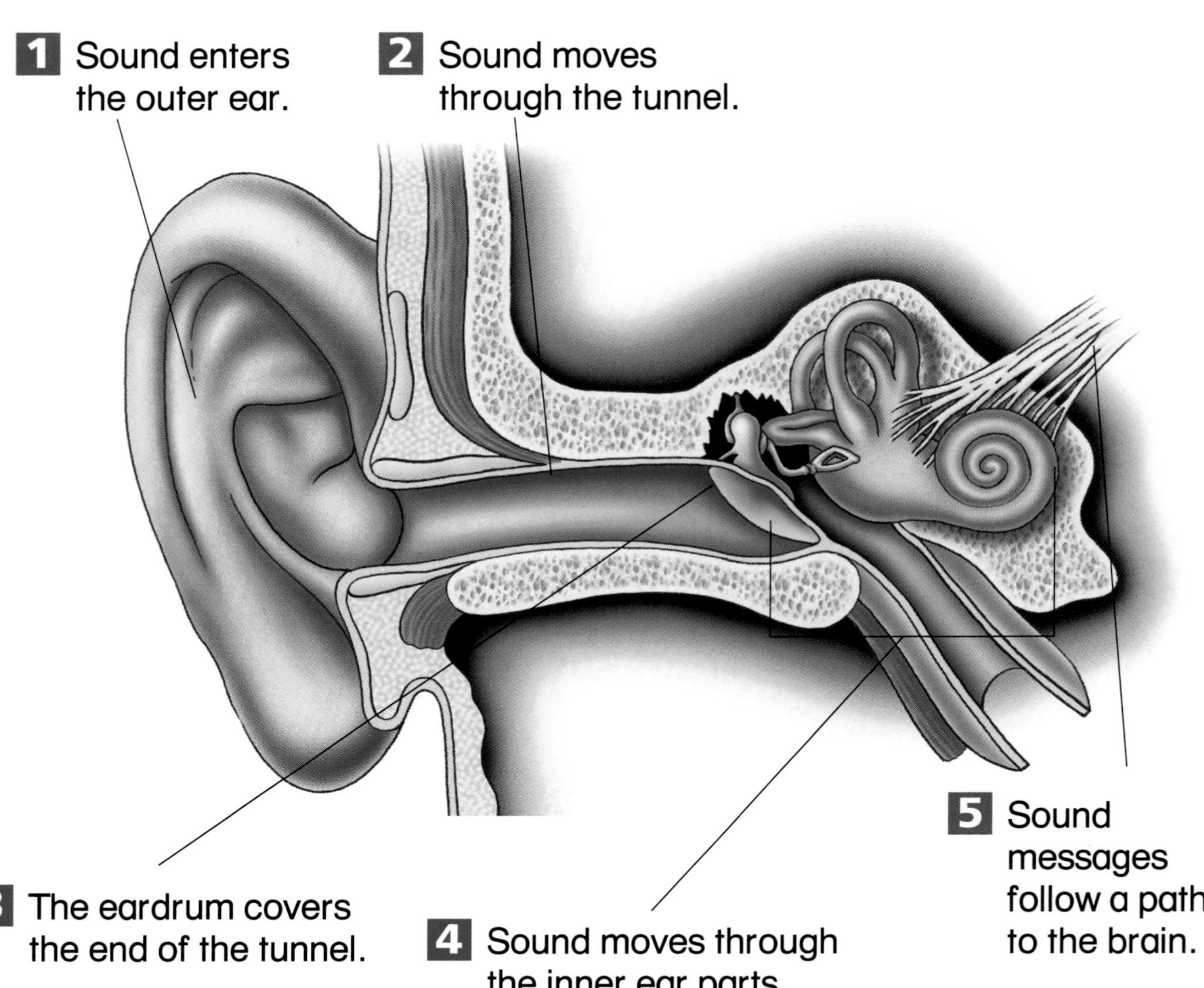

1 Sound enters the outer ear.
2 Sound moves through the tunnel.
3 The eardrum covers the end of the tunnel.
4 Sound moves through the inner ear parts.
5 Sound messages follow a path to the brain.

Muscles and Bones

Your body has many muscles. Muscles help your body move. Your body also has many bones. Bones hold your body up. Bones move when muscles pull them.

Using Measuring Tools

You can use tools to measure how long something is. Most scientists measure length in centimeters or meters.

Measure length with a metric ruler.

1. Find a pencil. Line up the eraser of the pencil with the end of the ruler.
2. Look at the tip of the pencil. Find the centimeter mark that is closest to the tip of the pencil.
3. About how long is the pencil? Record.

Measure length with a meter stick.

What is the length of your classroom? Measure with a meter stick.

Measure length with a tape measure.

Find something round in your classroom. Use a tape measure to measure around it.

Using a Thermometer

A thermometer measures the temperature. When the temperature gets warmer, the red line moves up. When it gets cooler, the red line moves down.

Some thermometers have a Celsius and Fahrenheit scale. Most scientists use the Celsius scale.

Measure temperature with a thermometer.

1. Put a thermometer in a cup of cold water.
2. Observe the red line in the thermometer.
3. Put the thermometer in a cup of warm water.
4. Observe the red line again.
5. How did the red line in the thermometer change?

Using a Pan Balance

A pan balance is used to measure mass. Mass is how much matter an object has. Make sure the two sides of a pan balance are level before you use it.

Measure mass with a pan balance.

1. Choose two objects. Which one do you think has more mass?
2. Put an object on each side of the pan balance.
3. Which side of the pan balance is lower? The object on the low side has more mass than the object on the high side.

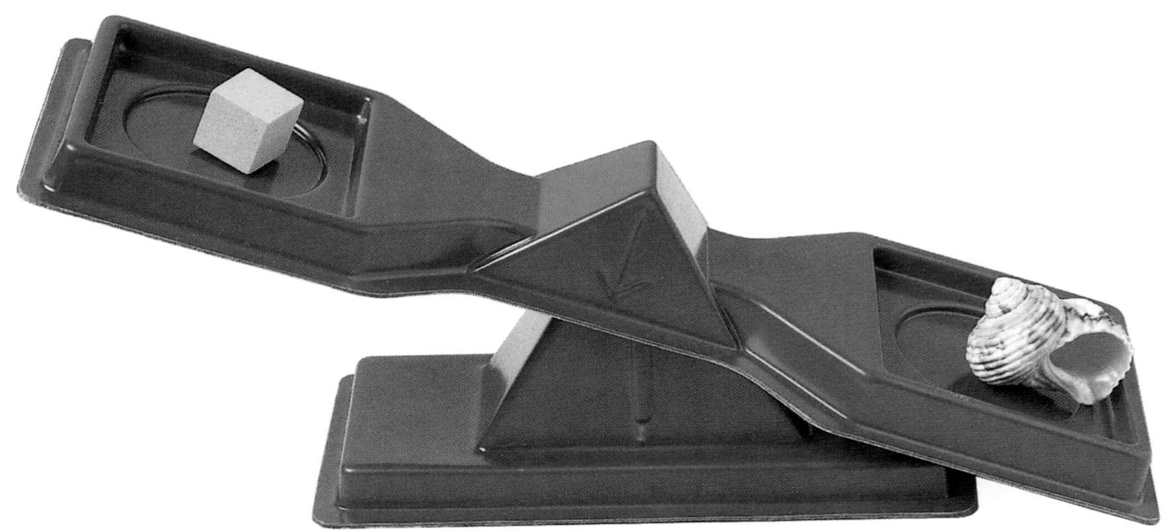

Using a Measuring Cup

You can use a measuring cup to measure volume. Volume is how much space something fills up. Most scientists use containers marked with milliliters to measure volume. The letters mL stand for milliliters.

Measure volume.

1. Find the 100 mL line on the measuring cup.
2. Put the measuring cup on a flat surface.
3. Move your head so that your eyes are even with the 100 mL line.
4. Pour water in the cup until it is even with the line.

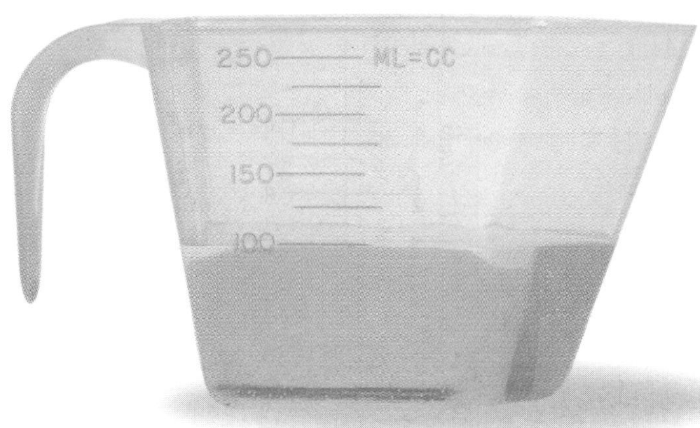

Using a Calculator

A calculator can help you do things, such as add and subtract. This chart shows how much paper a school recycled each month. Use a calculator to figure out how much paper they recycled in all.

1. To add a number, press the number. Then press the + sign.
2. Do this for each number in the chart.
3. When you have added all the numbers, press the = sign.
4. The answer should be 98.

Month	Paper Recycled in kilograms
September	7
October	12
November	13
December	9
January	11
February	14
March	9
April	15
May	8

Using a Computer

You can learn about science at a special Internet website. Go to **www.sfcience.com**.

1. Use the mouse to click on your grade.
2. Find a topic you would like to learn about. Click on that topic.
3. You can click on an arrow to go to another page. You can also click on words with lines under them.
4. Tell about 3 things that you learned at the website.

1,000 B.C.	725 B.C.	450 B.C.	175 B.C.	100 A.D.

450 B.C.
People fly the first kites.

250 B.C.
The heavy plow is invented.

200 B.C.
Archimedes shows how to use levers and pulleys.

1000 B.C.
People learn to make tools from iron.

50 B.C.
The wheelbarrow is invented.

105 A.D.
The first paper is made in China.

375 A.D.	650 A.D.	925 A.D.	1200 A.D.	1475 A.D.

500 A.D.
The first stirrups are used to ride horses.

868 A.D.
The oldest handprinted book is made.

1565 A.D.
The pencil is invented.

550 A.D.
Paper money is made in China.

1150 A.D.
People start to use bars of soap for the first time.

1285 A.D.
Eyeglasses are invented in Italy.

1453 A.D.
The first book is printed with a printing press.

1608 A.D.
The telescope is invented.

1609 A.D.
The first newspaper is printed in Germany.

1698 A.D.
Thomas Savery invents the steam engine.

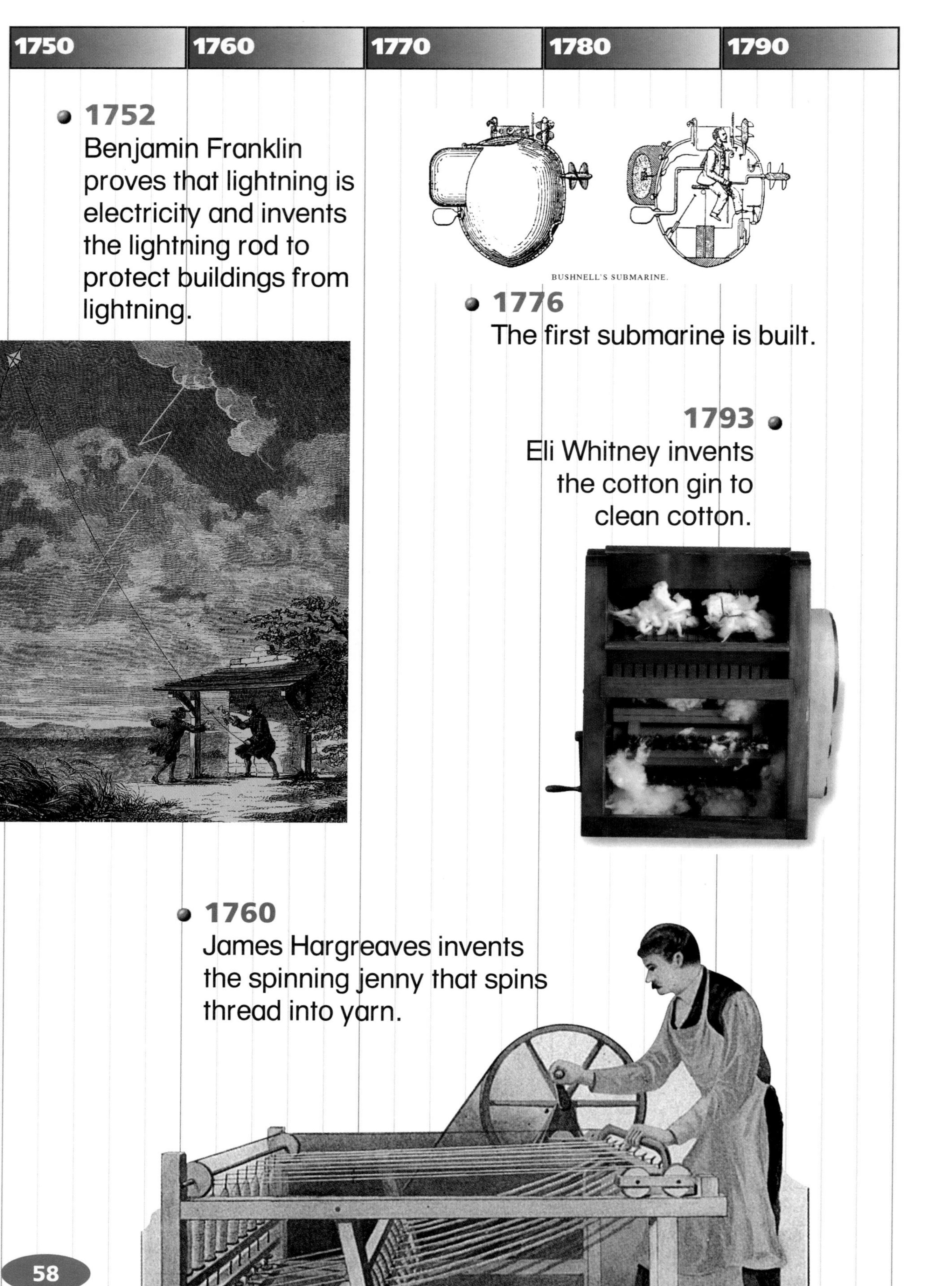

1752
Benjamin Franklin proves that lightning is electricity and invents the lightning rod to protect buildings from lightning.

1776
The first submarine is built.

1793
Eli Whitney invents the cotton gin to clean cotton.

1760
James Hargreaves invents the spinning jenny that spins thread into yarn.

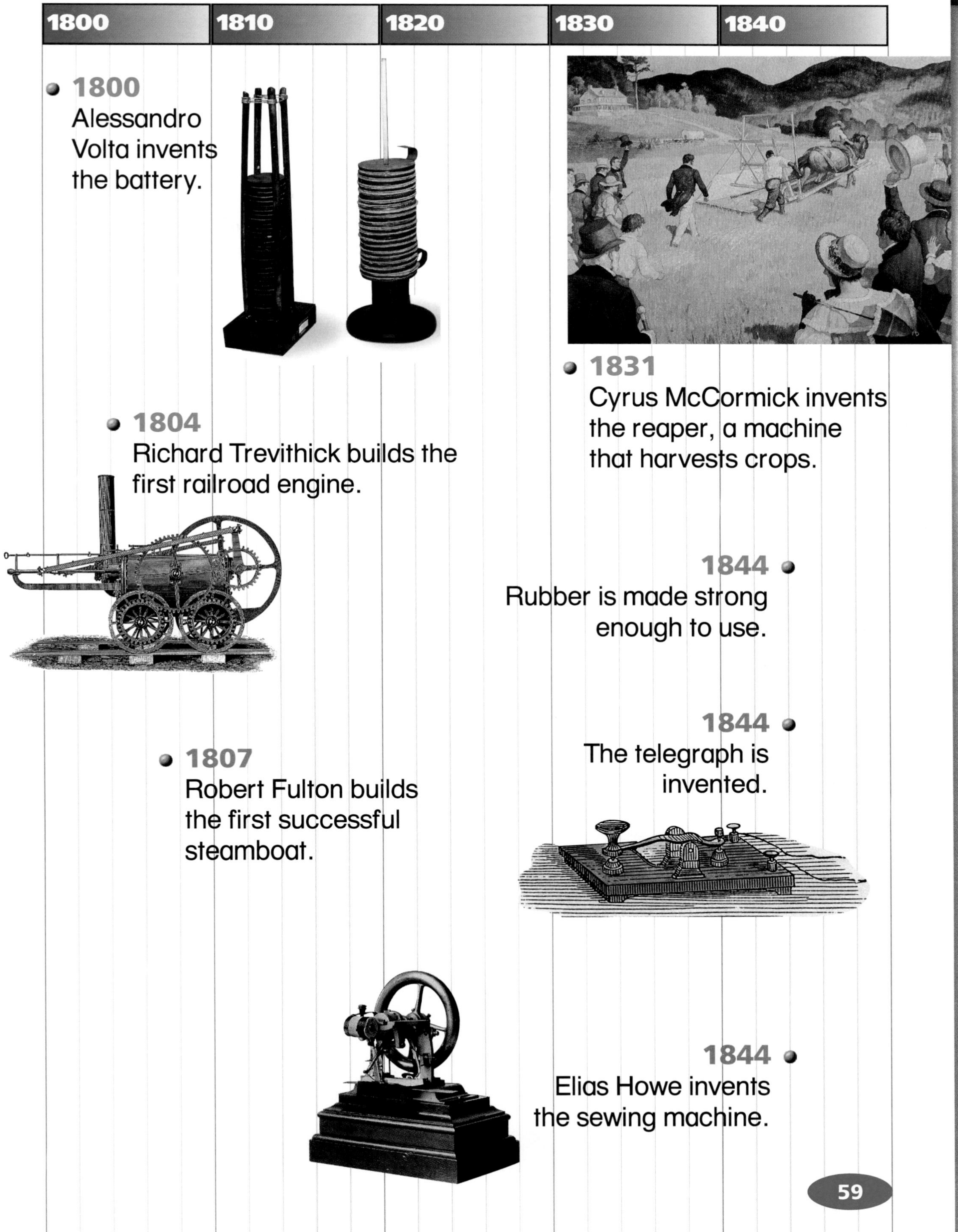
1800
1810
1820
1830
1840
1800
Alessandro Volta invents the battery.
1804
Richard Trevithick builds the first railroad engine.
1807
Robert Fulton builds the first successful steamboat.
1831
Cyrus McCormick invents the reaper, a machine that harvests crops.
1844
Rubber is made strong enough to use.
1844
The telegraph is invented.
1844
Elias Howe invents the sewing machine.
59

1850	1855	1860	1865	1870

1856
Henry Bessemer shows how to make strong steel.

1861
Coast to coast communication in the U.S.A. is made possible with the telegraph.

1858
The first rubber eraser is put on the end of a pencil.

1857
The passenger elevator is invented.

1861
Nicolaus August Otto makes the first engine powered by gasoline.

1863
James Plimpton makes the first set of roller skates.

1865
The first fax machines are used.

1873
The typewriter is invented.

1875	1880	1885	1890	1895

1876
The first telephone call is made.

1877
The record player is invented.

1879
The light bulb is invented.

1884
The fountain pen is invented.

1884
The first roller coaster is built.

1885
The car that uses gasoline is invented.

1889
The first dishwasher is invented.

1893
The zipper is invented.

1896
George Washington Carver, a scientist, makes many products from peanuts.

1900	1905	1910	1915	1920

1902
William Carrier makes the first air conditioner.

1903
The first crayons are made.

1903
The Wright brothers fly the first airplane.

1906
The first radio broadcast is heard.

1906
The first cartoon is made.

1907
Leo Baekeland invents plastic.

1913
The refrigerator is invented.

62

1925	1930	1935	1940	1945

1925
Masking tape is invented.

1927
Philo Farnsworth demonstrates the first television.

1928
Sir Alexander Fleming discovers penicillin.

1930
Clarence Birdseye introduces frozen foods.

1931
The Empire State Building is built.

1940
Nylon is invented.

1941
Les Paul builds the first electric guitar.

1946
ENIAC, the first computer, is built.

1947
The microwave oven is invented.

1948
The telephone answering machine is invented.

63

1950	1955	1960	1965	1970

1954
Color television is invented.

1957
The Soviet Union launches Sputnik, the first satellite into space.

1960
The photocopy machine is invented.

1961
Yuri Gagarin is the first man in space.

1964
Cassette tapes are invented.

1968
The first pair of running shoes is made.

1972
The first videotape machine is sold.

1974
The first bar codes appear in stores.

64

1975	1980	1985	1990	1995

1981
The first space shuttle is launched.

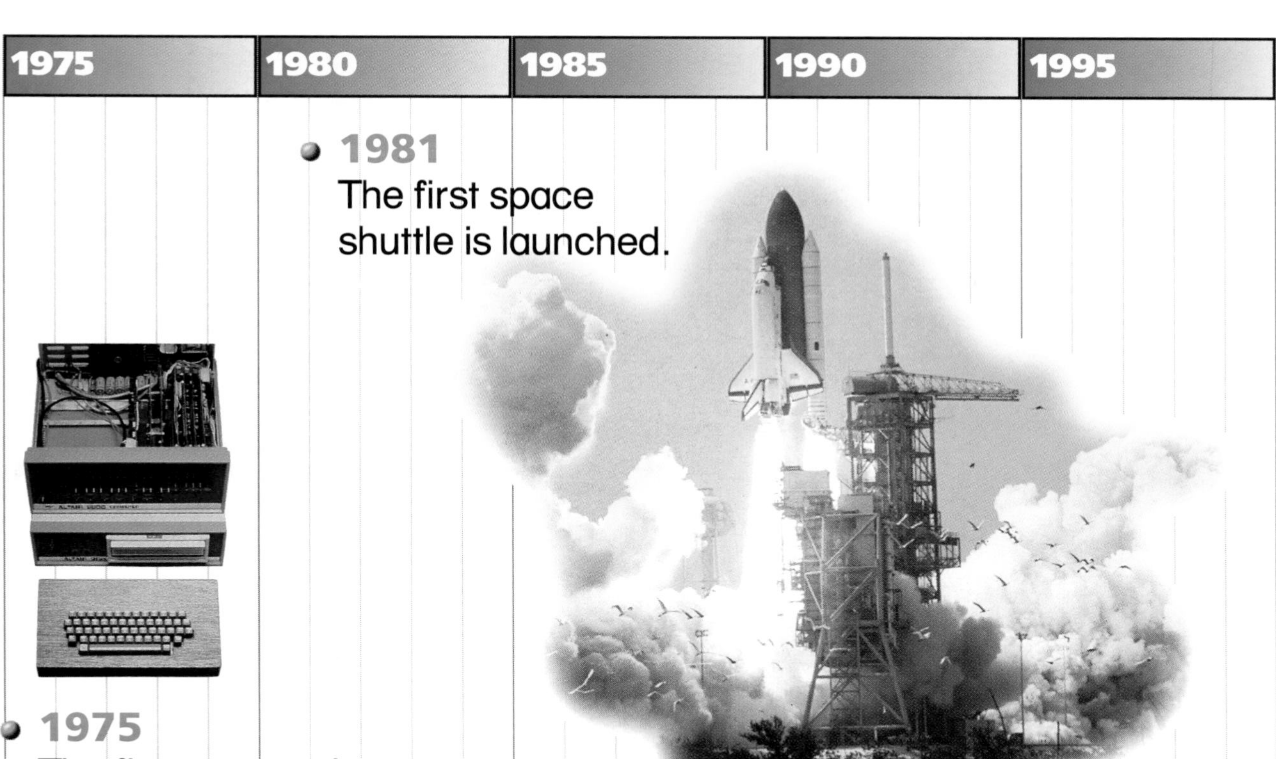

1975
The first personal computer goes on sale.

1983
Cellular phone networking starts in the U.S.A.

1985
The first compact discs are sold.

1990
The Hubble Space Telescope is launched.

1994
The Internet becomes popular.

Glossary/Index

A

adaptation, 34, 35. An adaptation is a part of or a behavior of a plant or animal that helps it stay alive. The webbed feet on a duck are an adaptation that help it swim.

amphibian, A28. An amphibian is a kind of animal. Amphibians live some of the time in water and some of the time on land. Frogs, toads, newts, and salamanders are amphibians.

anemometer, C28, C44. An anemometer measures how fast the wind is blowing.

animal, A28. An animal is a living thing. Most animals can move around on their own. Animals eat plants or other animals.

aquarium, 33. An aquarium is a tank or glass bowl in which living fish, other water animals, and water plants are kept

artery, D11, D16. An artery is a tube in the body that carries blood away from the heart.

astronaut, C54. An astronaut is a person who travels into space.

attract, B50, B60. Attract means to pull toward.

B

bones, 49. Bones are the hard part of the body. Bones hold the body up. Bones move when muscles pull them.

66

brain, D6, D16. The brain is a part of the body that is inside the head. The brain controls what the body does. It helps people move, think, feel, and remember.

C

camouflage, A42, A44. Camouflage is a color or shape that makes an animal hard to see.

cause, B44. A cause is a person, thing or event that makes something happen.

chemical change, 43. A chemical change causes matter to become a different kind of matter.

chrysalis, A34, A44. The caterpillar makes a covering called a chrysalis.

circuit, B56, B60. Electricity travels in a path called a circuit.

compost, C20. Compost is a mixture of plant wastes that rots. Compost can be added to soil to help plants grow.

condenses, C38, C44. When water vapor condenses, it changes from a gas to a liquid.

core, 47. The core is the center part of Earth.

crater, C50, C60. A crater is a hole in the ground that is shaped like a bowl. Rocks from space crashed into the moon and caused craters to form.

crust, 47. The crust is the outer layer of Earth.

67

D

digestion, D26, D30. The process of breaking down food is called digestion.

dinosaur, A52. A dinosaur is an extinct animal that lived millions of years ago. There were many different kinds of dinosaurs.

drought, C43, C44. A drought is a long period of time with no rain.

E

Earth, C48. Earth is the planet we live on. Earth is the third planet from the sun.

earthquake, C15. An earthquake is the shaking of the ground.

effect, B44. An effect is an event that is caused by an earlier event.

electricity, B56. Electricity is a form of energy. Electricity is used for lights, television, toaster and many other things.

endangered, A38, A44, 30, 31. When a plant or animal is endangered, it means that very few are living.

erosion, C12, C24. Erosion happens when soil or rock is carried away by water, wind, or other rocks.

68

esophagus, D28, D30. The esophagus is the part of the body that squeezes food down to the stomach.

evaporates, C38, C44. When water evaporates it changes into a gas called water vapor.

exercise, D34, D44. When you are active, your body is getting exercise. Walking, jumping rope, and playing tag are all ways to get exercise.

extinct, A58, A60. An animal that is extinct no longer lives on the earth. The dinosaur is an extinct animal.

F

flood, C43. A flood is a large amount of water on land that is usually dry.

flower, A15, A24. The flower is the part of a plant that makes seeds.

food chain, A40, A44. Plants use energy from the sun to make food; animals eat the plants for food; then other animals eat those animals; this is called a food chain.

Food Guide Pyramid, D22, D30. The Food Guide Pyramid shows the food groups. It shows what foods to eat in order to stay healthy.

force, B46, B60. Force is the push or pull that makes something move.

69

fossil, A50, A60. A fossil is a print or the remains of a plant or animal that lived long ago.

fuel, C18. Fuel is anything that can be burned to make a fire. Coal, wood, and oil are all fuels.

G

gas, B13, B20. A gas is a state of matter that can change shape and size. Air is made of gases.

germs, D40, D44. Germs are tiny living things. Some germs can make you sick.

globe, 46. A globe is a sphere with a map of Earth on it.

gravity, B48, B60. Gravity is the force that pulls things toward the center of the earth.

H

habitat, A38, A44. A place where a plant or animal lives is its habitat.

hatch, A32. To hatch is to come out from an egg.

heart, D10, D16. The heart is the part of the body that pumps blood to other parts of the body.

L

large intestine, D28, D30. The large intestine is a part of the body. Food that is not digested goes into the large intestine. Then it passes out of the body as solid waste.

lava, C14, C24. Lava is melted rock that comes from inside the earth.

leaves, A15, A24. Leaves are part of a plant. Leaves use light, air, and water to make sugars that plants need to grow.

life cycle, A32, A44. Some animals go through many changes as they grow. These changes are called a life cycle.

liquid, B13, B20. A liquid is a state of matter that can change shape. A liquid takes the shape of its container. Water and orange juice are liquids.

lungs, D10, D11. Lungs are the part of the body that take in air.

M

machine, 44. A machine is a tool that makes work easier.

magnet, B50. A magnet is an object that attracts some kinds of metal.

mammal, A28, A44. A mammal is a kind of animal that usually has fur or hair. Cats, horses, bats, and whales are all mammals.

mantle, 47. The mantle is the middle layer of Earth.

matter, B10, B20. Matter is anything that takes up space and has weight.

minerals, C11. Rocks are made of minerals.

moon, C50. The moon is an object in the sky that revolves around Earth.

muscles, 49. Muscles are the part of the body that gives the body shape and helps the body move. Leg muscles help you run.

N

natural resources, C18, C24. Natural resources are useful materials that come from the earth. Water, forests, oil, coal and gas are all natural resources.

nerves, D6, D16. Nerves are pathways in the body that carry messages to and from the brain.

nutrients, D28, D30. Nutrients are materials in food that people need to grow and stay healthy.

O

orbit, C56, C60. To orbit means to move around another object along a path. Earth and the other planets in our solar system orbit around the sun.

oxygen, D10. Oxygen is a gas we need to breathe. There is oxygen in air.

P

paleontologist, A58, A60. A scientist who studies fossils is called a paleontologist.

pan balance, 52. A pan balance is a tool used to measure mass. Mass is the amount of matter in an object.

phases, C51, C60. The shapes of the lighted part of the moon are called phases.

physical change, 42. A change in the size, shape, state, or appearance of matter is a physical change.

planet, C56. A planet is a body of matter that moves around the sun. The planets in our solar system are Mercury, Venus, Earth, Mars, Jupiter, Saturn, Uranus, Neptune, and Pluto.

pitch, B26, B40. Pitch is how high or low a sound is.

plant, A6. A plant is any living thing that can make its own food from light, air, and water.

pole, B50, B60. A pole is the place on a magnet that has the strongest push or pull.

properties, B8, B20. Some properties of objects are color, shape, and size.

pupa, A34, A44. When a caterpillar is changing inside its covering, it is called a pupa.

R

recycle, C20, C24. Recycle means to use something again.

repel, B50, B60. Repel means to push away.

reptiles, A28, A44. A reptile is a kind of animal. Most reptiles have scales. Snakes, lizards, and turtles are reptiles.

roots, A14, A24. Roots are a part of a plant. Roots take in water and hold plants in the soil.

S

saliva, D26. Saliva is the liquid in the mouth. Saliva helps people chew food and starts the process of digestion.

scatter, A20, A24. Scatter means to spread out.

season, C34. A season is one of the four parts of the year. The seasons are spring, summer, fall, and winter.

seed, A16. A seed is the part of a plant from which a new plant grows.

shadow, B38. A shadow is the shade made when an object blocks the light.

simple machine, End Matter 44, 45. A simple machine is a tool with few or no moving parts that makes work easier. A wheel and axle, inclined plane or ramp, lever, and pulley are four kinds of simple machines.

small intestine, D28, D30. The small intestine is a part of the body that helps digest food. Most of the digestion takes place in the small intestine.

soil, A8. Soil is the top layer of the earth. Plants grow in soil.

solar system, C46. The sun, the planets and their moons, and other objects that move around the sun form the solar system.

solid, B12, B20. A solid is a state of matter that takes up space and has its own shape. A book and a rock are examples of solids.

source, B28. A source is a place from which something comes.

states of matter, B12, B20. Three states of matter are solid, liquid, and gas.

stem, A12, A15, A24. The stem is the part of a plant that carries water to the leaves.

stomach, D 28, D29. The stomach is a part of the body. Food is mixed in the stomach until it becomes liquid.

T

tadpole, A32, A44. A tadpole is a very young frog or toad. Tadpoles have tails and live only in water.

telescope, C58, C60. A telescope makes objects that are far away look closer.

temperature, C28, 51. Temperature is how hot or cold something is.

terrarium, 32. A terrarium is a glass container in which plants or small land animals are kept.

thermometer, C28, C44, 51. A thermometer measures the temperature.

tornado, C42, C44. A tornado is a very strong wind that comes down from the clouds in the shape of a funnel. A tornado can harm objects in its path.

V

vein, D10, D11. A vein is a tube in the body that carries blood to the heart.

vibrate, B24, B40. Vibrate means to move back and forth. Sound happens when objects vibrate.

volcano, C14. A volcano is a mountain that erupts. When it erupts, lava comes out.

volume, B24, B40. Volume is how loud or soft a sound is.

W

water cycle, C38, C44. The way water moves from the clouds to the earth and back to the clouds is called the water cycle.

water vapor, C38. Water vapor is a form of water in the air. When liquid water evaporates, it changes to a gas called water vapor.

A

B

C

D

E

N

O

P

R

S

W

Acknowledgments

Illustration

Borders Patti Green
Icons Precision Graphics
Materials Icons Diane Teske Harris

Front Matter
iv BR Rob Simpson/Visuals Unlimited
iv-v B Walter Stuart
v BR Sinclear Stammers/SPL/Photo Researchers
viii T E. R. Degginger/Color-Pic, Inc.
ix John Edwards
x-xi T Donna Nelson
x B Myrleen Ferguson/PhotoEdit

Unit A
4 Marsha Winborn
6, 7, 26, 54 Walter Stuart
34a Claudia Sargent
46 Precision Graphics
46 Jean Hirashima

Unit B
4 Joann Daley
10 Simon Galkin
22 Kevin O' Malley
28 Carol Stutz
32 Tom Leonard
42 Dan Mcgeeham
44 Cathy Morrison
46b Pauline Phung
56 William Graham
58 Deborah Melmon

Unit C
4 Ken Tiessen
26 Doreen Gay- Kassel
30a, 31a Georgia C. Shola
46 Stacey Schuett
48 William Graham
56 J.B. Woolsey

Unit D
4 Anni Matsick
6, 10, 11, 29b John Edwards
18 Donna Nelson
22 William Graham
32 Deborah Melmon

Photography

Unless otherwise credited, all photographs are the property of Scott Foresman, a division of Pearson Education. Page abbreviations are asfollows: (T) top, (C) center, (B) bottom, (L) left, (R) right, (INS) inset.

Cover Clifton Carr/Minden Pictures

Unit A
1 Arie deZanger for Scott Foresman
1 Background Carr Clifton/Minden Pictures
2 TL George Hall/Check Six
2 BL Moshe Alamaro
2 B Louis Psilhoyos/Matrix International
3 T Courtesy Silicon Graphics
16 B H. Chaumeton/Nature, France
20 Background Robert Knauft/Biology Media/Photo Researchers
20 LB Richard Hutchings/Photo Researchers
21 RB Robert Knauft/Biology Media/Photo Researchers
22 RB John D. Cunningham/Visuals Unlimited
22 C Holt Studions/Nigel Catlin/Photo Researchers
23 RC John D. Cunningham/Visuals Unlimited
23 LB PhotoDisc, Inc.
28 T John Gerlach/Visuals Unlimited
28 C Hal Beral/Visuals Unlimited
28 RB Mary M. Thatcher/Photo Researchers
31 LT Rob Simpson/Visuals Unlimited
31 RC Michael Habicht/Animals Animals/Earth Scenes
31 LC Richard Day/Animals Animals/Earth Scenes
32 LB Gregory K. Scott/Photo Researchers
32 B Harry Rogers/Photo Researchers
32 RB Harry Rogers/Photo Researchers
33 T Stephen Dalton/Photo Researchers
33 LB Harry Rogers/NAS/Photo Researchers
34 LB Gustav Verderber/Visuals Unlimited
34 B Dr. E. R. Degginger FPSA/Color-Pic, Inc.
34 RB Dr. E. R. Degginger/Color-Pic, Inc.
35 C Dr. E. R. Degginger/Color-Pic, Inc.
35 T Dr. E. R. Degginger/Color-Pic, Inc.
38 B David M. Grossman/Photo Researchers
38 RB Beth Davidow/Visuals Unlimited
39 T Renee Lynn/Photo Researchers
39 RC Dan Guravich/Photo Researchers
42 B Bruce Watkins/Animals Animals/Earth Scenes
50 RT Sinclair Stammers/SPL/Photo Researchers
50 RC Albert Copley/Visuals Unlimited
50 RB Charlie Ott/Photo Researchers
50 B E. R. Degginger/Color-Pic, Inc.
50 LB E. R. Degginger/Color-Pic, Inc.
52 B A. J. Copley/Visuals Unlimited
53 LC Francois Gohier Pictures
53 RC Denver Museum of Natural History/Photo Researchers
58 B Francois Gohier Pictures
59 LB Courtesy of the Black Hills Institute of Geological Research, Inc., Hill City, SD/Black Hills Institute
59 RT Rich Frishman/Tony Stone Images

Unit B
1 NASA
2 T Thomas Zimmerman/Picture Perfect
2 B Courtesy LightVision Confectionary
3 Chris A. Crumley/Earth Water Stock Photography
3 INS Courtesy Shark Pod, Fort Lauderdale, FL
33 T Stock Market
36 LC Frank Siteman/Rainbow
48 B Tony Freeman/PhotoEdit

Unit C
1 Arie deZanger for Scott Foresman
1 Background Panoramic Images
2 T University of Bristol
2 B David Parker/ESA/SPL/Photo Reserachers
3 NASA
8 LB PhotoDisc, Inc.
10 B E. R. Degginger/Color-Pic, Inc.
12 B Jim Strawser/Grant Heilman Photography
14 B Soames Summerhays/Photo Researchers
15 T Carl Frank/Photo Researchers
18 B Ron Spomer/Visuals Unlimited
19 T Zigy Kaluzny/Tony Stone Images
22 B Richard Hutchings/Photo Researchers
28 RT Christian Grzimek/OKAPIA/Photo Researchers
28 B Rich Iwasaki/Tony Stone Images
34 LC S. Maslowski/Visuals Unlimited
34 B E. R. Degginger/Color-Pic, Inc.
35 RT Maslowski/Photo Researchers
35 T John D. Cunningham/Visuals Unlimited
36 RB Jeff Lepore/Photo Researchers
36 B John Gerlach/Visuals Unlimited
37 RT Ken Highfill/Photo Researchers
37 T D. Cavagnaro/Visuals Unlimited
42 LB Keith Kent/SPL/Photo Researchers
42 RB Merrilee Thomas/TOM STACK & ASSOCIATES
43 RB Adam Jones/Photo Researchers
50 B NASA
51 Right side Dr. E. R. Degginger/Color-Pic, Inc.
54 B NASA
55 T Hubble Space Telescope Institute/NASA
58 LB Mel Lindstrom/Lick Observatory/Photo Researchers
58 RB NASA

Unit D
1 Arie deZanger for Scott Foresman
1 Background Bob Schuchman/Phototake
2 T Dr. Susan Courtney/National Institute of Mental Health
2 B Davies & Starr/Liaison
3 Courtesy BBHExhibits, Inc.
20 Myrleen Ferguson/PhotoEdit
34 Myrleen Ferguson/PhotoEdit

Dr. Tim Cooney

Series Author, Professor of Earth Science and Science Education
University of Northern Iowa

"Science for all students," is the best way to express the intent of the National Science Education Standards. The statement reflects the social commitment that standards apply to students regardless of background (gender, ethnicity, economic condition), circumstance, or ambition. Before National Science Education Standards were developed, there was little available to show educators what a comprehensive K–12 science curriculum should aim for. Standards are criteria by which judgments can be made. Standards are broad, general statements of what is possible and do not define one, universal best approach. National Science Education Standards are limited to fundamental understandings and offer selection criteria that states, localities, and teachers can use to determine scientific subject matter to be studied.

National Science Education Standards

National Science Education Standards exist for l) content, 2) teaching, 3) assessment, 4) program, and 5) system.

- **Content Standards** define what ALL students should understand and be able to do as a result of their school learning experiences. They are voluntary, not federally mandated nor reducible to a set of minimum competencies.
- **Teaching Standards** provide a vision of what teachers need to understand and do to provide learning experiences for students that are aligned with content standards. They do not describe one best way to teach or learn.
- **Assessment Standards** identify essential characteristics of fair and accurate student assessments and program evaluations that are consistent with content standards at the classroom, school, district, state, and national levels. Assessment Standards are not tests nor do they describe a single strategy to judge student learning or a school program.
- **Program Standards** describe how content, teaching, and assessment are coordinated in school practice over a full range of schooling to provide all students the opportunity to learn science.
- **System Standards** describe how policies and practices outside of the immediate learning environment support high quality science programs.

Content Standards

The Content Standards are broken down for grades K–4, 5–8, and 9–12 into seven categories. These categories are: Science as Inquiry, Physical Science, Life Science, Earth and Space Science, Science and Technology, Science in Personal and Social Perspectives, and the History and Nature of Science. An eighth category, Unifying Concepts and Processes, is not broken down into grade levels, but should be developed over the entire K–12 science experience.

- **Science as Inquiry Standards** are the basic and controlling principles in the organization and experiences in students' science education. The standards on inquiry highlight the ability to do inquiry, which goes well beyond just using process skills such as measuring, observing, communicating, controlling variables, inferring, and experimenting. The Science as Inquiry Standards include the "processes of science", but go beyond by requiring that students combine process skills and scientific knowledge as they incorporate scientific reasoning and critical thinking to help develop their understanding of science. Today's students need to develop the ability to ask for information to use in answering questions; plan and conduct scientific investigations; use appropriate tools and equipment and experiences to extend their senses; and gather, analyze, and interpret data. Inquiry also includes using data and experiences to construct reasonable explanations and communicating about investigations and explanations.
- **Physical, Life, and Earth and Space Science Standards** express the primary subject matter of science. Science subject matter focuses on those science concepts, principles, and theories that are fundamental for all students to know and be able to use.
- **Science and Technology Standards** establish useful connections between the natural world and the designed world and offer essential decision-making abilities.
- **Science in Personal and Social Perspectives Standards** connect students with their social and personal world. In the elementary grades, these standards include personal health, environmental change, and science and technology in local challenges and society.
- **History and Nature of Science Standards** include an understanding of the nature of science and uses history in school science programs to clarify different aspects of scientific inquiry, science in society, and the human aspects of science.
- **Unifying Concepts and Processes Standards** provide students with powerful ideas that help them understand the natural world. These conceptual and procedural schemes that are integral to students' science learning experiences and include concepts and processes such as systems, organization, interactions, change, measurement, models, scale, adaptation, and explanation.

Scott Foresman *Science* and the National Science Education Standards

- **Scott Foresman *Science*** aligns with the structure of the Content Standards of the National Science Education Standards. At all grade levels, the subject matter is divided into four units: Life Science, Physical Science, Earth Science, and Human Body. Correlation of each chapter in **Scott Foresman *Science*** to the NSES Content Standards can be found in the Teacher's Editions as part of the Unit Planning Guides that begin each unit.
- Hands-on activities throughout the Student Edition and the Teacher's Edition of **Scott Foresman *Science*** support the goals of the Science as Inquiry standards. Correlation of all Investigate Activities and Experiment Activities to the Content Standards is provided on the Activity Videos. Extended Inquiry activities begin every unit in the Teacher's Edition. These activities follow methods of scientific inquiry suggested in the Science as Inquiry standards.
- Other features in the Student Edition and the Teacher's Edition provide connections to the other NSES Content Standards: Science and Technology; Science in Personal and Social Perspectives; History and Nature of Science; and Unifying Concepts and Principles.

Dr. Karen L. Ostlund

Series Author, Professor
The University of Texas at Austin

Hands-on and minds-on experiences are fundamental to the inquiry approach in science. **Scott Foresman *Science*** activities provide opportunities for students to investigate and inquire about the world. This emphasis on student observations and data gathering to learn science reflects the belief that students should use the process skills and thinking skills that scientists use to find out about the world and how it works.

Process skills are ways of thinking in science. The process skills that students will develop while using **Scott Foresman *Science*** include the following: Observing, Communicating, Classifying, Estimating and Measuring, Inferring, Predicting, Making Operational Definitions, Making and Using Models, Formulating Questions and Hypotheses, Collecting and Interpreting Data, Identifying and Controlling Variables, and Experimenting. These process skills are ways of thinking used in scientific inquiry or scientific methods, which are systematic approaches to problem solving. The use of scientific methods to solve problems in science will also help students to solve many other kinds of problems in their daily lives.

Student Edition Activities

Scott Foresman *Science* supports traditional content through the teaching of process skills and numerous hands-on activities throughout the Student Edition. Examples include:

- **Explore Activities** (grades K–6) are open-ended, one-page activities. Grades K–2 also have Science Center Explore Activities in the Flip Chart.
- **Investigate Activities** (grades 1–6) are two-page, step-by-step activities that provide either anticipatory or confirmatory hands-on experiences for students. Grades 1–2 also have Science Center Investigate Activities in the Flip Chart.
- **Experiment Activities** (grades K–6) are two- or three-page activities that use scientific methods to solve problems. Grades K–2 also have Science Center Experiment Activities in the Flip Chart.
- **Inquire Further** (grades K–6) ends each activity and provides suggestions for further inquiry.
- **Unit Performance Reviews** (grades K–6) at the end of each unit use short projects to assess different student intelligences.
- **Process Skills lessons** (grades K–6) in the student edition end matter provide further instruction in all of the process skills used in **Scott Foresman *Science***. In Kindergarten, these lessons are in the Student Workbook and the Teacher's Edition.

Teacher's Edition Activities

The **Scott Foresman *Science*** Teacher's Edition includes numerous activities to supplement the Student Edition.

- The **Activity Idea Bank** (grades K–6) includes extra science activity suggestions (a Science Center activity in grades K–2) as well as Cross-Curricular Options.
- **Extended Inquiry** activities (grades 1–6) are open-ended, long-term projects that begin each unit, using methods of inquiry suggested in the National Science Education Standards.
- **INQUIRY Additional Activity** (grades 3–6) is an open-ended activity suggestion that can be used to begin each lesson.

Additional Resources

The various ancillary booklets and other products in **Scott Foresman *Science*** include a variety of tools to support activities, such as:

- **Lab Manual** (grades 1–6) provides recording sheets for students' observations and data for each activity.
- **Process Skills blackline masters** (grades K–6) support the activities involving process skills in the end matter of the Student Edition.
- **Unit Equipment Kits** (grades K–6) provide many of the materials used in the Explore, Investigate, and Experiment activities. Each kit contains an **Equipment Kit Teacher's Guide** giving information on how to re-order materials.
- **Teacher Demonstration Kit** (grades K–6) provides one set of materials for each activity, so that teachers can rehearse activities prior to teaching activities in class.

Technology

Technology products that support activities in **Scott Foresman *Science*** include:

- **Activity Videos** (grades K–6) demonstrate every Investigate Activity and every Experiment Activity, aiding in teacher preparation and comfort with hands-on science. The National Science Education Standards Content Standard that each activity supports is emphasized and the main process skills involved in each activity are highlighted at point of use.
- At **www.sfscience.com** (grades K–6), students can join an interactive community accessible through your classroom in which they collect and share data, then publish their science efforts online. The Content Standards for Science as Inquiry from the National Science Education Standards are mirrored as a guide for conducting scientific investigations in the National Lab.
- **DataWonder** software can be used by students to organize and graph their data from activities.

Dr. Angie L. Matamoros

Series Author, Science Curriculum Specialist
Broward County Schools, Ft. Lauderdale, Florida

Assessment comes from the Latin word *assidere*, which means "to sit beside" and provide feedback, guidance, and support. A good assessment program is more about facilitating growth than it is about repeated testing. Good assessment systems are highly interactive, and provide teachers and students with information about students' evolving understandings, skills, knowledge, and their abilities to solve problems and think critically.

Student and Teacher's Editions

The Assessment System in **Scott Foresman *Science*** emphasizes frequent, informal assessments embedded both in science content and in classroom activities. Assessment in the Student Edition and in the Teacher's Edition includes the following alternatives:

- **Graphic Organizers** (grades 3–6) begin each chapter; students can assess their learning each lesson, then use their organizer as a study guide for review of the chapter.
- **Lesson Reviews** (grades 1–6) at the end of each lesson assess each lesson objective.
- **Chapter Reviews** (all grades) and **Unit Reviews** (grades 3–6) at the end of each chapter and unit use traditional items and extended responses to probe students' understanding.
- **Unit Performance Reviews** (grades 1–6) at the end of each unit use short projects to assess different student intelligences.
- A **Self-Assessment** section after each activity (grades 3–6) gives students the opportunity to evaluate their performance and compare it to the teacher's assessment of their progress.
- **Assessment Rubrics** in the Teacher's Edition help to assess the performance assessment that is part of the Chapter Review (grades 1–2) and the Unit Performance Review (grades 1–6).
- **Process Skills Development** (grades 1–6) charts in the Teacher's Edition help to assess the process skills that are used in activities.

Additional Resources

The various ancillary booklets include an assortment of assessment tools, such as:

- **Portfolio Ideas** (grades 1–6) for every chapter, organized by type of intelligence.
- **Graphic Organizers** (grades K–2) provided for every chapter help students understand and review chapter concepts.
- **Activity Rubrics** (grades 1–6) for all activities, provided to assist teachers in evaluating levels of student performance.
- **Lesson Assessments** (grades 3–6) combine traditional and alternative questions in an easy-to-grade format and probe students' conceptual understanding of each lesson.
- **Chapter Study Guides** (grades 3–6) provide writing and process skill application opportunities to prepare students for the Chapter Assessments.
- **Chapter Assessment** (all grades) in formats A and B (grades 3–6) and **Unit Assessment** (grades 3–6) in formats A and B combine traditional and open-ended assessment strategies.
- **Performance Assessment** for each chapter (grades 1–2) and each unit (all grades) provides hands-on tasks that use everyday materials to perform investigations and apply problem-solving skills in real-world settings.

Technology

Various technology products also facilitate formal and ongoing assessment.

- The **Production Studio** enables students to develop multimedia presentations that can be used as elements of their portfolios or as tools to assess students' synthesis of concepts.
- The **Practice & Assessment CD-ROM** provides students with an exciting way to review science concepts and assess their own mastery of the content objectives.
- **TestWorks™ CD-ROM** contains questions for all objectives that can be customized for individual and class needs.
- The **Teacher's Resource Planner CD-ROM** aids review of assessment tools.
- **KnowZone™** helps students increase their mastery of science concepts and practice test-taking skills.

Each **Scott Foresman *Science*** assessment component reveals different aspects of student performance and is an integral part of the curriculum. The **Scott Foresman *Science*** Assessment System features a range of different assessment strategies that provide you with a broad picture of student achievement designed to meet the needs of a diverse population of children who learn in different ways.

Kate Boehm Nyquist

Series Author, Science Writer and Curriculum Specialist
Mount Pleasant, South Carolina

It's no secret that engaged parents and other caregivers can make a real difference in a child's school performance. Research shows that at-home behaviors such as reading to children, helping with homework, and communicating high, but realistic, expectations can contribute to a student's achievement in school.[1] There is also a growing body of evidence that indicates meaningful family involvement at school can provide important benefits to students as well.[2] As a result, many schools across the country are now including collaboration with families—and the community in general—as an important part of their school improvement programs.

So how can busy teachers do more to encourage parental involvement in their science curriculum? A good first step is to provide numerous opportunities for parents and caregivers to become informed and involved. **Scott Foresman *Science*** offers many such opportunities and recommends teachers take advantage of the "built-in" school-home connection features of the program in the following ways.

1. **Connect parents and caregivers with the science curriculum their child is studying.** Sometimes science content can seem intimidating and best left to the "experts." But nothing could be further from the truth for our kids! Parents and caregivers are in a unique position to encourage observation and inquiry on a daily basis. Teachers can provide background information and activity suggestions for parents to use at home with the following tools from the **Scott Foresman *Science*** program:
   - **Family Activity Blackline Masters**—These letters home serve as a convenient way to update parents and caregivers on what their child is learning by explaining the main science concepts being taught in every chapter. Related home projects and activities are suggested and lists of chapter vocabulary words are provided. Parents often ask for recommended reading lists, so these family activity masters also provide topic-related literature references. Finally, a list of appropriate websites suggest further opportunities for families to explore the internet together. The Family Activity Blackline Masters are available for all grades (K–6) and are located in the Instructional Resources ancillary book.
   - **Notes for Home/Home Activity** — Annotations appear throughout the entire **Scott Foresman *Science*** program to cue teachers when to suggest relevant information or activities that are particularly suited for home follow-up. The idea is to provide a constant stream of information and ideas that will encourage parent/child interactions that are both educational and fun. Look for these annotations for all grades (K–6) in the following **Scott Foresman *Science*** program components: the Teacher's Edition, the Instructional Resources ancillary, the Lab Manual, the Teacher's Assessment Package and the Interactive Transparency Package.
2. **Invite parents and caregivers to participate in a science event at school.** Science is the perfect topic to bring parents, teachers, and students together for an evening of exploration and fun. One particularly successful outreach effort that has been enthusiastically embraced by the science education community is an event known as Family Science Night. **Scott Foresman *Science*** offers a detailed outline for teachers to create their own evening of science with the following feature:
   - **Family Science Night: A Blueprint for Success**—This informative guide helps teachers structure an outreach effort that can help shape positive attitudes while leading to greater science awareness and increased parent, child, and teacher interactions. General guidelines, templates for invitations, and even sample activities to use in a Family Science Night are provided. The SHAPE formula for success allows teachers to benefit from the experiences of many of their peers in conducting this special function. This helpful guide is found in the Instructional Resources ancillary book.
3. **Encourage parents and caregivers to take advantage of technology resources.** Kids love technology! Help parents learn to use a variety of media in helping their children learn about the world around them.
   - **Songs and Activities**—This audio package for primary students (K–2) brings science to life with special songs created for **Scott Foresman *Science*** by the Chidren's Television Workshop.™ Blackline masters of the lyrics and special activities for each song, in both English and Spanish, are ready to send home for the entire family to enjoy.
   - **The KnowZone™**—This world wide web based internet program allows students to prepare for and even practice taking tests in a fun, low-pressure environment. Fast-paced games review science content. When a child is ready, practice test-taking opportunities helps him or her prepare for state and local exams. A special Parent's Science Guide offers a friendly review of science content so parents and caregivers can "brush up" on their own knowledge to feel more confident in helping their kids study and prepare for science class.
4. **Counsel parents and caregivers to relax and have fun with science!** Parents often worry about not knowing all the answers to their kids' many science questions. Reassure parents that they are in fact, teaching the process of science when they research and explore with their children to find answers together. Children learn about science by playing and observing...and adults can learn in this way, too! Remind parents and caregivers that demonstrating a commitment to lifelong learning emphasizes the great value they place on education —and that legacy is perhaps the most valuable lesson of all!

References

1. ***Parental Engagements That Make a Difference***, Jeremy Finn, (ASCD Educational Leadership, vol.55, 1998)
2. ***A New Generation of Evidence—The Family Is Critical to Student Achievement***. Anne Henderson and Nancy Berla, (Center for Law and Education, Washington, D.C.).

Dr. Jack A. Gerlovich

Science Education Safety Consultant/Author
Des Moines, Iowa

Activities throughout **Scott Foresman *Science*** reinforce and extend science concepts using materials and procedures that are inherently safe. **Scott Foresman *Science*** teaches that safe procedure is part of sound scientific inquiry. Students who use this program learn not only how to safely investigate the topics at hand; they also develop safety habits that will serve them well in future scientific endeavors.

How does **Scott Foresman *Science*** accomplish this task? First and foremost, by performing the activities in the text, students learn that simple, safe materials can be used extensively to investigate science concepts. Second, safety reminders regarding procedure are given in the Student Edition whenever appropriate. These include Safety Note statements and the inclusion of safety goggles as a material in appropriate activities.

Safety Note *Safety notes at point of use throughout the program let you know when to exercise caution during activities.*

Third, the Teacher's Edition includes safety notes for the various student activities and teacher demonstrations that appear throughout the program. Following is a list of the most general of these tips for the elementary science classroom. If followed from the start, these guidelines should be easily assimilated into classroom procedures by teachers and students alike.

- The proper use of safety goggles that meet the American National Standards Institute (ANSI Z87.1) standards should be demonstrated to students. Safety goggles should be worn whenever the potential for eye injury exists; for example, when heating any substance, when using any chemicals including "ordinary" substances such as vinegar, and when using glassware. Even relatively safe items such as rubber bands and balloons can cause eye injury and warrant the use of goggles.
- To prevent student interference with each other and to assist the safe exit of students from the room in case of an emergency, teachers should try to ensure that rooms are not overcrowded, that students understand exit procedures, and that aisles are kept uncluttered.
- Teachers should periodically conduct simulations with students dealing with foreseeable emergencies. Examples might include exiting the room due to an emergency, coping with a fire, aiding someone who has been splashed by a substance, and helping a fall victim.
- Prior to using any equipment or substances, teachers should be certain they understand the proper function and hazards associated with the use of those items. This information should be communicated to the students.
- Unless you know the outcome is safe, you should never mix substances "just to see what happens." No hazardous substances are used in **Scott Foresman *Science***. However, the combining of certain substances might pose safety problems. For example, mixing ammonia with bleach produces particularly dangerous fumes. Notes about the dangers of mixing chemicals are included on the appropriate pages throughout the program.
- All equipment should be properly stored. The more dangerous items should be kept under lock and key.
- Whenever possible, plastic items should replace glass. If glass containers are essential, temperature- and break-resistant glassware should be selected.
- To prevent slipping and falls, any liquids spilled on tile or hardwood floors should be wiped up immediately.
- If the teacher cannot satisfy himself or herself that all foreseeable dangers have been reduced to an acceptable level, the activity should be altered or eliminated.

Teachers should be aware of all applicable federal, state, and local regulations and relevant guidelines from professional organizations which apply to the activities being performed. Examples would include Occupational Safety and Health Administration (OSHA) standards for workplace safety; state laws relating to safety goggles; local fire department requirements regarding the use of open flame, fire extinguishers, and fire blankets; and National Science Teachers Association (NSTA) suggestions regarding overcrowding. Refer to the following materials for other information about classroom safety.

Resources

Science Safety for Elementary School Teachers by Downs, G., et al. (Iowa State University Press, ISBN 0-81-381641-6)

Scott Foresman Science provides you with complete science content that supports the objectives of the *National Science Education Standards.*

Unit A Life Science

National Science Education Standards

- Characteristics of organisms
- Life cycles of organisms
- Organisms and environments

Chapter 1

Chapter 1 Plants

Lesson 1 What are some kinds of plants?
Lesson 2 What does a plant need to grow?
Lesson 3 Experiment with plants.
Lesson 4 What are the parts of a plant?
Lesson 5 How does a plant grow and change?
Lesson 6 What is inside a seed?
Lesson 7 How are seeds scattered?
Lesson 8 How do people use plants?

Chapter 2

Chapter 2 Animals

Lesson 1 What are some kinds of animals?
Lesson 2 How do frogs grow and change?
Lesson 3 How do butterflies grow and change?
Lesson 4 How can you make a model of a butterfly life cycle?
Lesson 5 Where do animals live?
Lesson 6 What do animals eat?
Lesson 7 How do animals protect themselves?

Chapter 3

Chapter 3 Fossils

Lesson 1 What are fossils?
Lesson 2 How do we learn about dinosaurs?
Lesson 3 What are some kinds of dinosaurs?
Lesson 4 How long were some dinosaurs?
Lesson 5 What happened to the dinosaurs?

Unit B Physical Science

National Science Education Standards

- Properties of objects and materials
- Position and motion of objects
- Light, heat, electricity, and magnetism

Chapter 1

Chapter 1 Matter

Lesson 1 What are the properties of objects?
Lesson 2 What is matter?
Lesson 3 What are the states of matter?
Lesson 4 How can matter be mixed?
Lesson 5 How can matter be changed?
Lesson 6 How fast can you melt an ice cube?

Chapter 2

Chapter 2 Sound, Heat, and Light

Lesson 1 How can you make sounds?
Lesson 2 What is pitch?
Lesson 3 What are some sources of heat?
Lesson 4 Which container will warm up fastest?
Lesson 5 What are some sources of light?
Lesson 6 How does light move?
Lesson 7 Experiment with shadows.

Chapter 3

Chapter 3 Force, Magnets, and Electricity

Lesson 1 What makes objects move?
Lesson 2 What is gravity?
Lesson 3 What is a magnet?
Lesson 4 What can a magnet attract?
Lesson 5 How many paper clips will a magnet pick up?
Lesson 6 How does electricity move?
Lesson 7 How do you use electricity safely?

Unit C Earth Science

- Properties of earth materials
- Objects in the sky
- Changes in earth and sky

Chapter 1
The Earth

Lesson 1 What are some features of the earth?
Lesson 2 What are rocks like?
Lesson 3 How can rocks and soil be changed?
Lesson 4 How do volcanoes and earthquakes change the earth?
Lesson 5 How can you make a model of a volcano?
Lesson 6 What resources do we get from the earth?
Lesson 7 How can you help protect the earth?
Lesson 8 What can be recycled?

Chapter 2
Weather and Seasons

Lesson 1 What can you tell about the weather?
Lesson 2 Experiment with temperature.
Lesson 3 What happens in spring and summer?
Lesson 4 What happens in fall and winter?
Lesson 5 Is there water in air?
Lesson 6 How does water vapor condense?
Lesson 7 What are some kinds of bad weather?

Chapter 3
The Solar System

Lesson 1 What causes day and night?
Lesson 2 What do we know about the moon?
Lesson 3 How can you record the phases of the moon?
Lesson 4 What is in our solar system?
Lesson 5 How do we learn about the solar system?

Unit D Human Body

- Personal health

Chapter 1
How Your Body Works

Lesson 1 What does the brain do?
Lesson 2 What do the heart and lungs do?
Lesson 3 How long can you blow bubbles?
Lesson 4 Experiment with exercise.

Chapter 2
Nutrition

Lesson 1 What foods help you stay healthy?
Lesson 2 Which foods will leave a greasy spot?
Lesson 3 What happens when you chew?
Lesson 4 How is food digested?

Chapter 3
Keeping Healthy

Lesson 1 Why is exercise important?
Lesson 2 How much exercise do you get?
Lesson 3 Why is it important to keep clean?
Lesson 4 How can you take care of yourself?

Scott Foresman *Science* Scope and Sequence

Scott Foresman *Science* provides you with complete science content that supports the objectives of the *National Science Education Standards.*

	National Science Education Standards: Grades K-4	National Science Education Standards: Grades 5-6	Grade K	Grade 1
Unit A Life Science	• The characteristics of organisms • Life cycles of organisms • Organisms and their environments	• Structure and function in living systems • Reproduction and heredity • Regulation and behavior • Populations and ecosystems • Diversity and adaptations of organisms	Chapter 1 Living and Nonliving Chapter 2 Animals Chapter 3 Plants	Chapter 1 Plants Chapter 2 Animals Chapter 3 Where Plants and Animals Live
Unit B Physical Science	• Properties of objects and materials • Position and motion of objects • Light, heat, electricity, and magnetism	• Properties and changes of properties in matter • Motions and forces • Transfer of energy	Chapter 1 Matter Chapter 2 Sound, Heat, and Light Chapter 3 Movement	Chapter 1 Grouping Objects Chapter 2 Sound, Light, and Heat Chapter 3 Moving and Working
Unit C Earth Science	• Properties of earth materials • Objects in the sky • Changes in earth and sky	• Structure of the earth system • Earth's history • Earth in the solar system	Chapter 1 Earth and Sky Chapter 2 Weather Chapter 3 Caring for Earth	Chapter 1 The Earth Chapter 2 Weather Chapter 3 The Sky
Unit D Human Body	• Personal health	• Personal health	Chapter 1 Human Body Chapter 2 Growing and Changing Chapter 3 Being Healthy	Chapter 1 The Senses Chapter 2 Growing and Changing Chapter 3 Taking Care of Your Health

Grade 2	Grade 3	Grade 4	Grade 5	Grade 6
Chapter 1 Plants **Chapter 2** Animals **Chapter 3** Fossils	**Chapter 1** How Plants Live and Grow **Chapter 2** How Animals Grow and Change **Chapter 3** Living Things and Their Environments **Chapter 4** Changing Environments	**Chapter 1** Plant Structure and Function **Chapter 2** Animal Structure and Function **Chapter 3** Energy in Ecosystems **Chapter 4** Surviving in the Environment	**Chapter 1** Comparing Living Things **Chapter 2** Reproduction and Change **Chapter 3** Adaptations **Chapter 4** Ecology	**Chapter 1** Structure and Function of Cells **Chapter 2** Reproduction and Heredity **Chapter 3** Changing and Adapting **Chapter 4** Ecosystems and Biomes
Chapter 1 Matter **Chapter 2** Sound, Heat, and Light **Chapter 3** Force, Magnets, and Electricity	**Chapter 1** Matter and How It Changes **Chapter 2** Forces, Machines, and Work **Chapter 3** Energy in Your World **Chapter 4** Sound	**Chapter 1** Measuring Matter **Chapter 2** Force and Motion **Chapter 3** Electricity and Magnetism **Chapter 4** Light and Sound	**Chapter 1** Classifying Matter **Chapter 2** Investigating Motion **Chapter 3** Forms of Energy **Chapter 4** Electrical Energy	**Chapter 1** Heat and Matter **Chapter 2** Changes in Matter **Chapter 3** Moving Objects **Chapter 4** Light, Color, and Sound
Chapter 1 The Earth **Chapter 2** Weather and Seasons **Chapter 3** The Solar System	**Chapter 1** Changes in the Earth's Surface **Chapter 2** Materials of the Earth **Chapter 3** The Sun, Planets, and Moon **Chapter 4** Clouds and Storms	**Chapter 1** Measuring Weather **Chapter 2** The Makeup of the Earth **Chapter 3** Exploring the Oceans **Chapter 4** Movements in the Solar System	**Chapter 1** The Changing Earth **Chapter 2** The Earth's Resources **Chapter 3** Climate **Chapter 4** Astronomy	**Chapter 1** Technology and Weather **Chapter 2** Earth Processes **Chapter 3** Exploring the Universe **Chapter 4** Resources and Conservation
Chapter 1 How Your Body Works **Chapter 2** Nutrition **Chapter 3** Keeping Healthy	**Chapter 1** The Body's Systems **Chapter 2** Staying Healthy	**Chapter 1** The Digestive, Circulatory, and Nervous Systems **Chapter 2** Keeping Your Body Systems Healthy	**Chapter 1** Respiration and Excretion **Chapter 2** Living a Healthy Life	**Chapter 1** Your Body's Control Systems **Chapter 2** Drugs and Your Body

Grade 2 Materials List

Materials Lists for Activities Quantities needed will vary based on class size and the way children are grouped for a particular activity. Items keyed with a diamond (◆) are available in the Unit Equipment Kit for that Unit. Each Unit Equipment Kit contains at least the minimum amount of each keyed item. To find out additional information about an item, refer to either the activity page number in this Teacher's Edition, or the Equipment Kit Teacher's Guide from your Unit Equipment Kit.

Unit A Life Science

Consumable Items	Minimum Amount	Page Numbers
art supplies		A17a, A23a, A33a, A43a
construction paper		A36–37, A37a
construction paper, green		A43
construction paper, yellow		A43
◆cork, size 7	25	A23a
crayons		A29, A41, A49, A59a
◆cup, plastic 9 oz cocktail	56	A7, A10–11, A17
◆feathers, down	.05 oz	A23a
foam tray		A59a
glue		A7
grocery bag		A10–11
index cards		A41
leaves		A51
magazines/ catalogs		A7
masking tape		A41
◆modeling clay, asst color	10 lb	A23a, A36–37, A51, A60–61
objects to imprint		A27
paint		A21
◆pan, foil 13x10x2"	4	A53a
paper		A29, A33a, A49, A59a
pencil		A29, A37a, A59a
◆pipe cleaner, 6" asst color	200	A36–37
◆plate, paper 9"	50	A41
◆sand, fine	2.5 kg	A53a
◆seeds, lima bean	8 oz	A18–19
◆seeds, pinto bean	1 lb	A7, A10–11, A17
shoe box with lid		A7
◆soil, seed starter mix	16 qt	A7, A10–11, A17
◆sponge, cellulose	8	A23a
stamp pad		A33a
water		A10–11, A17, A53a
◆yarn, red (skein)	4	A41, A56–57
Nonconsumable Items		
clock with second hand		A43
frog picture book		A33a
◆hand lens	16	A18–19
meter stick		A14, A56–57
metric ruler		A17
pictures of plants		A11a
plant		A17a
safety goggles		A36–37
scissors		A7, A36–37, A37a, A49, A56–57

Unit B Physical Science

Consumable Items	Minimum Amount	Page Numbers
12 oz soup can		B27a, B30–31
◆battery, size D	24	B37, B38–39, B57, B59a
brown paper bag		B13a
chalk		B11
craft stick		B19a
◆cup, foam 8 oz	8	B30–31
◆cup, plastic 10 oz	72	B15, B19a, B30–31
eraser		B11
folder		B39a
food coloring		B15
glue		B19a
ice cubes		B18–19
◆lid, plastic 10 oz	32	B15
making tape		B59a
◆miniature lamp, #14	8	B57
oil		B15
◆pan, foil 13x10x2"	8	B30–31
paper		B39a
pencil		B27, B39a
pencil, unsharpened		B51, B53
◆plate, foam 9"	35	B18–19
◆rubber band, #64	2 oz	B27
salt		B15
sand		B15
◆starch, liquid	1 qt	B19a
◆string, cotton	200 ft	B53
sugar		B15
water		B15
water, cool		B30–31
water, warm		B30–31
◆wire, insulated 22 gauge	100 ft	B57, B59a
Nonconsumable Items		
◆balance, primary small	8	B11
book		B27
clock with seconds		B18–19, B30–31
◆flashlight	8	B37, B38–39
◆magnet, donut 3 cm OD	24	B51, B53, B54–55, B55a, B61
measuring spoons (tbs, tsp)		B19a
metric ruler		B47
◆minature lamp, #14	8	B57, B59a
mirror (7x12)		B39a
paper clips		B11, B55a
paper clips, large		B54–55
safety goggles		B27, B57
◆thermometer, low temp	24	B30–31, B31a
toy or classroom object		B38–39
wood block		B11
Miscellaneous Items		
common classroom objects		B9, B13a, B27a, B37, B47, B49, B49a, B53, B55a, B61
metallic/non-metallic items		B59a
objects from desk		B25

Unit C Earth Science

Consumable Items	Minimum Amount	Page Numbers
art supplies		C53a, C59a
◆baking soda	454 g	C16–17
◆battery, size D	16	C49
brass fastener		C61
calendar		C53
cans		C40–41
cardboard		C43a
construction paper, blue		C7
craft sticks		C16–17, C21
crayons or markers		C23a, C53
◆cup, foam 8 oz	16	C13
◆cup, paper 3 oz	32	C29
◆cup, plastic 9 oz cocktail	64	C32–33, C39, C43a
diswashing soap		C16–17
◆food coloring, red 30 ml	1	C40–41
food scraps		C21
index cards		C13a
leaves, grass		C21
markers		C61
◆modeling clay	8 lb	C7, C16–17
◆pan, foil 13x10x2"	16	C13, C16–17
paper		C13a, C17a, C23a, C37a
paper towels		C43a
pencil		C13a
pencil, unsharpened with eraser		C29, C37a
◆plastic wrap, 50 sq ft	1	C39
◆plate, paper 9"	100	C61
◆sand, fine	2.5 kg	C7
◆soil, sandy	7.5 kg	C13, C21, C32–33
stickers		C49
◆straw, clear plastic	16	C29
tape		C23a, C39
◆vinegar, white	500 ml	C16–17
water		C13, C21, C32–33, C43a
water, ice		C40–41
water, warm		C39, C40–41
Nonconsumable Items		
blocks, wood or plastic		C17a
bulletin board		C23a
clock with seconds		C32–33, C39, C40–41
◆dropper, plastic	8	C43a
◆flashlight	8	C49
globe		C49
moon phase pictures		C53a
plastic jar with a lid		C21
push pin		C29, C37a
◆rock specimen pack	1	C13a
rocks		C7
safety goggles		C16–17, C29, C37a, C61
scissors		C37a, C61
space shuttle rocket pictures		C59a
teaspoon		C16–17
◆thermometer, low temp	24	C32–33
◆vial, plastic 70 ml	16	C16–17

Unit D Human Body

Consumable Items	Minimum Amount	Page Numbers
art supplies		D43a
◆bag, plastic zip lip 6x8"	64	D27
brown paper bag		D24–25
butter		D24–25
calendar		D38–39
carrot		D24–25
construction paper		D43a
crayons		D38–39, D39a
◆cup, plastic 9 oz cocktail	16	D12–13
glue		D23, D43a
magazine pictures		D43a
magazines/newspapers		D23
markers		D24–25, D39a
paper		D25a, D39a
paper, large piece		D23
pencil		D25a, D29a, D38–39, D39a
saltine crackers		D27
shoebox		D43a
snack foods		D24–25
◆straw, clear plastic	32	D12–13
tape		D39a
water		D12–13, D27
◆yarn, red (skein)	1	D29a
Nonconsumable Items		
clock with seconds		D12–13, D14–15, D35
meter stick		D29a
metric ruler		D7
scissors		D23, D43a